ERIK V. BOHN
University of British Columbia, Vancouver, British Columbia

INTRODUCTION TO ELECTROMAGNETIC FIELDS AND WAVES

ADDISON-WESLEY PUBLISHING COMPANY
Reading, Massachusetts · Menlo Park, California · London · Don Mills, Ontario

This book is in the
ADDISON-WESLEY SERIES IN ELECTRICAL ENGINEERING

Consulting Editors
DAVID K. CHENG
LEONARD A. GOULD
FRED K. MANASSE

PREFACE

Electromagnetic theory is one of the most important and also undoubtedly one of the most difficult subjects taught to electrical engineers and applied physicists. The subject matter involves many abstract physical and mathematical concepts. Considerable mathematical background is required before one can use electromagnetic theory to solve practical engineering problems. Furthermore, it is no easy matter at the introductory level to give meaningful experiments in time-varying electromagnetic fields. Consequently students are often inclined to explain field relations which are conceptually more difficult in terms of lumped-parameter circuit relations with which they have had considerable experimental contact. Since an important function of field theory is to analytically evaluate equivalent lumped-parameter circuit elements and to assign a precise meaning to terms such as induced voltage, voltage drop, and impedance, it is easy to see the conceptual difficulty faced by students before they acquire a fundamental understanding of electromagnetic theory.

The question then arises: how best to present electromagnetic theory at the introductory level? The first serious treatment is usually given after the student has had an elementary physics course in electricity and magnetism and courses in vector analysis and differential equations. The student will therefore have an elementary understanding of Faraday's law of electromagnetic induction and the Lorentz force. With this background, he has a foundation for a deductive, logical development of electromagnetic theory based on the Lorentz force and the Maxwell equations as postulates. Maxwell's first equation is essentially Faraday's law of electromagnetic induction. If a student accepts and understands Maxwell's first equation, he can equally well accept and understand Maxwell's second equation. In free space these equations are complementary, and there is no reason why they should not be treated together. Conceptually it can be of great benefit to a student if he realizes that **E** and **B** are *vector components* of the electromagnetic field. Such a point of view lays the foundation for understanding the transformation of field components between coordinate systems in relative motion. The student, without having to cope with any unnecessary conceptual problems, can thus accept the fact that a magnetic field in one coordinate system may appear as an electric field in a second coordinate system.

The classical approach based on Coulomb's law and the Biot-Savart law places such great emphasis on the independence of the **E** and **B** fields that it becomes difficult for a student to relate them in any meaningful manner. The Maxwell equations as well as numerous other laws are presented in a manner which is just adequate to solve the problems at hand. Lack of a fundamental approach becomes particularly noticeable when such quantities as induced voltage and impedance are discussed. The oversimplified concepts presented in a classical approach are often a hindrance to the student who wishes to obtain a fundamental understanding of electromagnetic theory. Furthermore, advanced treatments based on the Lorentz transformation differ completely from the classical approach.

From a conceptual standpoint the Lorentz force and the Maxwell equations leave little to be desired as postulates. They are simple, elegant, and form the basis for advanced treatments. This text, therefore, takes the Lorentz force and the Maxwell equations as postulates and presents electromagnetic theory from a deductive, logical point of view. For pedagogical reasons, and to impress on the student the generality of Maxwell's equations and the nature of the E and B fields, the formulation of the postulates is based on a number of descriptive "experiments." This is essentially the scientific approach, in which postulates or basic laws are accepted as such after they have been tested in a variety of experimental situations.

To keep the text within bounds the following points have been adhered to:

(1) The text is intended to cover the fundamental and introductory aspects of electromagnetic theory up to the level at which a student can profitably read literature on specific subjects and design techniques.

(2) The models used to represent macroscopic electromagnetic phenomena in material media have been kept as elementary as possible. This approach has the advantage of focusing attention on the electromagnetic aspects of the subject.

(3) An adequate background in physics and mathematics is assumed. In particular it is assumed that the student has had elementary courses in vector analysis, calculus, and electricity and magnetism. It is also assumed that the student has an elementary knowledge of atomic physics and semiconductor theory, and that he has had, or is concurrently taking, a course in network analysis and will therefore be acquainted with the phasor analysis of scalar fields. However, to assist the student in applying phasor analysis to vector fields, the text presents a discussion of the method wherever this seems helpful.

(4) General coordinates are used in developing the theory of wave guides, cavities, and space-charge waves, not because of the mathematical elegance of general coordinates, but because they offer a unified means for solving many problems. They permit one to give a unified treatment of TE, TM, and TEM waves in various coordinate systems and to express field components as directional derivatives of a scalar function. The transmission-line analog for wave guides is then readily obtainable. This approach eliminates the often repetitious manipulation of Maxwell's equations in various coordinate systems.

The choice of material in the text has been based on the following considerations:

Introductory courses in vector analysis usually stress cartesian coordinates. Emphasis on a particular coordinate system is undesirable in the development of electromagnetic theory. Consequently the emphasis in Chapter 1 is largely on geometric concepts and general coordinates.

One of the functions of electromagnetic theory is to predict theoretically the behavior of numerous electromagnetic devices. On the one hand no one wants to burden an introductory text with detailed design techniques. On the other hand a student cannot apply the theory with confidence unless he is shown how to manipulate the basic equations to yield numerical results. This text attempts a compromise, in that it gives a large number of numerical examples, using the type of data the student will encounter in practice or in the literature. However, the examples chosen, as well as the analysis used, are comparatively simple.

The text emphasizes development of fundamental and physical understanding of electromagnetic fields, as well as essential mathematical techniques. A student on first becoming acquainted with electromagnetic theory usually does not find formal vector manipulations very stimulating, even though he soon learns that vector identities and their manipulations provide the simplest way to derive electromagnetic relations. For this reason proofs in the text are often given in several ways; many proofs are based on physical considerations, which have greater appeal to students than formal vector manipulation and which also aid in the physical understanding of mathematical relations.

Since most specialized books on antennas do not devote much space to a fundamental discussion of antenna impedance, this aspect of antenna theory is handled with considerable care in this text. An attempt has been made to achieve a proper balance between the many important aspects of engineering electromagnetics. The topics treated are discussed in depth: there is a complete mathematical treatment using basic theory, followed in most cases by illustrative examples. Naturally the number of topics discussed must be limited if the text is to be held to a reasonable size, and therefore, since the text is of an introductory nature, it was decided to stress fundamentals and firmly established engineering applications.

Most of the material in Chapters 2 through 8 is suitable for an intermediate course in electromagnetic theory; it can also be used for review purposes in an advanced undergraduate course. An advanced undergraduate course can be based on the remaining chapters. Thus enough topics are covered to make the text flexible for classroom use and also suitable as a reference text for students. The material included is subject matter that is essential for a thorough introduction to the physical, mathematical, and engineering aspects of electromagnetic fields.

I should like to express my sincere appreciation to my colleague, Professor A. D. Moore, for his critical review of the first seven chapters.

Vancouver, B.C.   E. V. B.
May 1967

CONTENTS

To my children, Ehleen, Jan, and Mark

CHAPTER 1

INTRODUCTION TO VECTOR ANALYSIS

1-1 INTRODUCTION

The derivation of relationships between electromagnetic field components is considerably simplified if vector analysis is used. A vector is a quantity which requires three numbers to represent it in a given coordinate system. The three numbers are called the *scalar components* of the vector. A vector equation represents three equations relating scalar components in a manner which is independent of any particular coordinate system. Besides its mathematical elegance, vector analysis also allows a geometric interpretation to be given to equations. We shall see that this is of considerable importance in formulating the laws of electromagnetic theory. This chapter gives a review of vector analysis, with emphasis on the notation, theorems, and equations used in subsequent chapters.

1-2 SCALARS AND VECTORS

A *scalar* is a quantity which can be represented by one real number. For example, mass, length, time, and temperature are scalars. If a scalar is associated with every point of a region R, we say that a scalar field exists within R. An example of a scalar field would be the temperature distribution in a solid body.

Fig. 1-1. Vector addition.

A *vector* is a quantity which requires three numbers to represent it in a given coordinate system. The velocity of a particle is a vector and is represented by the components of velocity, u_1, u_2, and u_3 with respect to a given coordinate system. From a geometric point of view this implies that velocity has both a magnitude or length and an orientation or direction. We therefore represent a vector $\mathbf{A}$ graphically by a directed arrow (Fig. 1-1). The length of the arrow represents the magnitude A and the direction can be defined by the direction of a dimensionless unit vector $\mathbf{i}$ which is collinear with $\mathbf{A}$. Thus $\mathbf{A} = \mathbf{i}A$.

1

The sum of a vector **A** and a vector **B** is defined by the vector **C** = **A** + **B**, which forms a closed triangle with **A** and **B** as shown in Fig. 1–1.

The vector −**A** is defined by the equation **A** + (−**A**) = 0, and has the same magnitude as **A** but the opposite direction. The vector subtraction of **B** from **A** is defined by the vector addition of **A** and (−**B**).

1-3 VECTOR MULTIPLICATION

Since a vector has both magnitude and direction it is possible to define two kinds of product. We define the *scalar product* of **A** and **B** by the equation*

$$\mathbf{A} \cdot \mathbf{B} \triangleq AB \cos \theta = AB_p,$$

where θ is the angle included between **A** and **B** and where $B_p \triangleq B \cos \theta$ represents the perpendicular projection of **B** on **A** (Fig. 1–2).

The scalar product is distributive; that is,

$$\mathbf{A} \cdot (\mathbf{B} + \mathbf{C}) = \mathbf{A} \cdot \mathbf{B} + \mathbf{A} \cdot \mathbf{C}.$$

The proof is readily established with the aid of Fig. 1–3 by noting that the above equation can be written as $AD_p = A(B_p + C_p)$, where **D** $\triangleq$ **B** + **C**, and that $D_p = B_p + C_p$.

The *vector product* **C** = **A** × **B** is defined by the equation (see Fig. 1–4)

$$C = AB \, |\sin \theta|,$$

and by the requirement that **A**, **B**, and **C** form a right-handed system; that is, **C** has the direction of advance of a right-handed screw as **A** is rotated into **B**. The vector product can be written as

$$\mathbf{A} \times \mathbf{B} = \mathbf{A} \times \mathbf{B}_p, \tag{1-1}$$

where $\mathbf{B}_p$ is the vector formed by the projection of **B** onto a plane normal to **A** (Fig. 1–5). The vector product is distributive. That is,

$$\mathbf{A} \times (\mathbf{B} + \mathbf{C}) = \mathbf{A} \times \mathbf{B} + \mathbf{A} \times \mathbf{C}. \tag{1-2}$$

The proof can be established by taking a plane normal to **A** and projecting **B**, **C**, and **B** + **C** onto this plane (Fig. 1–6). The vector **A** × **B**$_p$ is obtained from **B**$_p$ by rotating it through 90° in a counterclockwise direction and multiplying it by A. We see, therefore, that triangle I is rotated through 90°, and that, after multiplication by A, it forms triangle II. Thus

$$\mathbf{A} \times (\mathbf{B} + \mathbf{C})_p = \mathbf{A} \times \mathbf{C}_p + \mathbf{A} \times \mathbf{B}_p,$$

and Eq. (1–2) follows from Eq. (1–1).

---

* The symbol $\triangleq$ indicates that the quantities are *equal by definition*.

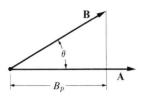

Fig. 1–2. The scalar product **A** · **B**.

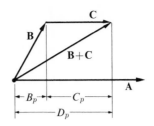

Fig. 1–3. The distributive law for the scalar product.

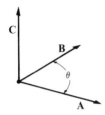

Fig. 1–4. The vector product **A** × **B**.

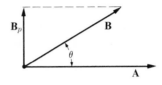

Fig. 1–5. The relation **A** × **B** = **A** × **B**$_p$.

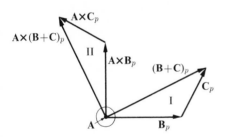

Fig. 1–6. The distributive law for the vector product.

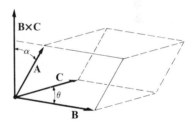

Fig. 1–7. The scalar triple product.

A scalar product of frequent occurrence is the *scalar triple product*,

$$\mathbf{A} \cdot (\mathbf{B} \times \mathbf{C}) = A \cos \alpha BC \sin \theta.$$

The right-hand side of the above equation represents the volume of the parallelepiped formed by the vectors **A**, **B**, and **C**, provided that $0 \leqq \alpha \leqq \pi/2$ (Fig. 1–7). If $\alpha > \pi/2$, we can replace **A** by −**A** and conclude that the scalar triple product represents the negative volume of the parallelepiped formed by the vectors −**A**, **B**, and **C**. Since the volume remains the same if we interchange the vectors **A**, **B**, and **C** in a cyclic manner, we have

$$\mathbf{A} \cdot (\mathbf{B} \times \mathbf{C}) = \mathbf{C} \cdot (\mathbf{A} \times \mathbf{B}) = \mathbf{B} \cdot (\mathbf{C} \times \mathbf{A}). \tag{1–3}$$

A vector identity of considerable importance is the *vector triple product*,

$$\mathbf{A} \times (\mathbf{B} \times \mathbf{C}) = (\mathbf{A} \cdot \mathbf{C})\mathbf{B} - (\mathbf{A} \cdot \mathbf{B})\mathbf{C}. \tag{1–4}$$

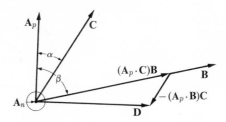

Fig. 1–8. The vector triple product.

To prove Eq. (1–4), we let

$$\mathbf{A} = \mathbf{A}_p + \mathbf{A}_n,$$

where the vectors $\mathbf{A}_p$ and $\mathbf{A}_n$ are, respectively, parallel to and normal to the plane P containing $\mathbf{B}$ and $\mathbf{C}$. We have

$$\mathbf{D} \triangleq \mathbf{A}_p \times (\mathbf{B} \times \mathbf{C}) = \mathbf{A} \times (\mathbf{B} \times \mathbf{C}),$$

and we see that $\mathbf{D}$ lies in the plane P (Fig. 1–8). The magnitude of $\mathbf{D}$ is given by

$$D = A_p BC \sin (\beta - \alpha) = (A_p C \cos \alpha)(B \sin \beta) - (A_p B \cos \beta)(C \sin \alpha),$$

where the angles α and β are as shown in the figure. The above expression can be written in terms of scalar products:

$$D = [(\mathbf{A}_p \cdot \mathbf{C})\mathbf{B} - (\mathbf{A}_p \cdot \mathbf{B})\mathbf{C}] \cdot \frac{\mathbf{D}}{D}.$$

Since $\mathbf{A}_p$ is perpendicular to $\mathbf{D}$, it follows that

$$(\mathbf{A}_p \cdot \mathbf{C})\mathbf{B} - (\mathbf{A}_p \cdot \mathbf{B})\mathbf{C} = \mathbf{D} + x\mathbf{A}_p,$$

where x is an unknown scalar. To determine x, we can scalar-multiply the above equation by $\mathbf{A}_p$. This yields $x = 0$, and we obtain

$$\mathbf{D} = (\mathbf{A}_p \cdot \mathbf{C})\mathbf{B} - (\mathbf{A}_p \cdot \mathbf{B})\mathbf{C}.$$

To complete the proof of Eq. (1–4), it is now sufficient to note that

$$\mathbf{A} \cdot \mathbf{C} = \mathbf{A}_p \cdot \mathbf{C}, \qquad \mathbf{A} \cdot \mathbf{B} = \mathbf{A}_p \cdot \mathbf{B}.$$

1–4 UNIT ORTHOGONAL VECTORS IN A CARTESIAN COORDINATE SYSTEM

In a cartesian coordinate system, x, y, z, we can represent a vector $\mathbf{u}$ in terms of its scalar components u_x, u_y, and u_z and the three unit vectors $\mathbf{i}_x$, $\mathbf{i}_y$, and $\mathbf{i}_z$ which have the direction of the x-, y-, and z-axes, respectively (Fig. 1–9):

$$\mathbf{u} = \mathbf{i}_x u_x + \mathbf{i}_y u_y + \mathbf{i}_z u_z.$$

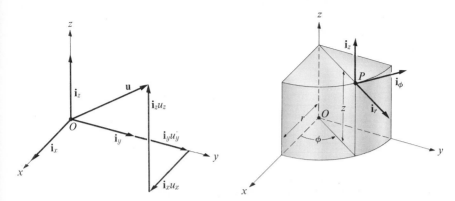

Fig. 1–9. A cartesian coordinate system.   **Fig. 1–10.** Cylindrical coordinates.

Unit vectors have the following properties:

1. They are of unit length. Thus

$$\mathbf{i}_x \cdot \mathbf{i}_x = \mathbf{i}_y \cdot \mathbf{i}_y = \mathbf{i}_z \cdot \mathbf{i}_z = 1.$$

2. They are mutually orthogonal. Thus

$$\mathbf{i}_x \cdot \mathbf{i}_y = \mathbf{i}_y \cdot \mathbf{i}_z = \mathbf{i}_z \cdot \mathbf{i}_x = 0.$$

3. They form a right-handed system. Thus

$$\mathbf{i}_x \times \mathbf{i}_y = \mathbf{i}_z, \qquad \mathbf{i}_y \times \mathbf{i}_z = \mathbf{i}_x, \qquad \mathbf{i}_z \times \mathbf{i}_x = \mathbf{i}_y.$$

To obtain the components u_x, u_y, and u_z when $\mathbf{u}$ is given, we can scalar-multiply $\mathbf{u}$ by $\mathbf{i}_x$, $\mathbf{i}_y$, and $\mathbf{i}_z$, respectively. For example,

$$u_x = \mathbf{u} \cdot \mathbf{i}_x.$$

1–5 UNIT ORTHOGONAL VECTORS IN A CYLINDRICAL COORDINATE SYSTEM

In the solution of many field problems we shall find that cartesian coordinates are not the most convenient ones, and that cylindrical or spherical coordinates are preferable. Figure 1–10 illustrates cylindrical coordinates r, ϕ, z, which are related to the cartesian coordinates x, y, z by the following equations:

$$x = r \cos \phi, \qquad y = r \sin \phi.$$

The unit vectors in cylindrical coordinates are $\mathbf{i}_r$, $\mathbf{i}_\phi$, and $\mathbf{i}_z$, respectively, and locally at any point P they form a right-handed orthogonal system. It should be noted that $\mathbf{i}_r$ and $\mathbf{i}_\phi$ depend on ϕ. By orthogonal projection of $\mathbf{i}_x$ and $\mathbf{i}_y$ onto $\mathbf{i}_r$ and $\mathbf{i}_\phi$, we can obtain the following relations:

$$\mathbf{i}_x = \mathbf{i}_r \cos \phi - \mathbf{i}_\phi \sin \phi, \qquad \mathbf{i}_y = \mathbf{i}_r \sin \phi + \mathbf{i}_\phi \cos \phi.$$

These equations can be used to convert the representation of a vector in cartesian coordinates to its representation in cylindrical coordinates. For example,

$$\mathbf{u} = \mathbf{i}_x u_x + \mathbf{i}_y u_y + \mathbf{i}_z u_z$$
$$= \mathbf{i}_r(u_x \cos \phi + u_y \sin \phi) + \mathbf{i}_\phi(-u_x \sin \phi + u_y \cos \phi) + \mathbf{i}_z u_z.$$

The r- and ϕ-components of $\mathbf{u}$ in cylindrical coordinates are then

$$u_r = u_x \cos \phi + u_y \sin \phi, \qquad u_\phi = -u_x \sin \phi + u_y \cos \phi.$$

1–6 UNIT ORTHOGONAL VECTORS IN A SPHERICAL COORDINATE SYSTEM

The unit vectors in a spherical coordinate system are $\mathbf{i}_r$, $\mathbf{i}_\theta$, and $\mathbf{i}_\phi$, and locally at any point P they form a right-handed orthogonal coordinate system (Fig. 1–11). The vector $\mathbf{i}_r$ is radially directed, $\mathbf{i}_\theta$ lies in a plane containing the z-axis and the point P and is directed in the sense of increasing θ. The vector $\mathbf{i}_\phi$ is normal to this plane and is directed in the sense of increasing ϕ. Note that the unit vectors at a point P depend on the coordinates θ, ϕ.

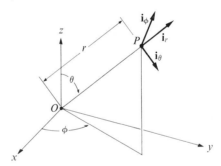

Fig. 1–11. Spherical coordinates.

The relationship between the coordinates of P in spherical and cartesian coordinates can be obtained by projecting P onto the x-, y-, and z-axes. Thus

$$x = r \sin \theta \cos \phi, \qquad y = r \sin \theta \sin \phi, \qquad z = r \cos \theta.$$

By orthogonal projection of the unit vectors $\mathbf{i}_x$, $\mathbf{i}_y$, and $\mathbf{i}_z$ onto the unit vectors $\mathbf{i}_r$, $\mathbf{i}_\theta$, and $\mathbf{i}_\phi$, we can obtain the following equations:

$$\mathbf{i}_x = (\mathbf{i}_r \sin \theta + \mathbf{i}_\theta \cos \theta) \cos \phi - \mathbf{i}_\phi \sin \phi,$$

$$\mathbf{i}_y = (\mathbf{i}_r \sin \theta + \mathbf{i}_\theta \cos \theta) \sin \phi + \mathbf{i}_\phi \cos \phi,$$

$$\mathbf{i}_z = \mathbf{i}_r \cos \theta - \mathbf{i}_\theta \sin \theta.$$

These equations can be used to convert the representation of a vector in cartesian coordinates to its representation in spherical coordinates. For example,

$$\mathbf{u} = \mathbf{i}_x u_x + \mathbf{i}_y u_y + \mathbf{i}_z u_z$$
$$= \mathbf{i}_r(u_x \sin\theta\cos\phi + u_y \sin\theta\sin\phi + u_z\cos\theta)$$
$$+ \mathbf{i}_\theta(u_x\cos\theta\cos\phi + u_y\cos\theta\sin\phi - u_z\sin\theta)$$
$$+ \mathbf{i}_\phi(-u_x\sin\phi + u_y\cos\phi).$$

The components of $\mathbf{u}$ in spherical coordinates are then

$$u_r = (u_x\cos\phi + u_y\sin\phi)\sin\theta + u_z\cos\theta,$$
$$u_\theta = (u_x\cos\phi + u_y\sin\phi)\cos\theta - u_z\sin\theta,$$
$$u_\phi = -u_x\sin\phi + u_y\cos\phi.$$

1-7 THE GRADIENT OF A SCALAR FUNCTION OF POSITION

Let U be a scalar function of the position P which has the cartesian coordinates x, y, z, and let

$$\mathbf{r} = \mathbf{i}_x x + \mathbf{i}_y y + \mathbf{i}_z z$$

represent the radius vector from the origin to P. The displacement

$$d\mathbf{r} = \mathbf{i}_x\, dx + \mathbf{i}_y\, dy + \mathbf{i}_z\, dz$$

results in a change in U given by

$$dU = \frac{\partial U}{\partial x}\, dx + \frac{\partial U}{\partial y}\, dy + \frac{\partial U}{\partial z}\, dz. \tag{1-5}$$

Equation (1–5) can be expressed as the scalar product of two vectors:

$$dU = \nabla U \cdot d\mathbf{r}, \tag{1-6}$$

where we define

$$\nabla \triangleq \mathbf{i}_x\frac{\partial}{\partial x} + \mathbf{i}_y\frac{\partial}{\partial y} + \mathbf{i}_z\frac{\partial}{\partial z} \tag{1-7}$$

as the *del operator*, and where

$$\nabla U \triangleq \mathbf{i}_x\frac{\partial U}{\partial x} + \mathbf{i}_y\frac{\partial U}{\partial y} + \mathbf{i}_z\frac{\partial U}{\partial z} \tag{1-8}$$

is defined as the *gradient* of U. The geometric significance of the vector ∇U is seen when we choose $d\mathbf{r}$ to be a displacement in the surface $U =$ const. It then follows from Eq. (1–6) that

$$\nabla U \cdot d\mathbf{r} = 0,$$

regardless of the direction of $d\mathbf{r}$. Thus ∇U is a vector normal to the surface $U = $ const. Since the shortest distance between two neighboring surfaces $U = c$ and $U = c + dc$ is along the normal to the surface, we may state that at each point ∇U has the direction of the greatest rate of change of U.

1–8 DIVERGENCE AND CURL IN CARTESIAN COORDINATES

In cartesian coordinates the scalar

$$\nabla \cdot \mathbf{B} \triangleq \frac{\partial B_x}{\partial x} + \frac{\partial B_y}{\partial y} + \frac{\partial B_z}{\partial z} \tag{1–9}$$

and the vector

$$\nabla \times \mathbf{B} \triangleq \mathbf{i}_x \times \frac{\partial \mathbf{B}}{\partial x} + \mathbf{i}_y \times \frac{\partial \mathbf{B}}{\partial y} + \mathbf{i}_z \times \frac{\partial \mathbf{B}}{\partial z} \tag{1–10}$$

are defined as the *divergence* of $\mathbf{B}$ (div $\mathbf{B}$), and the *curl* of $\mathbf{B}$ (curl $\mathbf{B}$), respectively. These definitions follow directly from definition (1–7) for del. Equation (1–10) is often expressed formally as a determinant:

$$\nabla \times \mathbf{B} = \begin{vmatrix} \mathbf{i}_x & \mathbf{i}_y & \mathbf{i}_z \\ \dfrac{\partial}{\partial x} & \dfrac{\partial}{\partial y} & \dfrac{\partial}{\partial z} \\ B_x & B_y & B_z \end{vmatrix}. \tag{1–11}$$

Equations (1–9), (1–10), and the operator representation (1–7) are often convenient in the derivation of vector identities. However, no physical insight is obtained from the operator representation. For our purposes the definition of gradient, divergence, and curl given by Eqs. (1–8), (1–9), and (1–10) are not adequate. In the next three sections we shall discuss general definitions which do not depend on a particular coordinate system. With the aid of these definitions we shall be able to determine representations for the gradient, divergence, and curl in coordinate systems other than cartesian ones.

1–9 GENERAL DEFINITION OF
DIVERGENCE OF A VECTOR FUNCTION

To understand the physical significance of the divergence of a vector let us consider an n-type semiconductor and let v be the volume bounded by an arbitrary surface S within the semiconductor (Fig. 1–12). The outward unit normal of S is $\mathbf{n}$. Due to thermal vibrations of the crystal structure, or due to external radiation, some of the bonds binding electrons to the atoms of the crystal are broken and free electrons are formed. Let ρ be the number of free electrons per unit volume and let $\mathbf{u}$ be their average velocity resulting from diffusion and from forces due to an external field. Let g be the effective number of free electrons generated each second in a unit volume. The total number of free electrons generated each second within v is

$$n_1 = \int_v g \, dv.$$

The total number of free electrons leaving v each second through the surface S is

$$n_2 = \int_S \rho \mathbf{u} \cdot \mathbf{n} \, ds.$$

The rate of increase of free electrons within v is given by

$$n_1 - n_2 = \int_v \frac{\partial \rho}{\partial t} \, dv.$$

Substituting for n_2 in the above equation yields

$$\int_v \left(g - \frac{\partial \rho}{\partial t} \right) dv = \int_S \rho \mathbf{u} \cdot \mathbf{n} \, ds. \quad (1\text{–}12)$$

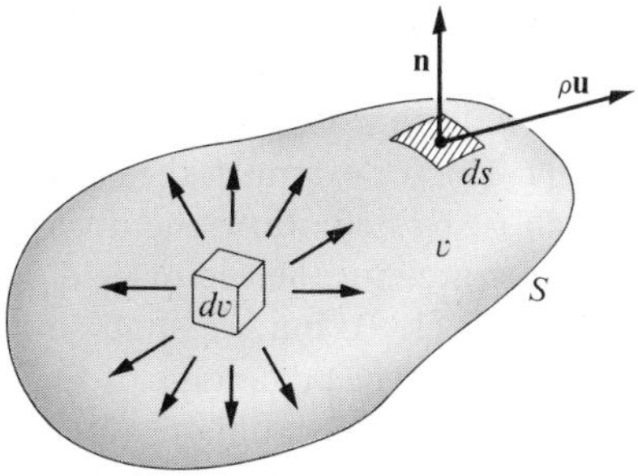

Fig. 1–12. Illustration of the divergence of a vector function.

The surface integral on the right represents the *flux* of electrons through S. From a physical point of view we would be interested in the flux per unit volume. This important physical quantity is defined as the *divergence* of $\rho \mathbf{u}$:

$$\operatorname{div} \rho \mathbf{u} \triangleq \lim_{v \to 0} \frac{1}{v} \int_S \rho \mathbf{u} \cdot \mathbf{n} \, ds. \quad (1\text{–}13)$$

In Eq. (1–12) we can choose S to be the surface of a sphere of radius r centered at a point P. If we let $r \to 0$, it follows that $v \to 0$, and Eqs. (1–12) and (1–13) yield

$$g - \frac{\partial \rho}{\partial t} = \lim_{v \to 0} \frac{1}{v} \int_S \rho \mathbf{u} \cdot \mathbf{n} \, ds = \operatorname{div} \rho \mathbf{u}. \quad (1\text{–}14)$$

Rearranging Eq. (1–14) yields the equation

$$\operatorname{div} \rho \mathbf{u} = g - \frac{\partial \rho}{\partial t}. \quad (1\text{–}15)$$

When $g = 0$, Eq. (1–15) is known as the *equation of continuity*. When $g = 0$, no free electrons are created or destroyed, and Eq. (1–15) then expresses the conservation of the number of free electrons. The same type of equation holds in many other physical situations, for example, in fluid flow and heat flow. We may therefore generalize Eq. (1–13) and state that when a vector **B** represents a *flux density*, then

$$\int_S \mathbf{B} \cdot \mathbf{n} \, ds$$

represents the *flux* of **B** through S and the *divergence* of **B** is the *flux per unit volume:*

$$\text{div } \mathbf{B} \triangleq \lim_{v \to 0} \frac{1}{v} \int_S \mathbf{B} \cdot \mathbf{n} \, ds. \tag{1–16}$$

In Eq. (1–16), v is the volume bounded by a well-behaved surface S.

The physical importance of the divergence of a vector is a consequence of the fact that it is a measure of the source density of the vector field. In Eq. (1–15), for example, the electron flux out of a unit volume is $g - (\partial\rho/\partial t)$, which is, by definition, the divergence of $\rho\mathbf{u}$. We consider the electron flux as the source for the vector field $\rho\mathbf{u}$. Definition (1–16) appears to differ from definition (1–9), but we shall show in Section 1–18 that the definitions are equivalent. The advantage of Eq. (1–16), however, is that it does not depend on a particular coordinate system. When we compare Eqs. (1–9) and (1–16), it would appear that a general representation for the del operator is given by

$$\nabla[\ ] \triangleq \lim_{v \to 0} \frac{1}{v} \int_S \mathbf{n}[\ ] \, ds. \tag{1–17}$$

We can then obtain Eq. (1–16) from Eq. (1–17) by introducing $\cdot \mathbf{B}$ into the square brackets. Thus

$$\nabla[\cdot \mathbf{B}] = \nabla \cdot \mathbf{B} = \lim_{v \to 0} \frac{1}{v} \int_S \mathbf{n} \cdot \mathbf{B} \, ds.$$

1–10 THE DIVERGENCE THEOREM; TUBES OF FLUX

A theorem of special significance in vector analysis is the *divergence theorem,* which states that

$$\int_v \text{div } \mathbf{D} \, dv = \int_S \mathbf{D} \cdot \mathbf{n} \, ds, \tag{1–18}$$

where v is the volume bounded by a well-behaved surface S.

We can see the usefulness of the divergence theorem if we reconsider Eq. (1–12) and take $\mathbf{D} = \rho\mathbf{u}$. With the aid of Eq. (1–18) we obtain

$$\int_v \left(g - \frac{\partial\rho}{\partial t} - \text{div } \rho\mathbf{u} \right) dv = 0. \tag{1–19}$$

Since the above integral vanishes for an arbitrary volume v, it follows that the integrand must vanish. This yields Eq. (1–15).

We can thus see that the divergence theorem is useful in deriving differential relationships between field vectors representing flux densities and the sources of the field flux.   The divergence theorem is also useful in the derivation of vector identities and in the manipulation of integral relationships between flux densities and the sources of the field flux.

To prove the divergence theorem, we can slice the volume v into N elemental volumes Δv_k $(k = 1, \ldots, N)$. If $N \to \infty$, then $\Delta v_k \to 0$, and Eq. (1–16) yields

$$\text{div } \mathbf{B}(P_k)\,\Delta v_k = \int_{S_k} \mathbf{B} \cdot \mathbf{n}\,ds,$$

where P_k is a suitably chosen interior point of the volume Δv_k and S_k represents the surface of Δv_k. We now form the sum

$$\sum_{k=1}^{N} \text{div } \mathbf{B}(P_k)\,\Delta v_k = \int_{S} \mathbf{B} \cdot \mathbf{n}\,ds. \tag{1–20}$$

The final surface integral is over the surface S which bounds v. We can see this by noting that the outward normals of the common surface of two adjacent volume elements are oppositely directed.   Thus, when the sum is formed, the integrals over elements of area internal to v cancel in pairs and we are left with the integral over the elements of area which form S and bound v.   If we let $\Delta v_k \to 0$, Eq. (1–20) yields the divergence theorem.

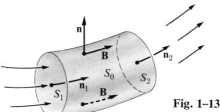

Fig. 1–13. A tube of flux.

When div $\mathbf{B} = 0$ throughout a volume v we have the important result that

$$\int_{S} \mathbf{B} \cdot \mathbf{n}\,ds = 0. \tag{1–21}$$

Equation (1–21) states that the resultant flux of $\mathbf{B}$ through the closed surface S is zero. This result allows us to introduce the concept of a *tube of flux*. To form a tube of flux we choose a surface S_0 for which $\mathbf{B} \cdot \mathbf{n} = 0$ at each point of S_0. Then we choose surfaces S_1 and S_2 to form a tubular volume v bounded by the surface $S = S_0 + S_1 + S_2$ (Fig. 1–13). If div $\mathbf{B} = 0$ throughout v, Eq. (1–21) holds. If we choose the normals $\mathbf{n}_1$ and $\mathbf{n}_2$ to have the direction of the vector field $\mathbf{B}$, we see from Fig. 1–12 that the outward normal over S_1 is $-\mathbf{n}_1$. Thus, since the surface integral over S_0 vanishes,

$$\int_{S_1} \mathbf{B} \cdot (-\mathbf{n}_1)\,ds + \int_{S_2} \mathbf{B} \cdot \mathbf{n}_2\,ds = 0.$$

The above equation can be written as

$$\int_{S_1} \mathbf{B} \cdot \mathbf{n}_1 \, ds = \int_{S_2} \mathbf{B} \cdot \mathbf{n}_2 \, ds. \tag{1–22}$$

Equation (1–22) states that the flux of **B** through the tubular region remains constant. Such a tubular region is called a tube of flux.

To illustrate these concepts, let us consider the *electric flux density* **D** of a uniform charge density ρ within a sphere of radius a. The center of the sphere is chosen as the origin of a spherical coordinate system. It can be shown that **D** is given by

$$\mathbf{D} = \begin{cases} \dfrac{Q}{4\pi r^3}\mathbf{r}, & r > a, \tag{1–23a} \\[2ex] \dfrac{Q}{4\pi a^3}\mathbf{r}, & r < a, \tag{1–23b} \end{cases}$$

where **r** is the radius vector from the origin to a field point P and where $Q = \frac{4}{3}\pi a^3 \rho$ is the total charge within the sphere. If $r > a$, we have

$$\nabla \cdot \mathbf{D} = \frac{Q}{4\pi}\left[\frac{\partial}{\partial x}\left(\frac{x}{r^3}\right) + \frac{\partial}{\partial y}\left(\frac{y}{r^3}\right) + \frac{\partial}{\partial z}\left(\frac{z}{r^3}\right)\right] = 0, \tag{1–24}$$

and if $r < a$, we have

$$\nabla \cdot \mathbf{D} = \frac{Q}{4\pi a^3}\left[\frac{\partial}{\partial x}(x) + \frac{\partial}{\partial y}(y) + \frac{\partial}{\partial z}(z)\right] = \rho. \tag{1–25}$$

We consider the charge to be the source of the electric flux. It follows from Eqs. (1–24) and (1–25) that the divergence of **D** gives us the source density ρ.

Let us compute the *electric flux* ϕ_e through an open surface S which is bounded by a sphere of radius $r > a$ and the cone $\theta = \theta_0$ (Fig. 1–14). We find, using Eq. (1–23) and noting that $\mathbf{n} = \mathbf{r}/r$, that

$$\phi_e = \int_S \mathbf{D} \cdot \mathbf{n} \, ds = \frac{Q}{4\pi r^2}\int_0^{\theta_0}(2\pi r \sin \theta)(r \, d\theta) = \frac{Q}{2}(1 - \cos \theta_0). \tag{1–26}$$

(Due to symmetry it is convenient to take the element of area ds to be the shaded strip shown in Fig. 1–14, which has a length of $2\pi r \sin \theta$ and a width of $r \, d\theta$.) The cone $\theta = \theta_0$ is a tube of flux and if $r > a$ the flux within the tube is given by Eq. (1–26).

With the aid of Eqs. (1–23), (1–24), and (1–25), we shall now illustrate the divergence theorem by evaluating both the surface and the volume integral. We choose S to be the surface of a sphere of radius b which is centered at P on the z-axis (Fig. 1–15). If $z + b < a$, the sphere S is com-

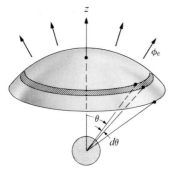

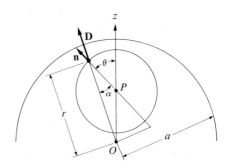

Fig. 1-14. The electric flux of a uniformly charged sphere.

Fig. 1-15. Illustration of the divergence theorem.

pletely within the charged sphere, and it follows from Eq. (1–25) that

$$\int_v \nabla \cdot \mathbf{D}\, dv = \tfrac{4}{3}\pi b^3 \rho = Q(b/a)^3. \qquad (1\text{–}27)$$

In order to evaluate the electric flux ϕ_e through S, we choose the element of area as

$$ds = (2\pi b \sin \theta)(b\, d\theta).$$

Thus, using Eq. (1–23b) and taking $\mathbf{n} \cdot \mathbf{r} = r \cos \alpha$, we obtain

$$\phi_e = \frac{Q}{4\pi a^3} \int_0^\pi r \cos \alpha\, (2\pi b \sin \theta)(b\, d\theta).$$

From Fig. 1–15 we see that $r \cos \alpha = b + z \cos \theta$. We can now evaluate the integral to obtain

$$\phi_e = Q(b/a)^3. \qquad (1\text{–}28)$$

Equation (1–28) is identical to Eq. (1–27), as required by the divergence theorem. Furthermore, if we compute the electric flux per unit volume and let $b \to 0$, we obtain the divergence of $\mathbf{D}$:

$$\lim_{b \to 0} Q(b/a)^3 / \tfrac{4}{3}\pi b^3 = \frac{3Q}{4\pi a^3} = \rho.$$

If the surface S is completely outside the charged sphere (see Eqs. 1–24 and 1–25), we have

$$\int_v \text{div}\, \mathbf{D}\, dv = \rho \tfrac{4}{3}\pi a^3 = Q \qquad (1\text{–}29)$$

and (see Eq. 1–23a)

$$\phi_e = \frac{Q}{4\pi} \int_0^\pi \frac{r \cos \alpha}{r^3} (2\pi b \sin \theta)(b\, d\theta).$$

We can best evaluate the above integral by expressing θ in terms of r. From the law of cosines, we have

$$r \cos \alpha = \frac{r^2 + b^2 - z^2}{2b}, \qquad r^2 = b^2 + z^2 + 2bz \cos \theta.$$

Thus

$$r \, dr = -bz \sin \theta \, d\theta \quad \text{and} \quad \phi_e = \frac{Q}{4z} \int_{b-z}^{b+z} \left(1 + \frac{b^2 - z^2}{r^2}\right) dr = Q,$$

as required by the divergence theorem (see Eq. 1–29).

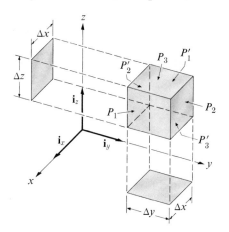

Fig. 1–16. A rectangular volume element in a cartesian coordinate system.

1–11 GENERAL DEFINITION OF THE GRADIENT OF A SCALAR FUNCTION

In cartesian coordinates the gradient of a scalar function U has been defined by Eq. (1–8). With the aid of ∇U we can determine the incremental change dU due to an elemental vector displacement $d\mathbf{r}$ (see Eq. 1–6). In order to obtain a general definition for the gradient of U we keep Eq. (1–17) in mind. Thus we anticipate that

$$\text{grad } U \triangleq \lim_{v \to 0} \frac{1}{v} \int_S \mathbf{n} U \, ds. \tag{1–30}$$

In order to show that definition (1–30) is equivalent to definition (1–8), we choose a cartesian coordinate system and consider an elemental volume $v = \Delta x \, \Delta y \, \Delta z$ (Fig. 1–16). The surface S bounding v has six plane faces. When P_1, P_1', P_2, P_2', P_3, P_3' are suitably chosen points in these faces, we have

$$\mathbf{n}(P_1) = \mathbf{i}_x = -\mathbf{n}(P_1'), \qquad \mathbf{n}(P_2) = \mathbf{i}_y = -\mathbf{n}(P_2'), \qquad \mathbf{n}(P_3) = \mathbf{i}_z = -\mathbf{n}(P_3'),$$

and

$$\int_S \mathbf{n}U \, ds = [U(P_1) - U(P_1')]\Delta y \, \Delta z \mathbf{i}_x + [U(P_2) - U(P_2')]\Delta x \, \Delta z \mathbf{i}_y$$
$$+ [U(P_3) - U(P_3')]\Delta x \, \Delta y \mathbf{i}_z.$$

Dividing by v and using Eq. (1-30) yields

$$\text{grad } U = \mathbf{i}_x \frac{\partial U}{\partial x} + \mathbf{i}_y \frac{\partial U}{\partial y} + \mathbf{i}_z \frac{\partial U}{\partial z}.$$

It follows that Eq. (1-30) is a generalization of Eq. (1-8). With the aid of Eq. (1-30) it is possible to prove that

$$\int_v \text{grad } U \, dv = \int_S \mathbf{n}U \, ds, \tag{1-31}$$

where v is the volume bounded by the surface S. The method of proof is identical to that of Eq. (1-18) given in Section 1-10.

1-12 GENERAL DEFINITION OF THE CURL OF A VECTOR FUNCTION

The form of Eqs. (1-16) and (1-30) suggests that a generalization of definition (1-10) for $\nabla \times \mathbf{B}$ can be obtained by inserting $\times \mathbf{B}$ into the square brackets in Eq. (1-17):

$$\text{curl } \mathbf{B} \triangleq \lim_{v \to 0} \frac{1}{v} \int_S \mathbf{n} \times \mathbf{B} \, ds. \tag{1-32}$$

That the two definitions (1-10) and (1-32) are equivalent can be seen by considering the elemental volume $v = \Delta x \, \Delta y \, \Delta z$ illustrated in Fig. 1-16. We have

$$\int_S \mathbf{n} \times \mathbf{B} \, ds = \mathbf{i}_x \times [\mathbf{B}(P_1) - \mathbf{B}(P_1')]\Delta y \, \Delta z + \mathbf{i}_y \times [\mathbf{B}(P_2) - \mathbf{B}(P_2')]\Delta x \, \Delta z$$
$$+ \mathbf{i}_z \times [\mathbf{B}(P_3) - \mathbf{B}(P_3')]\Delta x \, \Delta y.$$

Dividing by v and using Eq. (1-32), we obtain the equation

$$\text{curl } \mathbf{B} = \mathbf{i}_x \times \frac{\partial \mathbf{B}}{\partial x} + \mathbf{i}_y \times \frac{\partial \mathbf{B}}{\partial y} + \mathbf{i}_z \times \frac{\partial \mathbf{B}}{\partial z},$$

which is equivalent to Eq. (1-10).

The curl is an extremely important vector operation. In order to understand its physical significance let us investigate the application of Eq. (1-32) to the case of the rotation of a rigid body. Let us choose a circular rotor of radius a and width w which rotates with an angular velocity $\boldsymbol{\omega}$ (Fig. 1-17). The velocity at any point P on the rotor is given by

$$\mathbf{u} = \boldsymbol{\omega} \times \mathbf{r},$$

where $\mathbf{r}$ is the radius vector from the center O of the rotor to P. Let us suppose that $\mathbf{u}$ is known over the surface S of the rotor and that we wish to determine $\boldsymbol{\omega}$. With this in mind we consider the surface integral

$$\mathbf{I} \triangleq \int_S \mathbf{n} \times \mathbf{u} \, ds.$$

Since $\mathbf{n}(P_1) = -\mathbf{n}(P_2)$, where P_1 and P_2 are corresponding points on the sides S_1 and S_2 of the rotor, we see that only the edge S_0 contributes to $\mathbf{I}$. Over S_0 we have

$$\boldsymbol{\omega} \cdot \mathbf{n} = 0, \qquad \mathbf{n} \cdot \mathbf{r} = a.$$

Thus

$$\mathbf{n} \times \mathbf{u} = \mathbf{n} \times (\boldsymbol{\omega} \times \mathbf{r}) = a\boldsymbol{\omega}$$

and

$$\mathbf{I} = \int_{S_0} \mathbf{n} \times \mathbf{u} \, ds = a\boldsymbol{\omega}2\pi aw = 2\boldsymbol{\omega}v, \tag{1–33}$$

where $v = \pi a^2 w$ is the volume of the rotor.

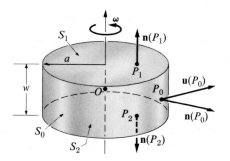

Fig. 1–17. A rotor with an angular velocity $\boldsymbol{\omega}$.

Taking $\mathbf{B} = \mathbf{u}$ in Eq. (1–32) and comparing it with Eq. (1–33), we see that

$$2\boldsymbol{\omega} = \operatorname{curl} \mathbf{u}. \tag{1–34}$$

Equation (1–34) allows us to state that the curl of a vector is a measure of the source of rotation of the vector field. For the rotor illustrated in Fig. 1–17 the source of rotation for the vector field $\mathbf{u}$ is the angular velocity $\boldsymbol{\omega}$.

With the aid of Fig. 1–17 we can obtain a different definition of curl which will subsequently prove to be useful. For the rotor we have shown that

$$\operatorname{curl} \mathbf{u} = \frac{1}{v} \int_S \mathbf{n} \times \mathbf{u} \, ds = \frac{1}{v} \int_{S_0} \mathbf{n} \times \mathbf{u} \, ds.$$

Let $ds = w \, dr$ and let us scalar-multiply the above equation by the unit vector $\mathbf{k} = \boldsymbol{\omega}/\omega$ (Fig. 1–17). We have

$$\mathbf{k} \cdot (\mathbf{n} \times \mathbf{u})\, dr = \mathbf{u} \cdot (\mathbf{k} \times \mathbf{n})\, dr = \mathbf{u} \cdot d\mathbf{r},$$

where dr is an elemental vector directed along the edge C_1 of the rotor. If we let $S_1 = \pi a^2$ and $v = wS_1$, we obtain

$$\mathbf{k} \cdot \operatorname{curl} \mathbf{u} = \frac{1}{S_1} \oint_{C_1} \mathbf{u} \cdot d\mathbf{r}, \qquad (1\text{–}35)$$

where the contour integral is along the contour C_1 defined by the edge of the rotor. Equation (1–35) can be generalized so that it applies to an arbitrary vector field $\mathbf{u}$:

$$\mathbf{n} \cdot \operatorname{curl} \mathbf{u} = \lim_{S \to 0} \frac{1}{S} \oint_C \mathbf{u} \cdot d\mathbf{r}. \qquad (1\text{–}36)$$

Here S is a surface bounded by a contour C and $\mathbf{n}$ is a unit normal to S. The contour C is traced out in a right-handed sense with respect to $\mathbf{n}$. That is, when $\mathbf{n}$ is moved along C in the direction indicated in Fig. 1–18, the vector $\mathbf{n} \times d\mathbf{r}$ will lie in S. It is important to remember this point, since it will be tacitly assumed that all contour integrals are evaluated in this manner. Failure to choose a right-handed sense could result in an incorrect sign in evaluating a contour integral.

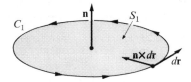

Fig. 1–18. Illustration defining the curl of a vector.

The contour integral in Eq. (1–36) is defined as the *circulation* of the vector field. Equation (1–36) defines the component of curl in the $\mathbf{n}$-direction as the *circulation per unit area* measured in a surface normal to $\mathbf{n}$. The source of the circulation can be found by evaluating the curl. For the rotor the circulation is

$$\oint_C \mathbf{u} \cdot d\mathbf{r} = (a\omega)(2\pi a),$$

and the circulation per unit area is 2ω, which is the component of curl $\mathbf{u}$ in the $\boldsymbol{\omega}$-direction. The source of the circulation is the angular velocity $\boldsymbol{\omega}$.

With the aid of Eq. (1–32), we can prove that

$$\int_v \operatorname{curl} \mathbf{B}\, dv = \int_S \mathbf{n} \times \mathbf{B}\, ds. \qquad (1\text{–}37)$$

The method of proof is identical to that of Eq. (1–18), given in Section 1–10.

1–13 STOKES' THEOREM

A theorem which we shall find very useful in electromagnetic theory is *Stokes' theorem:*

$$\int_S \mathbf{n} \cdot \text{curl } \mathbf{B} \, ds = \oint_C \mathbf{B} \cdot d\mathbf{r}. \tag{1–38}$$

Here the area S is bounded by a contour C which is traced through in a right-handed sense (Fig. 1–19).

To prove Stokes' theorem, we subdivide the surface S into N elemental areas ΔS_k. Applying Eq. (1–36) to ΔS_k yields

$$\mathbf{n} \cdot \text{curl } \mathbf{B}(P_k) \, \Delta S_k = \oint_{C_k} \mathbf{B} \cdot d\mathbf{r}, \tag{1–39}$$

where P_k is a suitably chosen interior point of ΔS_k. When we sum Eq. (1–39) over all N elements of area, we obtain

$$\sum_{k=1}^{N} \mathbf{n} \cdot \text{curl } \mathbf{B}(P_k) \, \Delta S_k = \oint_C \mathbf{B} \cdot d\mathbf{r}. \tag{1–40}$$

The final contour integral is over the contour C which bounds S. We can see this by noting that the part of the contour common to two adjacent areas within S is traced through in opposite senses and therefore contributes nothing to the final result. Equation (1–38) follows from Eq. (1–40) when we take the limit as $\Delta S_k \to 0$.

To illustrate Stokes' theorem let us consider the case of an infinitely long circular conductor of radius a which has a uniform current density $\mathbf{J} = \mathbf{i}_z J$ over its cross-sectional area (Fig. 1–20). It can be shown that the *magnetic field intensity* $\mathbf{H}$ resulting from this current is given by

$$\mathbf{H} = \begin{cases} \mathbf{i}_\phi \dfrac{Jr}{2}, & r < a, & \text{(1–41a)} \\[2ex] \mathbf{i}_\phi \dfrac{a^2 J}{2r}, & r > a, & \text{(1–41b)} \end{cases}$$

and that

$$\text{curl } \mathbf{H} = \begin{cases} \mathbf{J}, & r < a, & \text{(1–42a)} \\ 0, & r > a. & \text{(1–42b)} \end{cases}$$

Let us choose a contour C bounded by the circles $r = r_1$, $r = r_2$, and the angle α and evaluate the circulation of $\mathbf{H}$ around C (Fig. 1–21). If $r_2 < a$, we use Eq. (1–41a) and obtain

$$\oint_C \mathbf{H} \cdot d\mathbf{r} = \frac{J}{2} [r_2(r_2\alpha) - r_1(r_1\alpha)] = JS, \tag{1–43}$$

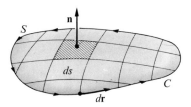

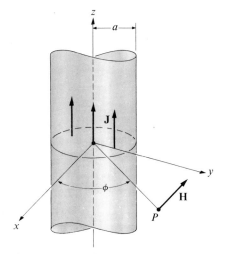

Fig. 1–19. A surface S bounded by a contour C.

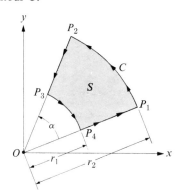

Fig. 1–20. An infinitely long circular conductor with a uniform axial current density $\mathbf{J}$.

Fig. 1–21. A contour C illustrating Stokes' theorem.

where S is the area bounded by C. From Eq. (1–42a) we have

$$\int_S \mathbf{n} \cdot \operatorname{curl} \mathbf{H}\, ds = JS. \qquad (1\text{–}44)$$

Equations (1–43) and (1–44) are equal, as required by Stokes' theorem. The current within C is JS, and this is considered as the source of the circulation for $\mathbf{H}$.

If $r_1 > a$, we use Eq. (1–41b) and obtain

$$\oint_C \mathbf{H} \cdot d\mathbf{r} = \frac{a^2 J}{2}\left[\frac{1}{r_2}\,(r_2\alpha) - \frac{1}{r_1}\,(r_1\alpha)\right] = 0. \qquad (1\text{–}45)$$

From Eq. (1–42b) we obtain

$$\int_S \mathbf{n} \cdot \operatorname{curl} \mathbf{H}\, ds = 0. \qquad (1\text{–}46)$$

Equations (1–45) and (1–46) are equal, as required by Stokes' theorem. The current within C is now zero, and consequently the circulation of $\mathbf{H}$ is also zero.

Equation (1–41a) can be written in the form

$$\mathbf{H} = \tfrac{1}{2}\mathbf{J} \times \mathbf{r}. \tag{1–47}$$

If we take a section of the conductor of length w we can establish an analogy with the rotor illustrated in Fig. 1–17 by noting that Eq. (1–47) is analogous with the equation

$$\mathbf{u} = \boldsymbol{\omega} \times \mathbf{r}. \tag{1–48}$$

The angular velocity is considered as the source of the rotation (circulation) for the vector field $\mathbf{u}$. By analogy we can state that the current density $\mathbf{J}$ is the source of the rotation (circulation) for the vector field $\mathbf{H}$.

1–14 SUMMARY OF GENERAL DEFINITIONS FOR GRADIENT, DIVERGENCE, AND CURL

For convenience we now summarize the results of the last four sections. The gradient of a scalar function U is defined by

$$\operatorname{grad} U \triangleq \lim_{v \to 0} \frac{1}{v} \int_S \mathbf{n}U \, ds. \tag{1–49}$$

The divergence of a vector function $\mathbf{B}$ is defined by

$$\operatorname{div} \mathbf{B} \triangleq \lim_{v \to 0} \frac{1}{v} \int_S \mathbf{n} \cdot \mathbf{B} \, ds. \tag{1–50}$$

The curl of a vector function $\mathbf{B}$ is defined by

$$\operatorname{curl} \mathbf{B} \triangleq \lim_{v \to 0} \frac{1}{v} \int_S \mathbf{n} \times \mathbf{B} \, ds. \tag{1–51}$$

The component of curl $\mathbf{B}$ in the direction of a unit surface normal $\mathbf{n}$ is defined by

$$\mathbf{n} \cdot \operatorname{curl} \mathbf{B} \triangleq \lim_{s \to 0} \frac{1}{S} \oint_C \mathbf{B} \cdot d\mathbf{r}. \tag{1–52}$$

The above equations are often abbreviated by use of the del operator ∇. We define

$$\nabla U \triangleq \operatorname{grad} U, \qquad \nabla \cdot \mathbf{D} \triangleq \operatorname{div} \mathbf{D}, \qquad \nabla \times \mathbf{B} \triangleq \operatorname{curl} \mathbf{B}. \tag{1–53}$$

It follows from Eqs. (1–49), (1–50), and (1–51) that the del operator is defined by

$$\nabla[\ ] \triangleq \lim_{v \to 0} \frac{1}{v} \int_S \mathbf{n}[\ ] \, ds. \tag{1–54}$$

The operations grad U, div $\mathbf{B}$, and curl $\mathbf{B}$ are obtained by inserting U, $\cdot \mathbf{B}$, and $\times \mathbf{B}$ in the brackets of Eq. (1–54). Since Eqs. (1–53) are identities, the question arises as to which notation is preferable. There are good reasons for both forms of notation and they both find widespread use in the literature. The del operator is extremely useful, since in most cases it can be treated as a vector. Because of this, vector identities are easily established by its use. If ∇ is considered as an operator, the left-hand side of Eqs. (1–53) are read as "del U," "del dot $\mathbf{D}$," and "del cross $\mathbf{B}$." However, these operations have an important physical significance which is obscured when ∇ is considered as an operator. The physical significance of these operations is more readily appreciated if we read ∇U, $\nabla \cdot \mathbf{D}$, and $\nabla \times \mathbf{B}$ as "grad U," "div $\mathbf{D}$," and "curl $\mathbf{B}$," that is, if we use the notation on the right-hand side of Eqs. (1–53). In this text both forms will be used. The forms grad U, div $\mathbf{D}$, and curl $\mathbf{B}$ will be chosen whenever the physical significance of the quantities under discussion is of some importance. In strictly mathematical manipulations, because of its convenience, the del notation ∇U, $\nabla \cdot \mathbf{D}$, and $\nabla \times \mathbf{B}$ will be used.

1-15 VECTOR IDENTITIES

In subsequent chapters we shall make use of a variety of vector identities involving the del operator. In this section the proof of these vector identities will be given. When we are establishing a vector identity we can proceed in two possible ways. We can express ∇ in a cartesian coordinate system and proceed directly, or we can make use of the general definitions (1–49), (1–50), and (1–51).

As an example let us consider the vector identity

$$\operatorname{div} \operatorname{curl} \mathbf{E} = 0. \tag{1–55}$$

In terms of the del operator the left-hand side of Eq. (1–55) is

$$\nabla \cdot (\nabla \times \mathbf{E}) = (\nabla \times \nabla) \cdot \mathbf{E}, \tag{1–56}$$

where we have considered ∇ as a vector and used the formula for the scalar triple product. Strictly speaking, we cannot equate $\nabla \times \nabla$ to zero, since ∇ is not a vector. Nevertheless, the result obtained by this operation is correct. To rigorously prove this result we could express Eq. (1–56) in cartesian coordinates. The result, however, is more conveniently obtained by using Eq. (1–18) and Stokes' theorem. Thus

$$\int_{v} \operatorname{div} \operatorname{curl} \mathbf{E} \, dv = \int_{S} \mathbf{n} \cdot \operatorname{curl} \mathbf{E} = \oint_{C} \mathbf{E} \cdot d\mathbf{r} = 0.$$

Since S is a closed surface, the contour C which bounds S can be taken to be any single point of S. Thus the contour integral is zero. Since the volume integral is zero for an arbitrary volume v, it follows that the integrand must be zero. This proves Eq. (1–55).

The vector identity

$$\operatorname{div}(c\mathbf{A}) = c \operatorname{div} \mathbf{A}, \tag{1–57}$$

where c is a constant, can be established in a cartesian coordinate system by the following manipulations:

$$\nabla \cdot (c\mathbf{A}) = \sum_u \mathbf{i}_u \cdot \frac{\partial}{\partial u}(c\mathbf{A}) = c \sum_u \mathbf{i}_u \cdot \frac{\partial \mathbf{A}}{\partial u} = c\nabla \cdot \mathbf{A}.$$

(The summation is over the values $u = x, y, z$.)

Let us now prove Eq. (1–57) with the aid of the divergence theorem. We have

$$\int_v \operatorname{div}(c\mathbf{A}) \, dv = \int_S c\mathbf{A} \cdot \mathbf{n} \, ds = c \int_S \mathbf{A} \cdot \mathbf{n} \, ds = \int_S c \operatorname{div} \mathbf{A} \, dv.$$

By means of these manipulations we again obtain a volume integral. Since v is arbitrary, the integrands of the volume integrals must be equal. This establishes Eq. (1–57).

If $\mathbf{A}$ is a constant and c variable, we have

$$\operatorname{div}(c\mathbf{A}) = \mathbf{A} \cdot \operatorname{grad} c. \tag{1–58}$$

In cartesian coordinates Eq. (1–58) can be proved by the following manipulations:

$$\nabla \cdot (c\mathbf{A}) = \sum_u \mathbf{i}_u \cdot \frac{\partial}{\partial u}(c\mathbf{A}) = \mathbf{A} \cdot \sum_u \mathbf{i}_u \frac{\partial c}{\partial u} = \mathbf{A} \cdot \nabla c.$$

To establish Eq. (1–58) without reference to a particular coordinate system, we can make use of the divergence theorem and Eq. (1–31). Thus

$$\int_v \operatorname{div}(c\mathbf{A}) \, dv = \mathbf{A} \cdot \int_S c\mathbf{n} \, ds = \int_v \mathbf{A} \cdot \operatorname{grad} c \, dv.$$

Since v is arbitrary the integrands of the volume integrals must be equal.

The vector identity

$$\operatorname{div}(\mathbf{A} \times \mathbf{C}) = \mathbf{C} \cdot \operatorname{curl} \mathbf{A}, \tag{1–59}$$

where $\mathbf{C}$ is a constant vector, can be proved in a similar manner. In cartesian coordinates we have

$$\nabla \cdot (\mathbf{A} \times \mathbf{C}) = \sum_u \mathbf{i}_u \cdot \frac{\partial}{\partial u}(\mathbf{A} \times \mathbf{C}) = \mathbf{C} \cdot \sum_u \mathbf{i}_u \times \frac{\partial \mathbf{A}}{\partial u} = \mathbf{C} \cdot \nabla \times \mathbf{A}.$$

An alternative proof of Eq. (1–59), which employs the divergence theorem and Eq. (1–37), is the following:

$$\int_v \operatorname{div}(\mathbf{A} \times \mathbf{C}) \, dv = \int_S \mathbf{n} \cdot (\mathbf{A} \times \mathbf{C}) \, ds = \mathbf{C} \cdot \int_S \mathbf{n} \times \mathbf{A} \, ds = \int_v \mathbf{C} \cdot \operatorname{curl} \mathbf{A} \, dv.$$

Since v is arbitrary, the integrands of the volume integrals must be equal, thus establishing Eq. (1–59).

A vector identity which finds frequent use in electromagnetic field theory is

$$\text{div}\,(\mathbf{A} \times \mathbf{B}) = \mathbf{B} \cdot \text{curl}\,\mathbf{A} - \mathbf{A} \cdot \text{curl}\,\mathbf{B}. \qquad (1\text{–}60)$$

In cartesian coordinates the proof of Eq. (1–60) makes use of the scalar triple product and proceeds as follows:

$$\nabla \cdot (\mathbf{A} \times \mathbf{B}) = \sum_u \mathbf{i}_u \cdot \frac{\partial}{\partial u}(\mathbf{A} \times \mathbf{B})$$

$$= \sum_u \left[\mathbf{B} \cdot \left(\mathbf{i}_u \times \frac{\partial \mathbf{A}}{\partial u} \right) - \mathbf{A} \cdot \left(\mathbf{i}_u \times \frac{\partial \mathbf{B}}{\partial u} \right) \right]$$

$$= \mathbf{B} \cdot \text{curl}\,\mathbf{A} - \mathbf{A} \cdot \text{curl}\,\mathbf{B}.$$

To establish Eq. (1–60) without reference to a particular coordinate system, we let P and P_0 be two neighboring points and let

$$\mathbf{B} \triangleq \mathbf{B}(P), \qquad \mathbf{B}_0 \triangleq \mathbf{B}(P_0),$$

$$\mathbf{A} \triangleq \mathbf{A}(P), \qquad \mathbf{A}_0 \triangleq \mathbf{A}(P_0).$$

The point P_0 is considered fixed, so that $\mathbf{A}_0$ and $\mathbf{B}_0$ are constant vectors. Consider now the vector

$$\mathbf{F} \triangleq (\mathbf{A} - \mathbf{A}_0) \times (\mathbf{B} - \mathbf{B}_0) = \mathbf{A} \times \mathbf{B} - \mathbf{A} \times \mathbf{B}_0 + \mathbf{B} \times \mathbf{A}_0 + \mathbf{A}_0 \times \mathbf{B}_0.$$

Taking the divergence of $\mathbf{F}$ and using Eq. (1–59) and the fact that

$$\text{div}\,(\mathbf{A}_0 \times \mathbf{B}_0) = 0$$

(see Problem 1–12) yields

$$\text{div}\,\mathbf{F} = \text{div}\,(\mathbf{A} \times \mathbf{B}) - \mathbf{B}_0 \cdot \text{curl}\,\mathbf{A} + \mathbf{A}_0 \cdot \text{curl}\,\mathbf{B}.$$

We now take $|P - P_0| = \varepsilon$, where ε is an arbitrarily small positive quantity, and we choose a sphere of radius ε centered at P_0. The magnitudes of the vectors $\mathbf{A} - \mathbf{A}_0$ and $\mathbf{B} - \mathbf{B}_0$ are both of the order of ε. Thus there exists a positive number M for which

$$|\mathbf{F} \cdot \mathbf{n}| \leqq M\varepsilon^2,$$

where $\mathbf{n}$ is the unit normal to the sphere. It follows from Eq. (1–50) that

$$|\text{div}\,\mathbf{F}| \leqq \frac{M\varepsilon^2(4\pi\varepsilon^2)}{4\pi\varepsilon^3/3} = 3M\varepsilon.$$

Thus, in the limit as $\varepsilon \to 0$, $\text{div}\,\mathbf{F} \to 0$, and we obtain Eq. (1–60) evaluated at P_0.

The identity

$$\text{div}\,(U\mathbf{A}) = U\,\text{div}\,\mathbf{A} + \mathbf{A} \cdot \text{grad}\,U \qquad (1\text{–}61)$$

can be established in a similar manner. In cartesian coordinates we have

$$\mathbf{\nabla} \cdot (U\mathbf{A}) = \sum_u \mathbf{i}_u \cdot \frac{\partial}{\partial u} (U\mathbf{A}) = \sum_u \left[U\mathbf{i}_u \cdot \frac{\partial \mathbf{A}}{\partial u} + \mathbf{A} \cdot \mathbf{i}_u \frac{\partial U}{\partial u} \right]$$

$$= U \mathbf{\nabla} \cdot \mathbf{A} + \mathbf{A} \cdot \mathbf{\nabla} U.$$

To establish Eq. (1-61) without reference to a particular coordinate system, we let

$$U \triangleq U(P), \qquad U_0 \triangleq U(P_0),$$

$$\mathbf{A} \triangleq \mathbf{A}(P), \qquad \mathbf{A}_0 \triangleq \mathbf{A}(P_0).$$

We consider P_0 as fixed, so that both U_0 and $\mathbf{A}_0$ are constants. If we take the divergence of the vector

$$\mathbf{F} \triangleq (U - U_0)(\mathbf{A} - \mathbf{A}_0) = U\mathbf{A} - U\mathbf{A}_0 - U_0\mathbf{A} + U_0\mathbf{A}_0$$

and use Eqs. (1-57) and (1-58), we obtain

$$\text{div } \mathbf{F} = \text{div } (U\mathbf{A}) - \mathbf{A}_0 \text{ grad } U - U_0 \text{ div } \mathbf{A}.$$

We now let $P \to P_0$, so that div $\mathbf{F} \to 0$. Thus, in the limit, we obtain Eq. (1-61) evaluated at P_0.

In the special case where $\mathbf{A} = \text{grad } U$, Eq. (1-61) takes the form

$$\text{div } (U \text{ grad } V) = \text{grad } U \text{ grad } V + U \text{ div grad } V.$$

The operator div grad occurs frequently; when it is applied to a scalar it is abbreviated as $\mathbf{\nabla}^2$ and is called the *Laplacian operator*. In cartesian coordinates the Laplacian operator is

$$\mathbf{\nabla}^2 \triangleq \frac{\partial^2}{\partial x^2} + \frac{\partial^2}{\partial y^2} + \frac{\partial^2}{\partial z^2}.$$

We now summarize the vector identities which we shall subsequently use in the development of electromagnetic field theory:

$$\text{div curl } \mathbf{E} = 0,$$

$$\mathbf{\nabla} \cdot (\mathbf{\nabla} \times \mathbf{E}) = 0, \tag{1-62}$$

$$\text{div } (\mathbf{A} \times \mathbf{B}) = \mathbf{B} \cdot \text{curl } \mathbf{A} - \mathbf{A} \cdot \text{curl } \mathbf{B},$$

$$\mathbf{\nabla} \cdot (\mathbf{A} \times \mathbf{B}) = \mathbf{B} \cdot (\mathbf{\nabla} \times \mathbf{A}) - \mathbf{A} \cdot (\mathbf{\nabla} \times \mathbf{B}), \tag{1-63}$$

$$\text{div } (U\mathbf{A}) = U \text{ div } \mathbf{A} + \mathbf{A} \cdot \text{grad } U,$$

$$\mathbf{\nabla} \cdot (U\mathbf{A}) = U \mathbf{\nabla} \cdot \mathbf{A} - \mathbf{A} \cdot \mathbf{\nabla} U, \tag{1-64}$$

$$\text{div } (U \text{ grad } V) = \text{grad } U \text{ grad } V + U \text{ div grad } V,$$

$$\mathbf{\nabla} \cdot (U \mathbf{\nabla} V) = \mathbf{\nabla} U \cdot \mathbf{\nabla} V + U \mathbf{\nabla}^2 V. \tag{1-65}$$

These vector identities need not be memorized. As the need arises they can be readily obtained by considering ∇ as a vector and using its representation in cartesian coordinates.

1-16 SOURCE POINTS AND FIELD POINTS

In electromagnetic field theory we consider that charges and currents at a source point Q set up an electromagnetic field at a field point P. The resultant field at P is obtained by summing (integrating) the effect of all sources. In subsequent chapters we shall see that for a vector source $\mathbf{J}$ at Q the resultant field vector at P has the form

$$\mathbf{F} = \int_v \frac{\mathbf{J}}{r}\, dv, \tag{1–66}$$

where r is the distance between P and Q. Thus

$$r^2 = (x_P - x_Q)^2 + (y_P - y_Q)^2 + (z_P - z_Q)^2.$$

The integration variables are x_Q, y_Q, and z_Q, so that $dv = dx_Q\, dy_Q\, dz_Q$. In order to distinguish between derivatives with respect to x_P, y_P, z_P and derivatives with respect to x_Q, y_Q, z_Q, we introduce a subscript on ∇:

$$\nabla_Q \triangleq \mathbf{i}_x \frac{\partial}{\partial x_Q} + \mathbf{i}_y \frac{\partial}{\partial y_Q} + \mathbf{i}_z \frac{\partial}{\partial z_Q},$$

$$\nabla_P \triangleq \mathbf{i}_x \frac{\partial}{\partial x_P} + \mathbf{i}_y \frac{\partial}{\partial y_P} + \mathbf{i}_z \frac{\partial}{\partial z_P}.$$

It is easily verified that we then have

$$\nabla_P \frac{1}{r} = -\mathbf{i}_x \frac{x_P - x_Q}{r^3} - \mathbf{i}_y \frac{y_P - y_Q}{r^3} - \mathbf{i}_z \frac{z_P - z_Q}{r^3} = -\nabla_Q \frac{1}{r}. \tag{1–67}$$

To see the usefulness of this simple result, let us compute the divergence of $\mathbf{F}$. We can differentiate under the integral sign, and since $\mathbf{J}$ is independent of P we can use Eq. (1–58) to obtain

$$\nabla_P \cdot \mathbf{F} = \int_v \nabla_P \cdot \frac{\mathbf{J}}{r}\, dv = \int_v \mathbf{J} \cdot \nabla_P \frac{1}{r}\, dv. \tag{1–68}$$

If any further manipulation of the volume integral in Eq. (1–68) is to be carried out, the integrand must be expressed in terms involving the divergence of a vector. It then becomes possible to apply the divergence theorem. The derivatives occurring in the divergence theorem are with respect to the integration variables, so that we must consider

$$\nabla_Q \cdot \frac{\mathbf{J}}{r} = \frac{1}{r} \nabla_Q \cdot \mathbf{J} + \mathbf{J} \cdot \nabla_Q \frac{1}{r} = \frac{1}{r} \nabla_Q \cdot \mathbf{J} - \mathbf{J} \cdot \nabla_P \frac{1}{r}.$$

Here we have used Eqs. (1–61) and (1–67). The seemingly trivial result given by Eq. (1–67) has allowed us to write the integrand in Eq. (1–68) in the form

$$\mathbf{J} \cdot \nabla_P \frac{1}{r} = \frac{1}{r} \nabla_Q \cdot \mathbf{J} - \nabla_Q \cdot \frac{\mathbf{J}}{r},$$

which then places us in a position where the divergence theorem can be applied. Thus

$$\nabla_P \cdot \mathbf{F} = \int_v \frac{\nabla_Q \cdot \mathbf{J}}{r} \, dv - \int_S \frac{\mathbf{n} \cdot \mathbf{J}}{r} \, ds. \qquad (1\text{–}69)$$

Here S is the surface which bounds v.

The type of manipulation used to obtain Eq. (1–69) will be used extensively in the subsequent chapters and should be thoroughly understood. It should be noted that the divergence of $\mathbf{F}$ is evaluated at P and that the divergence of $\mathbf{J}$ is evaluated at Q. We can drop the subscript letters provided that we understand at which point the divergence is to be evaluated. For example, in the divergence theorem we do not introduce the subscript Q, since it is tacitly assumed that the divergence is to be evaluated at Q.

1–17 GREEN'S THEOREM AND THE UNIQUENESS THEOREM

If we substitute

$$\mathbf{D}_1 = U \text{ grad } V,$$

$$\mathbf{D}_2 = V \text{ grad } U$$

into Eq. (1–18) and subtract the two equations, we obtain *Green's theorem*

$$\int_v (V \, \nabla^2 U - U \, \nabla^2 V) \, dv = \int_S \left(V \frac{\partial U}{\partial n} - U \frac{\partial V}{\partial n} \right) ds. \qquad (1\text{–}70)$$

Here the function $\partial U / \partial n = \mathbf{n} \cdot \text{grad } U$ is the rate of change of U in the direction of the surface normal $\mathbf{n}$.

Green's theorem is of importance because its application results in a simple method for solving *Poisson's equation*,

$$\nabla^2 U = -f, \qquad (1\text{–}71)$$

which occurs frequently in electromagnetic field problems. In Eq. (1–71) the function f is a piecewise continuous function of position. In order to use Green's theorem in the solution of Poisson's equation, we must choose $V = 1/r$ in Eq. (1–70). It can be shown (see Problem 1–13) that

$$\nabla^2 \frac{1}{r} = 0, \qquad r \neq 0. \qquad (1\text{–}72)$$

Because of Eq. (1–72), Eq. (1–70) reduces to

$$\int_v -\frac{f}{r}\,dv = \int_S \left(\frac{1}{r}\frac{\partial U}{\partial n} - U\frac{\partial}{\partial n}\frac{1}{r}\right) ds, \qquad (1\text{–}73)$$

provided that $r \neq 0$ within v. Here r is the distance between a source point Q and a field point P. Let us choose v to be bounded by a small sphere S_1 of radius a and by a large sphere S_2 of radius b. Both spheres are taken to be centered at the field point P (Fig. 1–22). We first consider S_2 and assume that a positive constant M exists for which

$$|U| \leqq \frac{M}{r}, \qquad \left|\frac{\partial U}{\partial r}\right| \leqq \frac{M}{r^2}, \qquad r \geqq b. \quad (1\text{–}74)$$

It follows from the conditions (1–74) that

$$\left|\int_{S_2}\left(\frac{1}{r}\frac{\partial U}{\partial r} - U\frac{\partial}{\partial r}\frac{1}{r}\right) ds\right| \leqq \frac{2M}{b}\frac{1}{b^2}4\pi b^2 \to 0$$

for $b \to \infty$, and we need therefore concern ourselves only with S_1. For S_1 we have

$$\left|\int_{S_1}\frac{1}{r}\frac{\partial U}{\partial n} ds\right| \leqq \frac{m}{a}4\pi a^2 \to 0$$

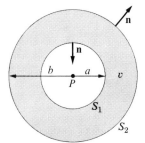

Fig. 1–22. Illustration of the derivation of Green's theorem.

for $a \to 0$. Here m is the maximum magnitude of $\partial U/\partial n$ on S_1. Thus, for $b \to \infty$, $a \to 0$, the only nonzero part of the surface integral in Eq. (1–73) (note that $\partial/\partial n = -\partial/\partial r$ on S_1) is

$$\int_{S_1} -U\frac{\partial}{\partial n}\frac{1}{r}\,ds = -U(P')\frac{1}{a^2}4\pi a^2 = -U(P')4\pi,$$

where P' is a suitably chosen interior point of the volume bounded by S_1. As $a \to 0$, $P' \to P$. Thus we obtain

$$U \triangleq U(P) = \frac{1}{4\pi}\int_v \frac{f}{r}\,dv. \qquad (1\text{–}75)$$

In most physical situations f represents the source density of a scalar field and the source is contained within a finite volume. It is then easily verified that Eq. (1–75) satisfies the conditions (1–74). We need only note that as $r \to \infty$, we have

$$U \simeq \frac{1}{4\pi r}\int_v f\,dv = \frac{Q}{4\pi r}$$

where $Q \triangleq \int_v f\,dv$ is the source of the scalar field. The solution (1–75) of Poisson's equation will play a fundamental role in the solution of electromagnetic field problems. The solution of Poisson's equation meeting the conditions (1–74) can be shown to be unique.

The uniqueness theorem states that there is only one solution U of Poisson's equation within a region v if U or $\partial U/\partial n$ is specified over the surface S which bounds v. We can prove the uniqueness theorem by assuming that there are two solutions U_1 and U_2 meeting all conditions and proving that $U_1 = U_2$. If we let $V = U_1 - U_2$, it follows that

$$\nabla^2 V = 0 \qquad \text{within } v, \qquad (1\text{–}76a)$$

$$V = 0 \quad \text{or} \quad \frac{\partial V}{\partial n} = 0 \qquad \text{over } S. \qquad (1\text{–}76b)$$

Using the vector identity (1–65) and Eq. (1–76a), we obtain

$$\text{div} (V \, \text{grad} \, V) = (\text{grad} \, V)^2.$$

Because of conditions (1–76b), the divergence theorem yields

$$\int_v (\text{grad} \, V)^2 \, dv = 0.$$

We must therefore have grad $V = 0$ and thus $V = \text{const} = c$. However, if $V = 0$ over S, it follows that $c = 0$. Thus $U_1 = U_2$, and there is only one solution. To make U unique for the case in which $\partial U/\partial u = 0$ over S, we need only specify the value of U at any one point of S.

1-18 ORTHOGONAL CURVILINEAR COORDINATES

Cartesian coordinates are convenient because the unit vectors $\mathbf{i}_x$, $\mathbf{i}_y$, and $\mathbf{i}_z$ are constant. However, the solution of field problems often takes a simpler form in a coordinate system which is not cartesian. We shall, therefore, be interested in representing the gradient of a scalar function and the divergence and curl of a vector function in a general curvilinear coordinate system. Let

$$u_1 = u_1(x, y, z), \qquad u_2 = u_2(x, y, z), \qquad u_3 = u_3(x, y, z).$$

The three surfaces defined by the equations $u_1 = c_1$, $u_2 = c_2$, and $u_3 = c_3$, where c_1, c_2, and c_3 are constants, are called *coordinate surfaces* and each pair of such surfaces intersect in a *coordinate curve*. The intersection of two coordinate curves determines a field point $P(u_1, u_2, u_3)$ (Fig. 1–23). If the coordinate surfaces intersect at right angles, the curvilinear coordinate system is called *orthogonal*. The cartesian coordinate system in which $u_1 = x$, $u_2 = y$, and $u_3 = z$ is the simplest of the orthogonal coordinate systems. In general, we let $\mathbf{i}_k$ represent a unit vector at P in the direction of the coordinate curve $u_k (k = 1, 2, 3)$. Note that in a coordinate system which is not cartesian,

$\mathbf{i}_k$ becomes a function of P. In a general orthogonal coordinate system we can represent a vector $\mathbf{E}$ in the form

$$\mathbf{E} = \mathbf{i}_1 E_1 + \mathbf{i}_2 E_2 + \mathbf{i}_3 E_3,$$

where E_1, E_2, and E_3 are the components of $\mathbf{E}$.

Let us consider the radius vector $\mathbf{r}$ from the origin to a point P. The differential of $\mathbf{r}$ is given by

$$d\mathbf{r} = \frac{\partial \mathbf{r}}{\partial u_1} du_1 + \frac{\partial \mathbf{r}}{\partial u_2} du_2 + \frac{\partial \mathbf{r}}{\partial u_3} du_3 = \mathbf{i}_1 h_1 \, du_1 + \mathbf{i}_2 h_2 \, du_2 + \mathbf{i}_3 h_3 \, du_3,$$

$$(1\text{-}77)$$

where we have set

$$h_k \triangleq \frac{dl_k}{du_k}, \qquad k = 1, 2, 3, \tag{1-78}$$

and where the dl_k are the components of $d\mathbf{r}$. The length dl of $d\mathbf{r}$ (note that the unit vectors are orthogonal) is determined by

$$(dl)^2 \triangleq d\mathbf{r} \cdot d\mathbf{r} = (dl_1)^2 + (dl_2)^2 + (dl_3)^2$$
$$= (h_1 \, du_1)^2 + (h_2 \, du_2)^2 + (h_3 \, du_3)^2. \tag{1-79}$$

We shall see that Eq. (1-79) is very useful in finding the parameters h_1, h_2, and h_3.

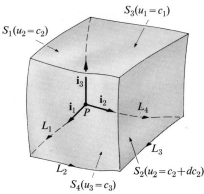

Fig. 1–23. Orthogonal curvilinear coordinates.

The area of the surface element in any of the coordinate planes is determined by multiplying the lengths of the appropriate line elements. For example, in the $u_2 = c_2$ plane, the element of area is

$$ds_2 = dl_1 \, dl_3 = h_1 h_3 \, du_1 \, du_3. \tag{1-80}$$

The volume element is a rectangular parallelepiped of volume

$$dv = dl_1 \, dl_2 \, dl_3 = h_1 h_2 h_3 \, du_1 \, du_2 \, du_3. \tag{1-81}$$

Let us now determine a representation for the gradient of a scalar function U in a general orthogonal coordinate system. The components of the gradient of U give the rates of change of U in the coordinate directions. These components (see Eq. 1–78) are

$$\frac{\partial U}{\partial l_k} = \frac{1}{h_1}\frac{\partial U}{\partial u_k}, \qquad k = 1, 2, 3.$$

Thus

$$\text{grad } U = \mathbf{i}_1 \frac{1}{h_1}\frac{\partial U}{\partial h_1} + \mathbf{i}_2 \frac{1}{h_2}\frac{\partial U}{\partial u_2} + \mathbf{i}_3 \frac{1}{h_3}\frac{\partial U}{\partial u_3}. \tag{1–82}$$

To determine div $\mathbf{D}$ in general coordinates, we apply Eq. (1–50) to an elemental volume dv (Fig. 1–23). Considering $\mathbf{D}$ as a flux density we find that the flux ϕ_2 of $\mathbf{D}$ through the coordinate surface S_1 into the volume dv (see Eq. 1–80) is

$$\phi_2 = \mathbf{D} \cdot \mathbf{i}_2\, ds_2 = D_2 h_1 h_3\, du_1\, du_3.$$

The flux ϕ_2' through the coordinate surface S_2 can be found by determining the change in ϕ_2 due to the change du_2:

$$\phi_2' = \phi_2 + \frac{\partial \phi_2}{\partial u_2}\, du_2.$$

The resultant flux flowing out of dv through the surfaces S_1 and S_2 is

$$\phi_2' - \phi_2 = \frac{\partial \phi_2}{\partial u_2}\, du_2 = \frac{\partial}{\partial u_2}(D_2 h_1 h_3)\, du_1\, du_2\, du_3.$$

We obtain similar expressions for the flux through the remaining surfaces bounding dv. These can be obtained from the above expression by a cyclic interchange of subscripts. With the aid of Eqs. (1–50) and (1–81), we obtain

$$\text{div } \mathbf{D} = \frac{1}{h_1 h_2 h_3}\left[\frac{\partial}{\partial u_1}(h_2 h_3 D_1) + \frac{\partial}{\partial u_2}(h_3 h_1 D_2) + \frac{\partial}{\partial u_3}(h_1 h_2 D_3)\right]. \tag{1–83}$$

The components of the curl of a vector function $\mathbf{A}$ can be obtained by evaluating the circulation of $\mathbf{A}$ around elemental rectangles in the coordinate planes. Consider the component $(\text{curl }\mathbf{A})_3$. The integral

$$I_1 \triangleq \int_{L_1} \mathbf{A} \cdot d\mathbf{r} = A_1\, dl_1 = A_1 h_1\, du_1$$

is evaluated by integrating along the coordinate line L_1 in the direction of increasing u_1 (see Fig. 1–23). The integral

$$I_3 \triangleq \int_{L_3} \mathbf{A} \cdot d\mathbf{r},$$

where the integration is along the coordinate line L_3 in the direction of increasing u_1, can be determined from the change in I_1 which results from the change in u_2. Thus

$$I_3 = I_1 + \frac{\partial I_1}{\partial u_2}\, du_2 = I_1 + \frac{\partial}{\partial u_2}(h_1 A_1)\, du_1\, du_2.$$

We obtain similar expressions for the integrals along the coordinate lines L_2 and L_4. Thus, since the contour C consists of L_1 and L_2 traced through in a positive sense and L_3 and L_4 traced through in a negative sense, we have

$$\oint_C \mathbf{A} \cdot d\mathbf{r} = I_1 + I_2 - I_3 - I_4 = \left[\frac{\partial}{\partial u_1}(h_2 A_2) - \frac{\partial}{\partial u_2}(h_1 A_1)\right] du_1\, du_2,$$

and Eq. (1–36) yields

$$(\operatorname{curl} \mathbf{A})_3 = \frac{1}{h_1 h_2}\left[\frac{\partial}{\partial u_1}(h_2 A_2) - \frac{\partial}{\partial u_2}(h_1 A_1)\right],$$

$$(\operatorname{curl} \mathbf{A})_1 = \frac{1}{h_2 h_3}\left[\frac{\partial}{\partial u_2}(h_3 A_3) - \frac{\partial}{\partial u_3}(h_2 A_2)\right], \qquad (1\text{–}84)$$

$$(\operatorname{curl} \mathbf{A})_2 = \frac{1}{h_3 h_1}\left[\frac{\partial}{\partial u_3}(h_1 A_1) - \frac{\partial}{\partial u_1}(h_3 A_3)\right],$$

where the remaining components of curl $\mathbf{A}$ have been determined by a cyclic interchange of subscripts.

Equations (1–84) allow us to express curl $\mathbf{A}$ formally in terms of a determinant:

$$\operatorname{curl} \mathbf{A} = \frac{1}{h_1 h_2 h_3}\begin{vmatrix} \mathbf{i}_1 h_1 & \mathbf{i}_2 h_2 & \mathbf{i}_3 h_3 \\ \dfrac{\partial}{\partial u_1} & \dfrac{\partial}{\partial u_2} & \dfrac{\partial}{\partial u_3} \\ h_1 A_1 & h_2 A_2 & h_3 A_3 \end{vmatrix}. \qquad (1\text{–}85)$$

With the aid of Eqs. (1–82) and (1–83) we can determine the Laplacian of a scalar function U:

$$\nabla^2 U = \frac{1}{h_1 h_2 h_3}\left[\frac{\partial}{\partial u_1}\left(\frac{h_2 h_3}{h_1}\frac{\partial U}{\partial u_1}\right) + \frac{\partial}{\partial u_2}\left(\frac{h_3 h_1}{h_2}\frac{\partial U}{\partial u_2}\right) + \frac{\partial}{\partial u_3}\left(\frac{h_1 h_2}{h_3}\frac{\partial U}{\partial u_3}\right)\right]. \quad (1\text{–}86)$$

The representation for ∇ in general coordinates can be determined with the aid of Eq. (1–54). The surface S is taken to be the one bounding the volume element dv illustrated in Fig. 1–23. For the coordinate surface S_1 we define an operator by the equation

$$\mathbf{O}_1 \triangleq \int_{S_1} \mathbf{i}_2[\ ]\, ds = \mathbf{i}_2[\ ]h_1 h_3\, du_1\, du_3.$$

The operator $\mathbf{O}_2$ for the surface S_2 can be obtained by evaluating the change in $\mathbf{O}_1$ due to the change in u_2. Thus

$$\mathbf{O}_2 = \mathbf{O}_1 + \frac{\partial \mathbf{O}_1}{\partial u_2}\, du_2 = \mathbf{O}_1 + \frac{\partial}{\partial u_2}\,(h_1 h_3 \mathbf{i}_2[\ ])\, du_1\, du_2\, du_3.$$

Noting that $\mathbf{n} = -\mathbf{i}_2$ over S_1 and that $\mathbf{n} = \mathbf{i}_2$ over S_2, we obtain

$$\int_{S_1+S_2} \mathbf{n}[\ ]\, ds = \mathbf{O}_2 - \mathbf{O}_1 = \frac{\partial}{\partial u_2}\,(h_1 h_3 \mathbf{i}_2[\ ])\, du_1\, du_2\, du_3. \qquad (1\text{–}87)$$

We obtain similar expressions for the remaining surfaces of dv. These can be obtained from Eq. (1–87) by a cyclic interchange of subscripts. Equation (1–54) then yields

$$\nabla[\ ] = \frac{1}{h_1 h_2 h_3}\left\{\frac{\partial}{\partial u_1}\,(h_3 h_2 \mathbf{i}_1[\ ]) + \frac{\partial}{\partial u_2}\,(h_1 h_3 \mathbf{i}_2[\ ]) + \frac{\partial}{\partial u_3}\,(h_2 h_1 \mathbf{i}_3[\ ])\right\}. \qquad (1\text{–}88)$$

The operations ∇U, $\nabla \cdot \mathbf{D}$, and $\nabla \times \mathbf{A}$ are obtained by inserting U, $\cdot\, \mathbf{D}$, and $\times\, \mathbf{A}$ into the square brackets of Eq. (1–88). Thus

$$\nabla U = \frac{1}{h_1 h_2 h_3}\left[\frac{\partial}{\partial u_1}\,(\mathbf{i}_1 h_3 h_2 U) + \frac{\partial}{\partial u_2}\,(\mathbf{i}_2 h_1 h_3 U) + \frac{\partial}{\partial u_3}\,(\mathbf{i}_3 h_2 h_1 U)\right], \qquad (1\text{–}89)$$

$$\nabla \cdot \mathbf{D} = \frac{1}{h_1 h_2 h_3}\left[\frac{\partial}{\partial u_1}\,(h_3 h_2 \mathbf{i}_1 \cdot \mathbf{D}) + \frac{\partial}{\partial u_2}\,(h_1 h_3 \mathbf{i}_2 \cdot \mathbf{D}) + \frac{\partial}{\partial u_3}\,(h_2 h_1 \mathbf{i}_3 \cdot \mathbf{D})\right],$$
$$\qquad (1\text{–}90)$$

$$\nabla \times \mathbf{A} = \frac{1}{h_1 h_2 h_3}\left[\frac{\partial}{\partial u_1}\,(h_3 h_2 \mathbf{i}_1 \times \mathbf{A}) + \frac{\partial}{\partial u_2}\,(h_1 h_3 \mathbf{i}_2 \times \mathbf{A}) + \frac{\partial}{\partial u_3}\,(h_2 h_1 \mathbf{i}_3 \times \mathbf{A})\right].$$
$$\qquad (1\text{–}91)$$

Equation (1–90) is identical to Eq. (1–83). However, Eqs. (1–89) and (1–91) appear to differ from Eqs. (1–82) and (1–85). Let us first consider Eq. (1–89) and apply it to the case in which $U = U_0 = $ const. Since the gradient of a constant is zero (see Problem 1–12), we obtain

$$\mathbf{F} \triangleq \frac{\partial}{\partial u_1}\,(\mathbf{i}_1 h_3 h_2) + \frac{\partial}{\partial u_2}\,(\mathbf{i}_2 h_1 h_3) + \frac{\partial}{\partial u_3}\,(\mathbf{i}_3 h_2 h_1) = 0. \qquad (1\text{–}92)$$

If U is variable, we must consider the term

$$\frac{\partial}{\partial u_1}\,(\mathbf{i}_1 h_3 h_2 U) = \mathbf{i}_1 h_3 h_2 \frac{\partial U}{\partial u_1} + U \frac{\partial}{\partial u_1}\,(\mathbf{i}_1 h_3 h_2)$$

Similar expressions are obtained for the remaining terms of Eq. (1–89).

Thus

$$\nabla U = \mathbf{i}_1 \frac{1}{h_1} \frac{\partial U}{\partial u_1} + \mathbf{i}_2 \frac{1}{h_2} \frac{\partial U}{\partial u_2} + \mathbf{i}_3 \frac{1}{h_3} \frac{\partial U}{\partial h_3} + U\mathbf{F}. \qquad (1\text{--}93)$$

Since $\mathbf{F} = 0$, we see that Eq. (1–89) is equivalent to Eq. (1–82).

Let us now consider Eq. (1–91). To show that Eq. (1–91) is equivalent to Eq. (1–85), we proceed in a manner similar to that used in obtaining Eq. (1–93). This first requires finding a simple vector $\mathbf{A}$ for which curl $\mathbf{A} = 0$. A suitable choice is

$$\mathbf{A} = \mathbf{i}_1 \frac{c_1}{h_1} + \mathbf{i}_2 \frac{c_2}{h_2} + \mathbf{i}_3 \frac{c_3}{h_3}, \qquad (1\text{--}94)$$

where c_1, c_2, and c_3 are arbitrary constants. For this choice of $\mathbf{A}$ (see Eq. 1–77), we have

$$\mathbf{A} \cdot d\mathbf{r} = d(c_1 u_1 + c_2 u_2 + c_3 u_3).$$

Hence

$$\oint_C \mathbf{A} \cdot d\mathbf{r} = 0 \qquad (1\text{--}95)$$

for any closed contour. It then follows from Eq. (1–52) that all components of curl $\mathbf{A}$ are zero and consequently that curl $\mathbf{A} = 0$. If we substitute Eq. (1–94) into Eq. (1–91), we obtain

$$\frac{1}{h_1 h_2 h_3} (c_1 \mathbf{F}_1 + c_2 \mathbf{F}_2 + c_3 \mathbf{F}_3) = 0, \qquad (1\text{--}96)$$

where

$$\mathbf{F}_1 \triangleq \frac{\partial}{\partial u_3} (h_2 \mathbf{i}_2) - \frac{\partial}{\partial u_2} (h_3 \mathbf{i}_3) = 0,$$

$$\mathbf{F}_2 \triangleq \frac{\partial}{\partial u_1} (h_3 \mathbf{i}_3) - \frac{\partial}{\partial u_3} (h_1 \mathbf{i}_1) = 0, \qquad (1\text{--}97)$$

$$\mathbf{F}_3 \triangleq \frac{\partial}{\partial u_2} (h_1 \mathbf{i}_1) - \frac{\partial}{\partial u} (h_2 \mathbf{i}_2) = 0.$$

The fact that $\mathbf{F}_1 = 0$ follows from Eq. (1–96) when we take $c_1 = 1$, $c_2 = c_3 = 0$. In a similar manner we can prove that $\mathbf{F}_2 = 0 = \mathbf{F}_3$.

If $\mathbf{A}$ is a general vector we must consider the term

$$\frac{\partial}{\partial u_1} (h_3 h_2 \mathbf{i}_1 \times \mathbf{A}) = \frac{\partial}{\partial u_1} (\mathbf{i}_3 h_2 h_3 A_2 - \mathbf{i}_2 h_2 h_3 A_3)$$

$$= \frac{\partial (h_2 A_2)}{\partial u_1} h_3 \mathbf{i}_3 - \frac{\partial (h_3 A_3)}{\partial u_1} h_2 \mathbf{i}_2$$

$$+ h_2 A_2 \frac{\partial}{\partial u_1} (h_3 \mathbf{i}_3) - h_3 A_3 \frac{\partial}{\partial u_1} (h_2 \mathbf{i}_2). \qquad (1\text{--}98)$$

Similar expressions are obtained for the remaining terms of Eq. (1–91). Thus

$$\text{curl } \mathbf{A} = \frac{1}{h_1 h_2 h_3} \begin{vmatrix} \mathbf{i}_1 h_1 & \mathbf{i}_2 h_2 & \mathbf{i}_3 h_3 \\ \dfrac{\partial}{\partial u_1} & \dfrac{\partial}{\partial u_2} & \dfrac{\partial}{\partial u_3} \\ h_1 A_1 & h_2 A_2 & h_3 A_3 \end{vmatrix}$$

$$+ \frac{1}{h_1 h_2 h_3} (h_1 A_1 \mathbf{F}_1 + h_2 A_2 \mathbf{F}_2 + h_3 A_3 \mathbf{F}_3). \quad (1–99)$$

Note that the term in parentheses in Eq. (1–99) can be obtained by choosing $c_k = h_k A_k$ in Eq. (1–94) and that it then corresponds to the left-hand side of Eq. (1–96). We can therefore conclude that this term vanishes; it then follows that Eq. (1–91) is equivalent to Eq. (1–85).

1–19 GRADIENT, DIVERGENCE, CURL, AND LAPLACIAN IN CYLINDRICAL COORDINATES

Cylindrical coordinates are defined by the equations

$$u_1 = r, \qquad u_2 = \phi, \qquad u_3 = z,$$

where $r^2 = x^2 + y^2$. The surface $r = $ const is a circular cylinder, the surface $\phi = $ const is a plane through the z-axis, and the surface $z = $ const is a plane normal to the z-axis (Fig. 1–10). The unit vectors in the direction of increasing r, ϕ, and z were taken to be $\mathbf{i}_r$, $\mathbf{i}_\phi$, and $\mathbf{i}_z$, respectively (see Section 1–5).

The length of a line element can be found with the aid of Fig. 1–24; it is given by

$$(dl)^2 = (dr)^2 + (r\,d\phi)^2 + (dz)^2.$$

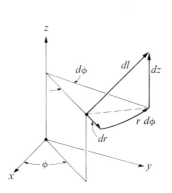

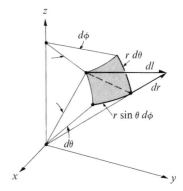

Fig. 1–24. A line element in cylindrical coordinates.

Fig. 1–25. A line element in spherical coordinates.

Comparing with Eq. (1–79) yields

$$h_1 = 1, \qquad h_2 = r, \qquad h_3 = 1.$$

The gradient, divergence, curl, and Laplacian in cylindrical coordinates can be obtained from Eqs. (1–82), (1–83), (1–85), and (1–86):

$$\nabla U = \mathbf{i}_r \frac{\partial U}{\partial r} + \mathbf{i}_\phi \frac{1}{r}\frac{\partial U}{\partial \phi} + \mathbf{i}_z \frac{\partial U}{\partial z}, \tag{1–100}$$

$$\nabla \cdot \mathbf{D} = \frac{1}{r}\left[\frac{\partial}{\partial r}(rD_r) + \frac{\partial D_\phi}{\partial \phi} + \frac{\partial}{\partial z}(rD_z)\right], \tag{1–101}$$

$$\nabla \times \mathbf{A} = \frac{1}{r}\begin{vmatrix} \mathbf{i}_r & \mathbf{i}_\phi r & \mathbf{i}_z \\ \dfrac{\partial}{\partial r} & \dfrac{\partial}{\partial \phi} & \dfrac{\partial}{\partial z} \\ A_r & rA_\phi & A_z \end{vmatrix}$$

$$= \mathbf{i}_r \frac{1}{r}\left(\frac{\partial A_z}{\partial \phi} - r\frac{\partial A_\phi}{\partial z}\right) + \mathbf{i}_\phi\left(\frac{\partial A_r}{\partial z} - \frac{\partial A_z}{\partial r}\right) + \mathbf{i}_z \frac{1}{r}\left[\frac{\partial}{\partial r}(rA_\phi) - \frac{\partial A_r}{\partial z}\right], \tag{1–102}$$

$$\nabla^2 U = \frac{1}{r}\left[\frac{\partial}{\partial r}\left(r\frac{\partial U}{\partial r}\right) + \frac{1}{r}\frac{\partial^2 U}{\partial \phi^2}\right] + \frac{\partial^2 U}{\partial z^2}. \tag{1–103}$$

1-20 GRADIENT, DIVERGENCE, CURL, AND LAPLACIAN IN SPHERICAL COORDINATES

Spherical coordinates are defined by the equations

$$u_1 = r, \qquad u_2 = \theta, \qquad u_3 = \phi,$$

where $r^2 = x^2 + y^2 + z^2$. The surface $r = $ const is a sphere of radius r, the surface $\theta = $ const is a cone of half-angle θ, and the surface $\phi = $ const is a plane which passes through the z-axis (Fig. 1–11). The unit vectors in the direction of increasing r, θ, and ϕ are taken to be $\mathbf{i}_r$, $\mathbf{i}_\theta$, and $\mathbf{i}_\phi$, respectively (see Section 1–6).

The length of a line element can be found with the aid of Fig. 1–25; it is given by

$$(dl)^2 = (dr)^2 + (r\,d\theta)^2 + (r\sin\theta\,d\phi)^2.$$

Comparing with Eq. (1–79) yields

$$h_1 = 1, \qquad h_2 = r, \qquad h_3 = r\sin\theta.$$

The gradient, divergence, curl, and Laplacian in spherical coordinates can be obtained from Eqs. (1–82), (1–83), (1–85), and (1–86):

$$\nabla U = \mathbf{i}_r \frac{\partial U}{\partial r} + \mathbf{i}_\theta \frac{1}{r} \frac{\partial U}{\partial \theta} + \mathbf{i}_\phi \frac{1}{r \sin \theta} \frac{\partial U}{\partial \phi}, \tag{1-104}$$

$$\nabla \cdot \mathbf{D} = \frac{1}{r^2 \sin \theta} \left[\frac{\partial}{\partial r} (r^2 \sin \theta D_r) + \frac{\partial}{\partial \theta} (r \sin \theta D_\theta) + \frac{\partial}{\partial \phi} (r D_\phi) \right], \tag{1-105}$$

$$\nabla \times \mathbf{A} = \frac{1}{r^2 \sin \theta} \begin{vmatrix} \mathbf{i}_r & \mathbf{i}_\theta r & \mathbf{i}_\phi r \sin \theta \\ \dfrac{\partial}{\partial r} & \dfrac{\partial}{\partial \theta} & \dfrac{\partial}{\partial \phi} \\ A_r & r A_\theta & r \sin \theta A_\phi \end{vmatrix}$$

$$= \mathbf{i}_r \frac{1}{r \sin \theta} \left[\frac{\partial}{\partial \theta} (\sin \theta A_\phi) - \frac{\partial A_\theta}{\partial \phi} \right] + \mathbf{i}_\theta \frac{1}{r \sin \theta} \left[\frac{\partial A_r}{\partial \phi} - \sin \theta \frac{\partial}{\partial r} (r A_\phi) \right]$$

$$+ \mathbf{i}_\phi \frac{1}{r} \left[\frac{\partial}{\partial r} (r A_\theta) - \frac{\partial A_r}{\partial \theta} \right], \tag{1-106}$$

$$\nabla^2 U = \frac{1}{r^2} \frac{\partial}{\partial r} \left(r^2 \frac{\partial U}{\partial r} \right) + \frac{1}{r^2 \sin \theta} \frac{\partial}{\partial \theta} \left(\sin \theta \frac{\partial U}{\partial \theta} \right) + \frac{1}{r^2 \sin^2 \theta} \frac{\partial^2 U}{\partial \phi^2}. \tag{1-107}$$

1-21 TWO-DIMENSIONAL COORDINATES

In the case of a two-dimensional field the scalar or vector functions associated with the field are independent of one of the coordinates, which we may take to be u_3. Thus, for a scalar function, $\partial U / \partial u_3 = 0$ and the gradient of U given by Eq. (1–82) may be expressed in the form

$$\nabla_T U \triangleq \mathbf{i}_1 \frac{1}{h_1} \frac{\partial U}{\partial u_1} + \mathbf{i}_2 \frac{1}{h_2} \frac{\partial U}{\partial u_2}, \tag{1-108}$$

which we define as the *transverse gradient* of U. We define ∇_T as the *transverse del operator*. The Laplacian of U, Eq. (1–86), takes the form

$$\nabla_T^2 U \triangleq \frac{1}{h_1 h_2} \left[\frac{\partial}{\partial u_1} \left(\frac{h_2}{h_1} \frac{\partial U}{\partial u_1} \right) + \frac{\partial}{\partial u_2} \left(\frac{h_1}{h_2} \frac{\partial U}{\partial u_2} \right) \right]. \tag{1-109}$$

1-22 TENSORS AND DYADICS

In many physical situations the components of a vector $\mathbf{D}$ are linear functions of the components of a vector $\mathbf{E}$. In cartesian coordinates we would then have equations of the form

$$D_x = a_{11}E_x + a_{12}E_y + a_{13}E_z,$$
$$D_y = a_{21}E_x + a_{22}E_y + a_{23}E_z, \qquad (1\text{--}110)$$
$$D_z = a_{31}E_x + a_{32}E_y + a_{33}E_z.$$

Equations (1–110) can be expressed in matrix form as

$$\begin{pmatrix} D_x \\ D_y \\ D_z \end{pmatrix} = \begin{pmatrix} a_{11} & a_{12} & a_{13} \\ a_{21} & a_{22} & a_{23} \\ a_{31} & a_{32} & a_{33} \end{pmatrix} \begin{pmatrix} E_x \\ E_y \\ E_z \end{pmatrix}. \qquad (1\text{--}111)$$

Equation (1–111) may be written as

$$\mathbf{D} = \mathbf{a} \cdot \mathbf{E}, \qquad (1\text{--}112)$$

where

$$\mathbf{a} \triangleq \begin{pmatrix} a_{11} & a_{12} & a_{13} \\ a_{21} & a_{22} & a_{23} \\ a_{31} & a_{32} & a_{33} \end{pmatrix}, \qquad (1\text{--}113)$$

and where the scalar product in Eq. (1–112) is used to indicate that the matrix $\mathbf{a}$ is to be multiplied by the matrix $\mathbf{E}$ according to the rules of matrix multiplication. However, we prefer to think of $\mathbf{D}$ and $\mathbf{E}$ as vectors, and then the question arises as to what meaning can be assigned to $\mathbf{a}$. To answer this question, we note that Eqs. (1–110) can be written in the form

$$D_x = (\mathbf{i}_x a_{11} + \mathbf{i}_y a_{12} + \mathbf{i}_z a_{13}) \cdot \mathbf{E},$$
$$D_y = (\mathbf{i}_x a_{21} + \mathbf{i}_y a_{22} + \mathbf{i}_z a_{23}) \cdot \mathbf{E},$$
$$D_z = (\mathbf{i}_x a_{31} + \mathbf{i}_y a_{32} + \mathbf{i}_z a_{33}) \cdot \mathbf{E}.$$

Hence we have

$$\mathbf{D} = \mathbf{i}_x(\mathbf{i}_x a_{11} + \mathbf{i}_y a_{12} + \mathbf{i}_z a_{13}) \cdot \mathbf{E} + \mathbf{i}_y(\mathbf{i}_x a_{21} + \mathbf{i}_y a_{22} + \mathbf{i}_z a_{23}) \cdot \mathbf{E}$$
$$+ \mathbf{i}_z(\mathbf{i}_x a_{31} + \mathbf{i}_y a_{32} + \mathbf{i}_z a_{33}) \cdot \mathbf{E}. \qquad (1\text{--}114)$$

When we compare Eqs. (1–114) and (1–112), we see that

$$\mathbf{a} \triangleq \mathbf{i}_x(\mathbf{i}_x a_{11} + \mathbf{i}_y a_{12} + \mathbf{i}_z a_{13}) + \mathbf{i}_y(\mathbf{i}_x a_{21} + \mathbf{i}_y a_{22} + \mathbf{i}_z a_{23})$$
$$+ \mathbf{i}_z(\mathbf{i}_x a_{31} + \mathbf{i}_y a_{32} + \mathbf{i}_z a_{33}). \qquad (1\text{--}115)$$

The quantity given by Eq. (1–115) is known as a *dyad*. We obtain a dyad from a vector by replacing the scalar components of the vector by vector components. We obtain the vector components of $\mathbf{a}$ from the rows of the matrix representation, Eq. (1–113), by considering the rows as vectors. The branch of mathematics which deals with vectors, dyads, and their generalization is known as *tensor calculus*. A scalar is a *tensor of rank zero*, a vector is a *tensor of rank one*, and a dyad is *tensor of rank two*. For our purposes it is sufficient to use a simpler terminology: these three quantities will be referred to as a *scalar*, a *vector*, and a *tensor*, respectively. In the case of Eq. (1–112), we can state that the tensor **a** operates on the vector **E** to give a new vector **D**.

We define the unit tensor **e** by the equation $\mathbf{e} \cdot \mathbf{E} = \mathbf{E} \cdot \mathbf{e} = \mathbf{E}$. The matrix representation of **e** is the unit matrix,

$$\mathbf{e} = \begin{pmatrix} 1 & 0 & 0 \\ 0 & 1 & 0 \\ 0 & 0 & 1 \end{pmatrix},$$

and the dyadic representation is $\mathbf{e} = \mathbf{i}_x\mathbf{i}_x + \mathbf{i}_y\mathbf{i}_y + \mathbf{i}_z\mathbf{i}_z$.

If we scalar-multiply Eq. (1–112) on the left by **E**, we obtain a quadratic form in E_x, E_y, and E_z:

$$\mathbf{E} \cdot \mathbf{D} = \mathbf{E} \cdot \mathbf{a} \cdot \mathbf{E} = a_{11}E_x^2 + a_{22}E_y^2 + a_{33}E_z^2 + (a_{12} + a_{21})E_xE_y$$
$$+ (a_{13} + a_{31})E_zE_x + (a_{23} + a_{32})E_yE_z.$$

A vector identity which occurs frequently in electromagnetic theory is

$$\nabla \times (\nabla \times \mathbf{A}) = \nabla(\nabla \cdot \mathbf{A}) - \nabla \cdot (\nabla\mathbf{A}). \qquad (1\text{–}116)$$

We can obtain Eq. (1–116) by considering ∇ as a vector and by formal use of the vector triple product. However, the question then arises as to what meaning can be given to the gradient of a vector. A definition becomes possible if we make use of tensors. By formally introducing **A** into the brackets in Eq. (1–54), we obtain

$$\nabla\mathbf{A} \triangleq \lim_{v \to 0} \frac{1}{v} \int_S \mathbf{n}\mathbf{A} \, ds, \qquad (1\text{–}117)$$

where the product **nA** is a tensor. If we represent **n** and **A** in a cartesian coordinate system, we have

$$\mathbf{n} = \mathbf{i}_xn_x + \mathbf{i}_yn_y + \mathbf{i}_zn_z, \qquad \mathbf{A} = \mathbf{i}_xA_x + \mathbf{i}_yA_y + \mathbf{i}_zA_z,$$

and the matrix representation for the tensor **nA** is

$$\mathbf{n}\mathbf{A} = \begin{pmatrix} n_xA_x & n_xA_y & n_xA_z \\ n_yA_x & n_yA_y & n_yA_z \\ n_zA_x & n_zA_y & n_zA_z \end{pmatrix}.$$

Equation (1–117) defines the gradient of a vector. If ∇ is considered a vector, the scalar product of the vector ∇ and the tensor $\nabla\mathbf{A}$ yields a vector represented by $\mathbf{\nabla} \cdot (\mathbf{\nabla} A)$. The question now remains whether the definition (1–117) is consistent with the identity (1–116). Using Eq. (1–51), we see that

$$\mathbf{\nabla} \times \mathbf{A} = \lim_{v_1 \to 0} \frac{1}{v_1} \int_{S_1} \mathbf{n}_1 \times \mathbf{A} \, ds_1,$$

$$\mathbf{\nabla} \times (\mathbf{\nabla} \times A) = \lim_{v \to 0} \frac{1}{v} \int_S \mathbf{n} \times (\mathbf{\nabla} \times \mathbf{A}) \, ds.$$

Thus

$$\mathbf{\nabla} \times (\mathbf{\nabla} \times \mathbf{A}) = \lim_{v \to 0} \lim_{v_1 \to 0} \frac{1}{vv_1} \int_S \int_{S_1} \mathbf{n} \times (\mathbf{n}_1 \times \mathbf{A}) \, ds_1 \, ds.$$

The triple vector product in the integrand can be expanded to yield

$$\mathbf{\nabla} \times (\mathbf{\nabla} \times \mathbf{A}) = \lim_{v_1 \to 0} \frac{1}{v_1} \int_{S_1} \mathbf{n}_1 \left[\lim_{v \to 0} \frac{1}{v} \int_S (\mathbf{n} \cdot \mathbf{A}) \, ds \right] ds_1$$

$$- \lim_{v \to 0} \frac{1}{v} \int_S \mathbf{n} \cdot \left[\lim_{v_1 \to 0} \frac{1}{v_1} \int_{S_1} \mathbf{n}_1 \mathbf{A} \, ds_1 \right] ds$$

$$= \mathbf{\nabla}(\mathbf{\nabla} \cdot \mathbf{A}) - \mathbf{\nabla} \cdot (\mathbf{\nabla} \mathbf{A}).$$

In the final step we have used Eqs. (1–49), (1–50), and (1–117). This establishes the validity of Eq. (1–116).

Care must be taken with the operation $\mathbf{\nabla} \cdot (\mathbf{\nabla} A)$, since it is not immediately apparent that $\mathbf{\nabla} A$ is a tensor. In cartesian coordinates $\mathbf{\nabla} A$ has a particularly simple form:

$$\mathbf{\nabla} A = \mathbf{i}_x \frac{\partial \mathbf{A}}{\partial x} + \mathbf{i}_y \frac{\partial \mathbf{A}}{\partial y} + \mathbf{i}_z \frac{\partial \mathbf{A}}{\partial z} .$$

Thus

$$\mathbf{\nabla} \cdot (\mathbf{\nabla} A) = \frac{\partial^2 \mathbf{A}}{\partial x^2} + \frac{\partial^2 \mathbf{A}}{\partial y^2} + \frac{\partial^2 \mathbf{A}}{\partial z^2} .$$

It would then appear that we could interpret $\mathbf{\nabla} \cdot (\mathbf{\nabla}[\ ])$ as the Laplacian operator $\mathbf{\nabla}^2[\ ]$. However, this is true only in cartesian coordinates.

1–23 VECTOR MECHANICS

Newton's law of motion for a particle of constant mass m under the influence of a force $\mathbf{F}$ is given by

$$m \frac{d\mathbf{u}}{dt} = \mathbf{F}, \tag{1–118}$$

where $\mathbf{u}$ is the velocity of the particle. We can express $\mathbf{u}$ in terms of the speed u and the unit vector $\mathbf{i}$ tangent to the path of the particle: $\mathbf{u} = \mathbf{i}u$. The

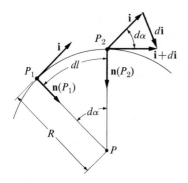

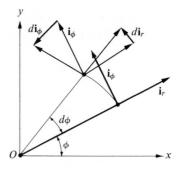

Fig. 1–26. The center of curvature of a curve.

Fig. 1–27. Differentials of the unit vectors $\mathbf{i}_r$ and $\mathbf{i}_\phi$.

acceleration is then given by

$$\frac{d\mathbf{u}}{dt} = \mathbf{i}\frac{du}{dt} + u\frac{d\mathbf{i}}{dt}. \tag{1–119}$$

Let us consider the change $d\mathbf{i}$ which occurs in the vector $\mathbf{i}$ during a time dt (Fig. 1–26). From the figure we see that $|d\mathbf{i}| = d\alpha$, where $d\alpha$ is the angle formed by the intersection of the normals to the trajectory at P_1 and P_2. Thus $d\mathbf{i} = \mathbf{n}\,d\alpha$, where $\mathbf{n}$ is a unit normal directed toward the *center of curvature P*. The center of curvature of a curve is determined by the intersection of two infinitesimally close normals. We can take the point of view that the particle moves from P_1 to P_2 along the *circle of curvature* of radius R whose center is at P. We see from Fig. 1–26 that the distance moved by the particle during a time dt is $dl = R\,d\alpha = u\,dt$. Thus $d\mathbf{i}/dt = \mathbf{n}(u/R)$, and we may therefore write Eq. (1–119) in the form

$$\frac{d\mathbf{u}}{dt} = \mathbf{i}\frac{du}{dt} + \mathbf{n}\frac{u^2}{R}. \tag{1–120}$$

From Eq. (1–120) we see that the component of acceleration in the tangential direction is du/dt, and that the component in the normal direction is u^2/R. The latter component is known as the *centripetal acceleration*.

In cylindrical coordinates r, ϕ, z, we can write

$$\mathbf{u} = \mathbf{i}_r\frac{dr}{dt} + \mathbf{i}_\phi r\frac{d\phi}{dt} + \mathbf{i}_z\frac{dz}{dt}.$$

Thus

$$\frac{d\mathbf{u}}{dt} = \mathbf{i}_r\frac{d^2r}{dt^2} + \mathbf{i}_\phi\frac{d}{dt}\left(r\frac{d\phi}{dt}\right) + \mathbf{i}_z\frac{d^2z}{dt^2} + \frac{dr}{dt}\frac{d\mathbf{i}_r}{dt} + r\frac{d\phi}{dt}\frac{d\mathbf{i}_\phi}{dt}. \tag{1–121}$$

From Fig. 1–27 we see that

$$d\mathbf{i}_r = \mathbf{i}_\phi \, d\phi, \qquad d\mathbf{i}_\phi = -\mathbf{i}_r \, d\phi.$$

Substituting these relations into Eq. (1–121) yields the representation of the acceleration in cylindrical coordinates. We can then express Eq. (1–118) in its cylindrical components:

$$m\left[\frac{d^2r}{dt^2} - r\left(\frac{d\phi}{dt}\right)^2\right] = F_r, \qquad \frac{m}{r}\frac{d}{dt}\left(r^2\frac{d\phi}{dt}\right) = F_\phi, \qquad m\frac{d^2z}{dt^2} = F_z. \quad (1\text{–}122)$$

Let us now consider the rotational motion of n rigidly connected particles. The equation of motion for the kth particle is

$$\mathbf{F}_k = m_k \frac{d\mathbf{u}_k}{dt}.$$

The *torque* on the kth particle is defined by the equation

$$\mathbf{T}_k \overset{\triangle}{=} \mathbf{r}_k \times \mathbf{F}_k = m_k \mathbf{r}_k \times \frac{d\mathbf{u}_k}{dt},$$

where $\mathbf{r}_k$ is the radius vector from the origin O to the kth particle. Note that $\mathbf{u}_k = d\mathbf{r}_k/dt$. The resultant torque on the system of n particles is given by

$$\mathbf{T} = \sum_{k=1}^{n} m_k \mathbf{r}_k \times \frac{d\mathbf{u}_k}{dt} = \frac{d}{dt}\left(\sum_{k=1}^{n} m_k \mathbf{r}_k \times \mathbf{u}_k\right) = \frac{d\mathbf{L}}{dt}, \qquad (1\text{–}123)$$

where

$$\mathbf{L} \overset{\triangle}{=} \sum_{k=1}^{n} m_k \mathbf{r}_k \times \mathbf{u}_k$$

is defined as the *angular momentum* with respect to the origin O. Equation (1–123) expresses the fact that the rate of change of angular momentum is equal to the applied torque.

As an example of Newton's law of motion, let us consider the case of planetary motion, in which a particle of mass m moves in the gravitational field of a second particle of mass $M \gg m$. The force on m is given by *Newton's law of gravitation*:

$$\mathbf{F} = -\frac{\gamma M m}{r^3}\,\mathbf{r},$$

where γ is the *gravitational constant* and $\mathbf{r}$ is a radius vector directed from M to m. Equation (1–118) has the form

$$\frac{d^2\mathbf{r}}{dt^2} = -\frac{\gamma M}{r^3}\,\mathbf{r}. \qquad (1\text{–}124)$$

(Note that m drops out). If we vector-multiply Eq. (1–124) by $\mathbf{r}$ we obtain

$$\frac{d}{dt}\left(\mathbf{r} \times \frac{d\mathbf{r}}{dt}\right) = 0.$$

Thus

$$\mathbf{r} \times \frac{d\mathbf{r}}{dt} = \mathbf{B}, \qquad (1\text{–}125)$$

where $\mathbf{B}$ is a constant vector. We can see the geometric significance of this result if we note that

$$|\mathbf{r} \times d\mathbf{r}| = |\mathbf{B}\, dt|$$

is the area swept out by the radius vector in time dt. Thus we have obtained *Kepler's first law of planetary motion*, which states that the radius vector sweeps out equal areas in equal times.

Vector multiplication of Eq. (1–124) by $\mathbf{B}$ yields

$$\frac{d}{dt}\left(\mathbf{B} \times \frac{d\mathbf{r}}{dt}\right) = \frac{\gamma M}{r^3}\, \mathbf{r} \times \left(\mathbf{r} \times \frac{d\mathbf{r}}{dt}\right). \qquad (1\text{–}126)$$

Noting that

$$\frac{d}{dt}(\mathbf{r} \cdot \mathbf{r}) = 2r\frac{dr}{dt} = 2\mathbf{r} \cdot \frac{d\mathbf{r}}{dt},$$

we see that the vector triple product in Eq. (1–126) can be written as

$$\mathbf{r} \times \left(\mathbf{r} \times \frac{d\mathbf{r}}{dt}\right) = \left(\mathbf{r} \cdot \frac{d\mathbf{r}}{dt}\right)\mathbf{r} - r^2\frac{d\mathbf{r}}{dt} = -r^3\frac{d}{dt}\left(\frac{\mathbf{r}}{r}\right).$$

Equation (1–126) can now be integrated with respect to t; it yields

$$\mathbf{B} \times \frac{d\mathbf{r}}{dt} = -\gamma M \frac{\mathbf{r}}{r} + \mathbf{C}, \qquad (1\text{–}127)$$

where $\mathbf{C}$ is a constant vector. The trajectory can be determined if we scalar-multiply Eq. (1–127) by $\mathbf{r}$ and use Eq. (1–125). The result is the conic section

$$r = \frac{B^2}{\gamma M - C\cos\theta},$$

where θ is the angle between $\mathbf{r}$ and $\mathbf{C}$.

GENERAL REFERENCE

M. R. Spiegel, *Vector Analysis*, Schaum's Outline Series. New York; Schaum Publishing Co., 1959.

PROBLEMS

1-1 Given that

$$A = \tfrac{1}{7}(i_x 2 + i_y 3 + i_z 6), \qquad B = \tfrac{1}{7}(i_x 3 - i_y 6 + i_z 2), \qquad C = \tfrac{1}{7}(i_x 6 + i_y 2 - i_z 3),$$

prove that **A**, **B**, and **C** are orthogonal unit vectors which form a right-handed system.

1-2 Given that

$$A = i_x \cos \alpha + i_y \sin \alpha,$$

$$B = i_x \cos \beta - i_y \sin \beta,$$

use the vector product $A \times B$ to prove that

$$\sin(\alpha + \beta) = \sin \alpha \cos \beta + \cos \alpha \sin \beta.$$

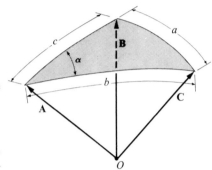

1-3 Consider the three unit vectors **A**, **B**, and **C** formed by three radial lines of a unit sphere (Fig. 1-28). Prove that

$$\cos \alpha = \cos b \cos c + \sin b \sin c \cos \alpha.$$

Figure 1-28

[*Hint:* Use $(A \times C) \cdot (A \times B)$ and apply the formulas for the scalar triple product and the vector triple product.]

1-4 Let $C = A - B$ and derive the law of cosines

$$C^2 = A^2 + B^2 - 2AB \cos \theta,$$

where θ is the angle between **A** and **B**.

1-5 Derive a vector identity for $\nabla \times (A \times B)$. What meaning can be given to the operation $(B \cdot \nabla)A$?

1-6 Given that S is a closed surface, prove that

$$\int_S n \, ds = 0.$$

[*Hint:* Use a cartesian coordinate system and project $n \, ds$ onto the coordinate planes.]

1-7 Determine the spherical coordinates of a point P on a unit sphere, given that

$$i_r = \tfrac{1}{2}(i_x + i_y + i_z\sqrt{2}), \qquad i_\theta = \tfrac{1}{2}(i_x + i_y - i_z\sqrt{2}), \qquad i_\phi = (1/\sqrt{2})(-i_x + i_y).$$

1-8 The rate of change of a scalar function U in the direction of a unit vector **n** is given by $\partial U / \partial n = \operatorname{grad} U \cdot n$. Use this formula to find $\partial U / \partial z$, where $U = 1/r$ and $r^2 = x^2 + y^2 + z^2$. Express the result in spherical coordinates.

1-9 A cylinder has elements which are parallel to the z-axis; its cross-sectional area in the xy-plane is S. Apply the divergence theorem to a unit length of the cylinder and prove that

$$\int_S \operatorname{div} \mathbf{D} \, ds = \oint_C \mathbf{D} \cdot \mathbf{n} \, dr.$$

Here $\mathbf{D} = \mathbf{i}_x D_x + \mathbf{i}_y D_y$, C is the contour in the xy-plane which bounds S, $\mathbf{n}$ is a unit outwardly directed normal of C, and dr is a line element of C.

1–10 Use the result in Problem 1–9, and by choosing $D_x = x$, $D_y = y$, show that the area bounded by a contour C in the xy-plane is given by

$$\tfrac{1}{2} \oint_C (x \, dy - y \, dx).$$

1–11 Prove Eqs. (1–42), given that $\mathbf{H}$ satisfies Eqs. (1–41). Use both cartesian and cylindrical coordinates. Which coordinate system is more convenient for the proof?

1–12 Given that U and C are constant, use Eqs. (1–49), (1–50), and (1–51) to prove that

$$\operatorname{grad} U = 0, \qquad \operatorname{div} \mathbf{C} = 0, \qquad \operatorname{curl} \mathbf{C} = 0,$$

[*Hint:* Consider the result given in Problem 1–6.]

1–13 Prove the following:

$$\text{(a)}\ \ \nabla^2 \frac{1}{r} = 0, \qquad \text{(b)}\ \ \nabla \cdot \frac{\mathbf{r}}{r^3} = 0, \qquad \text{(c)}\ \ \nabla \cdot \mathbf{r} = 3,$$

where $\mathbf{r} = \mathbf{i}_x x + \mathbf{i}_y y + \mathbf{i}_z z \neq 0$.

1–14 (a) Given that $U = \int_v (\rho/r) \, dv$, where

$$r^2 = (x_P - x_Q)^2 + (y_P - y_Q)^2 + (z_P - z_Q)^2,$$

prove that

$$\nabla_P U = \int_v \frac{1}{r} \nabla_Q \rho \, dv - \int_S \frac{\rho \mathbf{n}}{r} \, ds,$$

where S is the surface bounding v. [*Hint:* Use Eq. 1–31.]

(b) Given that $\mathbf{A} = \int_v (\mathbf{J}/r) \, dv$, prove that

$$\nabla_P \times \mathbf{A} = \int_v \frac{1}{r} \nabla_Q \times \mathbf{J} \, dv - \int_S \frac{\mathbf{n} \times \mathbf{J}}{r} \, ds.$$

[*Hint:* Use Eq. 1–37.]

1–15 Apply the result given in Problem 1–6 to the closed surface illustrated in Fig. 1–23, and prove Eq. (1–92).

1–16 For a contour C, $\oint_C d\mathbf{r} = 0$. Apply this result to the contours defined by the edges of the surface illustrated in Fig. 1–23, and prove Eqs. (1–97).

1–17 In what two-dimensional coordinate system is it permissible to write Eq. (1–109) in the form

$$\nabla_T^2 U = \frac{\partial^2 U}{\partial u_1^2} + \frac{\partial^2 U}{\partial u_2^2}$$

1–18 The cartesian components of two vectors **m** and **H** are related by the equations

$$m_x = \chi H_x - j\kappa H_y, \qquad m_y = j\kappa H_x + \chi H_y, \qquad m_z = \chi_z H_z.$$

By inverting these equations find the tensor **b** which relates **m** and **H** through the equation $\mathbf{H} = \mathbf{b} \cdot \mathbf{m}$.

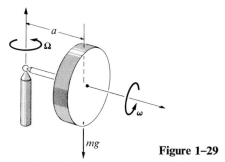

Figure 1–29

1–19 A gyroscope has an angular momentum $I\omega$ about its axis, which lies in a horizontal plane (Fig. 1–29). The moment of inertia I about the axis of rotation and the mass m are constant. The gyroscope is pivoted at a distance a from its center of gravity. Due to the force of gravitation, a torque is applied to the gyroscope, resulting in an angular precession Ω about the vertical axis. Determine a formula for Ω. Take $\Omega \ll \omega$.

THE ELECTROMAGNETIC FIELD

2–1 INTRODUCTION

In the simplest atomic theory of matter, macroscopic electromagnetic effects are considered to result from the forces exerted on each other by elementary positively and negatively charged particles. The elementary positive and negative charges are the proton and the electron, respectively. Protons, together with uncharged neutrons, can be bound by nuclear forces into a dense nucleus around which bound electrons circulate. The nucleus, together with the circulating electrons, forms an atom. In the non-ionized state of an atom the positive charge of the nucleus is balanced by the negative charge of the electrons. If some electrons are stripped from the atom by means of external forces the effective charge of the atom becomes positive. If the atom captures additional electrons the effective charge of the atom becomes negative. In either case the atom is ionized. Two ionized atoms or ions, due to their respective charges, exert an electrostatic force on each other. Atoms and molecules can be bound together by various kinds of interatomic forces to form gases, liquids, and solids.

If there are two uncharged solid particles in free space, it is possible by means of external forces, such as those obtained by means of friction, to remove electrons from one particle and place them on the other. The particles will then be oppositely charged to the same magnitude. When the particles are at rest with respect to each other, there is a force of attraction between them. When the particles have different relative velocities with respect to a common reference system, there is a force acting between them which differs from the force experienced when they are both at rest. We shall see that the force experienced by a moving charge can be most conveniently represented by means of electromagnetic field vectors, the *electric field intensity* **E** and the *magnetic flux density* **B**. The field vectors **E** and **B** are related to each other and to the sources of the field through field equations. In this chapter we shall formulate the field equations by discussing a series of simple experiments. We shall state the equations as postulates, since experimental evidence has verified their general validity for the analysis of electromagnetic phenomena.

2–2 ELECTRIC FIELD INTENSITY

Material media have electromagnetic effects depending only on the motions of the elementary charged particles of which they are composed. It is possible to develop a macroscopic theory of electromagnetism based entirely on the motion of point electric charges. For this reason, and also because of its simplicity and mathematical convenience, we introduce the concept of a *point electric charge*. A charged particle always has a distribution of charge throughout its volume. When a second charge interacts with the first, the electromagnetic forces alter the charge distribution. The change in charge distribution becomes smaller as the dimensions of the particle become smaller. In the limit as the dimensions of the particle approach zero, we obtain a point charge.

Fig. 2–1. Two point charges at rest.

The convenience of the concept of a point charge is that we need not be concerned with the change in charge distribution within the particle as other point charges are moved into its vicinity. Let us consider the situation shown in Fig. 2–1, where a point charge Q_1 is at a distance r from a second point charge Q_2. Both particles are considered to be at rest in free space. The particles experience forces represented by $\mathbf{F}_1$ and $\mathbf{F}_2 = -\mathbf{F}_1$, respectively, and mechanical constraints are necessary to hold the charges at rest. However, an attempt to describe electromagnetic effects in terms of forces between charges would result in relations of considerable complexity. It is much more convenient to express the force in terms of field vectors. Thus, if we consider Fig. 2–1 again, we can state that the charge Q_1 sets up an electric field intensity $\mathbf{E}_1$. If a charge Q_2 is placed in this field, it will experience a force linearly proportional to Q_2. Thus

$$\mathbf{F}_2 = Q_2 \mathbf{E}_1. \tag{2–1}$$

In the mks system of units, force, charge, and electric field intensity are measured in newtons (N), coulombs (C), and volts/meter (V/m), respectively (see Appendix C for a discussion of the mks system of units). It is convenient to consider the field $\mathbf{E}_1$ as existing independently of whether or not a test charge Q_2 is used. This abstract concept of a field vector is of tremendous importance, since it results in the simplest possible formulation of electromagnetic effects. With the aid of the field concept, we can remove the test charge Q_2 and consider the charge Q_1 and its associated field $\mathbf{E}_1$ alone.

Suppose that there are n distinct point charges Q_k ($k = 1, 2, \ldots, n$), in free space and that $\mathbf{E}_k$ is the electric field intensity at a field point P due to

Q_k alone. We obtain the resultant electric field intensity $\mathbf{E}$ at P by the vector sum

$$\mathbf{E} = \sum_{k=1}^{n} \mathbf{E}_k.$$

The above result is obtained by noting that $-\mathbf{E}_k$ is the mechanical force required to constrain a unit test charge at P under the influence of Q_k and that $-\mathbf{E}$ is the resultant mechanical force required to constrain the test charge under the influence of all n charges.

2-3   MAGNETIC FLUX DENSITY

When two charged particles have different relative velocities with respect to a common reference system, there is a force acting between them which differs from the force described by an electric field intensity. To understand the nature of this force and the necessity for introducing a new field vector to describe it, let us consider the experiment illustrated in Fig. 2-2, in which there is a steady flow of charges along a coil. The flow of charges constitutes a current i. Let us suppose that a test charge Q is moved infinitely slowly along a circular path C_0 which is coaxial with the coil. If there is a force on Q, it is due to the electric field set up by the charges in the coil. To demonstrate the nature of the magnetic field, it is convenient to consider the charges (the negative electrons) responsible for the current i to be electrically neutralized by positively charged atomic nuclei which are fixed in position. This does not change the current that is flowing. However, there is now no force acting on Q, provided that it is moved infinitely slowly along the path C_0.

Let us now constrain Q to move along C_0 with a velocity $\mathbf{u}$ directed as shown in the figure. We find that there is a radial force acting on Q directed toward the center of the circle, and that this force is proportional to the product Qui. We again prefer to consider this force as arising due to a field. It is evident that the field is not an electric field, since no single volume element of the coil has an effective charge. The field responsible for the force acting on the moving charge is represented by a vector $\mathbf{B}$, the magnetic flux density, which has the dimensions of webers/meter² (Wb/m²) in mks units. The force, assuming that $\mathbf{E} = 0$, is given by

$$\mathbf{F} = Q\mathbf{u} \times \mathbf{B}. \tag{2-2}$$

In general, both the electric and magnetic fields are present, and experimental evidence has shown that Eqs. (2-1) and (2-2) can be combined into a single equation which has general validity. This equation will be taken as the first of three postulates. The force given by this equation is known as the *Lorentz force*.

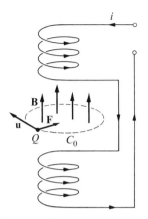

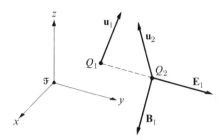

Fig. 2–3. A test charge Q_2 moving in the field of a point charge Q_1.

Fig. 2–2. The force on a moving charge due to a magnetic field.

Postulate 1. The force in newtons on a point charge Q moving with a velocity **u** is given by the Lorentz force

$$\mathbf{F} = Q(\mathbf{E} + \mathbf{u} \times \mathbf{B}), \qquad (2\text{–}3)$$

where **E** is the electric field intensity and **B** the magnetic flux density. In order for Eq. (2–3) to be correct, all quantities must be measured in the same reference system.

The distinction between the vectors **E** and **B**, which are used to represent different vector components of the force on a unit test charge, can be clarified if we consider Fig. 2–3. Let $\mathbf{E}_1$ and $\mathbf{B}_1$ represent the electric field intensity and magnetic flux density which are associated with a charge Q_1 as seen in a frame of reference $\mathscr{F}$ and let Q_2 be a test charge. When Q_1 is at rest, we have $\mathbf{B}_1 = 0$ and the force acting on Q_2 is given by

$$\mathbf{F}_2 = Q_2\mathbf{E}_1. \qquad (2\text{–}4)$$

Let us now suppose that Q_1 moves with a velocity $\mathbf{u}_1 \neq 0$ relative to $\mathscr{F}$. A magnetic field $\mathbf{B}_1$ is associated with the moving charge Q_1. However, when Q_2 is at rest in $\mathscr{F}$, $\mathbf{u}_2 = 0$, and the force acting on Q_2 is still given by Eq. (2–4). We can detect the magnetic field $\mathbf{B}_1$ if the test charge Q_2 moves with a relative velocity $\mathbf{u}_2 \neq 0$ with respect to $\mathscr{F}$ (note that this is the case illustrated in Fig. 2–2, where the test charge and the charges in the coil are all in motion).

In general, the sources of the electromagnetic field are the charge density ρ measured in coulombs/meter^3 (C/m^3), and the current density **J**, measured in amperes/meter^2 (A/m^2), and we anticipate the existence of equations relating **E**, **B**, ρ, and **J**. Two of these equations were discovered by Maxwell and are known as the *Maxwell equations*. Since a charge in motion constitutes a current, we anticipate a further equation relating **J** and ρ. This equation is

known as the *equation of continuity*. The next three sections will deal with
the formulation of the equation of continuity and the Maxwell equations as
postulates.

2–4 CURRENT IN CONDUCTORS
AND THE EQUATION OF CONTINUITY

In a conducting medium, electrons are free to move under the influence of an
external electric field. If there were no opposing mechanism the electrons
would accelerate and acquire high speeds. However, dislocations, defects,
and thermal vibrations of the crystal structure of a conductor all serve to
scatter the electrons. This scattering manifests itself macroscopically through
an average finite velocity acquired by the electrons. We also speak of the
conductor as having a resistance to the current. To a good approximation
the relation between the current density and the electric field intensity is given
in most conductors by

$$\mathbf{J} = \sigma\mathbf{E}, \tag{2–5}$$

where σ is the *conductivity*. We shall assume that σ is a constant for a given
conductor.

Let us now consider a very thin endless wire of cross-sectional area a
under the influence of an electric field $\mathbf{E}$ directed along the axis of the wire
(Fig. 2–4). When the cross-sectional dimensions of the wire approach zero,
we obtain a current filament. Let

$$v_e \triangleq \oint_C \mathbf{E} \cdot d\mathbf{r} \tag{2–6}$$

be the line integral of the tangential component of $\mathbf{E}$ taken along the axis C
of the filament. When we substitute Eq. (2–5) into Eq. (2–6) and note that the
current in the coil is determined by the relation $i\, dr = aJ\, dr$ and that $\mathbf{E}$ has
the direction of $d\mathbf{r}$, we obtain $v_e = iR$, where

$$R \triangleq \oint_C \frac{dr}{a\sigma} \tag{2–7}$$

represents the resistance of the wire. The quantity v_e defined by Eq. (2–6)
will be referred to as the *electromotive force* and abbreviated emf. Since v_e
has the dimensions of volts and not the dimensions of force, it is sometimes
referred to as *electromotance*. However, electromotance implies a motion of
some sort, which is not always the case. It would be convenient to designate
v_e as a voltage. This would imply that v_e has a unique value which, in general,
is not the case. The designation of emf for v_e appears to have more widespread appeal, and we shall adopt it here.

Let us now consider the current density in a conducting medium of
volume v bounded by a surface S. Let ρ be the charge density. The total

Fig. 2–4. Current in a thin endless ring due to an impressed electric field.

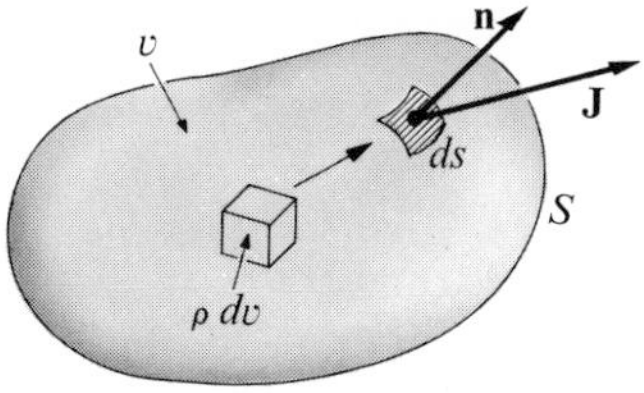

Fig. 2–5. Transport of charge from a volume and the associated current density.

charge within S is

$$Q = \int_v \rho \, dv. \tag{2-8}$$

If the charge within v changes with time a current density $\mathbf{J}$ must exist and the current flowing out of v (Fig. 2–5) is

$$i = \int_S \mathbf{J} \cdot \mathbf{n} \, ds.$$

We now accept as a postulate the principle of the conservation of charge, which states that in a conduction process charges are neither created or destroyed.

Postulate 2. The total charge within a closed system is invariant. Thus if there is a current i due to a transport of charge from a volume v, then i must equal the time rate of decrease, $-dQ/dt$, of the charge Q within v:

$$i = \int_S \mathbf{J} \cdot \mathbf{n} \, ds = -\frac{dQ}{dt}.$$

The above is a statement of the postulate. The following paragraph describes a consequence of the postulate which is made use of in Section 2–11, Eq. (2–42).

When the surface S is fixed, we have $dQ/dt = \partial Q/\partial t$. Substituting Eq. (2–8) and differentiating under the integral sign yields

$$\int_S \mathbf{J} \cdot \mathbf{n} \, ds = \int_v -\frac{\partial \rho}{\partial t} \, dv.$$

Applying the divergence theorem to the surface integral yields

$$\int_v \left(\operatorname{div} \mathbf{J} + \frac{\partial \rho}{\partial t} \right) dv = 0.$$

The above integral is zero for an arbitrary volume v. It follows that the integrand must equal zero, since otherwise we could find a volume v in which the integral differed from zero and we would have a contradiction. Equating the integrand to zero yields the *equation of continuity*

$$\text{div } \mathbf{J} + \frac{\partial \rho}{\partial t} = 0. \tag{2-9}$$

Postulate 2 thus states that the current density and the charge density are related to each other by the equation of continuity.

2-5 MAXWELL'S FIRST EQUATION

We shall now undertake the formulation of the first of the Maxwell equations. The general validity of the Maxwell equations can be illustrated by a variety of simple experiments. Some of the experiments we shall discuss are important in the historical development of electromagnetic theory. However, some of the experiments, for example experiments with perfect conductors or with time-varying electric fields, may be impractical to carry out accurately. These experiments should be considered as ideal experiments; they are presented here only to illustrate the general validity of Maxwell's equations.

Let us consider Faraday's experiment, in which a current filament of resistance R (see Eq. 2–7) is situated in a time-varying magnetic field (Fig. 2–6). Let

$$\phi_m \triangleq \int_S \mathbf{B} \cdot \mathbf{n} \, ds$$

be defined as the *magnetic flux* linked by the filament. The surface S is bounded by the filament but is otherwise arbitrary. When the magnetic flux ϕ_m changes with time, we find experimentally that there is a current i in the wire which is determined by the equation

$$\frac{\partial \phi_m}{\partial t} = -iR = -v_e, \tag{2-10}$$

where v_e is the electromotive force defined by Eq. (2–6), and where the partial derivative indicates that C and S do not change with time. We take the point of view that the free charges in the wire move under the influence of an electric field which is associated with the time-varying magnetic field. The direction of the line element $d\mathbf{r}$ of the filament has been chosen so that it forms a right-handed system with respect to the surface normal $\mathbf{n}$. If $d\phi_m/dt$ were positive, positive free charges in the wire would flow in a direction opposite to that chosen for $d\mathbf{r}$, and this accounts for the negative sign in Eq. (2–10). This equation is known as *Faraday's law of electromagnetic induction*. It is also Maxwell's first equation applied to the special case of a current filament. However, to illustrate the general validity of Maxwell's first equation, let us consider further experiments.

Suppose that we perform an ideal experiment in which we have a thin perfectly conducting wire with its ends connected to a closely spaced parallel-plate capacitor (Fig. 2–7). The contour C links a magnetic flux ϕ_m. Whenever

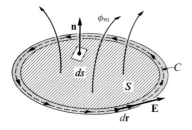

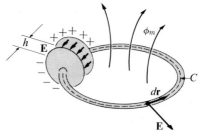

Fig. 2–6. A thin endless wire in a time-varying magnetic field.

Fig. 2–7. A perfectly conducting wire with two parallel perfectly conducting plates in a time-varying magnetic field.

ϕ_m changes, a current results, charging the capacitor plates. The charges on the plates result in an electric field **E** between the plates. Given that h is the distance between the plates, we observe experimentally that

$$\frac{\partial \phi_m}{\partial t} = -Eh = -v_e,$$

where v_e is the emf. Note that $\mathbf{E} \cdot d\mathbf{r} = 0$ along the perfectly conducting wire. Thus the capacitor field alone contributes to v_e.

As a final experiment, let us observe the effect of a time-varying magnetic field on a charge Q moving along a circular orbit of radius r with a velocity **u** (Fig. 2–8). Let the magnetic flux density **B** be uniform and normal to the plane of the path. When **B** is time-invariant, we note a force $Q\mathbf{u} \times \mathbf{B}$ acting on the charge. When **B** and ϕ_m are time-varying, we note an additional force acting on Q. This additional force has the direction of $-\mathbf{u}$ and therefore tends to make Q move in a direction opposite to that shown in the figure. We take the point of view that the additional force can be described by an electric field **E**, and we find that*

$$\frac{\partial \phi_m}{\partial t} = -2\pi r E = -v_e.$$

On the basis of these various experiments we postulate the general validity of the integral form of Maxwell's first equation,

$$\frac{\partial \phi_m}{\partial t} = -v_e, \qquad (2\text{–}11)$$

where

$$\phi_m \triangleq \int_S \mathbf{B} \cdot \mathbf{n} \, ds \qquad (2\text{–}12)$$

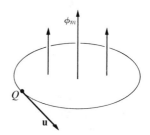

Fig. 2–8. A point charge moving in a time-varying magnetic field.

---

* The betatron, which is used to accelerate electrons, is based on this principle.

is the magnetic flux linked by C and where

$$v_e \triangleq \oint_C \mathbf{E} \cdot d\mathbf{r} \qquad (2\text{–}13)$$

is the emf evaluated along C. Equation (2–11) states that the negative rate of change of the magnetic flux linked by a contour C is equal to the emf evaluated along C. Stated in this manner, Maxwell's first equation is also Faraday's law of electromagnetic induction. Maxwell's first equation can also be stated in the following physical terms. Associated with a time-varying magnetic flux density $\mathbf{B}$ is an electric field intensity $\mathbf{E}$ which tends to circulate or curl around $\mathbf{B}$. We consider Eq. (2–11) to be valid for all physical situations involving electromagnetic phenomena. Maxwell's first equation and his second equation, which is discussed in the next section, form our third postulate.

2–6 MAXWELL'S SECOND EQUATION

Let us take a filamentary conductor and wind it into a long thin coil with n turns per unit length along a contour C. Let the cross-sectional dimensions of the coil be negligible compared with the length of C and let a represent the cross-sectional area of the coil. At two very closely spaced terminals, twisted leads are taken to a fluxmeter (Fig. 2–9). A fluxmeter is a ballistic galvanometer which is calibrated so that one can measure the magnetic flux linked by a wire connected to its terminals. Let a current i be linked by C.

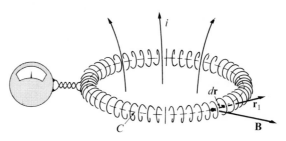

Fig. 2–9. A coil in the magnetic field of a current i.

Experimentally we can make the following observations. Associated with the current i is a magnetic flux density $\mathbf{B}$. The component of $\mathbf{B}$ in the direction of the unit tangent vector $\mathbf{r}_1$ of C results in a magnetic flux linking the turns of the coil. Given that N is the total number of turns and ϕ_m the average magnetic flux linked by one turn, the product $N\phi_m$ is designated as the number of *flux linkages*. The magnetic flux linking one turn of the coil is $a\mathbf{B} \cdot \mathbf{r}_1$. The same magnetic flux links $n\, dr$ turns, so that the number of flux linkages in an interval dr is

$$N \, d\phi_m = a\mathbf{B} \cdot \mathbf{r}_1 n \, dr = an\mathbf{B} \cdot d\mathbf{r}.$$

The total number of flux linkages is

$$N\phi_m = an \oint_C \mathbf{B} \cdot d\mathbf{r},$$

and can be measured by moving the coil to a position in which the magnetic field is negligible. Moving the coil causes the meter to deflect; we find that the meter reading is proportional to the product ani and is independent of the shape of the contour C. The fluxmeter reading is therefore

$$N\phi_m = kani,$$

where k is a constant. If the fluxmeter is calibrated to read flux in webers, we must choose $k = \mu_0 = 4\pi 10^{-7}$ henry/meter (H/m), which is known as the *permeability of free space*. Thus

$$N\phi_m/\mu_0 an = \oint_C \frac{\mathbf{B}}{\mu_0} \cdot d\mathbf{r} = i. \tag{2-14}$$

The current i linked by C can be written in terms of the current density $\mathbf{J}$:

$$i = \int_S \mathbf{J} \cdot \mathbf{n} \, ds. \tag{2-15}$$

Here S is an arbitrary surface bounded by C.

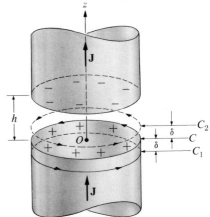

Fig. 2–10. Conduction current in a conductor and displacement current in a gap.

Equation (2–14) is incomplete and is not applicable to all physical situations. For example, consider a solid cylindrical conductor which has a constant and uniform axial current density $\mathbf{J} = \mathbf{i}_z J$. The current in the conductor is $i = \pi a^2 J$, where a is the radius of the conductor. A gap of width h is cut from the conductor, as illustrated in Fig. 2–10. Let S_1 and S_2 represent surfaces which are identical to the gap surface of the conductor and which are displaced a distance δ below and above the plane $z = 0$, respectively. Given that C_1 is the contour bounding S_1, it follows from Eqs. (2–14) and (2–15) that

$$\oint_{C_1} \frac{\mathbf{B_1}}{\mu_0} \cdot d\mathbf{r} = \int_{S_1} \mathbf{J} \cdot \mathbf{n}\, ds = \pi a^2 J, \qquad (2\text{–}16)$$

where $\mathbf{B_1}$ is the magnetic flux density for points on C_1. If we take Eq. (2–14) to be generally valid, it would follow that

$$\oint_{C_2} \frac{\mathbf{B_2}}{\mu_0} \cdot d\mathbf{r} = 0, \qquad (2\text{–}17)$$

since C_2 links no current. By taking $\delta \to 0$, we see that Eq. (2–17) contradicts Eq. (2–16). It is therefore essential that

$$\oint_{C_2} \frac{\mathbf{B_2}}{\mu_0} \cdot d\mathbf{r} = \pi a^2 J, \qquad (2\text{–}18)$$

in order to avoid the contradiction. The question now arises as to what meaning can be assigned to the right-hand side of Eq. (2–18), since C_2 links no current. To answer this question, we note that there is an electric field in the gap set up by the charges on the gap surfaces and that C_2 links this electric field. We can therefore consider the possibility of identifying the right-hand side of Eq. (2–18) with the rate of change of an electric flux linked by C_2. This would also result in both Maxwell's equations taking on a similar appearance. In both Eq. (2–11) and Eq. (2–18) we would then have a contour integral of a field vector being equated to the rate of change of a field flux. By investigating the gap region in greater detail we shall find that such a point of view is correct. To establish the desired result, we must relate $\mathbf{J}$ to the electric field in the gap. Given that q is the surface charge density on the gap surface at $z = 0$, the conservation of charge requires that

$$dq/dt = J. \qquad (2\text{–}19)$$

Due to the uniformity of q over the gap surface and due to the small gap width, we would find that a uniform electric field intensity $\mathbf{E} = \mathbf{i}_z E$ exists within the gap. The electric field intensity is proportional to q, so that we may write

$$E = q/\varepsilon_0, \qquad (2\text{–}20)$$

where the proportionality constant $1/\varepsilon_0$ can be found by measuring the charge density required to set up a field of 1 volt/meter (V/m). In the mks system of units, ε_0 is given very accurately by

$$\varepsilon_0 = (1/36\pi)10^{-9} \text{ farad/meter (F/m)},$$

and is called the *permittivity of free space* (for the exact value see Appendix C). From Eq. (2–20) we see that the product $\varepsilon_0 E$ has the dimensions of coulombs/meter^2, and we can therefore consider $\varepsilon_0 \mathbf{E}$ as an *electric flux density*. Combining Eqs. (2–18), (2–19), and (2–20) yields

$$\oint_{C_2} \frac{\mathbf{B}_2}{\mu_0} \cdot d\mathbf{r} = \frac{d\phi_e}{dt}, \qquad (2\text{–}21)$$

where

$$\phi_e \triangleq \oint_{S_2} \varepsilon_0 \mathbf{E}_2 \cdot \mathbf{n} \, ds \qquad (2\text{–}22)$$

is defined as the *electric flux* linked by C_2.

Having established Eq. (2–21) for the special case illustrated in Fig. 2–10, we can now use an ideal experiment to discuss its general validity. Consider once more Fig. 2–9. Suppose that no current is present, so that $i = 0$ and the coil is situated in free space in a time-varying electric field. For convenience in performing the experiment we can take $d\phi_e/dt$ to be constant, where ϕ_e is the electric flux linked by C. By withdrawing the coil from the electric field and measuring the magnetic flux that was linked by the coil, we can establish the validity of Eq. (2–21) for the situation illustrated in Fig. 2–9.

In a general case the contour C links both a current i and an electric flux ϕ_e. Combining Eqs. (2–14) and (2–21) into a single equation yields the integral form of Maxwell's second equation:

$$\oint_C \frac{\mathbf{B}}{\mu_0} \cdot d\mathbf{r} = i_T + \frac{d\phi_e}{dt}. \qquad (2\text{–}23)$$

Here i_T is the *total current* due to the movement of charges through a surface S linked by C and ϕ_e is the electric flux linked by C. Note that if we choose the contour C_1 (see Eq. 2–16), $\mathbf{E}$ is constant over S_1, since $\mathbf{J} = \sigma \mathbf{E}$ is constant. Thus $d\phi_e/dt = 0$ and Eq. (2–23) reduces to Eq. (2–16). If we choose C_2 (see Eq. 2–21), $i = 0$, and Eq. (2–23) reduces to Eq. (2–21). We see that the term $d\phi_e/dt$ is essential to avoid the contradiction that otherwise occurs between Eqs. (2–16) and (2–17). The term $d\phi_e/dt$ was originally introduced by Maxwell and called the *displacement current*. This can be misleading, since there is neither a displacement or a current associated with $d\phi_e/dt$. Despite this, it is quite common to designate $d\phi_e/dt$ as a displacement current.

2–7 THE INTEGRAL FORM OF MAXWELL'S EQUATIONS AS A POSTULATE

Equations (2–11) and (2–23) are the two Maxwell equations which we postulate to have general validity. These equations form our third postulate.

Postulate 3.   The field vectors $\mathbf{E}$ and $\mathbf{B}$ and the total current density $\mathbf{J}_T$ satisfy the integral form of Maxwell's equations:

$$\oint_C \mathbf{E} \cdot d\mathbf{r} = -\frac{d\phi_m}{dt}, \tag{2–24}$$

$$\oint_C \frac{\mathbf{B}}{\mu_0} \cdot d\mathbf{r} = i_T + \frac{d\phi_e}{dt}, \tag{2–25}$$

where

$$\phi_m \triangleq \int_S \mathbf{B} \cdot \mathbf{n}\, ds$$

is the magnetic flux linked by C,

$$\phi_e \triangleq \int_S \varepsilon_0 \mathbf{E} \cdot \mathbf{n}\, ds$$

is the electric flux linked by C, and where

$$i_T \triangleq \int_S \mathbf{J}_T \cdot \mathbf{n}\, ds$$

is the total current linked by C.

2–8 THE DIFFERENTIAL FORM OF MAXWELL'S EQUATIONS

With the aid of Stokes' theorem we can transform a contour integral into a surface integral.   Thus we have

$$\oint_C \mathbf{E} \cdot d\mathbf{r} = \int_S \mathbf{n} \cdot \operatorname{curl} \mathbf{E}\, ds,$$

$$\oint_C \mathbf{B} \cdot d\mathbf{r} = \int_S \mathbf{n} \cdot \operatorname{curl} \mathbf{B}\, ds, \tag{2–26}$$

and Maxwell's first equation (2–24) can be transformed into the equation

$$\int_S \left(\operatorname{curl} \mathbf{E} + \frac{\partial \mathbf{B}}{\partial t} \right) \cdot \mathbf{n}\, ds = 0. \tag{2–27}$$

The integral in Eq. (2–27) is zero for an arbitrary surface S.   This is possible only if

$$\operatorname{curl} \mathbf{E} = -\frac{\partial \mathbf{B}}{\partial t}, \tag{2–28}$$

since otherwise it would be possible to choose a surface S so that

$$\left(\operatorname{curl} \mathbf{E} + \frac{\partial \mathbf{B}}{\partial t} \right) \cdot \mathbf{n} > 0$$

over S, which would contradict Eq. (2–27).

Similarly, Maxwell's second equation (2–25) yields the differential equation

$$\text{curl}\,\frac{\mathbf{B}}{\mu_0} = \mathbf{J}_T + \varepsilon_0\,\frac{\partial \mathbf{E}}{\partial t}.$$ (2–29)

Equations (2–28) and (2–29) are Maxwell's equations in differential form. From these equations we can obtain some important results concerning magnetic and electric flux. To obtain these results we take the divergence of Eq. (2–28). Using del notation, we obtain

$$\mathbf{\nabla}\cdot(\mathbf{\nabla}\times\mathbf{E}) = 0 = -\frac{\partial}{\partial t}(\mathbf{\nabla}\cdot\mathbf{B}).$$

Here we have interchanged the order of the differentiations on the right-hand side. Integrating with respect to t yields $\mathbf{\nabla}\cdot\mathbf{B} = c_1$, where c_1 is independent of t.

Similarly, Eq. (2–29) yields

$$\frac{\partial}{\partial t}(\mathbf{\nabla}\cdot\varepsilon_0\mathbf{E}) + \mathbf{\nabla}\cdot\mathbf{J}_T = 0.$$ (2–30)

Given that ρ_T represents the total charge density, we can use the equation of continuity to write Eq. (2–30) in the form

$$\frac{\partial}{\partial t}(\mathbf{\nabla}\cdot\varepsilon_0\mathbf{E} - \rho_T) = 0.$$

Hence $\mathbf{\nabla}\cdot\varepsilon_0\mathbf{E} - \rho_T = c_2$, where c_2 is independent of t. The constants c_1 and c_2 must be zero. We can see this if we consider a static situation and let $\mathbf{J}_T$ and ρ_T and therefore also $\mathbf{B}$ and $\mathbf{E}$ slowly approach zero. Thus we obtain the two equations,

$$\text{div}\,\mathbf{B} = 0,$$ (2–31a)

$$\text{div}\,\varepsilon_0\mathbf{E} = \rho_T,$$ (2–31b)

which are of fundamental importance.

2–9 ELECTRIC AND MAGNETIC FLUX; COULOMB'S LAW

It is due to the validity of Eqs. (2–31) that we are justified in considering $\mathbf{B}$ and $\varepsilon_0\mathbf{E}$ as representing flux densities. This is made evident if we consider Fig. 2–11 and review the discussion in Section 1–10 dealing with tubes of flux. It follows from the divergence theorem and Eq. (2–31a) that

$$\int_v \text{div}\,\mathbf{B}\,dv = \int_S \mathbf{B}\cdot\mathbf{n}\,ds = 0,$$

where S is a closed surface which bounds the volume v. The above result

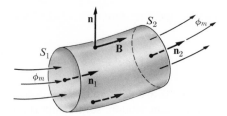

Fig. 2–11. A tube of magnetic flux.

implies that we can form a tube of flux in which the flux is constant:

$$\phi_m = \int_{S_1} \mathbf{B} \cdot \mathbf{n}_1 \, ds = \int_{S_2} \mathbf{B} \cdot \mathbf{n}_2 \, ds.$$

Here $\mathbf{n}_1$ and $\mathbf{n}_2$ are unit normals in the direction of the magnetic field.

A similar result follows for the electric flux density $\varepsilon_0 \mathbf{E}$ in a source-free region of space where $\rho_T = 0$. If $\rho_T \neq 0$, Eq. (2–31b) and the divergence theorem yield an important result known as *Gauss' law*, which states that

$$\int_v \operatorname{div} \varepsilon_0 \mathbf{E} \, dv = \int_S \varepsilon_0 \mathbf{E} \cdot \mathbf{n} \, ds = Q_T, \qquad (2\text{–}32)$$

where $Q_T \triangleq \int_v \rho_T \, dv$ is the *total charge* enclosed by S. In physical terms Gauss' law states that the total electric flux flowing out of a volume v is equal to the total charge within v.

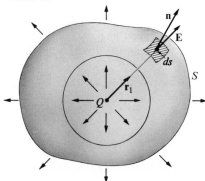

Fig. 2–12. Electric flux of a point charge through a surface S.

Gauss' law can be used to derive *Coulomb's law*, which gives the force on a point charge resulting from a second point charge. Consider Fig. 2–12, and let $\mathbf{r}_1$ be a unit radial vector from the point charge Q. Equation (2–32) applies for any surface S enclosing Q. When we choose a sphere of radius r

which is centered on the point charge we have $\mathbf{E} \cdot \mathbf{n} = E$ over S. Thus $4\pi r^2 \varepsilon_0 E = Q$ and

$$\mathbf{E} = \frac{Q}{4\pi\varepsilon_0 r^2}\mathbf{r}_1. \tag{2-33}$$

As a consequence of postulate 1 and Eq. (2-33), we can state that the force $\mathbf{F}_2$ on a test charge Q_2 placed in the field of a point charge Q_1 is

$$\mathbf{F}_2 = \frac{Q_2 Q_1}{4\pi\varepsilon_0 r^2}\mathbf{r}_1.$$

This relation is known as Coulomb's law. Its validity has been established by experimental means [1].*

2-10 MAGNETIC FIELD INTENSITY AND ELECTRIC FLUX DENSITY

We consider Eqs. (2-28), (2-29), and (2-31) to be generally valid, since they are derived from postulate 3. However, if material media are present in the field, these equations are not very convenient for the solution of problems. To obtain more suitable equations, we must investigate the electromagnetic properties of material media. In this section we must therefore anticipate the results to be derived in Section 3-5 and Section 6-7, which deal with material media. It will be shown in these sections that the electromagnetic properties of a dielectric and magnetic medium can be described by a *polarization* $\mathbf{P}$ and a *magnetization* $\mathbf{M}$, respectively. The reason for introducing these additional vectors can be made plausible if we take a closer look at the charges and currents which can exist in material media. Some charges, for example electrons in a conductor, are free to move and can cause a *charge density* ρ. In a dielectric we can have a *polarization charge density* ρ_p due to displaced charges which are locally bound to atoms. From a fundamental point of view we do not distinguish between free or bound charges, and we form the total charge density

$$\rho_T = \rho + \rho_p. \tag{2-34}$$

When the free charges move, a *current density* $\mathbf{J}$ results; when the polarization charges oscillate, a *polarization current density* $\mathbf{J}_p$ results. Furthermore, in a magnetic medium we can have a circular motion of charges about fixed axes. This motion results in a *magnetization current density* $\mathbf{J}_m$. From a fundamental point of view we do not distinguish between the various kinds of motion of charges, and we form the total current density

$$\mathbf{J}_T = \mathbf{J} + \mathbf{J}_p + \mathbf{J}_m. \tag{2-35}$$

---

* Numbers in brackets are cued to references at the end of each chapter.

It will be shown in Section 3–5 that $\mathbf{J}_p$ and ρ_p can be defined in terms of the polarization $\mathbf{P}$ (see Eqs. 3–21 and 3–27):

$$\mathbf{J}_p \triangleq \frac{\partial \mathbf{P}}{\partial t}, \qquad \rho_p \triangleq -\operatorname{div} \mathbf{P}, \tag{2–36}$$

and in Section 6–7 it will be shown that $\mathbf{J}_m$ can be defined in terms of the magnetization $\mathbf{M}$ (see Eq. 6–28):

$$\mathbf{J}_m \triangleq \operatorname{curl} \mathbf{M}.$$

With the aid of these relations, Eqs. (2–34) and (2–35) can be written in the form

$$\rho_T = \rho - \operatorname{div} \mathbf{P}, \qquad \mathbf{J}_T = \mathbf{J} + \frac{\partial \mathbf{P}}{\partial t} + \operatorname{curl} \mathbf{M}.$$

Substituting the above expression for $\mathbf{J}_T$ into Eq. (2–29) yields

$$\operatorname{curl} \left(\frac{\mathbf{B}}{\mu_0} - \mathbf{M} \right) = \frac{\partial}{\partial t} (\varepsilon_0 \mathbf{E} + \mathbf{P}) + \mathbf{J}. \tag{2–37}$$

Equation (2–37) can be simplified by the introduction of two vectors defined by

$$\mathbf{D} \triangleq \varepsilon_0 \mathbf{E} + \mathbf{P}, \qquad \mathbf{H} \triangleq \frac{\mathbf{B}}{\mu_0} - \mathbf{M}.$$

We then obtain

$$\operatorname{curl} \mathbf{H} = \frac{\partial \mathbf{D}}{\partial t} + \mathbf{J}. \tag{2–38}$$

The vector $\mathbf{H}$ is called the *magnetic field intensity* and the vector $\mathbf{D}$ the *electric flux density*. It should be noted that $\mathbf{D}$ is the electric flux density due to free charges while $\varepsilon_0 \mathbf{E}$ is the electric flux density due to all charges. This can be seen by substituting Eq. (2–34) into Eq. (2–31b) and making use of Eq. (2–36): $\operatorname{div} \varepsilon_0 \mathbf{E} = \rho - \operatorname{div} \mathbf{P}$. Hence

$$\operatorname{div} \mathbf{D} = \rho. \tag{2–39}$$

It follows from the divergence theorem and Eq. (2–39) that

$$\int_v \operatorname{div} \mathbf{D} \, dv = \int_S \mathbf{D} \cdot \mathbf{n} \, ds = Q, \tag{2–40}$$

where $Q \triangleq \int_v \rho \, dv$ is the *free charge* enclosed by S. Equation (2–40) expresses Gauss' law applied to the case of free charge.

Equation (2–38) is Maxwell's second equation in the most convenient form for the solution of field problems. The reason for introducing the vectors $\mathbf{D}$ and $\mathbf{H}$ is that these vectors are directly related to ρ and $\mathbf{J}$, quantities which are either directly given or comparatively easily evaluated. In Eq. (2–38) we no longer require an explicit consideration of the current densities J_p and J_m, which are difficult to evaluate directly. Thus in nearly all problems Eq. (2–38) and not Eq. (2–29) will be used.

2–11 SUMMARY OF THE POSTULATES

Because of their importance we now summarize the postulates and the equations of fundamental significance which have been derived from the postulates.

Postulate 1. The force in newtons on a point charge Q moving with a velocity $\mathbf{u}$ in an electromagnetic field is given by the Lorentz force

$$\mathbf{F} = Q(\mathbf{E} + \mathbf{u} \times \mathbf{B}). \tag{2–41}$$

Postulate 2. In a transport process charges are neither created nor destroyed. This conservation law requires that the equation of continuity hold:

$$\text{div } \mathbf{J} = -\frac{\partial \rho}{\partial t}. \tag{2–42}$$

Postulate 3. In a stationary medium the electric field intensity $\mathbf{E}$ and the magnetic flux density $\mathbf{B}$ are related by the integral form of the Maxwell equations:

$$\oint_C \mathbf{E} \cdot d\mathbf{r} = -\int_S \frac{\partial \mathbf{B}}{\partial t} \cdot \mathbf{n} \, ds, \tag{2–43a}$$

$$\oint_C \frac{\mathbf{B}}{\mu_0} \cdot d\mathbf{r} = \int_S \left(\mathbf{J}_T + \varepsilon_0 \frac{\partial \mathbf{E}}{\partial t} \right) \cdot \mathbf{n} \, ds. \tag{2–43b}$$

Here $\mathbf{J}_T$ is the total current density.

With the aid of Stokes' theorem, Eqs. (2–43) can be written in the differential form

$$\text{curl } \mathbf{E} = -\frac{\partial \mathbf{B}}{\partial t}, \tag{2–44a}$$

$$\text{curl } \frac{\mathbf{B}}{\mu_0} = \mathbf{J}_T + \varepsilon_0 \frac{\partial \mathbf{E}}{\partial t}. \tag{2–44b}$$

By taking the divergence of Eqs. (2–44), we have shown that

$$\text{div } \mathbf{B} = 0, \tag{2–45a}$$

$$\text{div } \varepsilon_0 \mathbf{E} = \rho_T, \tag{2–45b}$$

where ρ_T is the total charge density.

By introducing the magnetic field intensity **H** and the magnetic flux density **D**, we have seen that Eqs. (2–44) and (2–45) can be written as

$$\text{curl } \mathbf{E} = - \frac{\partial \mathbf{B}}{\partial t}, \tag{2–46a}$$

$$\text{curl } \mathbf{H} = \mathbf{J} + \frac{\partial \mathbf{D}}{\partial t}, \tag{2–46b}$$

$$\text{div } \mathbf{B} = 0, \tag{2–47a}$$

$$\text{div } \mathbf{D} = \rho. \tag{2–47b}$$

The free charge density ρ and the current density **J** are related by the equation of continuity. With the aid of Stokes' theorem, Eqs. (2–46) can be written in the integral form

$$v_e = - \frac{\partial \phi_m}{\partial t}, \tag{2–48a}$$

$$v_m = i + \frac{\partial \phi_e}{\partial t}, \tag{2–48b}$$

where

$$v_e \triangleq \oint_C \mathbf{E} \cdot d\mathbf{r} \tag{2–49}$$

is defined as the *electromotive force* (emf),

$$v_m \triangleq \oint_C \mathbf{H} \cdot d\mathbf{r} \tag{2–50}$$

is defined as the *magnetomotive force* (mmf),

$$\phi_m \triangleq \int_S \mathbf{B} \cdot \mathbf{n} \, ds \tag{2–51}$$

is defined as the *magnetic flux* linked by C,

$$\phi_e \triangleq \int_S \mathbf{D} \cdot \mathbf{n} \, ds \tag{2–52}$$

is defined as the electric flux linked by C, and

$$i \triangleq \int_S \mathbf{J} \cdot \mathbf{n} \, ds \tag{2–53}$$

is defined as the *current* linked by C. When we perform the contour integrations, we trace out the contour C in a positive sense with respect to the surface normal **n**.

Maxwell's first equation in the differential form (2–46a) states the following: Associated with a time-varying magnetic flux density **B** is an electric field intensity **E** which tends to circulate or curl around **B**. The integral form (2–48a) states that the negative rate of change of magnetic flux linked by a contour C is equal to the emf evaluated along C. Maxwell's second equation in the differential form (2–46b) states the following: Associated with a current density **J** and a time-varying electric flux density **D** is a magnetic field intensity **H** which tends to circulate or curl around the vector **J** $+ (\partial \mathbf{D}/\partial t)$. The integral form (2–48b) states that the sum of the current and the rate of change of electric flux linked by a contour C is equal to the mmf evaluated along C.

Equations (2–43), (2–44), (2–45), (2–46), (2–47), and (2–48) are of fundamental significance. With the aid of these equations we shall be able to solve all problems dealing with macroscopic electromagnetic phenomena. The range of problems that can be solved is so extensive that it is essential to discuss classes of problems. Thus in the subsequent chapters we shall apply these equations to problems in electrostatics, magnetostatics, quasi-stationary fields, microwaves, antennas, and the interaction of charged particles with fields.

2–12 ELECTROMAGNETIC FIELDS IN THE PRESENCE OF MOVING MATTER

In the integral form (2–48) of Maxwell's equations we have considered S and C as fixed in a frame of reference $\mathscr{F}$, and the electric and magnetic fields in $\mathscr{F}$ as time-varying. This is an unnecessary restriction, since we often find a situation in which C moves with respect to $\mathscr{F}$. Equations (2–48) can be easily generalized to include the case in which C or a part of C moves with respect to a fixed frame of reference. We have

$$v_e = - \frac{d\phi_m}{dt}, \qquad (2\text{–}54a)$$

$$v_m = i + \frac{d\phi_e}{dt}, \qquad (2\text{–}54b)$$

where

$$v_e \triangleq \oint_C \mathbf{E}_e \cdot d\mathbf{r} \qquad (2\text{–}55a)$$

and

$$v_m \triangleq \oint_C \mathbf{H}_e \cdot d\mathbf{r}. \qquad (2\text{–}55b)$$

Thus if C and therefore S change, we must compute the total derivatives. Furthermore, in computing v_e and v_m we must use the effective electromagnetic field vectors $\mathbf{E}_e$, $\mathbf{H}_e$, seen by an observer fixed to a field point on C. These field vectors are, in general, different from the field vectors **E**, **H**, seen by a fixed observer in $\mathscr{F}$.

Equations (2–54), when properly applied, often result in simple approximate solutions to difficult problems. However, no insight is obtained about the details of the field and this may limit the usefulness of Eqs. (2–54). It is not an easy matter to obtain exact solutions of Maxwell's equations in the presence of moving matter [2, 3, 4, 5]. In Appendix B, Eqs. (2–54) are used to derive the transformation equations relating field components in a moving and a fixed frame of reference. In this section, however, we shall restrict ourselves to relatively simple problems which illustrate the use of Eqs. (2–54) and which indicate how field components transform between different frames of reference.

We can obtain some physical insight into the nature of the transformation by considering the Lorentz force as viewed in two different frames of reference. When a test charge Q moves with a velocity $\mathbf{u}$ relative to a frame of reference $\mathscr{F}$, the force on Q as measured by an observer in $\mathscr{F}$ is

$$\mathbf{F} = Q(\mathbf{E} + \mathbf{u} \times \mathbf{B}),\qquad(2\text{–}56)$$

where $\mathbf{E}$ and $\mathbf{B}$ are field vectors in $\mathscr{F}$. When $\mathscr{F}'$ is a frame of reference moving with Q, the force on Q as measured by an observer in $\mathscr{F}'$ is

$$\mathbf{F}' = Q\mathbf{E}',\qquad(2\text{–}57)$$

where $\mathbf{E}'$ is a field vector in $\mathscr{F}'$. From a physical standpoint it seems reasonable to expect that $\mathbf{F} = \mathbf{F}'$, so that the force is invariant. This is true provided that relativistic effects can be neglected, which is the case in most engineering problems (see Appendix B). Thus

$$\mathbf{E}' = \mathbf{E} + \mathbf{u} \times \mathbf{B}\qquad(2\text{–}58)$$

is one of the transformations which relate field vectors in $\mathscr{F}$ and $\mathscr{F}'$. An alternative derivation of Eq. (2–58) based on Eq. (2–54a) is given in Appendix B.

As an example let us consider the case of a cylindrical conductor which moves with a velocity $\mathbf{u} = \mathbf{i}_x u$ relative to a frame of reference $\mathscr{F}$, in which a uniform and constant magnetic field $\mathbf{B} = \mathbf{i}_z B$ exists (Fig. 2–13). An observer in $\mathscr{F}$ notices that a free charge Q in the conductor experiences a Lorentz force

$$\mathbf{F} = Q\mathbf{u} \times \mathbf{B},$$

which causes the charge to move to the end of the cylinder. The displaced free charges set up an electric field $\mathbf{E}$, and equilibrium is reached when the resultant force on a charge within the conductor is zero. Thus

$$\mathbf{E} + \mathbf{u} \times \mathbf{B} = 0.\qquad(2\text{–}59)$$

We can obtain the electric field seen by an observer in $\mathscr{F}'$ moving with the conductor from Eq. (2–58). Within the conductor $\mathbf{E}' = 0$, as required by the condition for equilibrium. At sufficiently large distances from the

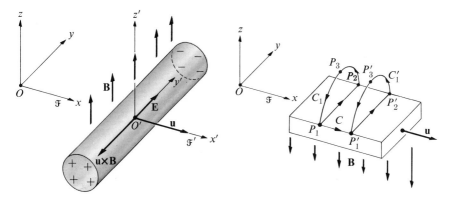

Fig. 2–13. A conducting cylinder moving in a uniform magnetic field.   **Fig. 2–14.** A conducting slab moving in a uniform magnetic field.

cylinder the electric field intensity $\mathbf{E}$ due to the surface charges is negligible. It follows from Eq. (2–58) that in this region the observer in $\mathscr{F}'$ sees an electric field intensity given by

$$\mathbf{E}' = \mathbf{u} \times \mathbf{B}. \tag{2–60}$$

Thus the observer in $\mathscr{F}'$ sees an electric field which results from inserting the cylindrical conductor in a uniform electric field given by Eq. (2–60).

Consider now a second example, in which a conducting slab moves with a velocity $\mathbf{u} = \mathbf{i}_x u$ relative to a frame of reference in which there is a uniform and constant magnetic field $\mathbf{B} = -\mathbf{i}_z B$ (Fig. 2–14). Due to the Lorentz force, charges are displaced and an electric field $\mathbf{E}$ results. As a first approximation let us assume that the electric field is uniform throughout the conductor and that $\mathbf{E} = \mathbf{i}_y E$. Let C_1 be a contour fixed in $\mathscr{F}$ and situated as shown in the figure. Since $d\phi_m/dt = 0$ for the contour C_1, we have

$$\oint_{C_1} \mathbf{E} \cdot d\mathbf{r} = 0. \tag{2–61}$$

Consider now a line $P_1'P_2'$ fixed in the conductor and let C be the contour determined by the sequence of points $P_1P_1'P_2'P_2P_3P_1$. When we apply Eq. (2–54a) it is important to note that the contour C is traced through in a right-handed sense with respect to the surface normal $\mathbf{n}$ (see the discussion following Eq. 1–36). For the case in which a conductor is present, it is convenient to choose the sense of direction of the current to be the same as that chosen for C. This will be the case if $v_e > 0$, which requires that $-(d\phi_m/dt) > 0$. The latter condition is fulfilled when $\mathbf{B}$ and $\mathbf{n}$ tend to be oppositely directed. This choice has been made in Fig. 2–14; the same choice will be made in all subsequent examples. Since the line $P_1'P_2'$ moves with a velocity $\mathbf{u}$, the flux linked by C changes. Given that w is the width of the conductor, we have

$$- \frac{d\phi_m}{dt} = uBw.$$

When we apply Eq. (2–54a), we note that $\mathbf{E}_e = \mathbf{E}$ along the sections of C at rest in $\mathscr{F}$ and that $\mathbf{E}_e = \mathbf{E}'$ along $P_1'P_2'$. Since $\mathbf{E} \cdot d\mathbf{r} = 0$ along P_1P_1' and P_2P_2', we obtain

$$\int_{P_2P_3P_1} \mathbf{E} \cdot d\mathbf{r} + \int_{P_1'}^{P_2'} \mathbf{E}' \cdot d\mathbf{r} = uBw, \qquad (2\text{–}62)$$

where the integral on the left-hand side of Eq. (2–62) is evaluated along the path $P_2P_3P_1$. From Eq. (2–61) it follows that

$$\int_{P_2P_3P_1} \mathbf{E} \cdot d\mathbf{r} = - \int_{P_1}^{P_2} \mathbf{E} \cdot d\mathbf{r}. \qquad (2\text{–}63)$$

Substituting Eq. (2–63) into Eq. (2–62) yields

$$\int_{P_1}^{P_2} -\mathbf{E} \cdot d\mathbf{r} + \int_{P_1'}^{P_2'} \mathbf{E}' \cdot d\mathbf{r} = uBw. \qquad (2\text{–}64)$$

If we now make use of our assumption concerning the uniformity of $\mathbf{E}$ and $\mathbf{E}'$ throughout the slab, we can evaluate the integrals in Eq. (2–64) and obtain

$$E' = E + uB. \qquad (2\text{–}65)$$

Equation (2–65) is the y-component of Eq. (2–58). We have, in effect, given a very simple and not very rigorous derivation of Eq. (2–58).

If the slab is a perfect conductor, $\mathbf{E}' = 0$, and Eq. (2–64) yields

$$V = uBw, \qquad (2\text{–}66)$$

where

$$V \triangleq \int_{P_1}^{P_2} -\mathbf{E} \cdot d\mathbf{r} \qquad (2\text{–}67)$$

is defined as the *voltage* between P_1 and P_2.

Let a thin wire of cross-sectional area a and conductivity σ be placed along the path $P_1P_3P_2$ and let sliding contacts be placed at P_1 and P_2 (Fig. 2–15). Due to the charges on the slab, an electric field $\mathbf{E}$ is set up in the wire and a current i results. For the fixed path illustrated in Fig. 2–15, $d\phi_m/dt = 0$, and with the help of Eq. (2–67) we obtain

$$\int_{P_2P_3P_1} \mathbf{E} \cdot d\mathbf{r} = \int_{P_1}^{P_2} -\mathbf{E} \cdot d\mathbf{r} = V. \qquad (2\text{–}68)$$

Within the wire $\mathbf{E}$ has the direction of $d\mathbf{r}$ and the following relations hold:

$$\mathbf{E} \cdot d\mathbf{r} = \frac{J\,dr}{\sigma} = \frac{i\,dr}{a\sigma}.$$

Equation (2–68) can therefore be written in the form

$$V = iR, \qquad (2\text{–}69)$$

where

$$R \triangleq \int_{P_2 P_3 P_1} \frac{dr}{a\sigma} \qquad (2\text{–}70)$$

is the resistance of the wire. Equation (2–69) states that a current i is driven through a resistance R by a voltage V. Since V is given by Eq. (2–66), we say that the voltage is a *motion-induced voltage* caused by the motion of the conductor through a magnetic field **B**. It should be pointed out that we have tacitly assumed that **B** is not changed by i. In effect this means that either the magnetic field due to i must be negligible compared with **B** or that we must compensate for its effect on **B**. In practical devices this compensation is often accomplished by means of external compensating coils which are excited by the current i.

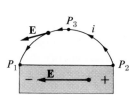

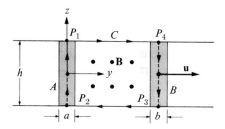

Fig. 2–15. A cross-sectional view of the conduction slab illustrated in Fig. 2–14.

Fig. 2–16. A simple electromechanical energy converter.

Figure 2–16 illustrates a very simple electromechanical energy converter which converts mechanical energy into electrical energy. Two perfectly conducting infinite plane sheets are parallel to the y-axis and a distance h apart. Two conducting slabs A and B of infinite length in the x-direction make perfect contact with the sheets. Slab A is fixed while slab B is movable and their conductivities are σ_a and σ_b, respectively. Let a uniform magnetic field $\mathbf{B} = \mathbf{i}_x B$ be applied and let the movable slab be pulled by a mechanical force $\mathbf{F}_{\text{mech}}$ in the direction of the y-axis with a velocity **u**. The Lorentz force causes a displacement of charge in slab B, and the resulting electric field in slab A produces a current i. Let us determine a relationship between i, σ_a, σ_b, u, and B for the case in which $(a/h) \ll 1$ and $(b/h) \ll 1$, and in which i causes a negligible change in **B**. A contour C is chosen, as shown in Fig. 2–16. The conditions that a and b are small compared with h allow us to neglect the magnetic flux in the slabs not linked by C. Equation (2–54a) yields

$$\int_{P_2}^{P_1} \mathbf{E} \cdot d\mathbf{r} + \int_{P_4}^{P_3} \mathbf{E}' \cdot d\mathbf{r} = uBh. \qquad (2\text{–}71)$$

The current densities in A and B are given, respectively, by

$$\mathbf{J}_a = \sigma_a \mathbf{E}, \qquad \mathbf{J}_b = \sigma_b \mathbf{E}',$$

and the current per unit length of the slabs is

$$i = aJ_a = bJ_b.$$

If we introduce

$$R_a = \frac{h}{a\sigma_a}, \qquad R_b = \frac{h}{b\sigma_b},$$

the resistance of a unit length of slab A and slab B, respectively, we find when we substitute the above relations into Eq. (2–71) that

$$Eh + E'h = i(R_a + R_b) = uBh. \tag{2–72}$$

In order to interpret Eq. (2–72), we assume that slab B has infinite conductivity so that $\mathbf{E}' = 0$. We may then consider the moving slab as a voltage generator which has zero internal resistance and the voltage generated by the motion of the slab (see Eq. 2–67) is given by $V = uBh$. In the case of a finite σ_b the internal resistance of the generator is accounted for by R_b. The generated voltage remains the same and Eq. (2–72) states that the voltage V drives a current i through a resistance $R_a + R_b$. The electrical energy dissipated in the resistance comes from the mechanical source which does work in pulling the slab. The following power equality must hold:

$$F_{\text{mech}}u = i^2(R_a + R_b) = iuBh.$$

Thus

$$\mathbf{F}_{\text{mech}} = \mathbf{i}_y iBh$$

is the mechanical force on slab B. This in turn implies that the magnetic field $\mathbf{B}$ exerts a force $\mathbf{F} = -\mathbf{i}_y iBh$ on slab B.

As a final example of the use of Eq. (2–54a), let the $\mathbf{B}$-field in the previous example vary according to the equation

$$B = B_m \cos \omega_1 t,$$

and let the center of slab B be determined by

$$y = y_0 - \frac{u_m}{\omega_2} \cos \omega_2 t.$$

During the time dt, the change in magnetic flux linked by C due to $\mathbf{B}$ varying is

$$d\phi_{m1} = hy(-dB) = h\left(y_0 - \frac{u_m}{\omega_2} \cos \omega_2 t\right)(B_m \omega_1 \sin \omega_1 t \, dt),$$

and the change in magnetic flux linked by C due to C moving is

$$d\phi_{m2} = (h \, dy)(-B) = (hu_m \sin \omega_2 t \, dt)(-B_m \cos \omega_1 t).$$

Thus

$$-\frac{d\phi_m}{dt} = -hB_m\omega_1\left(y_0 - \frac{u_m}{\omega_2}\cos\omega_2 t\right)\sin\omega_1 t + hB_m u_m \sin\omega_2 t \cos\omega_1 t.$$

$$(2\text{-}73)$$

The right-hand side of Eq. (2-73) will now replace the right-hand side of Eq. (2-71) and will then become the induced voltage. The induced voltage consists of two terms, a *transformer-induced voltage*,

$$V_1 = -hB_m\omega_1\left(y_0 - \frac{u_m}{\omega_2}\cos\omega_2 t\right)\sin\omega_1 t,$$

which arises because of the change in magnetic flux linked by a fixed C, and a *motion-induced voltage*,

$$V_2 = hB_m u_m \sin\omega_2 t \cos\omega_1 t,$$

which arises because of the change in magnetic flux linked by C due to the motion of C.

There are a variety of ways of formulating the basic laws of electromagnetism. The reason for the particular choice of postulates given here is the fact that they are easily verified by simple experiments. However, we could also postulate that the force on a test charge transform from one frame of reference to another so as to satisfy the relativity principle. With the aid of the relativistic Lorentz transformation and some suitable assumptions, we become able to derive the Maxwell equations [6]. This possibility, which sheds additional light on the nature of the electromagnetic field, is discussed in Appendix B. However, all that is actually done is to replace one set of postulates by another set.

REFERENCES

1. S. J. PLIMPTON and W. F. LAWTON, "A very accurate test of Coulomb's law of force between charges," *Phys. Rev.* **50**, 1066–1071, 1936

2. R. M. FANO, L. J. CHU, and R. B. ADLER, *Electromagnetic Fields, Energy and Forces.* New York: John Wiley & Sons, 1960

3. H. A. HAUS and J. P. PENHUNE, *Case Studies in Electromagnetism.* New York: John Wiley & Sons, 1960

4. A. SOMMERFELD, *Electrodynamics.* New York: Academic Press, 1964

5. W. K. PANOSKY and M. PHILLIPS, *Classical Electricity and Magnetism.* Reading, Mass.: Addison-Wesley, 1956

6. R. S. ELLIOT, "Relativity and electricity," *IEEE Spectrum*, 140–152, March 1966

PROBLEMS

2–1 A circular copper ring which has a radius of 10 cm and a circular cross section of radius 0.1 cm is situated in a time-varying magnetic field. The magnetic flux is normal to the plane of the ring and changes at the rate of 4×10^{-3} (Wb/m²)/sec. The conductivity of the copper is $\sigma = 5.80 \times 10^7$ mhos/m. Determine the current in the ring.

2–2 Consider a betatron in which an electron is moving in a circular orbit of radius $r = 0.5$ m. The magnetic flux linked by the orbit changes by 0.08 Wb in 10^{-3} sec. Determine the emf for the orbit. What are the forces acting on the electron due to the magnetic and electric fields?

2–3 Consider a nonequilibrium charge distribution ρ in a uniform infinite conducting medium. Take $\mathbf{D} \cong \varepsilon_0\mathbf{E}$ for a conductor and prove that

$$\frac{\partial \rho}{\partial t} + \frac{\sigma}{\varepsilon_0}\,\rho = 0.$$

For a copper conductor $\sigma = 5.80 \times 10^7$ mhos/m; determine the time constant for the decay of the charge density.

2–4 In an electrostatic generator of the Van de Graaf type, charges are sprayed onto a moving dielectric belt. Given that the breakdown strength of air is $E = 30 \times 10^3$ V/cm, determine the maximum surface charge density q that can be sprayed onto the belt. Assume that the thickness of the belt is negligible compared with its width of 0.5 m. Assume that the belt has a linear speed of 20 m/sec; determine the current i and the magnetic field intensity $\mathbf{H}$. Assume that $\mathbf{H}$ is tangential to the belt and normal to the belt velocity. Can you justify this assumption for a very wide belt? [*Hint:* Use Gauss' law to establish the relationship between $\mathbf{E}$ and q and use Eq. (2–48b) to establish the relation between i and $\mathbf{H}$.]

2–5 The z-component of the magnetic flux density of a radially symmetric electromagnet is given by

$$B_z = B_0[1 - (r/a)^2]\sin \omega t,$$

where r is the radial coordinate. Determine the component E_ϕ of the electric field intensity associated with the time-varying magnetic field.

2–6 A charge Q moves along the x-axis with a velocity $\mathbf{u} = d\mathbf{r}/dt$ (Fig. 2–17). Determine the electric flux linked by a circular path of radius a centered on the axis and normal to $\mathbf{u}$. (a) Assuming that $\mathbf{B}$ is tangential to the circle, prove that

$$\mathbf{B} = \frac{1}{c^2}\,\mathbf{u} \times \mathbf{E},$$

where $c = 1/\sqrt{\mu_0\varepsilon_0}$. How would you justify the assumption made concerning the direction of $\mathbf{B}$? (b) Consider the moving charge as a current element, so that $Q\mathbf{u} \triangleq i\,d\mathbf{r}$, and prove the *Biot-Savart law*,

$$d\mathbf{H} = \frac{i\,d\mathbf{r} \times \mathbf{r}}{4\pi r^3}.$$

2-7 Suppose that a dielectric sphere of radius a and permittivity ε is placed in a uniform static electric field $\mathbf{i}_z E_0$. It can be shown (Fig. 2-18) that

$$\mathbf{E} = \begin{cases} -\operatorname{grad} U_1, & r < a, \\ -\operatorname{grad} U_2, & r > a, \end{cases}$$

where

$$U_1 = -\frac{3E_0 r \cos \theta}{\varepsilon_r + 2}, \qquad U_2 = -E_0 r \cos \theta + E_0 a^3 \frac{\varepsilon_r - 1}{\varepsilon_r + 2} \frac{\cos \theta}{r^2}$$

and where $\varepsilon_r = \varepsilon/\varepsilon_0$. (a) Assuming the above result to be true, determine the electric flux linked by a contour C defined by the circle $\theta = \text{const}$, $r = \text{const}$. (b) Suppose that E_0 changes at a uniform rate; use the integral form of Maxwell's second equation (2-48b) to find H_ϕ. The symmetry of the field leads one to conclude that $H_z = H_\theta = 0$. Is this conclusion compatible with the differential form of Maxwell's equations (Eqs. 2-46)? Note how easily the problem is solved when one uses the integral form. Would you expect this to be always the case? If E_0 did not change at a uniform rate, would you expect complications? Explain. (c) Using the formula for $\mathbf{H}$ derived in part (b), justify the following statement. The term $d\phi_e/dt$ can be neglected in a problem if either the rate $d\mathbf{E}/dt$ or the system dimensions can be chosen sufficiently small.

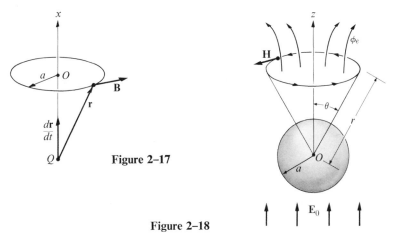

Figure 2-17

Figure 2-18

2-8 An electric field intensity $\mathbf{E} = \mathbf{E}_0 \sin \omega t$ is normal to the plane of a circle C of radius a which is situated in free space. Given that $E_0 = 10^4 \text{ V/m}$ and $a = 10 \text{ cm}$, determine the frequency at which the maximum rate of change of electric flux linked by C is $d\phi_e/dt = 1 \text{ C/sec}$. (Note that this is equivalent to a current of one ampere.) If you had no further information about the symmetry of the field, could you use the integral form of Maxwell's second equation to find the component of $\mathbf{H}$ tangential to C? Explain.

2-9 A thin circular ring of radius r is rotated with an angular velocity ω about an axis normal to a uniform and constant magnetic field $\mathbf{B}$. Determine the current in the ring, given that it has a conductivity of σ and a cross-sectional area of a. The following values are given: $\sigma = 5.80 \times 10^7$ mhos/m (copper), $r = 10^{-2}$ m, $a = 10^{-6}$ m^2, $B = 0.1$ Wb/m^2, and the ring turns at a rate of 100 rev/sec. Determine the resistance of the ring, the maximum emf and the maximum current in the coil. [*Hint:* Consider the coil as fixed and the magnetic field as time-varying.] The magnetic flux density at the center of a thin ring can be shown to be given in magnitude by the formula

$$B_c = \frac{\mu_0 i}{2\pi r}.$$

Compute B_c and compare it with B. Does i affect B to any extent?

2–10 (a) With the aid of Eq. (2–58) and by taking $\mathbf{E}_e = \mathbf{E}'$, show that Eq. (2–54a) reduces to

$$\oint_C (\mathbf{u} \times \mathbf{B}) \cdot d\mathbf{r} = -\frac{d\phi_m}{dt}.$$

(b) A rectangular coil of dimensions a and b is rotated with an angular velocity ω about its axis of symmetry, which is perpendicular to a magnetic field $\mathbf{B}$ (Fig. 2–19). For this coil, evaluate both sides of the equation given in part (a) and show that they are equal.

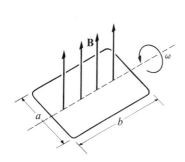

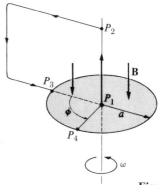

Figure 2–19   **Figure 2–20**

2–11 Figure 2–20 illustrates a Faraday disk. It consists of a circular plane conductor rotated in a uniform and constant magnetic field which is parallel to the axis of rotation. An external wire is connected to a sliding contact at P_2 on the axis and to a sliding contact at P_3 on the rim of the disk. Given that the disk and the axis are perfect conductors, apply Eq. (2–54a) to the contour C shown in the figure and determine an expression for the voltage

$$V = \int_{P_3}^{P_1} -\mathbf{E} \cdot d\mathbf{r},$$

where the integral is evaluated along the path $P_1P_4P_3$. Does the result depend on the angle ϕ?

2–12 The radius of a thin conducting circular ring changes at a rate dr/dt. The ring is situated in a uniform and constant magnetic field which is normal to the plane of the ring. Use Eq. (2–54a) and show that

$$\mathbf{E'} = \frac{dr}{dt}\mathbf{r} \times \mathbf{B},$$

where $\mathbf{r_1}$ is a unit radial vector. Note that this result is equivalent to that obtained by using Eq. (2–58).

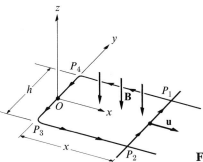

Figure 2–21

2–13 A thin filamentary conductor of cross-sectional area a and conductivity σ_a has the shape shown in Fig. 2–21, where two sides are parallel to the x-axis a distance h apart and one side coincides with the y-axis. A second thin straight conductor of cross-sectional area b and conductivity σ_b makes a sliding contact at P_1 and P_2 with the first conductor and remains parallel to the y-axis as it moves with a velocity $\mathbf{u} = i_x u$. A uniform and constant magnetic field $\mathbf{B} = -i_z B$ is applied. Determine the motion-induced voltage

$$V \triangleq \int_{P_1}^{P_2} -\mathbf{E} \cdot d\mathbf{r}$$

and the current i resulting from this voltage. Assume that i has negligible effect on $\mathbf{B}$.

CHAPTER 3

THE ELECTROSTATIC FIELD

3–1 INTRODUCTION

In the case of static fields the two Maxwell equations (2–46) become independent of each other. This results in a considerable simplification, since it is then possible to discuss the electric and magnetic fields separately. A question arises concerning the practical usefulness of the results obtained for static fields, since most practical applications involve time-varying fields. We shall see in Section 9–2 that sinusoidally varying electromagnetic fields propagate as waves with a speed c. Given that the frequency of oscillation is f, we have the relation

$$f\lambda = c,$$

where λ is the wavelength. Suppose that a represents the largest physical dimension of the system under discussion; the static field will be a good approximation provided that the wavelength is large compared with a (see Section 11–11):

$$a/\lambda = af/c \ll 1. \tag{3–1}$$

The same conclusion is reached in the special case illustrated in Fig. 2–18 (see Problem 2–7). The solution of this problem shows that $d\phi_e/dt$ is proportional to the product $a(dE_0/dt)$, where a is the radius of the sphere. The term $d\phi_e/dt$, which couples the two Maxwell equations, is negligible if dE_0/dt is negligible (the case of a static field) or if a is negligible. Thus it follows that the static field can yield a good approximation, even at very high frequencies, provided that the physical dimensions are sufficiently small.

3–2 THE STATIC ELECTRIC FIELD OF FREE CHARGES

For the case of a static field Maxwell's first equation in the differential and integral form (see Eqs. 2–46 and 2–48) yields

$$\text{curl } \mathbf{E} = 0, \qquad v_e = \oint_C \mathbf{E} \cdot d\mathbf{r} = 0. \tag{3–2}$$

The two equations given by (3–2) are equivalent, since one can obtain the second from the first by applying Stokes' theorem. Equations (3–2) are both satisfied if we choose*

$$E = -\text{grad } U,$$

which we can see when we substitute this expression into Eqs. (3-2):

$$\nabla \times E = -\nabla \times (\nabla U) = 0,$$

$$\oint_C -E \cdot dr = \oint_C \text{grad } U \cdot dr = \oint_C dU = 0.$$

Thus the electrostatic field is characterized by the fact that the electric field intensity can be expressed as the negative gradient of a scalar function U. The function U is called the *electric scalar potential*, or simply the *potential*.

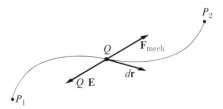

Fig. 3-1. A test charge in a static electric field.

Let us consider a test charge Q at rest in an electric field. We assume that Q does not alter the existing charge distribution. This is the case for point charges. Otherwise we must consider Q to be infinitesimally small or consider all other charges as fixed in position so that they assume the properties of point charges. The charge Q experiences a force given by QE and a mechanical force

$$F_{\text{mech}} = -QE$$

is required to hold the charge in position (Fig. 3-1). Let us compute the mechanical work done in moving a unit positive test charge from a position P_1 to a position P_2. We move the charge infinitely slowly so that we need not concern ourselves with dynamical effects. The mechanical work done is

$$W_{\text{mech}} = \int_{P_1}^{P_2} F_{\text{mech}} \cdot dr = \int_{P_1}^{P_2} \text{grad } U \cdot dr = \int_{P_1}^{P_2} dU = V, \quad (3-3)$$

where $V = U(P_2) - U(P_1)$ is the *potential difference* between the points P_2 and P_1. For computational reasons it is often convenient to consider V as positive. We then take P_2 to be at a higher potential than P_1 so that mechanical work is done in moving a positive unit charge from P_1 to P_2.

In the case of an isolated point charge Q in free space, the simplest approach when we wish to determine the quantities **D**, **E**, and U is by use of

---

* The minus sign is chosen so that **E** has the direction of decreasing potential.

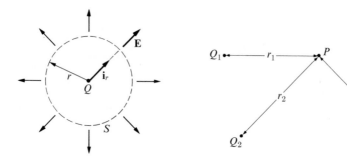

Fig. 3–2. The electric field of a point charge.

Fig. 3–3. The potential of n point charges.

Gauss' law (see Eq. 2–40). For the surface S in Gauss' law we choose a sphere of radius r centered at the point charge (see Fig. 3–2), so that the surface normal $\mathbf{n}$ is also the unit radial vector $\mathbf{i}_r$. Due to symmetry, $\mathbf{D}$ has the direction of $\mathbf{i}_r$ and D is constant over S. Gauss' law yields

$$\mathbf{D} = \frac{Q}{4\pi r^2}\mathbf{i}_r$$

and the electric field intensity is

$$\mathbf{E} = \frac{Q}{4\pi\varepsilon_0 r^2}\mathbf{i}_r.$$

In order to determine the potential U due to the point charge we note that

$$dU = \operatorname{grad} U \cdot d\mathbf{r} = -\mathbf{E} \cdot d\mathbf{r}.$$

If we choose $d\mathbf{r} = \mathbf{i}_r\, dr$, we obtain

$$dU = -\frac{Q\, dr}{4\pi\varepsilon_0 r^2}.$$

Integrating from infinity to a position P a distance r from Q yields

$$U = \frac{Q}{4\pi\varepsilon_0 r}, \tag{3–4}$$

where we have taken $U(\infty) = 0$. It follows from Eq. (3–3) that U is equal to the mechanical work done in bringing a positive unit test charge from infinity to a distance r from the point charge Q.

When there are n point charges, we can find the potential at a field point P by superposition (Fig. 3–3)

$$U = \frac{1}{4\pi\varepsilon_0}\sum_{k=1}^{n}\frac{Q_k}{r_k}. \tag{3–5}$$

A continuous distribution of charge results in a charge density ρ. The potential due to a continuous distribution of charge can be found by the following heuristic argument. The element of charge in a volume element dv is $\rho \, dv$, and this is considered to be a point charge (Fig. 3–4). The elemental potential at a field point P due to this charge is

$$dU = \frac{\rho \, dv}{4\pi\varepsilon_0 r}. \tag{3–6}$$

Thus, by superposition, we find that

$$U = \frac{1}{4\pi\varepsilon_0} \int_v \frac{\rho \, dv}{r}. \tag{3–7}$$

The resulting expression for U is correct. However, the derivation is not rigorous. The element of charge $\rho \, dv$ is not a point charge; it only appears approximately as a point charge if r is sufficiently large. A rigorous proof

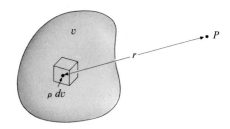

Fig. 3–4. Potential of a continuous distribution of charges.

can be obtained by solving Poisson's equation, which we shall now derive. The electric flux density in free space is $\mathbf{D} = \varepsilon_0\mathbf{E}$. Thus, substituting this relation into Eq. (2–47b), we obtain

$$\text{div } \mathbf{D} = \varepsilon_0 \text{ div } \mathbf{E} = \rho.$$

Substituting $\mathbf{E} = -\text{grad } U$ yields Poisson's equation,

$$\nabla^2 U = -\frac{\rho}{\varepsilon_0}. \tag{3–8}$$

We saw in Chapter 1 (recall Eq. 1–75) that Poisson's equation can be solved with the aid of Green's theorem. The solution is given by Eq. (3–7).

3-3 THE POTENTIAL DUE TO A DIPOLE

The potential at a field point P due to two charges Q and $-Q$ situated on the z-axis and separated by a distance l (Fig. 3–5) is

$$U = \frac{Q}{4\pi\varepsilon_0}\left(\frac{1}{r_2} - \frac{1}{r_1}\right). \tag{3–9}$$

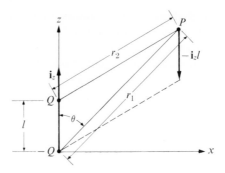

Fig. 3-5. Potential of a dipole.

If $l \ll r_1$, we can use the differential $d(1/r)$ to approximate the difference $[(1/r_2) - (1/r_1)]$. Thus

$$d\left(\frac{1}{r}\right) = \operatorname{grad} \frac{1}{r} \cdot d\mathbf{r} \cong \left(\frac{1}{r_2} - \frac{1}{r_1}\right), \qquad (3\text{-}10)$$

where $d\mathbf{r} = -\mathbf{i}_z l$ and where $\mathbf{i}_z$ is the unit vector directed from the charge $-Q$ to the charge Q. Substituting Eq. (3-10) into Eq. (3-9) yields

$$U = -\frac{Ql}{4\pi\varepsilon_0} \operatorname{grad} \frac{1}{r} \cdot \mathbf{i}_z.$$

The *dipole moment* $\mathbf{m}$ of the two charges is defined by the equation

$$\mathbf{m} \triangleq \mathbf{i}_z \lim_{l\to 0} Ql. \qquad (3\text{-}11)$$

Evidently as $l \to 0$ it is necessary that $Q \to \infty$ in order that the product Ql approach a finite value m. For the potential we obtain, as $l \to 0$,

$$U = -\frac{m}{4\pi\varepsilon_0} \operatorname{grad} \frac{1}{r} \cdot \mathbf{i}_z. \qquad (3\text{-}12)$$

The function U given by Eq. (3-12) is the potential due to a dipole. A dipole is formed by two charges Q and $-Q$ which satisfy the relation (3-11). When the dipole is at the origin so that $r^2 = x^2 + y^2 + z^2$, it is convenient to express U in spherical coordinates. This is done by noting that

$$\operatorname{grad} \frac{1}{r} \cdot \mathbf{i}_z = \frac{\partial}{\partial z} \frac{1}{r} = -\frac{\cos\theta}{r^2}.$$

Thus Eq. (3-12) takes the form

$$U = \frac{m}{4\pi\varepsilon_0} \frac{\cos\theta}{r^2}. \qquad (3\text{-}13)$$

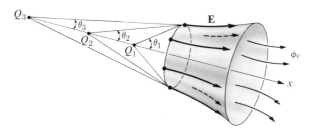

Fig. 3–6. Streamlines for three collinear point charges.

3–4 TUBES OF ELECTRIC FLUX; STREAMLINES

The line element of a *streamline* is defined by the equation

$$d\mathbf{r} = dc\mathbf{E}, \qquad (3\text{–}14)$$

where dc is an infinitesimally small scaling factor. In the case of fluid flow, $\mathbf{E}$ would represent the fluid velocity and $d\mathbf{r}$ would give the direction of motion of the fluid particles. Hence the name streamlines for the curves composed of the elements $d\mathbf{r}$. In the case of an electric field, $d\mathbf{r}$ gives the direction in which a positive test charge tends to move, provided that the test charge does not alter the charge distribution. In cartesian coordinates Eq. (3–14) reduces to the system of differential equations

$$\frac{dx}{E_x} = \frac{dy}{E_y} = \frac{dz}{E_z}. \qquad (3\text{–}15)$$

When $\mathbf{E}$ is a known function of position, the differential equations (3–15) can be solved and yield a family of curves which define the streamlines. However, in most cases the solution of the differential equations is not an easy matter. If the charge distribution has an axis of symmetry, it is often possible to determine the streamlines by considering them to bound a tube of constant electric flux (see Section 1–10). As an example, let us determine the equation for the streamlines of a collinear distribution of three point charges Q_1, Q_2, and Q_3 (Fig. 3–6). The desired result is most conveniently obtained with the aid of Gauss' law by noting that the streamlines form tubes of electric flux and that within such a tube the flux remains constant. Let us consider a tube of flux T_f defined by the angles θ_1 and θ_2. The angle θ_1 defines an area*

$$\Omega_1 = 2\pi(1 - \cos\theta_1)$$

on a unit sphere centered at Q_1. Thus Q_1 contributes an electric flux

$$\phi_{e_1} = \frac{\Omega_1}{4\pi} \cdot Q_1 = \frac{Q_1}{2}(1 - \cos\theta_1)$$

---

* The area Ω_1 is known as a *solid angle*.

to T_f and the total electric flux in T_f due to the three charges is

$$\phi_e = \frac{Q_1}{2}(1 - \cos\theta_1) + \frac{Q_2}{2}(1 - \cos\theta_2) + \frac{Q_3}{2}(1 - \cos\theta_3).$$

The streamlines are defined by the equation $\phi_e = \text{const.}$

3–5 DIELECTRICS AND THE POLARIZATION VECTOR

A dielectric solid consists of nuclei at fixed sites around which electrons circulate in bound orbits. In the case of a perfect dielectric there are no free electrons and the conductivity is zero. However, the electrons can still be displaced from the equilibrium orbits and this displacement can result in an effective charge density and an effective current density. Let us consider an individual atom in a dielectric material. Under the action of an electric field $\mathbf{E}$ the negative electrons are displaced from their equilibrium orbits about the positive nucleus. Due to this displacement, the atom appears as a dipole and we speak of it as being polarized. The *polarization* or *dipole moment* of the atom is defined by the equation (Fig. 3–7)

$$\mathbf{P} = \mathbf{k}Ql,$$

where $\mathbf{k}$ is a unit vector directed from the effective electron charge $-Q$ to the effective nucleus charge Q. The potential due to the polarized atom at a field point P (see Eq. 3–12) is

$$U = -\frac{1}{4\pi\varepsilon_0}\operatorname{grad}\frac{1}{r}\cdot\mathbf{P}. \tag{3–16}$$

In a dielectric solid we have a large number of atoms attached to fixed sites. Let there be N atoms in a volume element Δv. We define a macroscopic polarization vector $\mathbf{P}$ as the *dipole moment per unit volume*,

$$\mathbf{P} \triangleq \lim_{\Delta v \to 0} \frac{1}{\Delta v} \sum_{k=1}^{N} \mathbf{P}_k. \tag{3–17}$$

Here $\mathbf{P}_k$ is the dipole moment of the kth atom.

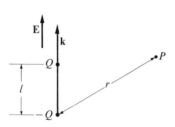

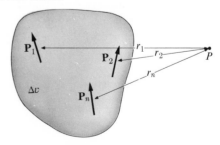

Fig. 3–7. Polarization of an atom.   Fig. 3–8. Potential due to polarized atoms.

It follows from Eq. (3–16) that the elemental polarization potential ΔU_p at a field point P (Fig. 3–8) is

$$\Delta U_p = -\frac{1}{4\pi\varepsilon_0} \sum_{k=1}^{N} \operatorname{grad} \frac{1}{r_k} \cdot \mathbf{P}_k. \qquad (3\text{–}18)$$

Since the volume element is considered to be infinitesimally small, we can set $r \cong r_k$, where r is the distance from P to an interior point of the volume element. Thus with the aid of Eq. (3–17) we can express Eq. (3–18) in the form

$$\Delta U_p \cong -\frac{1}{4\pi\varepsilon_0} \operatorname{grad} \frac{1}{r} \cdot \mathbf{P}\, \Delta v.$$

Summing over all volume elements and taking the limit as $\Delta v \to 0$, we obtain

$$U_p = -\frac{1}{4\pi\varepsilon_0} \int_v \mathbf{P} \cdot \operatorname{grad}_P \frac{1}{r}\, dv = \frac{1}{4\pi\varepsilon_0} \int_v \mathbf{P} \cdot \operatorname{grad}_Q \frac{1}{r}\, dv$$

$$= \frac{1}{4\pi\varepsilon_0} \int_v \mathbf{P} \cdot \operatorname{grad} \frac{1}{r}\, dv. \qquad (3\text{–}19)$$

In the integrands of the integrals we have used subscripts P and Q to distinguish between differentiations with respect to the coordinates of the field point P and the coordinates of the source point Q (see Eq. 1–67). In the final integral, for simplicity, we omit the subscript Q. Let us substitute the vector identity

$$\nabla \cdot \left(\frac{\mathbf{P}}{r}\right) = \mathbf{P} \cdot \nabla \frac{1}{r} + \frac{1}{r} \nabla \cdot \mathbf{P}$$

into Eq. (3–19). This yields

$$U_p = \frac{1}{4\pi\varepsilon_0} \int_v \left(\operatorname{div} \frac{\mathbf{P}}{r} - \frac{1}{r}\operatorname{div} \mathbf{P}\right) dv$$

$$= \frac{1}{4\pi\varepsilon_0} \int_S \frac{\mathbf{P} \cdot \mathbf{n}}{r}\, ds + \frac{1}{4\pi\varepsilon_0} \int_v -\frac{\operatorname{div} \mathbf{P}}{r}\, dv, \qquad (3\text{–}20)$$

where we use the divergence theorem to obtain the surface integral. When we compare Eq. (3–20) with Eq. (3–7), we see that we can interpret the polarization potential as resulting from a *polarization charge density*

$$\rho_p \overset{\triangle}{=} -\operatorname{div} \mathbf{P} \qquad (3\text{–}21)$$

distributed throughout the volume of the dielectric and a *polarization surface charge density*

$$\sigma_p \overset{\triangle}{=} \mathbf{P} \cdot \mathbf{n} \qquad (3\text{–}22)$$

distributed over the surface of the dielectric. Besides the distribution of polarization charges, we can also have a distribution of free charges specified by the charge density ρ. The total potential due to all charges is

$$U = \frac{1}{4\pi\varepsilon_0} \int_v \frac{\rho + \rho_p}{r}\, dv + \frac{1}{4\pi\varepsilon_0} \int_S \frac{\sigma_p}{r}\, ds. \qquad (3\text{--}23)$$

We shall now give an alternative interpretation of the results expressed by Eqs. (3–21) and (3–22). This requires that we have a closer look at the polarization within the dielectric. We therefore cut a cylinder of polarized material out of the dielectric. When we remove the cylinder for examination, we must consider the charges as fixed, so that the charge distribution is not affected. The axis of the cylinder is taken parallel to the polarization $\mathbf{P}$ and its dimensions are taken sufficiently small so that we may consider $\mathbf{P}$ as uniform throughout the cylinder (Fig. 3–9). Let a be the area of one of the parallel cylinder faces and let the normal $\mathbf{n}$ of the upper face make an angle θ with respect to $\mathbf{P}$. Due to polarization we observe the positive end of the dipoles distributed over the upper face. This distribution of charge results in a surface charge density σ_p. A similar situation exists at the lower face of the cylinder; since we have taken the dipole distribution in the cylinder as uniform, the surface charge density will be $-\sigma_p$. The surface charges result in the cylinder appearing as a dipole, and the magnitude of the dipole moment is

$$m = \sigma_p a l.$$

The volume of the cylinder is $al \cos \theta$. Thus the magnitude of the polarization (the dipole moment per unit volume) is

$$P = \frac{\sigma_p a l}{al \cos \theta},$$

which yields

$$\sigma_p = P \cos \theta = \mathbf{P} \cdot \mathbf{n}.$$

This result is identical to Eq. (3–22). In order to discuss the polarization charge density we consider an arbitrary volume v within a dielectric (Fig. 3–10). Let S be the surface which bounds v. As the dielectric becomes polarized, charges (the displaced electrons) are transported through the surface. The amount of charge transported through a surface element ds is

$$\sigma_p\, ds = \mathbf{P} \cdot \mathbf{n}\, ds,$$

where σ_p is the polarization surface charge density on S. Thus the total charge transported out of v through the surface S is

$$Q = \int_S \mathbf{P} \cdot \mathbf{n}\, ds. \qquad (3\text{--}24)$$

This charge transport results in a charge density ρ_p within v. Since an outward

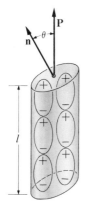
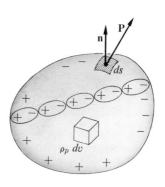

Fig. 3–9. Polarization surface charge density.   **Fig. 3–10.** Polarization charge density.

flow of charge results in a decrease in the charge density, we have

$$Q = -\int_v \rho_p \, dv. \tag{3–25}$$

If we apply the divergence theorem to Eq. (3–24) and equate the result to Eq. (3–25), we obtain

$$\int_v (\text{div } \mathbf{P} + \rho_p) \, dv = 0.$$

Since the above integral is zero for an arbitrary volume v, it follows that the integrand must be identically zero. This yields div $\mathbf{P} = -\rho_p$, which is identical to Eq. (3–21).

Since ρ_p is a charge density resulting from the transport of charges, it must satisfy the equation of continuity (2–42) and a current density $\mathbf{J}_p$ is associated with the charge transport. Thus

$$\text{div } \mathbf{J}_p = -\partial \rho_p / \partial t,$$

where $\mathbf{J}_p$ is defined as the *polarization current density*. Eliminating ρ_p from this equation with the aid of Eq. (3–21) yields

$$\text{div} \left(J_p - \frac{\partial \mathbf{P}}{\partial t} \right) = 0. \tag{3–26}$$

Since $\mathbf{J}_p = 0$ when $\mathbf{P} = 0$, it follows from Eq. (3–26) that

$$\mathbf{J}_p \triangleq \partial \mathbf{P} / \partial t. \tag{3–27}$$

Equation (3–27) defines the polarization current density as the time rate of change of polarization.

3-6 THE ELECTRIC FLUX DENSITY

We shall find it convenient to distinguish between the charge density ρ due to free charges and the polarization charge density ρ_p due to bound charges. The total charge density is $\rho_T = \rho + \rho_p$. From a fundamental point of view we consider all charges to be in free space. We must therefore use Eq. (2–45b) in the form

$$\text{div } \mathbf{D}_0 = \rho + \rho_p = \varepsilon_0 \text{ div } \mathbf{E}, \qquad (3\text{–}28)$$

where the subscript zero is used to indicate that the vector $\mathbf{D}_0 = \varepsilon_0 \mathbf{E}$ is the electric flux density resulting from all charges. Substituting $\mathbf{E} = -\text{grad } U$ into Eq. (3–28) yields Poisson's equation,

$$\nabla^2 U = -\frac{1}{\varepsilon_0}(\rho + \rho_p),$$

which has the solution (see Eq. 3–7)

$$U = \frac{1}{4\pi\varepsilon_0} \int_v \frac{\rho + \rho_p}{r}\, dv. \qquad (3\text{–}29)$$

The function U is the same as that given by Eq. (3–23), with the exception of the surface integral. This is a consequence of the fact that the solution given by Eq. (3–29) is valid only if the volume charge density is a piecewise continuous function of position. If there is a surface charge density σ_p, the volume charge density will then be infinite for points on the surface. Actually, a surface charge density is a mathematical abstraction, since charges are always distributed throughout a volume. However, the concept of a surface charge is very convenient, since it often approximates a physical situation with great accuracy. When charges are crowded very densely near a surface S into a volume element $dv = h\, ds$, we can express the element of charge dQ in the volume element in the form (Fig. 3–11) $dQ = \rho\, dv = \sigma\, ds$, where

$$\sigma \triangleq \lim_{h \to 0} \rho h$$

is defined as the *surface charge density*.* When h is negligible compared with

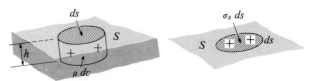

Fig. 3–11. Surface charge density.

---

* For cases in which there is a possibility of confusion with the symbol for conductivity, we shall represent the surface charge density by σ_s.

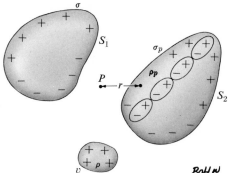

Fig. 3–12. Free charges in the presence of a conductor and a dielectric.

the surface dimensions, we can replace the volume distribution of charge near the surface by a surface charge distribution with negligible error.

In the case of a thin wire it is usually convenient to replace the volume charge density ρ by an equivalent *linear charge density* along the axis of the wire. The linear charge density is defined by

$$q \triangleq \lim_{a \to 0} \rho a$$

where a is the cross-sectional area of the wire.

In a general situation we can have a free charge density ρ within a volume v situated near a dielectric of volume v_2 and a conductor of surface area S_1 (Fig. 3–12). Due to the electric field of the free charges the dielectric becomes polarized and the free charges on the conductor surface move until a condition of equilibrium is established. This occurs when the resultant electric field intensity due to all charges is normal to the surface S_1. The potential at a field point P is then given by

$$U = \frac{1}{4\pi\varepsilon_0} \int_v \frac{\rho}{r} \, dv + \frac{1}{4\pi\varepsilon_0} \int_{v_2} \frac{\rho_p}{r} \, dv + \frac{1}{4\pi\varepsilon_0} \int_{S_2} \frac{\sigma_p}{r} \, ds + \frac{1}{4\pi\varepsilon_0} \int_{S_1} \frac{\sigma}{r} \, ds.$$

$$(3\text{–}30)$$

Here S_2 is the surface which bounds v_2. If ρ, ρ_p, σ_p, and σ are known, the electric field intensity $\mathbf{E}$ and the electric flux density $\mathbf{D}_0$ due to all charges are given by $\mathbf{E} = -\text{grad } U$ and $\mathbf{D}_0 = \varepsilon_0 \mathbf{E}$. However, ρ_p and σ_p are never given directly, since they depend on $\mathbf{E}$. The solution of a general field problem is therefore very complicated. Considerable simplification is achieved, however, if the explicit consideration of ρ_p and σ_p can be eliminated.

When we use Eq. (3–21) to eliminate ρ_p in Eq. (3–28), we obtain

$$\text{div} (\varepsilon_0 \mathbf{E} + \mathbf{P}) = \rho.$$

The vector

$$\mathbf{D} \triangleq \varepsilon_0 \mathbf{E} + \mathbf{P} \qquad (3\text{–}31)$$

is of special significance, and is defined as the *electric flux density*. Since div $\mathbf{D} = \rho$, $\mathbf{D}$ is actually the electric flux density due to free charges. The distinction between $\mathbf{D}$ and $\mathbf{D}_0$, the electric flux density due to all charges, should be noted (see Eq. 3–28). We have seen that the introduction of the vector $\mathbf{D}$ results in Maxwell's second equation taking the form given by Eq. (2–46b), which is very convenient for computational reasons.

For many dielectric materials the polarization is proportional to the electric field intensity. We then have

$$\mathbf{P} = \varepsilon_0 \chi_e \mathbf{E},$$

where χ_e is defined as the *electric susceptibility*. Equation (3–31) now has the form

$$\mathbf{D} = \varepsilon \mathbf{E}, \tag{3–32}$$

where $\varepsilon \triangleq \varepsilon_0(1 + \chi_e)$ is defined as the *permittivity* of the dielectric. Equation (3–32) is very convenient in problems dealing with dielectrics. The polarization of the dielectric is expressed in terms of the *relative permittivity* $\varepsilon_r \triangleq \varepsilon/\varepsilon_0$ and the polarization charges need not, therefore, be explicitly considered. Numerical values of ε_r for various materials are given in Table 3–1.

As an example of the convenience of the vector $\mathbf{D}$ in the solution of field problems, let us consider the case of a spherical conductor of radius a placed in an infinite uniform dielectric medium of permittivity ε. Let the charge on the conductor be Q. Suppose that we choose the center of the sphere as the origin of a spherical coordinate system and that $r > a$. It follows from Gauss' law that the electric flux density is given by

$$\mathbf{D} = \frac{Q}{4\pi r^2} \mathbf{i}_r.$$

Note that this is the same result for the charged sphere situated in free space. The electric field intensity in the dielectric is obtained from (3–32):

$$\mathbf{E} = \frac{Q}{4\pi \varepsilon r^2} \mathbf{i}_r.$$

The polarization $\mathbf{P}$ can be obtained from Eq. (3–31):

$$\mathbf{P} = (\varepsilon - \varepsilon_0)\mathbf{E} = (1 - 1/\varepsilon_r)\mathbf{D}.$$

Since $\rho = 0$ for $r > a$, we have div $\mathbf{D} = 0$, and we then see from Eq. (3–21) that the polarization charge density is zero. However, if we note that $\mathbf{n} = -\mathbf{i}_r$, it follows from Eq. (3–22) that there is a polarization surface charge density on the dielectric surface formed by the sphere which is given by

$$\sigma_p = \mathbf{P} \cdot \mathbf{n} = -(1 - 1/\varepsilon_r)\sigma,$$

where $\sigma = Q/4\pi a^2$ is the surface charge density on the sphere due to the free charges. We see that the dielectric reduces the *effective surface charge density*

Table 3–1

RELATIVE PERMITTIVITY OF VARIOUS
MATERIALS

Material	ε_r
Polystyrene	2.6
Mylar	3.2
Quartz	3.8
Mica	5.4
Oil	2.2–2.8
Water	81

and that the *effective total charge* Q_e on the spherical interface is

$$Q_e = Q + 4\pi a^2 \sigma_p = \frac{1}{\varepsilon_r} Q.$$

If we let $a \rightarrow 0$ we obtain a point charge. Thus we can make the following statement. If we have determined the potential of a system of free charges in free space, we can determine the potential of the same system of free charges in an infinite dielectric medium by simply replacing ε_0 by ε in the equation for U. However, note that this is the case only so long as $\rho_p = 0$. If the dielectric is finite or not uniform we shall have, in general, a nonzero ρ_p and more complicated boundary conditions. The evaluation of the potential U then becomes a difficult problem. In special cases a simple solution is still possible. For the discussion of such a case see Section 3–8, Example 2.

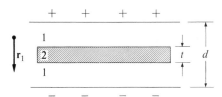

Fig. 3–13. A parallel-plate capacitor.

3–7 ELECTRIC FIELD INTENSITY
IN A PARALLEL-PLATE CAPACITOR

As an illustration of a simple problem dealing with the polarization of a dielectric, let us consider the parallel-plate capacitor in Fig. 3–13. The area of one plate is A and the distance d between the plates is taken sufficiently small so that we can consider the surface charge density on the plates as uniform. Between the plates there is a dielectric slab of thickness t. The free space and dielectric regions are represented by 1 and 2, respectively, and the fields in these regions are given corresponding subscripts. For charge distributions having a sufficient degree of symmetry, the application of Gauss' law proves to be the simplest means for the solution of field problems.

Let us consider an element of area a of the capacitor plate and let σ be the surface charge density (Fig. 3–14). We enclose the charge $a\sigma$ in a cylinder, as shown in the figure. The electric field is negligible outside the plates. Thus, given that S represents the surface of the cylinder, we have

$$\phi_e = a\sigma = \int_S \mathbf{D}_1 \cdot \mathbf{n} \, ds = D_1 a$$

and

$$\mathbf{D}_1 = \sigma \mathbf{r}_1, \qquad \mathbf{E}_1 = \frac{\sigma}{\varepsilon_0} \mathbf{r}_1,$$

where $\mathbf{r}_1$ is a unit vector directed as shown in Fig. 3–14. We can determine the field in the dielectric by two possible methods. Let us first consider the charges in the dielectric resulting from polarization. Since the polarization is uniform, $\rho_p = 0$ (see Eq. 3–21). There is a surface charge distribution σ_p on the lower surface (see Eq. 3–22) given by

$$\sigma_p = \mathbf{P} \cdot \mathbf{r}_1 = \varepsilon_0 \chi_e \mathbf{E}_2 \cdot \mathbf{r}_1. \tag{3–33}$$

In effect, the surface charges on the upper and lower surfaces of the dielectric form a parallel-plate capacitor in which there is a flux density $\mathbf{D}_p = -\sigma_p \mathbf{r}_1$.

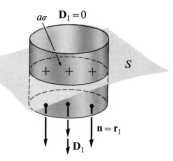

Fig. 3–14. Surface charge density of a perfect conductor.

Given that $\mathbf{D}_0$ is the flux density in region 2 due to all charges, we have

$$\mathbf{D}_0 = (\sigma - \sigma_p)\mathbf{r}_1, \qquad \varepsilon_0 \mathbf{E}_2 = (\sigma - \sigma_p)\mathbf{r}_1 = (\sigma - \varepsilon_0 \chi_e E_2)\mathbf{r}_1,$$

which yields $\varepsilon \mathbf{E}_2 = \sigma \mathbf{r}_1$. Substituting this result into Eq. (3–33) yields

$$\sigma_p = \frac{\chi_e}{1 + \chi_e} \sigma.$$

Note that the magnitude $E_2 = \sigma/\varepsilon = (\sigma - \sigma_p)/\varepsilon_0$ of the electric field intensity in the dielectric region 2 is smaller than the magnitude $E_1 = \sigma/\varepsilon_0$ of the electric field intensity in the free-space region 1. The difference

$$E_1 - E_2 = \sigma_p/\varepsilon_0$$

results from the fact that within the dielectric the electric field intensity $\mathbf{E}_2$ due to the polarization charges is directed oppositely to $\mathbf{E}_1$. In region 1 the electric field intensity due to the polarization charges is zero.

Let us now solve the same problem with the aid of the vector $\mathbf{D}$ and Eq. (3–32). The vector $\mathbf{D}$ is the electric flux density due to the free charges. Thus

$$\mathbf{D}_1 = \mathbf{D}_2 = \sigma\mathbf{r}_1,$$

where $\mathbf{D}_2$ is the electric flux density in region 2. With the aid of Eq. (3–32) we obtain

$$\varepsilon_0\mathbf{E}_1 = \mathbf{D}_1 = \sigma\mathbf{r}_1, \qquad \varepsilon\mathbf{E}_2 = \sigma\mathbf{r}_1, \qquad (3\text{–}34)$$

which is the same result obtained previously. We see that the use of $\mathbf{D}$ results in a substantial simplification of the problem, since we need not concern ourselves explicitly with the polarization charges.

3–8 CAPACITANCE

Let us consider two conductors with a charge of Q and $-Q$, respectively. In the interior of a conductor charges can move freely and a state of equilibrium is reached when the force acting on a charge is zero. Thus $\mathbf{E} = 0 = \mathbf{D}$ within the conductor, and it follows that

$$\text{div } \mathbf{D} = \rho = 0.$$

Hence there are no charges within the conductor and the charge distribution is entirely on the surface of the conductor. There can be no tangential component of $\mathbf{E}$ on the surface, since this would result in a movement of charge. Thus the situation illustrated in Fig. 3–14 exists at the surface and we can determine the surface charge density by applying Gauss' law to the cylinder shown. We obtain the equation $\sigma = \mathbf{D} \cdot \mathbf{n}$, which states that the surface charge density is the source of the electric flux density at the surface. Since $\mathbf{E}$ is normal to the conductor surface, we have

$$dU = \text{grad } U \cdot d\mathbf{r} = -\mathbf{E} \cdot d\mathbf{r} = 0,$$

provided that $d\mathbf{r}$ is a vector tangent to the surface. Thus the surface of the conductor is an equipotential surface where $U = $ constant.

The *capacitance* of two conductors S_1 and S_2 is defined (Fig. 3–15) by the equation

$$C = Q/V, \qquad (3\text{–}35)$$

where V is the potential difference between the conductors. Here V is deter-

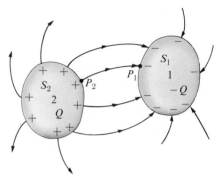

Fig. 3–15. Electric field due to charged conductors.

mined by the equation

$$V = \int_{P_1}^{P_2} -\mathbf{E} \cdot d\mathbf{r} = U(P_2) - U(P_1)$$

and Q is the charge on S_2. It is important to note how Q and V are to be taken, since otherwise C may acquire a meaningless negative sign. This possibility can be avoided if we take the convention of assuming that S_2 is charged positively, so that $Q > 0$. If we move a unit positive test charge from S_1 to S_2, mechanical work must be done, since the test charge is repelled by S_2. Thus $V > 0$, and Eq. (3–35) would give $C > 0$. However, we could move the test charge from S_2 to S_1. In this case $V < 0$, but we must now choose $-Q$, the charge on S_1, and Eq. (3–35) would again give $C > 0$. In computing V, we can choose any path connecting two points P_1 and P_2 on the conductors.

Example 1. Let us compute the capacitance of the parallel-plate capacitor in Fig. 3–13. The electric field intensity is piecewise uniform and has a magnitude of σ/ε_0 in region 1 and a magnitude of σ/ε in region 2 (see Eq. 3–34). Thus

$$V = \frac{\sigma}{\varepsilon_0}(d - t) + \frac{\sigma}{\varepsilon}t.$$

The charge on the upper plate is given by $Q = \sigma A$ and the capacitance is

$$C = \frac{A\varepsilon_0}{d}\frac{1}{1 + (1/\varepsilon_r - 1)(t/d)}.$$

In a general case we can have a system of n conductors. Let the charge on the kth conductor be Q_k and let its surface potential be U_k. The potential at a field point P is given by

$$U = \frac{1}{4\pi\varepsilon_0}\sum_{i=1}^{n} Q_k \int_{S_k} \frac{\sigma_k/Q_k}{r}\,ds,$$

where σ_k is the surface charge density on the surface S_k of the kth conductor.

Let us now choose the point P on $S_1, \ldots, S_n$, so that we obtain equations of the form

$$U_1 = a_{11}Q_1 + a_{12}Q_2 + \cdots + a_{1n}Q_n,$$

$$U_n = a_{n1}Q_1 + a_{n2}Q_2 + \cdots + a_{nn}Q_n, \tag{3-36}$$

where the coefficients a_{lk} depend only on the geometry of the system of conductors. We shall prove that $a_{lk} = a_{kl}$. To establish this result we consider two different charge distributions Q_k and Q_k' on the conductors. The field vectors and potentials due to these two distributions are taken as $\mathbf{E}$, $\mathbf{D}$, U and $\mathbf{E}'$, $\mathbf{D}'$, U', respectively. Since $\rho = \rho' = 0$ within the volume bounded by the conductors, we have

$$\nabla \cdot \mathbf{D} = \nabla \cdot \mathbf{D}' = 0.$$

Thus we have

$$\nabla \cdot (U\mathbf{D}' - U'\mathbf{D}) = \mathbf{D}' \cdot \nabla U - \mathbf{D} \cdot \nabla U' = -\mathbf{D}' \cdot \mathbf{E} + \mathbf{D} \cdot \mathbf{E}' = 0.$$

Applying the divergence theorem to the above result yields the *reciprocity theorem*,

$$\sum_{k=1}^{n} \int_{S_k} (U\mathbf{D}' - U'\mathbf{D}) \cdot \mathbf{n} \, ds = \sum_{k=1}^{n} (U_k Q_k' - U_k' Q_k) = 0, \tag{3-37}$$

where

$$Q_k = \int_{S_k} \mathbf{D} \cdot \mathbf{n} \, ds = \int_{S_k} \sigma_k \, ds$$

is the charge on the kth conductor for the unprimed case.

We now consider case 1, in which $Q_k = 0$ for $k \neq m$ and in which $Q_m \neq 0$, and case 2, in which $Q_k' = 0$ for $k \neq l$ and $Q_l' \neq 0$.

From Eqs. (3-36) we obtain, for case 1,

$$U_l = a_{lm}Q_m,$$

and for case 2,

$$U_m' = a_{ml}Q_l'.$$

Equation (3-37) now reduces to $U_l Q_l' = U_m' Q_m$, which yields

$$a_{lm}Q_m Q_l' = a_{ml}Q_l' Q_m,$$

and we obtain the desired result that $a_{ml} = a_{lm}$.

The linear equations (3-36) can be solved for the Q_k's. This yields the system of linear equations,

$$Q_1 = C_{11}U_1 + C_{12}U_2 + \cdots + C_{1n}U_n,$$

$$Q_n = C_{n1}U_1 + C_{n2}U_2 + \cdots + C_{nn}U_n, \tag{3-38}$$

where $C_{kl} = C_{lk}$. The C_{kk} are called the *coefficients of capacitance* and the C_{kl} $(k \neq l)$ are called the *coefficients of electrostatic induction*.

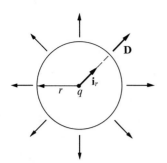

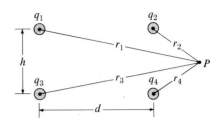

Fig. 3–16. Electric field of a line source.

Fig. 3–17. An infinitely long four-wire straight transmission line.

A very important practical application of Eqs. (3–38) is in the case of multiwire infinitely long straight transmission lines. Let us first consider a uniform linear distribution of charge along a single infinitely long straight line and let q be the linear charge density. A charge distribution of this type is known as a *line source* (Fig. 3–16). Because of cylindrical symmetry, **D** can be found by applying Gauss' law to a cylinder S of unit length which is coaxial with the line. Since $\mathbf{D} \cdot \mathbf{n} = 0$ over the faces of the cylinder, we find that

$$q = \int_S \mathbf{D} \cdot \mathbf{n}\, ds = 2\pi r D.$$

Thus

$$\mathbf{E} = \frac{q}{2\pi\varepsilon_0 r}\, \mathbf{i}_r.$$

The potential can be found from the relation

$$dU = -\mathbf{E} \cdot d\mathbf{r} = -\frac{q}{2\pi\varepsilon_0}\frac{dr}{r},$$

where we have chosen $d\mathbf{r} = \mathbf{i}_r\, dr$. Integration yields

$$U = -\frac{q}{2\pi\varepsilon_0} \ln r, \tag{3–39}$$

where, for simplicity, we have taken the integration constant to be zero.

Let us now consider the configuration of four straight transmission lines illustrated in Fig. 3–17. All conductors have equal radii a and we take $a \ll d$, $a \ll h$. We first consider a general case in which the linear charge density and the potential of the kth conductor are q_k and U_k, respectively. To a good approximation the transmission lines can be considered as line sources. It follows from Eq. (3–39) that the potential at a field point P is

$$U = -\frac{1}{2\pi\varepsilon_0} \sum_{k=1}^{4} q_k \ln r_k.$$

When the field point P is taken on the surface of conductor 1 we have $r_1 = a$, the potential is U_1, and the distances r_k are approximately

$$r_2 \cong d, \qquad r_3 \cong h, \qquad r_4 \cong \sqrt{d^2 + h^2}.$$

Thus

$$U_1 \cong - \frac{1}{2\pi\varepsilon_0} (q_1 \ln a + q_2 \ln d + q_3 \ln h + q_4 \ln \sqrt{d^2 + h^2}). \quad (3\text{–}40)$$

Similarly, if the field point is taken on conductors 2, 3, and 4, respectively, we obtain

$$U_2 \cong - \frac{1}{2\pi\varepsilon_0} (q_1 \ln d + q_2 \ln a + q_3 \ln \sqrt{d^2 + h^2} + q_4 \ln h),$$

$$U_3 \cong - \frac{1}{2\pi\varepsilon_0} (q_1 \ln h + q_2 \ln \sqrt{d^2 + h^2} + q_3 \ln a + q_4 \ln d), \quad (3\text{–}41)$$

$$U_4 \cong - \frac{1}{2\pi\varepsilon_0} (q_1 \ln \sqrt{d^2 + h^2} + q_2 \ln h + q_3 \ln d + q_4 \ln a).$$

The equations (3–40) and (3–41) correspond to the system of equations (3–36). We see that

$$a_{11} = a_{22} = a_{33} = a_{44} \cong - \frac{1}{2\pi\varepsilon_0} \ln a,$$

$$a_{12} = a_{21} = a_{34} = a_{43} \cong - \frac{1}{2\pi\varepsilon_0} \ln d,$$

$$a_{13} = a_{31} = a_{24} = a_{42} \cong - \frac{1}{2\pi\varepsilon_0} \ln h,$$

$$a_{14} = a_{41} = a_{23} = a_{32} \cong - \frac{1}{2\pi\varepsilon_0} \ln \sqrt{d^2 + h^2}.$$

Let us now consider the special case in which the lines 1 and 2 form a transmission line pair with a potential difference V and in which lines 3 and 4 are grounded so that $U_3 = U_4 = 0$. Because of the symmetry we can set

$$U_1 = V/2, \qquad U_2 = -V/2, \qquad q_1 = q,$$

and $q_2 = -q$. The charges on lines 1 and 2 attract charges from the ground and lines 3 and 4 become charged. Let kq be the linear charge density of line 4. The factor k is determined by the condition that $U_4 = 0$ (we could also use $U_3 = 0$ with identical results). From Eqs. (3–41) we find that

$$k = \frac{\ln (\sqrt{d^2 + h^2}/h)}{\ln (d/a)}.$$

The capacitance per unit length of the transmission line pair 1 and 2 can be found from Eq. (3–35):

$$C = q/V = \frac{\pi \varepsilon_0}{\ln (d/a) - k \ln (\sqrt{(d^2 + h^2)}/h)}.$$

Example 2. As a final example, which illustrates a case in which the dielectric is not uniform, let us compute the capacitance per unit length of a coaxial cable of inner and outer radius a and b, respectively, and in which the permittivity is a linear function of the radial coordinate r:

$$\varepsilon = \varepsilon_1 + (\varepsilon_2 - \varepsilon_1) \frac{r - a}{b - a}.$$

Here ε_1 and ε_2 are constant. Let V be the potential difference between the conductors and let q be the charge per unit length on the inner conductor. Gauss' law applied to a cylinder concentric with the inner conductor yields

$$\mathbf{D} = \frac{q}{2\pi r} \mathbf{i}_r.$$

Thus

$$\mathbf{E} = \frac{q}{2\pi \varepsilon r} \mathbf{i}_r.$$

We can determine the capacitance per unit length from the equation

$$V = \int_a^b \frac{q}{2\pi \varepsilon r} dr = \frac{q(b - a)}{2\pi(\varepsilon_1 b - \varepsilon_2 a)} \ln \frac{\varepsilon_1 b}{\varepsilon_2 a},$$

which yields

$$C = \frac{2\pi(\varepsilon_1 b - \varepsilon_2 a)}{(b - a) \ln (\varepsilon_1 b/\varepsilon_2 a)}.$$

If we wish to find the polarization charge density within the dielectric, we can proceed as follows. We first find the polarization from the relation

$$\mathbf{P} = (\varepsilon - \varepsilon_0)\mathbf{E} = \left(1 - \frac{\varepsilon_0}{\varepsilon}\right) \frac{q}{2\pi r} \mathbf{i}_r.$$

We can then find the polarization charge density by using Eqs. (3–21) and (1–101):

$$\rho_p = -\frac{1}{r} \frac{\partial}{\partial r} (r P_r) = -\frac{q \varepsilon_0 (\varepsilon_2 - \varepsilon_1)}{2\pi \varepsilon^2 r(b - a)}.$$

PROBLEMS

3–1 Two point charges are a distance d apart (Fig. 3–18). Given that $Q_2/Q_1 = \frac{1}{4}$, determine the equation of the critical streamline for which $\mathbf{E}(P) = 0$. What is the angle α? Determine the location of the critical point P at which the streamline meets the x-axis.

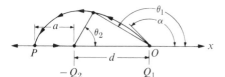

Figure 3–18

3–2 Two infinitely thin straight conducting wires are parallel and a distance d apart. The linear charge densities are q and $-q$, respectively. Prove that the streamlines are circles.

3–3 Determine the differential equations for a streamline in cylindrical coordinates.

3–4 Use Coulomb's law to determine the electric field intensity of a line source in free space having a linear charge density q. Which is more convenient for solving this problem, Coulomb's law or Gauss' law?

3–5 A spherical capacitor has an inner conductor of radius a which is covered with a concentric dielectric shell of outside radius b. The outer conductor of the capacitor has a radius c (Fig. 3–19). Determine the electric field intensity in regions 1 and 2 for a case in which a potential difference V is applied between the conductors. Determine the capacitance.

3–6 A parallel-plate capacitor has an area A; the distance d between the plates is sufficiently small so that the surface charge density on the plates can be taken as uniform. The permittivity $\varepsilon(x)$ is a linear function of the distance x from one of the plates and $\varepsilon(0) = \varepsilon_1$, $\varepsilon(d) = \varepsilon_2$. (a) Determine the capacitance. (b) Determine the polarization charge density ρ_p and the polarization surface charge density σ_p.

3–7 A coaxial cable has an inner conductor of radius a and an outer conductor of radius c. The medium between the conductors consists of two dielectric cylinders of permittivity ε_1 and ε_2, as shown in Fig. 3–20. Given that the breakdown strengths of the dielectrics are E_{c1} and E_{c2}, respectively, determine the potential difference that can be applied before breakdown occurs in one of the dielectrics. What relationship must hold between a, b, ε_1 and ε_2 in order that breakdown will occur simultaneously in both dielectrics?

3–8 A coaxial cable has an inner conductor of radius a and an outer conductor of radius b. The permittivity is ε. Determine the capacitance per unit length.

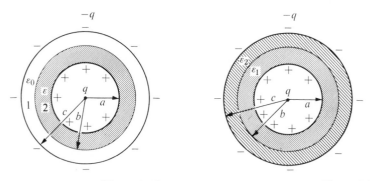

Figure 3–19   **Figure 3–20**

3–9 A straight two-wire transmission line has linear charge densities of q and $-q$, respectively. The conductor radii are equal to a and the distance between centers is d. Given that $a \ll d$, show that the capacitance per unit length is

$$C \cong \frac{\pi \varepsilon_0}{\ln (d/a)}.$$

Given that $a = 0.163$ in., $d = 10$ in., determine C. Assume that the breakdown strength of air is 30 kV/cm; determine the maximum voltage that can be applied before breakdown occurs.

3–10 Consider a point charge Q in free space at a distance r from the center of a spherical conductor of radius $a < r$. (a) Suppose that the spherical conductor has a zero charge. Use the reciprocity theorem to prove that its surface potential is

$$U_1 = Q/4\pi\varepsilon_0 r.$$

(b) Suppose that the spherical conductor is grounded ($U_1 = 0$). Use the reciprocity theorem to prove that its charge is

$$Q_1 = -(a/r)Q.$$

[*Hint:* Take the point charge to be an infinitely small conductor 2 and consider the primed case of Eq. (3–37) to correspond to the choice of zero charge on conductor 2 ($Q_2' = 0$) and a charge $Q_1' = Q$ on the sphere.] (c) Prove parts (a) and (b) by determining the coefficients a_{11} and a_{12} in Eq. (3–36) and using the reciprocity condition $a_{12} = a_{21}$. [*Hint:* Consider case 1 in which $Q_1 = 1$, $Q_2 = 0$, and case 2 in which $Q_1 = 0$, $Q_2 = 1$.]

3–11 Consider an infinite uniform dielectric medium of permittivity ε situated in a uniform electric field. The electric flux density is **D**. A thin plane circular disk is cut out of the dielectric and the axis of the disk-shaped cavity makes an angle θ with respect to **D**. Show that the components of the electric field intensity in the cavity parallel and normal to the axis are

$$E_1 = (D \cos \theta)/\varepsilon_0, \qquad E_2 = (D \cos \theta)/\varepsilon,$$

respectively.

3–12 The total charge Q_p of a polarized dielectric is given by

$$Q_p = \int_S \sigma_p \, ds + \int_v \rho_p \, dv,$$

where S bounds the dielectric volume v. Prove that $Q_p = 0$.

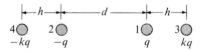

Figure 3–21

3–13 In Chapter 10 we shall see that transmission lines are used as wave guides. A quantity of importance is the *characteristic impedance* $Z_0 = 1/cC$, where $c = 3 \times 10^8$ m/sec is the speed of light and C is the capacitance per unit length (see

Eq. 10–31). Consider the four-wire line illustrated in Fig. 3–21, where all conductors have equal radii b. The even- and odd-numbered conductors are connected conductively together at suitable intervals so that $U_1 = U_3 = V/2$, $U_2 = U_4 = -V/2$, where $V = U_1 - U_2$ is the potential difference.   (a) Given that $Z_0 = 400\ \Omega$, $b = 0.163$ in., $d = 12$ in., evaluate h. [*Hint:* Assume a value for h, determine k, and then use the given value of Z_0 to determine a new value for h. This procedure can be continued iteratively.]   (b) Given that the breakdown strength of air is 30 kV/cm, determine the maximum value of V.

CHAPTER 4

THE SOLUTION OF
ELECTROSTATIC FIELD PROBLEMS

4-1 INTRODUCTION

We saw in Chapter 3 that for charge distributions having spherical or cylindrical symmetry, Gauss' law can be used to obtain $\mathbf{D}$ directly. We can then find the potential function by integrating the tangential component of $\mathbf{E}$ along a suitable path. In general, this is not possible and we must develop methods of solving for a potential function which satisfy prescribed boundary conditions.

For a static electric field in a dielectric medium of permittivity ε, the electric flux density can be expressed in the form

$$\mathbf{D} = -\varepsilon \operatorname{grad} U, \qquad (4\text{-}1)$$

where U is the potential. Substituting into Eq. (2–47b) yields

$$\operatorname{div}(\varepsilon \operatorname{grad} U) = -\rho. \qquad (4\text{-}2)$$

The permittivity ε is often piecewise uniform. In regions in which ε is uniform, we obtain Poisson's equation

$$\nabla^2 U = -\rho/\varepsilon, \qquad (4\text{-}3)$$

which has a particular solution (see Eqs. 1–71 and 1–75)

$$U_1 = \frac{1}{4\pi} \int_v \frac{\rho}{\varepsilon r}\, dv, \qquad (4\text{-}4)$$

provided that ρ/ε is a piecewise continuous function of position.* The solution U_1 is unique for the case of free charges embedded in an infinite uniform dielectric and for the boundary condition $U(\infty) = 0$ at infinity. In general, however, the dielectric has finite dimensions and conductors may be present. The solution U_1 will then no longer satisfy the boundary conditions and we must add to U_1 a suitable solution of Laplace's equation,

$$\nabla^2 U_2 = 0, \qquad (4\text{-}5)$$

* For a rigorous mathematical discussion, see O. Kellogg, *Foundations of Potential Theory*, New York, Dover Publications, 1953.

so that the boundary conditions can be satisfied. The solution $U = U_1 + U_2$ of Poisson's equation satisfying the boundary conditions determines the potential function from which the electric field intensity and the electric flux density can be found.

From a physical point of view we could consider the solution U as resulting from a distribution of charges throughout the volume and over the surfaces of the material media in the field. The solution then takes the form (3-30), where ρ_p, σ_p, and σ must be evaluated by some suitable means.

In this chapter we shall develop both a mathematical and a physical approach for finding the solution of Laplace's equation which meets specified boundary conditions. Because of the uniqueness theorem (see Section 1-17) we can use a physical approach to obtain a solution, whenever this appears convenient.

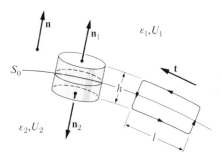

Fig. 4–1. Boundary conditions.

4-2 BOUNDARY CONDITIONS

Let us consider a surface S_0 which forms the interface for a medium 1 of permittivity ε_1 and a medium 2 of permittivity ε_2 (Fig. 4–1). The field vectors and potentials in the two media are given corresponding subscripts and are related to each other in a manner prescribed by our postulates. For example, Gauss' law,

$$Q = \int_S \mathbf{D} \cdot \mathbf{n}\, ds,$$

must be satisfied for any surface S which bounds the charge Q. Let us choose a small flat cylinder situated at the interface, as shown in Fig. 4–1. The area a of the cylinder face is chosen sufficiently small so that the surface charge density σ, which is due to free charge embedded in the interface, is nearly uniform within the cylinder. Gauss' law yields

$$a\sigma = \mathbf{D}_1 \cdot \mathbf{n}_1 a + \mathbf{D}_2 \cdot \mathbf{n}_2 a + O(h),$$

where $O(h)$ indicates terms of the order of h which represent the electric flux through the sides of the cylinder. We now let $h \to 0$ and obtain

$$\sigma = \mathbf{D}_1 \cdot \mathbf{n} - \mathbf{D}_2 \cdot \mathbf{n} = -\varepsilon_1 \frac{\partial U_1}{\partial n} + \varepsilon_2 \frac{\partial U_2}{\partial n}, \qquad (4\text{-}6)$$

where $n_1 = -n_2 = n$ and where $\partial U/\partial n$ is the derivative of U evaluated in the direction of n. If $\sigma = 0$, we have $D_1 \cdot n = D_2 \cdot n$ and the boundary condition states that the normal component of the electric flux density is continuous. If medium 2 is a conductor we have $D_2 = 0$ and

$$\sigma = -\varepsilon_1 \frac{\partial U_1}{\partial n}. \qquad (4\text{–}7)$$

Equation (4–7) will prove useful in determining the surface charge density on a conductor. The boundary condition given by Eq. (4–6) accounts for the relationship which exists between the charge density on a surface and the normal components of electric flux density on either side of the surface.

A second boundary condition is obtained from the fact that the electric field intensity must satisfy Eq. (3–2),

$$\oint_C E \cdot dr = 0,$$

for any contour C. Let us choose the path along the interface illustrated in Fig. 4–1. We take the path length l short enough so that E_1 and E_2 are nearly uniform along the path. Thus

$$E_1 \cdot lt + E_2 \cdot (-lt) + O(h) = 0,$$

where t is a unit vector tangent to the surface S_0. We let $h \rightarrow 0$ and obtain $E_1 \cdot t - E_2 \cdot t = 0$ and

$$-\frac{\partial U_1}{\partial t} + \frac{\partial U_2}{\partial t} = 0. \qquad (4\text{–}8)$$

Equation (4–8) is satisfied if we take $U_1 = U_2$ on the surface S_0, and the equation states that the tangential component of the electric field intensity is continuous at the boundary.

4–3 THE METHOD OF IMAGES

It can be shown that the potential due to a point charge,

$$U = Q/4\pi\varepsilon_0 r,$$

where $r^2 = x^2 + y^2 + z^2 \neq 0$, is a solution of Laplace's equation. Thus

$$\nabla^2 \frac{1}{r} = 0. \qquad (4\text{–}9)$$

When we differentiate both sides of Eq. (4–9) with respect to z we find, by interchanging the order of differentiations, that

$$\nabla^2 \frac{\partial}{\partial z} \frac{1}{r} = 0.$$

Thus $(\partial/\partial z)(1/r) = -z/r^3$ is a solution of Laplace's equation. This function has the form of a dipole potential (see Eq. 3–13). A process of successive differentiations of $1/r$ yields an infinite number of solutions of Laplace's equation. By taking a linear combination of these solutions we can obtain a solution satisfying prescribed boundary conditions. However, we shall first discuss a more convenient method, the so-called *method of images*, for solving a special class of field problems.

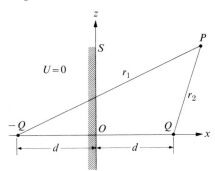

Fig. 4–2. A point charge situated near a plane conductor.

Let us consider the problem illustrated in Fig. 4–2, in which a point charge Q is at a distance d from a plane conductor which we take to have zero potential. The charge Q will attract charges from infinity, resulting in a surface charge density σ. The solution of Poisson's equation for this case has the form (see Eq. 3–30)

$$U = \frac{Q}{4\pi\varepsilon_0 r_1} + \frac{1}{4\pi\varepsilon_0} \int_S \frac{\sigma}{r} \, ds.$$

The function U must satisfy the condition that $U = 0$ on S. This condition determines σ. However, in this problem it is more convenient to use the method of images. Let us consider the function

$$U = \frac{Q}{4\pi\varepsilon_0} \left(\frac{1}{r_1} - \frac{1}{r_2} \right), \tag{4–10}$$

which is the potential due to charges Q and $-Q$, situated as shown in Fig. 4–2. It follows from Eq. (4–9) that U satisfies Laplace's equation when $r_1 \neq 0$. Furthermore, since $r_1 = r_2$ when the field point P is on S, we have $U = 0$ as required. Equation (4–10) is the unique solution to the problem. It is remarkable that the problem can be solved in this simple manner. The charge $-Q$ is called the *image charge* of Q. Essentially what we have done is to replace the unknown surface charge distribution by an equivalent single image charge which gives the same potential; that is,

$$-\frac{Q}{4\pi\varepsilon_0 r_2} = \frac{1}{4\pi\varepsilon_0} \int_S \frac{\sigma}{r} \, ds, \qquad x > 0.$$

The method of images is essentially a physical approach. The unknown charge distribution over a surface S is replaced by one or more equivalent image charges within the volume v bounded by S. The image charges set up the same electric field intensity outside v as the surface charges. Thus we can obtain the force acting on Q by applying Coulomb's law:

$$F = -i_x \frac{Q^2}{16\pi\varepsilon_0 d^2} \cdot$$

The surface charge density σ on the conductor surface can be found with the aid of Eq. (4–7):

$$\sigma = -\frac{Qd}{2\pi r^3}, \tag{4–11}$$

where $r^2 = y^2 + z^2$.

It is instructive to consider the change in Eq. (4–10) when the free-space region is replaced by a uniform dielectric of permittivity ε. From the discussion given at the end of Section 3–6, we can conclude that U is determined by simply replacing ε_0 by ε in Eq. (4–10). To interpret this simple result we can consider the point charge Q to be replaced by a charged conducting sphere with an infinitesimally small radius. As explained in Section 3–6, the induced surface charge on the dielectric surface adjacent to the sphere can be combined with the charge on the sphere to yield an effective charge $Q_e = Q/\varepsilon_r$, which we consider to be in free space. Since they are related to the free charges, the electric flux density and the surface charge density σ on the plane conductor remain unaffected by the presence of the dielectric. However, there is a polarization surface charge density given by

$$\sigma_p = P \cdot (-i_x) = -(\varepsilon - \varepsilon_0)E_x = -(\varepsilon - \varepsilon_0)\frac{\sigma}{\varepsilon}$$

on the dielectric surface at $x = 0$. The resultant surface charge density along the interface at $x = 0$ is

$$\sigma + \sigma_p = \frac{\sigma}{\varepsilon_r} = -\frac{Qd}{2\pi\varepsilon_r r^3} \cdot$$

The charged interface can be replaced by an image charge $-Q_e$. The resultant potential due to all charges is given by Eq. (4–10), where Q is replaced by Q_e. It is important to note that we consider all charges to be in free space. It follows from

$$\text{div } D = 0, \qquad P = (\varepsilon - \varepsilon_0)\frac{D}{\varepsilon},$$

that

$$\rho_p = -\text{div } P = 0.$$

Thus there is no volume distribution of charge and the electric field is due to the charge Q and the induced charges on the interfaces. The reduction in potential is a consequence of the smaller effective charge.

4-4 EXAMPLES OF THE METHOD OF IMAGES

In this section we shall discuss a variety of examples showing the usefulness of the method of images for solving a special class of field problems. The image method is applicable only when the charge distribution has a spherical or cylindrical symmetry. The placement of the image charges depends on the boundary conditions and is essentially a geometric problem.

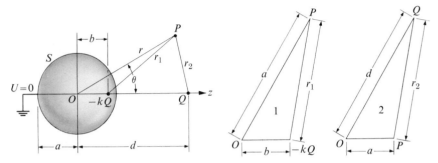

Fig. 4-3. A point charge situated near a grounded spherical conductor.

Fig. 4-4. Similar triangles for satisfying boundary conditions.

Example 1. A point charge Q is a distance d from the center of a grounded ($U = 0$) spherical conductor of radius a (Fig. 4-3). We consider a conductor as grounded when it is conductively connected to an unlimited source of charge at infinity. The point charge Q can therefore attract a charge $-kQ$ from infinity and the sphere acquires a surface charge density σ. Let us use the method of images to evaluate σ. If the field point P is outside the sphere, the distribution of charge on the surface of the sphere can be replaced by a single image charge $-kQ$ at a distance b from the center. Thus

$$U = \frac{Q}{4\pi\varepsilon_0}\left(\frac{1}{r_2} - \frac{k}{r_1}\right).$$

The unknown quantities k and b are determined by the boundary condition which requires that $U = 0$ on S. We must then have

$$k = \frac{r_1}{r_2} = \text{const.} \tag{4-12}$$

The ratio r_1/r_2 must be constant for any position of P on the sphere. We can satisfy this condition if we choose the triangles 1 and 2 illustrated in Fig. 4-4 to be similar. This yields

$$\frac{a}{d} = \frac{r_1}{r_2} = \frac{b}{a} = k.$$

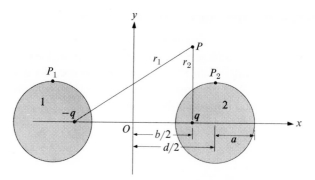

Fig. 4–5. A two-wire transmission line.

Thus $b = a^2/d$ and $k = a/d$. To determine σ we introduce polar coordinates so that

$$r_2^2 = r^2 + d^2 - 2rd \cos\theta, \qquad r_1^2 = r^2 + b^2 - 2rb \cos\theta,$$

and use Eq. (4–7):

$$\sigma = -\varepsilon_0 \frac{\partial u}{\partial r}\bigg]_{r=a} = -\frac{Q}{4\pi}\left[a\left(\frac{k}{r_1^3} - \frac{1}{r_2^3}\right) + \left(\frac{d}{r_2^3} - \frac{kb}{r_1^3}\right)\cos\theta \right].$$

Since

$$\frac{d}{r_2^3} - \frac{kb}{r_1^3} = \frac{1}{r_2^3}\left(d - \frac{b}{k^2}\right) = 0 \qquad \text{and} \qquad \frac{k}{r_1^3} - \frac{1}{r_2^3} = \frac{k(1 - k^2)}{r_1^3},$$

we obtain

$$\sigma = -\frac{Qak(1 - k^2)}{4\pi r_1^3}.$$

Example 2. Figure 4–5 illustrates an open-wire transmission line composed of parallel conducting circular cylinders of radii a_1 and a_2, respectively, which are charged to a potential difference of V volts. The method of images can be used to determine the potential. Let q be the charge per unit length on cylinder 2. We can replace the surface charge distribution on the conductors by line sources a distance b apart, as shown in the figure. The potential at a field point P due to the line sources (see Eq. 3–39) is

$$U = \frac{q}{2\pi\varepsilon_0} \ln \frac{r_1}{r_2}.$$

Due to symmetry, we can take the surface potentials of cylinders 1 and 2 as $U_1 = -V/2$ and $U_2 = V/2$, respectively. When the field point P is taken to coincide with any point P_2 on the surface of conductor 2, we have

$$\frac{V}{2} = \frac{q}{2\pi\varepsilon_0} \ln k, \qquad (4\text{–}13)$$

where k is a constant given by

$$k = \frac{r_1}{r_2} > 1. \tag{4-14}$$

We now let

$$r_1^2 = (x + b/2)^2 + y^2, \qquad r_2^2 = (x - b/2)^2 + y^2,$$

and square Eq. (4–14). This yields the equation of the circle defining the surface of conductor 2. Thus $(x - d/2)^2 + y^2 = a^2$, where

$$d = b \frac{k^2 + 1}{k^2 - 1}, \tag{4-15}$$

$$a = \frac{bk}{k^2 - 1}. \tag{4-16}$$

Equations (4–15) and (4–16) relate the known radius a and the distance between centers d to the unknown quantities k and b of the image line. Eliminating b from these equations yields

$$k^2 - \frac{d}{a} k + 1 = 0. \tag{4-17}$$

Since $k = r_1/r_2 > 1$, the desired root of Eq. (4–17) is

$$k = \frac{d}{2a} + \sqrt{(d/2a)^2 - 1}. \tag{4-18}$$

Equation (4–15) yields $b = \sqrt{d^2 - 4a^2}$.

The potential function for this problem is now completely determined. If we wish to determine the capacitance per unit length, $C = q/V$, we can use Eqs. (4–13) and (4–18):

$$C = \frac{\pi \varepsilon_0}{\ln\left[(d + \sqrt{d^2 - 4a^2})/2a\right]}. \tag{4-19}$$

Example 3. A spherical conductor of radius a is placed in a uniform electric field $\mathbf{E}_0 = \mathbf{i}_z E_0$ (Fig. 4–6). Let us use the method of images to determine the surface charge density and the maximum electric field intensity. The uniform field $\mathbf{E}_0$ can be considered as a primary field; it can be determined from the potential

$$U_p = -E_0 z = -E_0 r \cos \theta.$$

The primary field polarizes the sphere, resulting in a secondary field due to the surface charges. As seen from an external field point P, the surface charges appear equivalent to a dipole located at the origin. The dipole has a potential of the form (see Eq. 3–13)

$$U_s = \frac{A \cos \theta}{r^2},$$

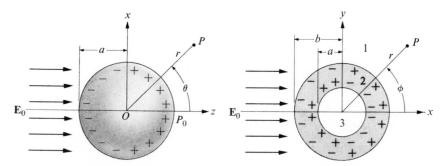

Fig. 4–6. A spherical conductor placed in a uniform electric field.

Fig. 4–7. A hollow dielectric cylinder placed in a uniform electric field.

where A is a constant. The resultant potential is

$$U = -E_0 r \cos \theta + \frac{A \cos \theta}{r^2}.$$

The boundary condition requires that $U = 0$ when $r = a$. This yields

$$A = E_0 a^3.$$

The surface charge density can be determined from Eq. (4–7):

$$\sigma = -\varepsilon_0 \frac{\partial U}{\partial r}\Bigg]_{r=a} = 3\varepsilon_0 E_0 \cos \theta.$$

The maximum field strength occurs at the point P_0 and has a magnitude

$$E_x = -\frac{\partial U}{\partial x}\Bigg]_{x=a} = 3E_0.$$

Thus the effect of the secondary field is to increase the primary field strength at P_0 by a factor of 3.

Example 4. A hollow infinitely long circular dielectric cylinder is placed in a uniform electric field, as shown in Fig. 4–7. Let us determine the effectiveness of the dielectric in screening region 3 from the primary field in region 1. The primary potential is $U_p = -E_0 x$. Since the electric field is independent of z, Laplace's equation reduces to the two-dimensional form

$$\nabla_T^2 U = \frac{\partial^2 U}{\partial x^2} + \frac{\partial^2 U}{\partial y^2} = 0. \tag{4–20}$$

We now have $r^2 = x^2 + y^2$ and it can be shown that $U = \ln r$ is a solution of Eq. (4–20). Substituting this function into Eq. (4–20), we can successively differentiate both sides of the equation with respect to x and y to obtain further solutions. For example,

$$\frac{\partial}{\partial x}(\ln r) = \frac{x}{r^2}$$

is a solution of Eq. (4-20). A potential of the form $\ln r$ results from a line source which is a uniform distribution of charge along an infinitely long straight line. A potential of the form x/r^2 results from two line sources infinitely close together and oppositely charged to the same magnitude. We designate it a *two-dimensional dipole*.

The primary field $\mathbf{E}_0$ results in a polarization of the dielectric. As seen from a field point P in region 1, the polarization charges appear equivalent to a two-dimensional dipole located at the origin. For the secondary potential we therefore set

$$U_s = \frac{A \cos \phi}{r}.$$

The resultant potential in region 1 is

$$U_1 = -E_0 r \cos \phi + \frac{A \cos \phi}{r}.$$

When P is in region 3 the polarization charges appear uniformly distributed, resulting in a uniform field. Thus we set

$$U_3 = -E_3 r \cos \phi,$$

where $\mathbf{E}_3$ represents the assumed uniform electric field intensity. In region 2 the potential is taken as a linear combination of the potential of a uniform and a two-dimensional dipole field. Thus

$$U_2 = Br \cos \phi + \frac{C \cos \phi}{r}.$$

The assumed potentials are solutions of Laplace's equation in two dimensions. Note that the solutions chosen are based on physical considerations concerning the type of field that is expected. If we can determine the unknown constants A, B, and C so that the boundary conditions are satisfied, then we have determined the unique solution.

The boundary conditions at $r = a$ are $U_2 = U_3$ and

$$-\varepsilon_0 \frac{\partial U_3}{\partial r} = -\varepsilon \frac{\partial U_2}{\partial r},$$

which yield

$$B = -(\varepsilon_r + 1)E_3/2\varepsilon_r, \qquad C = -a^2(\varepsilon_r - 1)E_3/2\varepsilon_r. \tag{4-21}$$

The boundary conditions at $r = b$ are $U_1 = U_2$ and

$$-\varepsilon_0 \frac{\partial U_1}{\partial r} = -\varepsilon \frac{\partial U_2}{\partial r},$$

which yield

$$E_0 + A/b^2 = -\varepsilon_r B + \varepsilon_r C/b^2, \qquad -E_0 + A/b^2 = B + C/b^2. \quad (4\text{--}22)$$

Eliminating A between Eqs. (4–22) and substituting Eqs. (4–21) yields the ratio

$$\frac{E_3}{E_0} = \frac{4\varepsilon_r}{(\varepsilon_r + 1)^2}\left[1 - \left(\frac{\varepsilon_r - 1}{\varepsilon_r + 1}\frac{a}{b}\right)^2\right]^{-1},$$

which is a measure of the effectiveness of the dielectric cylinder in screening region 3 from the applied field $\mathbf{E}_0$.

Let us now consider the case of a solid cylinder where $a = 0$. Region 3 no longer exists and we now have $C = 0$. Solving Eqs. (4–22) for B yields $B = -2E_0/(\varepsilon_r + 1)$. The potential within the dielectric is

$$U_2 = -\frac{2E_0 x}{\varepsilon_r + 1},$$

which results in a uniform electric field intensity of magnitude

$$E_2 = \frac{2E_0}{\varepsilon_r + 1} < E_0.$$

The reduction in the electric field intensity inside the cylinder is due to the polarization charges on the surface of the cylinder which set up an electric field intensity

$$\mathbf{E}_p = -\frac{\varepsilon_r - 1}{\varepsilon_r + 1}\mathbf{E}_0.$$

Since the polarization is proportional to the field $\mathbf{E}_2 = \mathbf{E}_p + \mathbf{E}_0$, we see that the surface charges tend to depolarize the dielectric. The reduction in the polarizing field strength can be expressed in the form

$$E_2 = E_0 - N_x \frac{P_x}{\varepsilon_0},$$

where N_x is defined as the *depolarization factor* for the x-axis.

It follows from Eqs. (3–31) and (3–32) that $\mathbf{P} = (\varepsilon - \varepsilon_0)\mathbf{E}$. In our case $P_x = (\varepsilon - \varepsilon_0)E_2$, and we find that $N_x = \frac{1}{2}$. We can obtain the depolarization factors $N_y = \frac{1}{2}$ and $N_z = 0$ in a similar manner. The latter result follows from the fact that if a field is applied along the z-axis there are no polarization charges and hence no depolarizing effect.

Example 5. Let us consider two semi-infinite dielectric media which have a plane interface at $x = 0$ (Fig. 4–8). A point charge Q is placed in medium 1 at a distance d from the interface. This charge will polarize both dielectrics. If medium 1 were of infinite extent, the potential due to a point charge (see

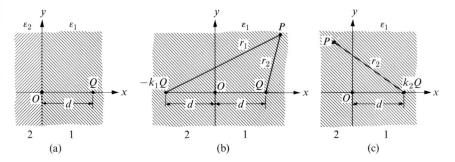

Fig. 4–8. A point charge Q in one of two semi-infinite dielectrics.

Eq. 4–4 and Section 3–6) would be given by

$$U_P = Q/4\pi\varepsilon_1 r_2,$$

which we may consider as the primary potential. If the field point is in medium 1 the effect of the polarization charges will appear equivalent to a point charge $-k_1 Q$ situated in a medium of permittivity ε_1, as shown in Fig. 4–8b. (For convenience we consider all image charges to be situated in the same medium as Q.) The factor k_1 accounts for the imperfect image of the charge Q (note that $k_1 = 1$ when medium 2 is a conductor). The potential in medium 1 is given by

$$U_1 = \frac{Q}{4\pi\varepsilon_1}\left(\frac{1}{r_2} - \frac{k_1}{r_1}\right), \qquad x > 0. \tag{4–23}$$

If the field point is in medium 2 we observe the effect of the charge Q and the polarization charges in medium 1 and 2. We account for all observed charges by an equivalent point charge $k_2 Q$ located as shown in Fig. 4–8c. The potential in medium 2 is given by

$$U_2 = k_2 Q/4\pi\varepsilon_1 r_2, \qquad x < 0. \tag{4–24}$$

The boundary conditions at $x = 0$ require that $U_1 = U_2$ and

$$-\varepsilon_1 \frac{\partial U_1}{\partial x} = -\varepsilon_2 \frac{\partial U_2}{\partial x}.$$

We find that

$$k_1 = \frac{\varepsilon_2 - \varepsilon_1}{\varepsilon_2 + \varepsilon_1}, \qquad k_2 = \frac{2\varepsilon_1}{\varepsilon_2 + \varepsilon_1}.$$

It is instructive to discuss the solution of this problem from a fundamental point of view, in which the charge Q and the polarization charges are considered to be in free space. We take the point charge to be a spherical conductor S_c with an infinitesimally small radius. It follows from the uniformity of ε in regions 1 and 2 that

$$\rho_p = -\text{div } \mathbf{P} = (\varepsilon_0 - \varepsilon) \text{ div } \mathbf{E} = 0.$$

There is, however, a polarization surface charge density σ_p on the interface S at $x = 0$ and a polarization surface charge density σ_p' on the interface S_c. It was shown in Section 3–6 that σ_p' results in an effective charge $Q_e = (\varepsilon_0/\varepsilon_1)Q$ uniformly distributed over S_c. (Note that this result is not affected by the presence of the surface charges on S, since the radius of the sphere is infinitesimally small.)

Several methods can be used to determine σ_p. Given that σ_{pk} is the polarization surface charge density on S for medium k ($k = 1, 2$) we can determine the resultant σ_p on the interface from the equation

$$\sigma_p = \sigma_{p1} + \sigma_{p2} = \left[(\varepsilon_1 - \varepsilon_0) \frac{\partial U_1}{\partial x} - (\varepsilon_2 - \varepsilon_0) \frac{\partial U_2}{\partial x} \right]_{x=0}.$$

A second method for determining σ_p is to consider σ_p as a charge distribution in free space and apply Gauss' law to an elemental cylinder (see Fig. 4–1 and Eq. 4–6):

$$\sigma_p = (\varepsilon_0 E_{x1} - \varepsilon_0 E_{x2})_{x=0} = \varepsilon_0 \left(\frac{\varepsilon_2}{\varepsilon_1} - 1 \right) E_{x2} \Bigg]_{x=0}.$$

Here we have made use of the condition that the normal component of $\mathbf{D}$ must be continuous. The evaluation of σ_p by the above methods is left as an exercise. Here we shall use Eqs. (4–10) and (4–11) to determine σ_p. It was shown that the image charge $k_1 Q_e$ is equivalent to a surface charge distribution where

$$\sigma_p = - \frac{\varepsilon_0 Q k_1 d}{2 \varepsilon_1 \pi r^3}$$

and where $r^2 = y^2 + z^2$. If P is in region 1 the field is considered to be due to a point charge Q_e and a charge distribution σ_p over the interface S. The latter distribution can be replaced by an image charge $-k_1 Q_e$ located at $x = -d$ on the x-axis. If P is in region 2 the charge distribution over S can be replaced by an image charge $-k_1 Q_e$ located at $x = d$ on the x-axis. This image charge appears superimposed on the charge Q_e and we then observe an effective charge

$$Q_e - k_1 Q_e = k_2 Q_e$$

at $x = d$. Note that we consider all charges to be in free space. However, the potentials determined by this approach are the same as those given by Eqs. (4–23) and (4–24).

It is important to note that it is not always possible to replace a surface charge distribution by one or more equivalent point charges. However, it is evident from the examples discussed that the method of images, when applicable, is an extremely simple and powerful technique. Further insight into the method of images can be obtained if we consider the solution of Laplace's equation from a strictly mathematical viewpoint. In Section 4–3 it was shown that an infinite number of solutions of Laplace's equation can be obtained by successively differentiating $1/r$ with respect to x, y, and z. The method of images is essentially restricted to problems that can be solved using simple solutions of the type x, $1/r$ and x/r^3. (In the two-dimensional case the corresponding solutions are x, $\ln r$ and x/r^2.) In general, in order to satisfy the boundary conditions, we need an infinite number of solutions of the type obtained by successive differentiations. In such cases it is essential to use a different approach, the so-called method of separation of variables. This technique, which is a general one, is discussed in the next three sections.

4–5 THE SOLUTION OF LAPLACE'S EQUATION IN CARTESIAN COORDINATES

In cartesian coordinates Laplace's equation has the form

$$\frac{\partial^2 U}{\partial x^2} + \frac{\partial^2 U}{\partial y^2} + \frac{\partial^2 U}{\partial z^2} = 0. \tag{4–25}$$

Equation (4–25) has the important property that solutions can be obtained by the *separation of variables*. We say that the variables are separable if a solution of the form $U = f(x)g(y)h(z)$ is possible. Substituting U into Eq. (4–25) and dividing the result by U yields

$$\frac{1}{f}\frac{d^2 f}{dx^2} + \frac{1}{g}\frac{d^2 g}{dy^2} + \frac{1}{h}\frac{d^2 h}{dz^2} = 0. \tag{4–26}$$

The variables in Eq. (4–26) can be separated by differentiating with respect to x, y, and z, respectively. For example, differentiating with respect to x yields the equation

$$\frac{d}{dx}\left(\frac{1}{f}\frac{d^2 f}{dx^2}\right) = 0. \tag{4–27}$$

Equation (4–27) is an ordinary differential equation in one variable. Integrating once with respect to x yields

$$\frac{d^2 f}{dx^2} + k_1^2 f = 0, \tag{4–28}$$

where k_1 is an integration constant. In a similar manner we obtain

$$\frac{d^2 g}{dy^2} + k_2^2 g = 0, \tag{4–29}$$

$$\frac{d^2 h}{dz^2} + k_3^2 h = 0. \tag{4–30}$$

The constants k_1, k_2, and k_3 are not independent. Substituting Eqs. (4–28), (4–29), and (4–30) into Eq. (4–26) yields

$$k_1^2 + k_2^2 + k_3^2 = 0. \qquad (4-31)$$

The separation of variables has reduced the partial differential equation (4–25) into three ordinary differential equations (4–28), (4–29), and (4–30), where the condition (4–31) must be satisfied.

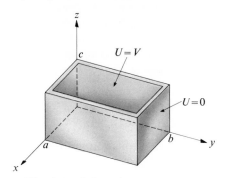

Fig. 4–9. A box-shaped capacitor.

As an example of this method, let us consider the box-shaped capacitor illustrated in Fig. 4–9, which has its sides and bottom at zero potential and its top at a potential V. (Note that there must be an infinitesimally small gap between the top and the sides to prevent the capacitor from discharging.) The dimensions of the box are a, b, and c, respectively, and we wish to find the solution of Laplace's equation which satisfies the boundary conditions. The function fgh will meet the boundary conditions on the sides and bottom of the box if we choose

$$f(0) = 0 = f(a), \qquad g(0) = 0 = g(b), \qquad h(0) = 0. \qquad (4-32)$$

The solution of Eqs. (4–28), (4–29), and (4–30) meeting the conditions (4–32) are

$$f = \sin \frac{\pi m x}{a}, \qquad m = 1, 2, \ldots,$$

$$g = \sin \frac{\pi n y}{b}, \qquad n = 1, 2, \ldots,$$

$$h = \sinh \beta_{mn} z.$$

Here we have taken $k_1 = \pi m/a$, $k_2 = \pi n/b$ to satisfy the boundary conditions and we have taken

$$k_3 = j\beta_{mn} = j\sqrt{(\pi m/a)^2 + (\pi n/b)^2}$$

in order to satisfy the condition (4–31).

A solution of Laplace's equation meeting the conditions (4–32) is

$$U_{mn} = C_{mn} \sin \frac{\pi m x}{a} \sin \frac{\pi n y}{b} \sinh \beta_{mn} z, \qquad (4\text{–}33)$$

where C_{mn} is an arbitrary constant. In order to find a solution U that also meets the boundary condition

$$U(z = c) = V, \qquad (4\text{–}34)$$

we take a linear combination of the functions U_{mn}:

$$U = \sum_{m=1}^{\infty} \sum_{n=1}^{\infty} C_{mn} \sin \frac{\pi m x}{a} \sin \frac{\pi n y}{b} \sinh \beta_{mn} z. \qquad (4\text{–}35)$$

Equation (4–35) is a Fourier series in x and y. The coefficients C_{kl} can be found from the condition (4–34) if we multiply by

$$\sin \frac{\pi k x}{a} \sin \frac{\pi l y}{b}$$

and integrate over the range $0 \leq x \leq a, \, 0 \leq y \leq b$. Since

$$\int_0^a \sin \frac{\pi k x}{a} \sin \frac{\pi l x}{a} \, dx = \begin{cases} a/2, & k = l, \\ 0, & k \neq l, \end{cases}$$

and

$$\int_0^a \sin \frac{\pi k x}{a} \, dx = \begin{cases} 2a/\pi k, & k = 1, 3, 5, \ldots, \\ 0, & k = 0, 2, 4, \ldots, \end{cases}$$

we obtain

$$C_{kl} = \begin{cases} \dfrac{16V}{\pi^2 k l \sinh \beta_{kl} c}, & k, l \text{ both odd,} \\ 0, & k, l \text{ not both odd.} \end{cases}$$

The solution is

$$U = \frac{16V}{\pi^2} \sum_{m=1,3,5,\ldots}^{\infty} \sum_{n=1,3,5,\ldots}^{\infty} \frac{\sinh \beta_{mn} z}{m n \sinh \beta_{mn} c} \sin \frac{\pi m x}{a} \sin \frac{\pi n y}{a}. \qquad (4\text{–}36)$$

4–6 THE SOLUTION OF LAPLACE'S EQUATION IN CYLINDRICAL COORDINATES

Let us assume that the potential U is independent of the z-coordinate. Thus we obtain Laplace's equation in the form (see Eq. 1–103)

$$r \frac{\partial}{\partial r} \left(r \frac{\partial U}{\partial r} \right) + \frac{\partial^2 U}{\partial \phi^2} = 0. \qquad (4\text{–}37)$$

Equation (4–37) can be solved by separation of variables. We substitute

$U = f(r)g(\phi)$ and proceed exactly as we did with Eq. (4–26). This yields

$$r \frac{d}{dr}\left(r \frac{df}{dr}\right) = n^2 f, \qquad \frac{d^2 g}{d\phi^2} = -n^2 g, \qquad (4\text{–}38)$$

where n is a constant. In the special case of $n = 0$ we have $g = \text{const}$ and $U = c \ln r$, where c is an arbitrary constant. When $n \neq 0$ we find that $f = r^n$, $g = e^{\pm jn\phi}$. Thus

$$U_n = r^n(C_n \sin n\phi + D_n \cos n\phi), \qquad (4\text{–}39)$$

where C_n and D_n are arbitrary constants, is a solution of Eq. (4–37).

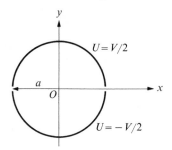

Fig. 4–10. A capacitor formed by splitting a thin conducting circular cylindrical shell into two halves.

As an example, let us determine the potential function for a capacitor formed by splitting a thin conducting circular cylindrical shell into two halves (Fig. 4–10). The boundary values are given by

$$U(a, \phi) = \begin{cases} V/2, & 0 < \phi < \pi, \\ -V/2, & \pi < \phi < 2\pi. \end{cases} \qquad (4\text{–}40)$$

Here a is the radius of the cylinder and V the potential difference. The potential U must be finite at $r = 0$. Thus we must take $n > 0$. Furthermore, n must be an integer, since U is a single-valued function of ϕ. We can therefore represent U as a linear combination of the U_n given by Eq. (4–39) in the form

$$U = \sum_{n=1}^{\infty} r^n(C_n \sin n\phi + D_n \cos n\phi).$$

The coefficients C_m and D_m are obtained by introducing the conditions (4–40), multiplying by $\sin m\phi$ and $\cos m\phi$, respectively, and integrating over the range $0 \leqq \phi \leqq 2\pi$. We find that

$$C_m = \begin{cases} \dfrac{2V}{\pi m}\left(\dfrac{1}{a^m}\right), & m = 1, 3, 5, \ldots, \\[2mm] 0, & m = 2, 4, 6, \ldots, \end{cases}$$

and $D_m = 0$. The potential U is given by

$$U = \frac{2V}{\pi} \sum_{n=1,3,5,\ldots}^{\infty} \left(\frac{r}{a}\right)^n \frac{1}{n} \sin n\phi, \qquad r < a. \qquad (4\text{–}41)$$

Equation (4-41) gives the potential at field points within the cylinder. Suppose that we now wish to determine the potential U' outside the cylinder. The *principle of inversion* allows us to determine U', the potential outside a circular cylinder C, from the potential U, inside C. To discuss the method of inversion, we let $rr' = a^2$, where a is the radius of the inversion cylinder. The principle of inversion states that if $U = U(r, \phi)$ is a solution of Laplace's equation (4-37), then $U' = U(a^2/r', \phi)$ is a solution of Eq. (4-37), where r is replaced by r'. The proof is established by noting that

$$\partial r/\partial r' = -(r/a)^2.$$

Thus

$$r' \frac{\partial U'}{\partial r'} = -r \frac{\partial U}{\partial r}$$

and we obtain the desired result that

$$r' \frac{\partial}{\partial r'}\left(r' \frac{\partial U'}{\partial r'}\right) = r \frac{\partial}{\partial r}\left(r \frac{\partial U}{\partial r}\right).$$

If we apply the principle of inversion to Eq. (4-41), we obtain

$$U' = \frac{2V}{\pi} \sum_{n=1,3,5,\ldots}^{\infty} \left(\frac{a}{r'}\right)^n \frac{1}{n} \sin n\phi, \qquad r' > a,$$

for the potential outside the cylinder.

4-7 THE SOLUTION OF LAPLACE'S EQUATION IN SPHERICAL COORDINATES

When we equate Eq. (107) to zero we obtain Laplace's equation in spherical coordinates. To solve this equation by the separation of variables we substitute $U = f(r)g(\theta)h(\phi)$ into Eq. (1-107). The differential equation obtained for g requires an extensive discussion in the case in which $dh/d\phi \neq 0$. We shall therefore restrict our discussion to axial symmetric fields in which $\partial U/\partial \phi = 0$. Thus we can take $h = 1$. Substituting U into Laplace's equation yields

$$\frac{1}{f}\frac{d}{dr}\left(r^2 \frac{df}{dr}\right) + \frac{1}{g \sin \theta} \cdot \frac{d}{d\theta}\left(\sin \theta \frac{dg}{d\theta}\right) = 0. \tag{4-42}$$

The variables can be separated by the method used in obtaining Eq. (4-28) from Eq. (4-26). Thus

$$\frac{d}{dr}\left(r^2 \frac{df}{dr}\right) - n(n + 1)f = 0, \tag{4-43a}$$

$$\frac{d}{d\theta}\left(\sin \theta \frac{dg}{d\theta}\right) + n(n + 1)g \sin \theta = 0, \tag{4-43b}$$

where $n(n + 1)$ is a constant. Equation (4-43b) can be simplified by means of the substitution $u = \cos \theta$. Thus

$$\frac{d}{du}\left[(1 - u^2)\frac{dg}{du}\right] + n(n + 1)g = 0. \tag{4–44}$$

Equation (4–44) is known as *Legendre's equation*. It can be shown that n must be an integer if one of the solutions of Legendre's equation is to remain finite at $u = \pm 1$. This solution, normalized so that $g(1) = 1$, is known as the *Legendre polynomial of order n:*

$$g = P_n(u). \tag{4–45}$$

(See Appendix A–1 for a discussion of the properties of Legendre polynomials.)
To determine a solution of Eq. (4–43a) we substitute

$$f = r^k \tag{4–46}$$

and find that

$$k(k + 1) = n(n + 1). \tag{4–47}$$

Solutions of Eq. (4–47) are $k = n$ and $k = -n - 1$. A general solution of Eq. (4–43a) is therefore

$$f = A_n r^n + B_n r^{-n-1}.$$

Combining this with Eq. (4–45) yields the function

$$U_n = (A_n r^n + B_n r^{-n-1})P_n(\cos \theta), \tag{4–48}$$

which is a solution of Laplace's equation. A general solution having axial symmetry is

$$U = \sum_{n=0}^{\infty}(A_n r^n + B_n r^{-n-1})P_n(\cos \theta). \tag{4–49}$$

As an example of Eq. (4–49) let us consider the function $U = 1/r_1$, where

$$r_1^2 = x^2 + y^2 + (z - b)^2 = r^2 + b^2 - 2rb \cos \theta.$$

In cartesian coordinates it is relatively easy to show that $1/r_1$ is a solution of Laplace's equation. Let us now consider the representation of this solution in spherical coordinates. Expanding $1/r_1$ in a Taylor series in b/r and r/b, respectively, yields

$$\frac{1}{r_1} = \frac{1}{r}P_0(\cos \theta) + \frac{b}{r^2}P_1(\cos \theta) + \cdots, \quad \frac{b}{r} < 1, \tag{4–50}$$

$$\frac{1}{r_1} = \frac{1}{b}P_0(\cos \theta) + \frac{r}{b^2}P_1(\cos \theta) + \cdots, \quad \frac{r}{b} < 1. \tag{4–51}$$

A heuristic consideration would indicate that since $1/r_1$ is a solution of Laplace's equation, the terms in the above expansions should also be solutions. That this is correct can be seen from Eq. (4–49) by choosing $A_n = 0$,

$B_n = b^n$ to obtain Eq. (4–50) and by choosing $A_n = 1/b^{n+1}$, $b_n = 0$ to obtain Eq. (4–51). We can recognize the fact that the coefficient of $(b/r)^n$ in Eq. (4–50) is the Legendre polynomial $P_n(u)$ by noting that the coefficient must satisfy Eq. (4–44) and that if we take $\theta = 0$ we find that the coefficient is unity, thus satisfying the normalization condition for the Legendre polynomials.

Let us consider once more Example 1 of Section 4–4, which was solved by the method of images, and let us now obtain the solution with the aid of Eq. (4–49) (see Fig. 4–3). We consider the point charge to set up a primary potential U_p which we can express in the form

$$U_p = \frac{Q}{4\pi\varepsilon_0 r_2} = \frac{Q}{4\pi\varepsilon_0 d}\left[P_0(\cos\theta) + \frac{r}{d}P_1(\cos\theta) + \cdots\right], \qquad (4\text{–}52)$$

where $1/r_2 = (r^2 + d^2 - 2rd\cos\theta)^{-1/2}$ has been expanded in a Taylor series in $r/d < 1$. For the secondary potential U_s due to the sphere we must have $\lim_{r\to\infty} U_s = 0$. Thus we choose $A_n = 0$ in Eq. (4–49) and take U_s in the form

$$U_s = \frac{B_0}{r}P_0(\cos\theta) + \frac{B_1}{r^2}P_1(\cos\theta) + \cdots \qquad (4\text{–}53)$$

The resultant potential, $U = U_p + U_s$ must satisfy the condition that $U = 0$ for $r = a$. Since the Legendre polynomials are orthogonal functions (see Appendix A–12), this requires that the coefficient of $P_n(\cos\theta)$ equal zero:

$$\frac{B_n}{a^{n+1}} + \frac{Q}{4\pi\varepsilon_0 d}\left(\frac{a}{d}\right)^n = 0.$$

Solving for B_n and substituting into Eq. (4–49) yields

$$U_s = -\frac{Q}{4\pi\varepsilon_0 d}\left(\frac{a}{r}\right)\left[P_0(\cos\theta) + \frac{a^2}{rd}P_1(\cos\theta) + \frac{a^4}{d^2 r^2}P_2(\cos\theta) + \cdots\right]$$

$$= -\frac{Q}{4\pi\varepsilon_0 d}\frac{a}{\sqrt{r^2 + b^2 - 2rb\cos\theta}} = -\frac{kQ}{4\pi\varepsilon_0 r_1},$$

where we have used Eq. (4–50) and have taken $b = a^2/d$, $k = a/d$, and $r_1 = r^2 + b^2 - 2rb\cos\theta$. This is the same result obtained previously. It is evident that the method of images is more direct and requires fewer mathematical manipulations. However, in many cases the method of images is not applicable.

As an example of the failure of the method of images, let us consider the problem illustrated in Fig. 4–11, in which a spherical conductor of radius a is covered by a dielectric shell of outer radius b and a point charge Q is at a distance d from the center of the sphere. The problem is to determine the

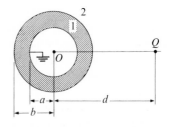

Fig. 4–11. A point charge near a grounded
spherical conductor which is covered with
a dielectric shell.

potential at any field point. Equation (4–52) gives the primary potential due
to the point charge. In medium 2 we choose a secondary potential for which
$\lim_{r \to \infty} U_s = 0$. Thus (see Eq. 4–53)

$$U_s = \frac{Q}{4\pi\varepsilon_0 r}\left[C_0 P_0(\cos\theta) + \frac{C_1}{r}P_1(\cos\theta) + \cdots\right].$$

The resultant potential in medium 2 is $U_2 = U_p + U_s$. In medium 1 we
take (see Eq. 4–49)

$$U_1 = \frac{Q}{4\pi\varepsilon_0}\left[(A_0 + B_0/r)P_0(\cos\theta) + (A_1 r + B_1/r^2)P_1(\cos\theta) + \cdots\right].$$

$$(4\text{--}54)$$

Let us consider the sphere as grounded so that $U_1 = 0$ for $r = a$. Since
the Legendre polynomials are orthogonal functions we must set the coefficient
of $P_n(\cos\theta)$ in Eq. (4–54) equal to zero for $r = a$. Thus

$$a^n A_n + B_n/a^{n+1} = 0, \qquad n = 0, 1, 2, \ldots$$

The boundary conditions at $r = b$ are

$$U_1 = U_2, \qquad -\varepsilon\frac{\partial U_1}{\partial r} = -\varepsilon_0 \frac{\partial U_2}{\partial r}.$$

Equating like coefficients of $P_n(\cos\theta)$ on both sides of the above equations
yields

$$b^n A_n + B_n/b^{n+1} = C_n/b^{n+1} + b^n/d^{n+1},$$

$$\varepsilon_r[nb^{n-1}A_n - (n+1)B_n/b^{n+2}] = nb^{n-1}/d^{n+1} - (n+1)C_n/b^{n+2}.$$

Eliminating C_n from the above equations, we find that

$$B_n = -a^{2n+1}A_n,$$

$$A_n = \frac{2n+1}{d^{n+1}}\frac{1}{(\varepsilon_r + 1)n + 1 + (\varepsilon_r - 1)(n+1)(a/b)^{2n+1}}.$$

The coefficients in the infinite series (4–54) are now known and the problem can be considered as solved. There seems to be no way of summing the
series into a finite form which would be the case if the method of images were
applicable.

4–8 POISSON'S INTEGRAL

The solution of Laplace's equation by the separation of variables is a general technique which is formally relatively simple. However, it has the disadvantage of yielding infinite series as solutions, even in cases in which a closed form of solution is possible. Furthermore, slow convergence may limit the usefulness of the series solution. In this section we shall discuss the representation of a potential function in a closed integral form. We shall limit the discussion to boundary value problems in two dimensions. The extension of the method to be discussed to three dimensions is relatively straightforward and is left as an exercise (see Problem 4–12).

A closed integral form for the solution of Laplace's equation in two dimensions can be obtained with the aid of Green's theorem. Let us apply Eq. (1–70) to a cylinder of unit length in the direction of the z-axis of a cylindrical coordinate system and let U and V be two solutions of Laplace's equation within the cylinder. The volume integral of Eq. (1–70) will then vanish. Over the faces of the cylinder we have, for a two-dimensional field,

$$\frac{\partial U}{\partial z} = 0, \qquad \frac{\partial V}{\partial z} = 0.$$

Thus

$$\oint_C \left(V \frac{\partial U}{\partial n} - U \frac{\partial V}{\partial n} \right) dh = 0, \qquad (4\text{–}55)$$

where we have taken $ds = (1)\, dh$ for the element of area in Eq. (1–70), and where dh is the element of arc for the contour C. The derivatives are taken in the direction of the outward normal of C.

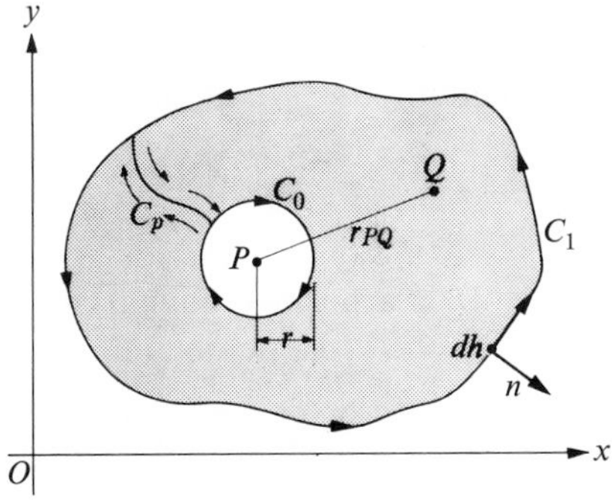

Fig. 4–12. Illustration of the derivation of Poisson's integral.

Equation (4–55) can be used to determine the potential U at an interior field point P in terms of the potential distribution along a contour C_1 enclosing P (see Fig. 4–12). To determine U we first enclose P in a circle C_0 of radius r, as shown in the figure, and choose a suitable solution V of Laplace's equation. The contour C is composed of C_1, C_0, and an arbitrary path C_p connecting C_1 and C_0. Let the arc length h be measured along the contour C in a positive sense. The integration back and forth over the path C_p contributes nothing to the final result because of the opposed normals at each point along the path. We are therefore left with the integrals along C_1 and C_0. We let I_0 and I_1 represent the integrals evaluated along C_0 and C_1, respectively, and thus we can write Eq. (4–55) in the form

$$I_0 + I_1 = 0 \qquad (4\text{–}56)$$

Consider now the integral I_1. Since $\partial U/\partial n$ is not known on C_1, we must require that

$$V = 0 \qquad (4\text{–}57)$$

on C_1 in order to evaluate I_1. Thus

$$I_1 = -\oint_{C_1} U \frac{\partial V}{\partial n} \, dh. \qquad (4\text{–}58)$$

The values of U are specified on C_1 so that I_1 may be evaluated after a suitable V has been chosen. Consider now I_0. The choice of V is governed by the fact that we wish to determine $U(P)$ from I_0 by letting $r \to 0$. To accomplish this objective requires that V have a singularity at P. A solution of Laplace's equation in two dimensions having a singularity at P (see Eq. 3–39) is

$$V_1 = \ln r_{PQ}, \qquad (4\text{–}59)$$

where $r_{PQ}^2 = (x_P - x_Q)^2 + (y_P - y_Q)^2$, and where Q is any point within C_1. However, V_1 will not satisfy the condition (4–57). Thus we choose

$$V = \ln r_{PQ} + W, \qquad (4\text{–}60)$$

where W is a solution of Laplace's equation which remains finite on and within C_1 and is chosen so that the condition (4–57) is satisfied. The function V is called the *Green's function* for the problem and is uniquely determined by these conditions. We are now in a position to evaluate I_0. On C_0, let

$$\left| \frac{\partial U}{\partial n} \right| \leqq M, \qquad dh = r \, d\phi,$$

where M is a positive bound on the normal derivative. Thus, noting that $-\partial V/\partial n = \partial V/\partial r$, we obtain

$$\lim_{r \to 0} \left| \oint_{C_0} V \frac{\partial U}{\partial n} \, dh \right| \leqq \lim_{r \to 0} M 2\pi r \ln r = 0.$$

The nonzero part of I_0 is given by

$$I_0 = \lim_{r \to 0} \oint_{C_0} - U \frac{\partial V}{\partial n} \, dh = 2\pi U(P).$$

Substituting I_1 and I_0 into Eq. (4–56) yields *Poisson's integral:*

$$U(P) = \frac{1}{2\pi} \oint_C U \frac{\partial V}{\partial n} \, dh. \qquad (4\text{–}61)$$

Here we have deleted the subscript on C_1. Equation (4–61) expresses the potential at P in terms of the potential distribution along the contour C and the normal derivative of Green's function. The problem is formally solved as soon as Green's function has been determined.

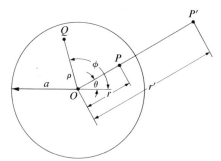

Fig. 4–13. Illustration of the derivation of the Green's function for a circle.

The Green's function for a circle can be determined by the method of images. Let us consider a circular cylinder of radius a (Fig. 4–13). The potential V which satisfies the conditions (4–57) and (4–60) can be considered to result from a line source at P and an image line source at P'. The point P' is determined by the condition that $V = 0$ on C. Using the geometric approach discussed in Section 4–4, Example 1, we can show that we must have

$$\frac{r_{PQ}}{r_{P'Q}} = \frac{r}{a} = \frac{a}{r'},$$ (4–62)

when Q is on C. Thus

$$V = \ln \frac{r_{PQ}}{r_{P'Q}} + k,$$

where k is a constant. If the point Q is on C, we find with the aid of Eq. (4–62) that $k = -\ln (r/a)$. Thus Green's function for the circle is

$$V = \ln \frac{a r_{PQ}}{r r_{P'Q}},$$

where

$$r_{PQ}^2 = \rho^2 + r^2 - 2\rho r \cos (\phi - \theta),$$

$$r_{P'Q}^2 = \rho^2 + r'^2 - 2\rho r' \cos (\phi - \theta).$$

The normal derivative of V on C is

$$\frac{\partial V}{\partial \rho}\bigg]_{\rho=a} = \frac{1}{a} \frac{a^2 - r^2}{a^2 + r^2 - 2ar \cos (\phi - \theta)},$$

and Poisson's integral for the circle is

$$U(r, \theta) = \frac{1}{2\pi} \int_0^{2\pi} U(a, \phi) \frac{a^2 - r^2}{a^2 + r^2 - 2ar \cos (\phi - \theta)} \, d\phi.$$ (4–63)

As an example of the use of Poisson's integral, let us solve the problem illustrated in Fig. 4–10 and discussed in Section 4–6. Introducing the potential distribution given by Eq. (4–40) and substituting $\alpha = \phi - \theta$, we obtain

$$U(r, \theta) = \frac{V}{\pi} \int_{-\theta}^{\pi-\theta} \frac{ar(a^2 - r^2) \cos \alpha}{(a^2 + r^2)^2 - 4a^2r^2 \cos^2 \alpha} \, d\alpha.$$

The integral can be evaluated by means of the substitution

$$\tan \psi = \frac{2ar \sin \alpha}{a^2 - r^2}.$$

Thus

$$U(r, \theta) = \frac{V}{2\pi} \int_{\alpha=-\theta}^{\alpha=\pi-\theta} d\psi = \frac{V}{\pi} \arctan \frac{2ay}{a^2 - r^2}. \tag{4–64}$$

The closed form given by Eq. (4–64) is more convenient than the infinite series (4–41). In general, however, Poisson's integral must be evaluated by numerical means.

4-9 ANALYTIC FUNCTIONS; SOLUTION OF LAPLACE'S EQUATION IN TWO DIMENSIONS

A function $F(z) = U + jV$ of the complex variable $z = x + jy$ is called *analytic* within a region R if the derivative

$$\frac{dF}{dz} = \lim_{\Delta z \to 0} \frac{\Delta F}{\Delta z} \tag{4–65}$$

exists within R independent of the direction chosen for Δz. The necessary and sufficient conditions for F to be analytic are known as the *Cauchy-Riemann equations:*

$$\frac{\partial U}{\partial x} = \frac{\partial V}{\partial y}, \qquad \frac{\partial U}{\partial y} = -\frac{\partial V}{\partial x}. \tag{4–66}$$

The necessity of the conditions (4–66) can be seen if we choose $\Delta z = \Delta x$ and $\Delta z = j \Delta y$ in Eq. (4–65), respectively, and equate the derivatives:

$$\frac{dF}{dz} = \frac{\partial U}{\partial x} + j \frac{\partial V}{\partial x} = \frac{1}{j} \cdot \frac{\partial U}{\partial y} + \frac{\partial V}{\partial y}. \tag{4–67}$$

Equating the real and imaginary parts of Eq. (4–67) yields the Cauchy-Riemann equations.

When we eliminate V from Eqs. (4–66), we find that

$$\frac{\partial^2 U}{\partial x^2} + \frac{\partial^2 U}{\partial y^2} = 0. \tag{4–68}$$

A similar result is obtained for V. Thus if $F(z) = U + jV$ is an analytic function of z, then both U and V are solutions of Laplace's equation (4–68). This fact is extremely useful and allows us to solve boundary-value problems by determining a suitable analytic function.

If we consider U as the potential function of an electrostatic field, the electric field intensity is given by[†]

$$\mathbf{E} = -\mathbf{i}_x \frac{\partial U}{\partial x} - \mathbf{i}_y \frac{\partial U}{\partial y}.$$

Instead of the vector representation for $\mathbf{E}$, we shall now use a complex number representation of the form

$$E \triangleq E_x + jE_y = -\left(\frac{\partial U}{\partial x} + j\frac{\partial U}{\partial y}\right) = -\left(\frac{\partial V}{\partial y} + j\frac{\partial U}{\partial y}\right) = -\left(\frac{dF}{dz}\right)^*,$$

$$(4\text{–}69)$$

where the asterisk denotes *complex conjugate*. The latter result follows from the Cauchy-Riemann equations and the fact that the derivative of an analytic function is independent of the increment chosen for dz (in the above case $dz = j\,dy$). Because E can be obtained from F in the manner indicated by Eq. (4–69), we shall refer to F as the *complex potential*.

The curve $U = $ const defines an equipotential curve. A streamline is defined by the equation $dz = dcE$, where dc is an elemental real scaling factor. Substituting into Eq. (4–69) yields

$$(dF)^* = -\frac{|dz|^2}{dc}.$$

Thus dF is real on a streamline. In order that dF be real we must have $V = $ const. Thus the curves $V = $ const define the streamlines. If $\mathbf{E} \neq 0$, it follows from $\mathbf{E} = -\text{grad }U$ that $\mathbf{E}$ is normal to the equipotential curve at any field point. It follows that the equipotential curves are orthogonal to the streamlines, with the exception of singular points where $\mathbf{E} = 0$.

Let us determine the electric flux per unit length ϕ_e between two streamlines $V = V_1$ and $V = V_2$[‡] (Fig. 4–14). In free space we have

$$\phi_e = \varepsilon_0 \int_{V_1}^{V_2} |E\,dz|.$$

The integral can be evaluated if we note that

$$E = |E|\,e^{j\theta}, \qquad dz = |dz|\,e^{j(\theta+\pi/2)} = j\,|dz|\,e^{j\theta}.$$

[†] Note that V no longer represents a potential difference and that z is now a point in the xy-plane.

[‡] In the case of two-dimensional fields, quantities such as flux, charge, surface charge density, current, and capacitance are computed on the basis of a unit length of the medium along a direction normal to the field.

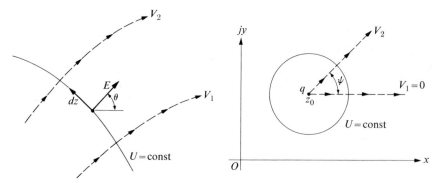

Fig. 4-14. Streamlines and equipotentials in two dimensions.

Fig. 4-15. Streamlines and equipotentials of a line source.

Thus $jE\,dz^* = |E\,dz| = -j\,dF^* = -dV$, and we obtain the result

$$\phi_e = \varepsilon_0(V_1 - V_2). \tag{4-70}$$

The electric flux between two streamlines can be obtained from the difference in value of the two streamlines.

The potential due to a line source in free space is given by Eq. (3-39):

$$U = -\frac{q}{2\pi\varepsilon_0}\ln r,$$

where q is the charge per unit length and r is the distance between the line source and the field point. When we set $z - z_0 = re^{j\psi}$, we see that the complex potential of a line source is

$$F = -\frac{q}{2\pi\varepsilon_0}\ln(z - z_0), \tag{4-71}$$

where $V = -(q/2\pi\varepsilon_0)\psi$. The electric flux per unit length between the streamlines $V_1 = 0$ and $V_2 > V_1$ can be obtained from Eq. (4-70); it is (Fig. 4-15)

$$\phi_e = \frac{q}{2\pi}\psi.$$

In general, the type of problem that we can solve using analytic functions is illustrated in Fig. 4-16. A cylindrical conductor is at a potential U_0 and is under the influence of a line source situated at z_0. The solution U of Laplace's equation is to be found which satisfies the boundary condition $U = U_0$ on the conductor surface and has a singularity at z_0 corresponding to the line source. The problem can be solved by mapping the shaded region onto a half-plane, as shown in Fig. 4-17, by means of a transformation or mapping function $w = w(z)$. The line source maps to a position w_0. In the w-plane the

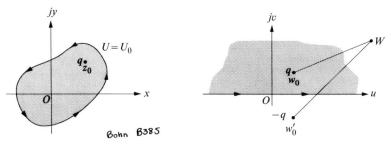

Fig. 4–16. The z-plane representation of a line source inside a cylindrical conductor.

Fig. 4–17. The w-plane representation of the mapping function $w(z)$.

complex potential can be found using the method of images, and has the form (see Eq. 4–71)

$$F = \frac{q}{2\pi\varepsilon_0} \ln \frac{w - w_0'}{w - w_0}. \tag{4-72}$$

When we express F in terms of z we obtain an analytic function of z, and the desired solution is given by $U = \text{Re}\,[F]$. Note that we can use the Taylor series $w - w_0 = c_1(z - z_0) + \cdots$ to show that the function

$$F = -\frac{q}{2\pi\varepsilon_0} \ln (z - z_0) + \cdots$$

has the specified singularity at z_0. In general, there is often more than one conductor and line sources may not be present. In the next section we shall discuss the *Schwartz-Christoffel transformation*, which maps the interior of a polygon onto a half-plane. With the aid of this transformation we can determine the complex potential for a variety of two-dimensional boundary-value problems.

4–10 THE SCHWARTZ-CHRISTOFFEL TRANSFORMATION

The problem of mapping the interior of a closed polygon of n sides onto a half-plane can be solved by the Schwartz-Christoffel transformation. When we are discussing the mapping function $w = w(z)$, it is convenient to consider that a point z on the polygon contour and the corresponding point w on the real w-axis move in a positive sense along the contours (Fig. 4–18). Consider a neighborhood of the corner $w_1 = w(z_1)$ and let $dw = w - w_1$ and $dz = z - z_1$. In the w-plane the argument of dw at the points P_1 and P_2 is given by

$$\arg\,[dw] = \pi, \qquad \arg\,[dw] = 0,$$

respectively. Thus the change in the argument of dw as we move from P_1 to

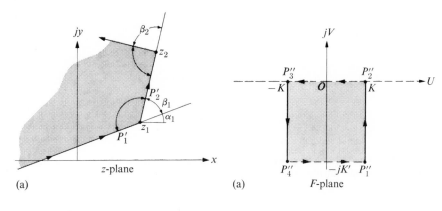

(a)   z-plane

(a)   F-plane

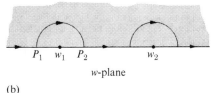

(b)   w-plane

(b)   w-plane

Fig. 4–18. The mapping of a polygon of n sides onto a half-plane.

Fig. 4–19. The mapping of a rectangle onto a half-plane.

P_2 is $\Delta \arg [dw] = -\pi$. In the z-plane we have

$$\arg [dz] = \pi + \alpha_1 \quad \text{at } P_1', \qquad \arg [dz] = \alpha_1 + \beta_1 \quad \text{at } P_2'.$$

Thus $\Delta \arg [dz] = \beta_1 - \pi$, and we find that

$$\Delta \arg \left[\frac{dz}{dw}\right] = \beta_1 - \pi + \pi,$$

$$\arg \left[\frac{dz}{dw}\right] = \alpha_1 + \beta_1 - \frac{\beta_1}{\pi} \arg [w - w_1], \qquad |w - w_1| \ll 1.$$

We can obtain similar expressions for each corner of the polygon. Thus the function

$$\arg \left[\frac{dz}{dw}\right] = \arg [c_1] - \frac{\beta_1}{\pi} \arg [w - w_1] - \cdots - \frac{\beta_n}{\pi} \arg [w - w_n]$$

has the proper mapping property at each corner. This function yields the differential equation for the Schwartz-Christoffel transformation,

$$\frac{dz}{dw} = c_1(w - w_1)^{-\beta_1/\pi} \cdots (w - w_n)^{-\beta_n/\pi}. \tag{4–73}$$

Here c_1 is an arbitrary constant. Note that the angles $\beta_1, \ldots, \beta_n$ give the angular change in the direction of motion of z as it passes through the corresponding corners $z_1, \ldots, z_n$ on the polygon contour.

As an example of the Schwartz-Christoffel transformation, let us consider the mapping problem illustrated in Fig. 4–19, in which the interior of a rectangle of width $2K$ and height K' in the F-plane is to be mapped onto the lower half of the w-plane. The interval $k \leq w \leq 1$ is to map onto the line $F = K + jV$, where $-K' \leq V \leq 0$ and where $F = 0$ when $w = 0$.

Tracing through the contour of the rectangle in a positive sense, we note that we have $\beta/\pi = \frac{1}{2}$ at each corner. Thus, taking $c_1 = 1$ and $z = F$ in Eq. (4–73), we obtain

$$\frac{dF}{dw} = \frac{1}{(w-1)^{1/2}(w-k)^{1/2}(w+1)^{1/2}(w+k)^{1/2}} = \frac{1}{\sqrt{(w^2 - k^2)(w^2 - 1)}}.$$

Integration yields the mapping function

$$F = \int_0^w \frac{dw}{\sqrt{(w^2 - k^2)(w^2 - 1)}}. \tag{4–74}$$

If we substitute $w = uk$ into Eq. (4–74), we find that

$$K \triangleq F(k, \pi/2) = \int_0^1 \frac{du}{\sqrt{(1 - u^2)(1 - k^2u^2)}}, \tag{4–75}$$

where $F(k, \pi/2)$ is the *complete elliptic integral of the first kind*. For a given value of K we can use tables to determine k.†

As w increases from $w = k$ to $w = 1$, F changes by $-jK'$. Thus

$$-jK' = \int_k^1 \frac{dw}{\sqrt{(w^2 - k^2)(w^2 - 1)}}.$$

Substituting $w^2 = 1 - (k'u)^2$, where $k' \triangleq \sqrt{1 - k^2}$, into the above integral shows that

$$K' = F(k', \pi/2). \tag{4–76}$$

4–11 EXAMPLES OF THE SCHWARTZ-CHRISTOFFEL TRANSFORMATION

Example 1. A circular infinitely long straight transmission line of radius A has a charge per unit length of q and is situated near a grounded conducting boundary formed by two semi-infinite parallel planes with a connecting step of height B. We wish to compare the capacitance of the system with the case of a plane conducting boundary where $B = 0$. For convenience, we normalize

---

† E. Jahnke and F. Emde, *Tables of Functions*, Dover Publications, New York, 1943.

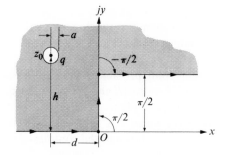

Fig. 4-20. The z-plane representation of a line source and a conducting boundary formed by two semi-infinite parallel planes and a connecting step.

all distance, so that the height of the step is $\pi/2$ (Fig. 4–20) and so that

$$a \triangleq \pi A/2B, \qquad h \triangleq \pi H/2B, \qquad d \triangleq \pi D/2B.$$

We take $a \ll h$, $a \ll d$. The shaded region shown in the figure can be mapped onto a half-plane by means of the Schwartz-Christoffel transformation. In tracing through the contour in a positive sense, we note that the angular change at $z = 0$ and $z = j\pi/2$, corresponding to the points $w = 0$ and $w = 1$, is $\pi/2$ and $-\pi/2$, respectively. Equation (4–73) yields

$$\frac{dz}{dw} = c_1 \sqrt{\frac{w-1}{w}}. \tag{4–77}$$

The integration can be performed by means of the substitution $w = \cosh^2 p$, and we obtain the equation

$$z = c_1(\cosh p \sinh p - p) + c_2,$$

where c_2 is an integration constant. We can express this equation in terms of w by noting that

$$e^p = \cosh p + \sinh p = \sqrt{w} + \sqrt{w-1}.$$

Thus

$$z = c_1[\sqrt{w(w-1)} - \ln(\sqrt{w} + \sqrt{w-1})] + c_2.$$

The conditions that $z = 0$ for $w = 0$ and $z = j\pi/2$ for $w = 1$ yield $c_1 = 1$ and $c_2 = j\pi/2$. (Note that $e^{j\pi/2} = j$.) The mapping function is

$$z = \sqrt{w(w-1)} - \ln(\sqrt{w} + \sqrt{w-1}) + j\frac{\pi}{2}.$$

Suppose that w_0 is the point corresponding to z_0; the complex potential in the w-plane is given by Eq. (4–72) (see Fig. 4–21). Since the normalized transmission line radius a is small, its circumference will map approximately onto a circle of radius a'. To determine a' in terms of a, we note that line elements in the two planes are related by the derivative dz/dw. Thus we can

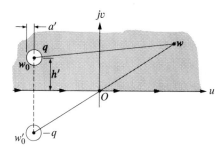

Fig. 4–21. The w-plane representation of the mapping function $w(z)$.

find a' from the equation (see Eq. 4–77)

$$\frac{a}{a'} = \left| \frac{dz}{dw} \right|_{w=w_0} = \left| \sqrt{\frac{w_0 - 1}{w_0}} \right|. \tag{4–78}$$

From the figure we see that

$$h' = \text{Im}\,[w_0]. \tag{4–79}$$

The potential U is given by the real part of F (see Eq. 4–72). Thus

$$U = \frac{q}{2\pi\varepsilon_0} \ln \left| \frac{w - w_0'}{w - w_0} \right|.$$

If the point w is taken on the surface of the transmission line which has a potential of U_0, we have $U = U_0$, $|w - w_0| \cong a'$, and $|w - w_0'| \cong 2h'$. The capacitance per unit length is

$$C' = q/U_0 \cong \frac{2\pi\varepsilon_0}{\ln\,(2h'/a')},$$

where a' and h' are given by Eqs. (4–78) and (4–79).

The capacitance C' can now be compared with the capacitance

$$C = \frac{2\pi\varepsilon_0}{\ln\,(2H/A)},$$

for the case of a plane ground surface where $B = 0$.

Example 2. We wish to determine an approximate formula for the capacitance of a parallel-plate capacitor which takes the edge effect into account (Fig. 4–22). The difference in potential between the plates is U_0 and the dimensions of the plate are taken to be large compared with the distance d between the plates, so that the field may be approximated by a two-dimensional field. The capacitor plates are represented in the z-plane by the two lines $z = x$ and $z = x + jd$, respectively, where $x < 0$. In order to distinguish between the two sides of a plate, we must consider that the z-plane is cut open along these lines. In tracing through the contour defined by both

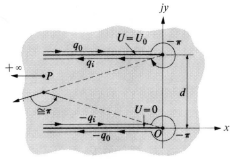

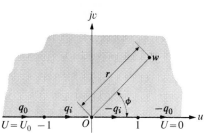

Fig. 4–22. The edge of a parallel-plate capacitor in the z-plane.

Fig. 4–23. The w-plane representation of the mapping function $w(z)$.

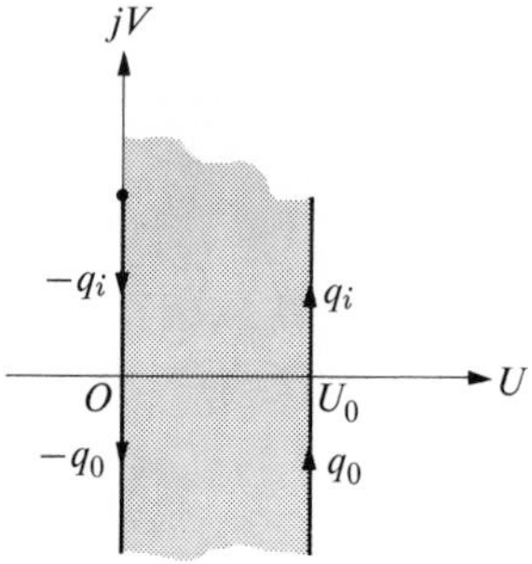

Fig. 4–24. The F-plane representation of the complex potential.

sides of the plates, we note that the angular change at the points $z = jd$, $z = \infty$, $z = 0$ is $-\pi$, π, and $-\pi$, respectively. (To determine the angular change at $z = \infty$, we take the point $P = x + jd/2$ shown in Figure 4–22 and let $x \to -\infty$.) The corresponding points in the w-plane (see Fig. 4–23) are taken at $w = -1$, $w = 0$, and $w = 1$, respectively. Thus

$$\frac{dz}{dw} = c_1 \frac{(w + 1)(w - 1)}{w}$$

and we obtain

$$z = c_1 \left(\frac{w^2}{2} - \ln w \right) + c_2.$$

The conditions that $z = jd$ for $w = -1$ and $z = 0$ for $w = 1$ (note that $e^{j\pi} = -1$) yield

$$c_1 = -d/\pi, \qquad c_2 = d/2\pi,$$

and the desired transformation is

$$z = \frac{d}{\pi} \left(\frac{1 - w^2}{2} + \ln w \right). \tag{4–80}$$

In order to determine the complex potential $F = U + jV$, we map the upper half of the w-plane onto the infinite strip shown in Fig. 4-24. The equipotential curves in the z-plane then map onto straight lines parallel to the jV-axis in the F-plane. The desired mapping is accomplished by the function $\ln w$. Thus

$$F = -j\frac{U_0}{\pi}\ln w \tag{4-81}$$

is the complex potential.

The charge and capacitance per unit length are obtained with the aid of Eq. (4-70), which gives the electric flux between two streamlines. To determine the streamlines we substitute

$$w = re^{j\phi} \tag{4-82}$$

into Eq. (4-81). Taking the imaginary part of F yields the equation of a streamline:

$$V = -\frac{U_0}{\pi}\ln r. \tag{4-83}$$

Substituting Eq. (4-82) into Eq. (4-80) and taking $\phi = 0$ and $\phi = \pi$, respectively, yields the equations for the upper and lower plate in the z-plane:

$$z = x + jd, \quad \text{upper plate, } \phi = \pi,$$

$$z = x \quad\quad\quad \text{lower plate, } \phi = 0.$$

Here

$$x = \frac{d}{\pi}\left(\frac{1 - r^2}{2} + \ln r\right). \tag{4-84}$$

For a given value of $x < 0$, Eq. (4-84) yields two values of r. For the inside of the plates the range for r is $0 \leq r \leq 1$; for the outside of the plates the range for r is $1 \leq r \leq \infty$.

With the aid of Eqs. (4-70) and (4-83), we can determine the electric flux and the magnitude q of the charge per unit length on a section of the plate from $x = x_1$ to $x = x_2$. Thus, taking $U_0 > 0$, we have

$$q = \varepsilon_0 |V_2 - V_1| = \frac{\varepsilon_0 U_0}{\pi}\left|\ln\frac{r_2}{r_1}\right|, \tag{4-85}$$

where r_k is one of the two values of r corresponding to x_k. Let us apply Eq. (4-85) to determine the charges per unit length q_i and q_0 for the inside and outside of the upper plate for a section from $x_1 = 0$ to $x_2 = -l$. We take $l \gg d$. From Eq. (4-84) we see that $r_1 = 1$ for $x_1 = 0$. For $x_2 = -l$ there are two solutions for r_2 corresponding to the ranges of r for the inside and outside of the plates. In the case of $l/d \gg 1$, we can obtain approximate solutions directly from Eq. (4-84). These are given by

$$-l \cong \frac{d}{\pi} \ln r_2, \qquad \text{inside} \tag{4-86a}$$

$$-l \cong -\frac{r_2^2 d}{2\pi} \qquad \text{outside.} \tag{4-86b}$$

Using Eq. (4-85) and Eq. (4-86a) yields $q_i \cong \varepsilon_0 l U_0/d$. Similarly, using Eq. (4-85) and Eq. (4-86b) yields

$$q_0 \cong \frac{\varepsilon_0 U_0}{2\pi} \ln \frac{2\pi l}{d}.$$

The capacitance per unit length of a section of length l is

$$C = \frac{q_i + q_0}{U_0} = \frac{\varepsilon_0}{d}\left(l + \frac{d}{2\pi} \ln \frac{2\pi l}{d}\right).$$

Thus at each edge a length

$$\frac{d}{2\pi} \ln \frac{2\pi l}{d}$$

must be added to the capacitor dimensions to account for the edge effect.

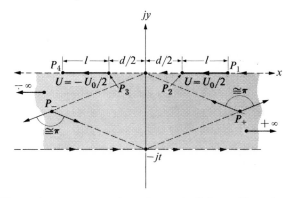

Fig. 4-25. The z-plane representation of two parallel metallic strips on a dielectric substrate of thickness t.

Example 3. It is often necessary to estimate the capacitance of metallic films on dielectric substrates [1, 2]. In material such as barium titanate, the permittivity is extremely large ($\varepsilon_r > 1000$), so that we can assume that the electric flux outside the material is negligible compared with the electric flux within the material. The surface of the dielectric then consists of equipotentials formed by the metallic film and of streamlines corresponding to the direction of the electric field intensity.

Let us consider Fig. 4-25, which illustrates an infinite dielectric plate of thickness t. Two metallic films are deposited as shown; the potential difference

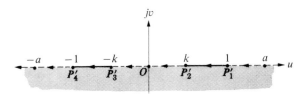

Fig. 4–26. The w-plane representation of the mapping function $w(z)$.

between the films is U_0. We first map the shaded region onto a half-plane by means of a transformation $w = w(z)$ (Fig. 4–26). We can find the function w with the aid of the Schwartz-Christoffel transformation by noting that in tracing through the contour in a positive sense the angular change at $x = \pm\infty$ corresponding to the points $w = \pm a$ are both π. (We can readily see this when we consider the points P_+ and P_- shown in the figure and take $P_+ \to \infty$, $P_- \to -\infty$.) Thus

$$\frac{dz}{dw} = \frac{-2ac_1}{(w - a)(w + a)} = c_1\left(\frac{1}{w + a} - \frac{1}{w - a}\right),$$

and we obtain

$$z = c_1 \ln\frac{w + a}{w - a} + c_2.$$

The constants c_1 and c_2 are determined by the conditions that $z = -jt$ for $w = \infty$ and $z = 0$ for $w = 0$. We find that

$$z = \frac{t}{\pi}\left(\ln\frac{w + a}{w - a} - j\pi\right),$$

from which we obtain $e^{\pi z/t}e^{j\pi} = (w + a)/(w - a)$, and finally $w/a = \tanh(\pi z/2t)$.

The constants a and k are determined by the conditions that $w = 1$ for $z = (d/2) + l$ and $w = k$ for $z = d/2$, which yields

$$\frac{1}{a} = \tanh\frac{\pi}{4t}(d + 2l), \qquad \frac{k}{a} = \tanh\frac{\pi d}{4t}.$$

Thus

$$k = \frac{\tanh(\pi d/4t)}{\tanh[\pi(d + 2l)/4t]}. \tag{4–87}$$

The complex potential F can now be obtained by mapping the shaded region of the w-plane onto the rectangular region illustrated in Fig. 4–19. The mapping function is given by Eq. (4–74) and the rectangle in the F-plane can be considered to be a section of a parallel-plate capacitor. The potential difference is $U_0 = 2K$ and the charge per unit length of the plates can be obtained with the aid of Eq. (4–70), where we replace ε_0 by ε:

$$\phi_e = q = \varepsilon(V_1 - V_2) = \varepsilon K'.$$

The capacitance per unit length is

$$C = q/U_0 = \varepsilon K'/2K. \tag{4–88}$$

We can evaluate the parameter k in terms of the given dimensions from Eq. (4–87) and determine K and K' from Eqs. (4–75) and (4–76).

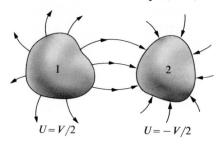

Fig. 4–27. Insulation resistance of two conductors in an infinite conducting medium.

4–12 INSULATION RESISTANCE

Let us consider two perfect conductors 1 and 2 situated in a conducting medium (Fig. 4–27). Let V be the potential difference between the conductors and let the conductivity σ be uniform. The current density is given by

$$\mathbf{J} = \sigma\mathbf{E} \tag{4–89}$$

and it follows from the equation of continuity that

$$\operatorname{div} \mathbf{J} = 0 \tag{4–90}$$

for a steady flow of charge. Substituting Eq. (4–89) into Eq. (4–90) and noting that $\mathbf{D} = \varepsilon\mathbf{E}$, we obtain

$$\operatorname{div} \mathbf{D} = \rho = 0.$$

The charge in each volume element of the conducting medium is zero, due to the fact that as much charge enters as leaves each volume element. The electric field is therefore due to the surface charges on the conductors. The total current leaving conductor 1 is

$$i = \int_{S_1} \mathbf{J} \cdot \mathbf{n}\, ds = \sigma \int_{S_1} \mathbf{E} \cdot \mathbf{n}\, ds = \frac{\sigma}{\varepsilon} \int_{S_1} \mathbf{D} \cdot \mathbf{n}\, ds = \frac{\sigma Q}{\varepsilon},$$

where Q is the charge on conductor 1. The *insulation resistance* is defined by the equation

$$R \triangleq V/i = \frac{\varepsilon V}{\sigma Q}.$$

Since $Q = CV$, where C is the capacitance, we see that

$$R = \varepsilon/\sigma C. \tag{4-91}$$

Thus the problem of determining the insulation resistance of a medium can be solved by determining the capacitance of the conductors in a non-conducting medium having the same permittivity. All the problems discussed in this chapter can be considered as problems in determining the steady current density $\mathbf{J}$ in a conducting medium. Given that σ is the conductivity of the medium, $\mathbf{J}$ is given by Eq. (4-89).

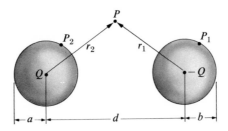

Fig. 4-28. Insulation resistance of two spherical conductors in an infinite conducting medium.

As an example of the evaluation of insulation resistance let us consider two spherical conductors embedded in an infinite conducting medium of conductivity σ and permittivity ε (Fig. 4-28). The radii of the spheres are a and b, respectively, and the distance between centers is d. We take $a \ll d$, $b \ll d$, so that, to a good approximation, we may replace the surface charges on the spheres by equivalent point charges located at the centers. The potential is given by

$$U \simeq \frac{Q}{4\pi\varepsilon}\left(\frac{1}{r_2} - \frac{1}{r_1}\right).$$

If the field point P is at P_1, we have

$$U_1 \simeq \frac{Q}{4\pi\varepsilon}\left(\frac{1}{d} - \frac{1}{b}\right),$$

and if the field point is at P_2, we have

$$U_2 = \frac{Q}{4\pi\varepsilon}\left(\frac{1}{a} - \frac{1}{d}\right).$$

The potential difference is $V = U_2 - U_1$ and the capacitance is

$$C \simeq \frac{4\pi\varepsilon}{(1/a) + (1/b) - (2/d)}.$$

It follows from Eq. (4–91) that the insulation resistance is given by

$$R \cong \frac{1}{4\pi\sigma}\left(\frac{1}{a} + \frac{1}{b} - \frac{2}{d}\right).$$

The current density within the medium is given by

$$\mathbf{J} = -\sigma \operatorname{grad} U.$$

REFERENCES

1. H. R. KAISER and P. S. CASTRO, "Capacitance between thin film conductors on a high dielectric constant substrate," *Proc. IRE*, October 1962, **50**, pages 2142–2143

2. P. N. WOLFE, "Capacitance calculation for several simple two-dimensional geometries," *Proc. IRE*, October 1962, **50**, pages 2131–2132

GENERAL REFERENCES

P. MOON and E. S. SPENCER, *Field Theory for Engineers*, New York: D. Van Nostrand, 1961

W. R. SMYTHE, *Static and Dynamic Electricity*, New York: McGraw-Hill, 1950

F. OLLENDORF, *Potentialfelder der Electrotechnik*, Berlin: Julius Springer, 1932

E. WEBER, *Electromagnetic Fields*, Volume 1, New York: John Wiley & Sons, 1950

PROBLEMS

4–1 Consider the spherical conductor and point charge discussed in Section 4–4, Example 1. For a sphere which is not grounded and whose charge is zero, determine the potential U at any field point and the surface charge density on the sphere. [*Hint:* Introduce a second image charge inside the sphere to satisfy the condition of zero charge on the sphere. Locate the image charge so that the boundary condition $U = $ const is satisfied on the sphere.] Show that the area S on the sphere which has the same polarity of surface charge density as the point charge is given by

$$S = \frac{\pi a}{d}[(d + a)^2 - d(d^2 - a^2)^{2/3}].$$

4–2 Expand Eq. (4–19) in a Taylor series in a/d and determine the percentage error for the approximate formula for C given in Problem 3–9.

4–3 An infinitely long circular cylindrical conductor of radius a is placed in a uniform electric field $\mathbf{E}_0$ which is perpendicular to the axis of the cylinder. Determine the surface charge density σ on the cylinder. Show that the magnitude of the electric field intensity at the surface of the cylinder is $2E_0 \cos \phi$, where ϕ is the angle between the unit radius vector $\mathbf{i}_r$ and $\mathbf{E}_0$.

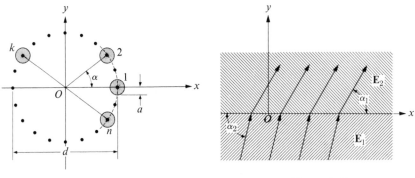

Figure 4–29   **Figure 4–30**

4–4 Consider n infinitely long cylindrical conductors of equal radii a which are uniformly spaced on a circular cylindrical surface of radius $d \gg a$ (Fig. 4–29). The conductors have a charge per unit length of q/n. Determine an approximate expression for the maximum magnitude of the electric field intensity. [*Hint:* Consider the field of conductor k to be uniform in the region around conductor 1 and use the result of Problem 4–3.]

4–5 Determine the force **F** acting on the point charge Q for the situation illustrated in Fig. 4–8(a). Can you account for the fact that the force on the image charge is not $-\mathbf{F}$?

4–6 Consider two semi-infinite dielectric media of permittivity ε_1 and ε_2, respectively, which have a common boundary at $y = 0$ (Fig. 4–30). Uniform electric field intensities exist in both regions and are given by $\mathbf{E}_1$ and $\mathbf{E}_2$. Show that $\mathbf{E}_1$ and $\mathbf{E}_2$ must be coplanar and that

$$\varepsilon_1 \tan \alpha_1 = \varepsilon_2 \tan \alpha_2.$$

4–7 Consider a uniform electric field $\mathbf{E}_0$ in an infinite medium of permittivity ε_1. Given a spherical cavity of radius a formed and filled with a medium of permittivity ε_2, determine the potential and the electric field intensity within the cavity. For a case in which $\varepsilon_1 = \varepsilon_0$, determine the depolarization factors for a cartesian coordinate system.

Consider the case in which $\varepsilon_1 = \varepsilon_0$ and $\varepsilon_2 \to \infty$. Show that the external field is the same as in the case of a spherical conductor filling the cavity. Show that the surface charge density of the conductor is equal to the polarization surface charge density of the dielectric. Are the internal fields the same? Explain.

4–8 Determine the polarization surface charge density σ_p on the interface of the dielectrics illustrated in Fig. 4–8(a). Use the two methods mentioned in Section 4–4, Example 5.

4–9 A hemispherical conductor of radius a is placed on a plane conductor (Fig. 4–31). Determine the potential U and the surface charge density σ which results from a point charge Q which is situated on the x-axis at a distance d from the origin.

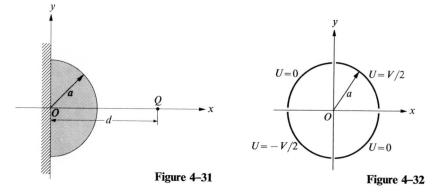

Figure 4–31   **Figure 4–32**

4–10 Consider a two-dimensional electric field in the xy-plane. The field is symmetrical about the y-axis, so that the potential has the form

$$U = f_0 + f_2 y^2 + f_4 y^4 + \cdots,$$

where $f_k \triangleq f_k(x)$. Prove that

$$f_2 = -\tfrac{1}{2} f_0^{(2)}, \qquad f_4 = \frac{1}{4!} f_0^{(4)}, \ldots,$$

where $f^{(n)}$ represents the nth derivative of f with respect to x.

4–11 Prove Poisson's integral representation for the potential $U(P)$ at a point P inside a closed surface S:

$$U(P) = \int_S -U \frac{\partial V}{\partial n}\, ds.$$

Here $V = V(P, Q)$ is the Green's function which satisfies the conditions that $V = (1/r_{PQ}) + W$ and that $V = 0$ for points Q on S. The function W is a solution of Laplace's equation which remains finite within S.

4–12 Determine Green's function for a sphere of radius a and show that

$$U(r, \theta_P, \phi_P) = \frac{a}{4\pi} \int_0^{2\pi} \int_0^{\pi} U(a, \theta_Q, \phi_Q) \frac{a^2 - r^2}{(a^2 + r^2 - 2ar \cos \gamma)^{3/2}} \sin \theta_Q\, d\theta_Q\, d\phi_Q,$$

where

$$\cos \gamma \triangleq \cos \theta_P \cos \theta_Q + \sin \theta_Q \sin \theta_P \cos (\phi_P - \phi_Q).$$

4–13 Prove the principle of inversion in spherical coordinates. If $U(r, \theta, \phi)$ is a solution of Laplace's equation in the coordinates r, θ, and ϕ, the function

$$U'(r', \theta, \phi) = \frac{a}{r'} U(a^2/r', \theta, \phi)$$

is a solution of Laplace's equation in the coordinates $r' = a^2/r$, θ, ϕ.

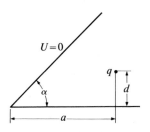

Figure 4-33   **Figure 4-34**

4-14 A capacitor is formed by splitting an infinitesimally thin conducting circular cylinder of radius a into four quadrants (Fig. 4-32). The potential distribution on the surface of the cylinder is given by

$$U(a, \phi) = \begin{cases} V/2, & 0 < \phi < \pi/2, \\ 0, & \pi/2 < \phi < \pi, 3\pi/2 < \phi < 2\pi, \\ -V/2, & \pi < \phi < 3\pi/2. \end{cases}$$

a) Use Poisson's integral (4-63) to show that the potential function for $r < a$ is

$$U = \frac{V}{2\pi}\left(\arctan\frac{2ax}{a^2 - r^2} + \arctan\frac{2ay}{a^2 - r^2}\right).$$

(b) Determine U by the separation of variables. (c) Use the principle of inversion and find U for $r > a$.

4-15 Solve Problem 4-1 by separating the variables in a spherical coordinate system.

4-16 Two plane conductors make an angle α with respect to each other and are under the influence of a line source which has a charge per unit length q (Fig. 4-33). Determine the complex potential. For what values of α can a solution be found using the method of images?

4-17 Figure 4-34 illustrates the cross section of a strip transmission line. The inner conductor of width a has negligible thickness and is symmetrically situated with respect to the outer plane conductors. Let U_0 be the potential of the inner conductor and let the outer conductors be grounded. Determine the capacitance per unit length, given that the medium has a permittivity of ε. [*Hint:* Consider a mirror image of the transmission line about the lower conductor and map the shaded region shown in the figure onto a half-plane.]

4-18 Determine the insulation resistance of a unit length of coaxial cable. The insulation has a permittivity of ε and a conductivity σ. The inner and outer conductors have radii given by a and b, respectively.

If the length of the cable is doubled, does the resistance increase or decrease? Explain.

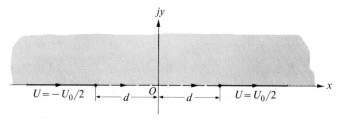

Fig. 4–35. The z-plane representation of two semi-infinite conductors with a gap of $2d$.

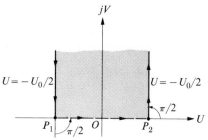

Fig. 4–36. The w-plane representation of the mapping function.

4–19   Two semi-infinite plane conductors have a gap of $2d$ between them (Fig. 4–35). The potential difference is U_0. Map the upper half of the z-plane onto the semi-infinite strip shown in Fig. 4–36, and prove that the complex potential is given by

$$F = (U_0/\pi) \arcsin (z/d).$$

CHAPTER 5

ENERGY AND FORCES IN ELECTROSTATIC FIELDS

5-1 INTRODUCTION

It was shown in Chapter 3 that the potential difference between two points P_1 and P_2 is equal to the mechanical work done in moving a positive unit point charge from P_1 to P_2 (see Eq. 3–3). We can consider that any static charge distribution results from charges being moved from infinity to their final positions in the field. Work is done in moving the charges, and since the process is reversible, we consider that the field contains energy. In this chapter we shall derive various expressions for electrostatic field energy. Furthermore, we shall also discuss forces and torques on conductors, since these are directly related to changes in field energy which result from elemental displacements.

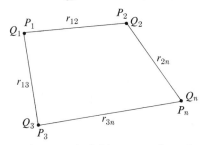

Fig. 5–1. Electrostatic field energy of n point charges.

5-2 ELECTROSTATIC FIELD ENERGY

Let us suppose that a point charge Q_1 is located in free space at a point P_1 (Fig. 5–1). The potential at a point P_2 due to Q_1 is

$$U_2 = \frac{Q_1}{4\pi\varepsilon_0 r_{12}},$$

where r_{12} is the distance between points P_1 and P_2. If a second charge Q_2 is moved from infinity to the point P_2, the mechanical work done is

$$W_2 = U_2 Q_2 = \frac{Q_1 Q_2}{4\pi\varepsilon_0 r_{12}}. \tag{5-1}$$

We can also consider the charge Q_2 as fixed and move the charge Q_1 from infinity to P_1. The work done is again W_2:

$$W_2 = U_1 Q_1 = \frac{Q_2 Q_1}{4 \pi \varepsilon_0 r_{21}}. \tag{5–2}$$

Since $r_{12} = r_{21}$, we can combine Eqs. (5–1) and (5–2) into the symmetrical form

$$W_2 = \tfrac{1}{2}(Q_1 U_1 + Q_2 U_2),$$

which can be generalized to the case of n charges:

$$W_n = \frac{1}{2} \sum_{k=1}^{n} Q_k U_k, \tag{5–3}$$

where

$$U_k \triangleq \frac{1}{4 \pi \varepsilon_0} \sum_{\substack{j=1 \\ j \neq k}}^{n} \frac{Q_j}{r_{jk}} \tag{5–4}$$

is the potential at P_k due to the $n-1$ charges Q_j $(j \neq k)$.

The most convenient proof of Eq. (5–3) is by mathematical induction. We have shown that the expression is correct for $n = 2$. Let us assume that it is correct for $n-1$ charges. When Q_n is not present, the potential at P_k due to the $n-1$ charges is given by

$$U_k - \frac{Q_n}{4 \pi \varepsilon_0 r_{kn}},$$

where U_k is defined by Eq. (5–4). Thus, since $r_{kn} = r_{nk}$,

$$2W_{n-1} = \sum_{k=1}^{n-1} \left(U_k - \frac{Q_n}{4 \pi \varepsilon_0 r_{kn}} \right) Q_k = \sum_{k=1}^{n-1} Q_k U_k - Q_n U_n.$$

If we now bring the charge Q_n from infinity to the position P_n, the field energy is increased by the amount $Q_n U_n$. Thus

$$W_n = W_{n-1} + Q_n U_n = \frac{1}{2} \sum_{k=1}^{n-1} Q_k U_k + \tfrac{1}{2} Q_n U_n,$$

which establishes the validity of Eq. (5–3) for all n.

When the charge distribution is continuous, we can consider the charge $\rho \, \Delta v$ within a volume element Δv to be concentrated as a point charge within the volume element. Thus, letting W_e represent the electrostatic field energy, we have

$$W_e = \lim_{\Delta v \to 0} \frac{1}{2} \sum \rho U \, \Delta v = \frac{1}{2} \int_v \rho U \, dv. \tag{5–5}$$

In Eq. (5–5) it is possible to express ρ and U in terms of $\mathbf{D}$ and $\mathbf{E}$, thus yielding an alternative expression for W_e. This expression is obtained with the aid of the vector identity

$$\nabla \cdot (-U\mathbf{E}) = \nabla \cdot (U \nabla U) = \nabla U \cdot \nabla U + U \nabla^2 U = \mathbf{E} \cdot \mathbf{E} - \frac{\rho}{\varepsilon_0} U.$$

Here we have made use of Poisson's equation (4–3). Substituting $\mathbf{D} = \varepsilon_0 \mathbf{E}$ and making use of the vector identity, we obtain

$$\int_v \rho U \, dv = \int_v \mathbf{D} \cdot \mathbf{E} \, dv + \varepsilon_0 \int_v \nabla \cdot (U\mathbf{E}) \, dv$$

$$= \int_v \mathbf{D} \cdot \mathbf{E} \, dv + \varepsilon_0 \int_S U\mathbf{E} \cdot \mathbf{n} \, ds, \tag{5–6}$$

where S is the surface that bounds the volume v. Here we have made use of the divergence theorem to obtain the surface integral. In general, in order for S to enclose the entire field, we must choose a sphere with an infinitely large radius (the infinite sphere). If the field point P is sufficiently far removed from the charges, it follows from Eq. (4–4) that (see Fig. 5–2)

$$U \cong \frac{1}{4\pi\varepsilon_0 r} \int_v \rho \, dv = \frac{Q}{4\pi\varepsilon_0 r}.$$

The charge distribution appears as a point charge, and we have the following bounds as $r \to \infty$:

$$E \leqq c_1/r^2, \quad \left| \int_S U\mathbf{E} \cdot \mathbf{n} \, ds \right| \leqq \frac{c_2}{r^3} \int_S ds = 4\pi c_2/r, \tag{5–7}$$

where c_1 and c_2 are positive constants. Thus, if $r \to \infty$, the surface integral in Eq. (5–6) vanishes and we obtain

$$W_e = \tfrac{1}{2} \int_v \rho U \, dv = \tfrac{1}{2} \int_v \mathbf{D} \cdot \mathbf{E} \, dv. \tag{5–8}$$

Equation (5–8) can be shown to remain valid if a dielectric is present. In order to prove this, we must determine the work done in polarizing the dielectric (see Problem 5–1).

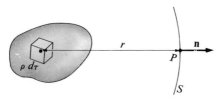

Fig. 5–2. Potential of a finite distribution of charge for large r.

In the derivation of Eq. (5–8) we have assumed that we have a volume distribution of charge. However, in the case of conductors, we have a surface distribution of charge. Equation (5–8) may be applied to a conductor surface if we take $dv = h\,ds$ as the volume element and define

$$\sigma \stackrel{\triangle}{=} \lim_{h \to 0} \rho h$$

as the surface charge density, so that $\sigma\,ds = \rho\,dv$. Equation (5–8) now takes the form

$$W_e = \tfrac{1}{2} \int_S \sigma U\,ds. \tag{5–9}$$

Let us apply Eq. (5–9) to the case of two conductors 1 and 2 charged to potentials U_1 and U_2, respectively. The surface S in Eq. (5–9) now consists of the two surfaces S_1 and S_2. Thus

$$W_e = \frac{U_2}{2} \int_{S_2} \sigma\,ds + \frac{U_1}{2} \int_{S_1} \sigma\,ds = \tfrac{1}{2}(U_2 - U_1)Q = \frac{QV}{2}, \tag{5–10}$$

where Q is the charge on conductor 2 and V is the potential difference. Equation (5–10) may also be derived by a more elementary consideration. Let the capacitance of the conductors be C and the potential difference v. When an element of charge dq is moved from conductor 1 to conductor 2, the mechanical work done is

$$dW_{\text{mech}} = v\,dq = \frac{1}{C} q\,dq.$$

Thus, integrating from an initial state $q = 0$ to a final state $q = Q$, we obtain

$$W_{\text{mech}} = Q^2/2C = QV/2.$$

It is possible to interpret the integral in Eq. (5–8) in the following manner. When we have a parallel-plate capacitor of unit area, we can find the electrostatic field energy by the preceding consideration; it is given by Eq. (5–10). Since $Q = D$ and $V = Ed$, we obtain (Fig. 5–3)

$$W_e = \frac{DEd}{2},$$

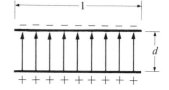

Fig. 5–3. Field energy of a parallel-plate capacitor.

and the *energy density per unit volume* is

$$\tfrac{1}{2}\mathbf{D} \cdot \mathbf{E}. \tag{5–11}$$

In the case of a general electrostatic field, we can take a family of equipotential surfaces spaced a small distance apart extending over the complete field (Fig. 5–4). We consider the equipotential surfaces as conductors and assign a surface charge density $\sigma = \mathbf{D} \cdot \mathbf{n}$ to both the upper and lower sides of the surface. In terms of the original field nothing is changed, since the surface charges cancel each other. However, we can consider the volume elements bounded by the surfaces as parallel-plate capacitors whose energy density is given by Eq. (5–11). Integrating over the field yields Eq. (5–8). This interpretation of the field energy allows us to interpret the expression (5–11) as representing an energy density.

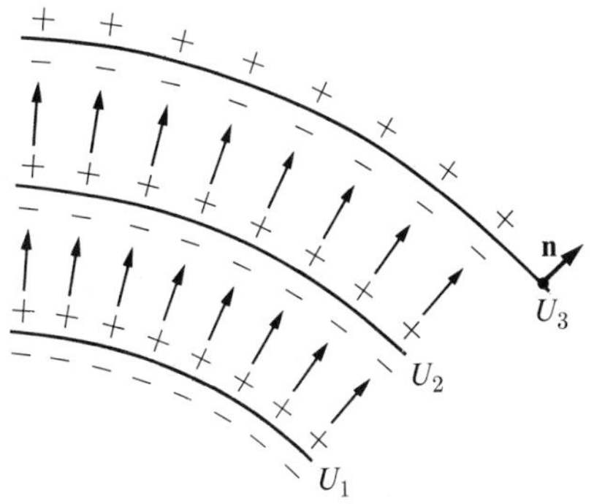

Fig. 5–4. Field energy of a general electrostatic field.

5–3 FORCES AND TORQUES IN AN ELECTROSTATIC FIELD

A problem of considerable practical importance is the evaluation of the force and torque acting on a charged conductor under the influence of an electric field. Consider the two charged conductors illustrated in Fig. 5–5. In principle, we can determine the force $\mathbf{F}$ by applying Coulomb's law to the elements of surface charge and then integrating over both surfaces. This approach is appealing in that the forces are physically evident. However, the integration is mathematically complicated and an energy method is usually more suitable. The energy method is based on the evaluation of the energy change caused by an elemental displacement of the system.

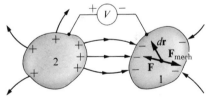

Fig. 5–5. Forces between charged conductors.

Consider the conductor 1 shown in Fig. 5–5. A mechanical force $\mathbf{F}_{\mathrm{mech}} = -\mathbf{F}$ is required to hold conductor 1 in a state of rest. Let us consider the case in which the conductors have been charged by a battery and the battery removed. For an elemental displacement $d\mathbf{r}$ of conductor 1 we have $Q = \mathrm{const}$, and the mechanical work done is

$$dW_{\mathrm{mech}} = \mathbf{F}_{\mathrm{mech}} \cdot d\mathbf{r} = -\mathbf{F} \cdot d\mathbf{r}.$$

The change in field energy is

$$dW_e = dW_{\mathrm{mech}} = \mathrm{grad}\, W_e \cdot d\mathbf{r}.$$

Thus $(\text{grad } W_e + \mathbf{F}) \cdot d\mathbf{r} = 0$. Since $d\mathbf{r}$ is arbitrary we must have

$$\mathbf{F} = -\text{grad } W_e, \qquad Q = \text{const.} \tag{5-12}$$

If we substitute Eq. (5-10) into Eq. (5-12) and note that

$$\frac{\partial}{\partial u}\left(\frac{1}{C}\right) = -\frac{1}{C^2}\frac{\partial C}{\partial u}, \qquad u = x, y, z,$$

we obtain

$$\mathbf{F} = -\frac{Q^2}{2}\text{grad}\frac{1}{C} = \frac{V^2}{2}\text{grad } C. \tag{5-13}$$

In computing the gradient in Eq. (5-13), we consider the capacitance to be a function of the position of the conductor.

The force $\mathbf{F}$ does not depend on the manner in which we evaluate it. Equation (5-13) can also be derived if we consider that the battery remains connected during the displacement. The energy relations are then different, since the battery also does work. For a displacement $d\mathbf{r}$ the change in field energy is

$$dW_e = dW_{\text{mech}} + dW_b, \tag{5-14}$$

where $dW_b = V\,dQ$ is the work done by the battery and dQ is the charge transferred from conductor 1 to conductor 2. It follows from Eq. (5-10) that if $V = \text{const}$, then $dW_e = (V/2)\,dQ$. We see that $dW_b = 2dW_e$. Substituting into Eq. (5-14) yields

$$dW_e = -dW_{\text{mech}} = \mathbf{F} \cdot d\mathbf{r} = \text{grad } W_e \cdot d\mathbf{r}.$$

Thus

$$\mathbf{F} = \text{grad } W_e, \qquad V = \text{const.} \tag{5-15}$$

Note that the forces given by Eqs. (5-12) and (5-15) are identical. However, the condition under which the gradient is to be computed differs. This is made evident if we substitute

$$W_e = QV/2 = V^2C/2$$

into Eq. (5-15). We obtain $\mathbf{F} = (V^2/2)\text{grad } C$, which is identical to Eq. (5-13).

The torque $\mathbf{T}$ acting on a conductor can be found in a similar manner. A mechanical torque $\mathbf{T}_{\text{mech}}$ must be applied to prevent the conductor from rotating. Let us consider an elemental rotation $d\theta$ about a fixed axis and take $Q = \text{const}$. The mechanical work done is

$$dW_{\text{mech}} = T_{\text{mech}}\,d\theta = -T\,d\theta$$

and the change in field energy is

$$dW_e = dW_{\text{mech}} = \frac{\partial W_e}{\partial \theta}\,d\theta.$$

Thus
$$T = - \frac{\partial W_e}{\partial \theta}, \qquad Q = \text{const.}$$

If $V = \text{const}$ it can be shown that

$$T = \frac{\partial W_e}{\partial \theta}, \qquad V = \text{const.} \qquad (5\text{--}16)$$

As an example of Eq. (5–12), let us compute the force acting on the plates of a parallel-plate capacitor. The capacitance of a parallel-plate capacitor of area A, permittivity ε_0, and spacing x is $C = A\varepsilon_0/x$. The force in the direction of increasing x can be determined from Eq. (5–13):

$$F_x = \frac{V^2}{2} \frac{\partial C}{\partial x} = - \frac{V^2 C}{2x}.$$

The minus sign indicates that the force is one of attraction. Note that we consider x to be negligible compared with the dimensions of the plate so that we can neglect the fringing field at the edges. The computed force is, therefore, correct only for a section of area A of an infinite parallel-plate capacitor. However, for most practical applications, the error is negligible.

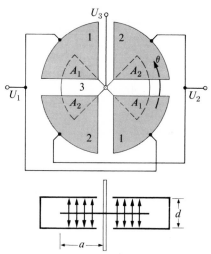

Fig. 5–6. A four-quadrant electrometer.

As an example of Eq. (5–16), consider Fig. 5–6, which illustrates a four-quadrant electrometer. The quadrants consist of conducting plates and are connected in pairs as shown. The potential of pair 1 is U_1 and that of pair 2 is U_2. The center vane is at a potential U_3 and is in equilibrium between the torque resulting from the electrical forces and the mechanical restoring torque due to the suspension. Equation (5–16) will be used to determine an expression for the angular deflection θ in terms of the applied potentials. It should be noted that the torque results from the force between the charges at the edges of the conductors. Thus a fringing field is essential to obtain a force (Fig. 5–7). It is evident that the computation of the torque on the basis of Coulomb's law would be extremely complicated. The energy method is simpler, since an elemental displacement does not change the fringing field, and hence this field need not be considered in computing the torque with the aid of Eq. (5–16). The change in field energy results from the change in the uniform part of the field which can be approximated by a parallel-plate capacitor field and is easily evaluated.

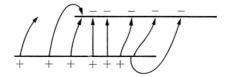

Fig. 5–7. Electrostatic forces in an electrometer.

The vane forms parallel-plate capacitors with the quadrants. Thus the capacitance of pair 1 and the vane is

$$C_1 = 4 \frac{\varepsilon_0 A_1}{d}$$

and the field energy is

$$W_1 = \frac{4\varepsilon_0 A_1}{d} (U_3 - U_1)^2.$$

The field energy due to pair 2 and the vane results in a similar expression, and the total field energy is

$$W = \frac{4\varepsilon_0}{d} [(U_3 - U_1)^2 A_1 + (U_3 - U_2)^2 A_2].$$

We obtain the torque by noting that $\partial A_2 / \partial \theta = a^2/2 = -\partial A_1 / \partial \theta$ and applying Eq. (5–16). Thus

$$T = \frac{\partial W}{\partial \theta} = \frac{2\varepsilon_0 a^2}{d} (U_2 - U_1)(U_1 + U_2 - 2U_3).$$

The mechanical torque, which is proportional to the angular displacement, is negatively directed, so that $T_{\text{mech}} = -k\theta = -T$, and we obtain the desired formula:

$$\theta = \frac{2\varepsilon_0 a^2}{kd} (U_2 - U_1)(U_1 + U_2 - 2U_3). \tag{5–17}$$

5-4 PERTURBATION OF ELECTROSTATIC FIELD ENERGY

In many technical measurements we are interested in the perturbing effect of a small material body on the electromagnetic field. It is fortunate that we can solve this problem by use of the divergence theorem and a vector identity. To derive the desired perturbation formula, we consider two fields ε_1, $\mathbf{D}_1$, $\mathbf{E}_1$, U_1, and ε_2, $\mathbf{D}_2$, $\mathbf{E}_2$, U_2 resulting from the same charge distribution $\rho_1 = \rho_2 = \rho$. We take $\varepsilon_1 = \varepsilon_2$, with the exception of a volume v_m where $\varepsilon_1 \neq \varepsilon_2$. We wish to determine an expression for the change in field energy resulting from changing the permittivity of the volume v_m from ε_1 to ε_2 under the condition that the free charges remain fixed. The difference in field energy is

$$\Delta W \triangleq W_2 - W_1 = \tfrac{1}{2} \int_v (\mathbf{D}_2 \cdot \mathbf{E}_2 - \mathbf{D}_1 \cdot \mathbf{E}_1)\, dv$$

$$= \tfrac{1}{2} \int_v (\mathbf{E}_2 + \mathbf{E}_1) \cdot (\mathbf{D}_2 - \mathbf{D}_1)\, dv$$

$$+ \tfrac{1}{2} \int_v (\mathbf{D}_1 \cdot \mathbf{E}_2 - \mathbf{D}_2 \cdot \mathbf{E}_1)\, dv.$$

We shall show that under the assumed conditions the first integral, I, on the right-hand side of the above expression is zero. Thus

$$\Delta W = \tfrac{1}{2} \int_v (\varepsilon_1 - \varepsilon_2)\mathbf{E}_1 \cdot \mathbf{E}_2\, dv = \tfrac{1}{2} \int_{v_m} \left(\frac{1}{\varepsilon_2} - \frac{1}{\varepsilon_1}\right) \mathbf{D}_1 \cdot \mathbf{D}_2\, dv. \quad (5\text{–}18)$$

We can restrict the range of integration to the volume v_m, since $\varepsilon_1 = \varepsilon_2$ for points outside v_m. Equation (5–18) is the desired perturbation formula.

To prove that the integral I is zero, we set

$$U \triangleq U_1 + U_2, \qquad \mathbf{E} \triangleq \mathbf{E}_1 + \mathbf{E}_2 = -\operatorname{grad} U, \qquad \mathbf{D} \triangleq \mathbf{D}_2 - \mathbf{D}_1,$$

and note that div $\mathbf{D} = \rho_2 - \rho_1 = 0$. With the aid of the vector identity

$$\mathbf{\nabla} \cdot (U\mathbf{D}) = U\mathbf{\nabla} \cdot \mathbf{D} + \mathbf{D} \cdot \mathbf{\nabla}U = \mathbf{D} \cdot \mathbf{\nabla}U,$$

we obtain

$$\mathbf{E} \cdot \mathbf{D} = -\mathbf{D} \cdot \mathbf{\nabla}U = -\mathbf{\nabla} \cdot (U\mathbf{D}).$$

The divergence theorem yields

$$\int_v \mathbf{E} \cdot \mathbf{D}\, dv = -\int_S U\mathbf{D} \cdot \mathbf{n}\, ds. \quad (5\text{–}19)$$

The integral vanishes if we choose the infinite sphere for S (see Eq. 5–7). In the above derivation we have assumed that the charge density ρ is a piecewise continuous function of position. The case in which a conductor is present requires a separate discussion, since there is then a surface charge density and ρ is infinite. In the case of conductors, Eq. (5–18) will remain valid if we specify that the conductor charge Q is unaffected by the perturbation. This is accomplished by removing the voltage source from the conductors. The proof is established by noting that on a conductor S_c both U_1 and U_2 are constant. Thus $U = U_c = $ const and since $Q_1 = Q_2 = Q$, we have

$$\int_{S_c} U \mathbf{D} \cdot \mathbf{n} \, ds = U_c(Q_2 - Q_1) = 0.$$

To illustrate Eq. (5–18), let us determine the change in the capacitance of two conductors due to the introduction of a small dielectric sphere of radius a into the field at a point P (Fig. 5–8). The permittivity of the sphere is $\varepsilon_2 = \varepsilon$ and the conductors are originally in free space ($\varepsilon_1 = \varepsilon_0$). Since the sphere is small we can consider it to be situated in a uniform primary field $\mathbf{E}_1 = \mathbf{E}_1(P)$ which results in a uniform field $\mathbf{E}_2$ within the sphere. We determine the change in capacitance by computing the change in field energy under the condition that the charge on the conductors remains constant. Equation (5–18) yields

$$\Delta W = \left(\frac{1}{\varepsilon} - \frac{1}{\varepsilon_0}\right)\frac{2\pi a^3}{3} \mathbf{D}_1 \cdot \mathbf{D}_2.$$

The electric flux density within the sphere (see Problem 4–7) is given by

$$\mathbf{D}_2 = \frac{3\varepsilon_r}{2 + \varepsilon_r} \mathbf{D}_1. \tag{5–20}$$

Thus

$$\Delta W = 2\frac{1 - \varepsilon_r}{2 + \varepsilon_r} \pi\varepsilon_0 a^3 E_1^2.$$

The change in capacitance can be found from the equation (note that $Q = $ const)

$$W_2 = \frac{Q^2}{2(C + \Delta C)} = W_1 + \Delta W.$$

This yields $\Delta W \cong -(V^2/2)\,\Delta C$, where V is the potential difference between the conductors. Thus

$$\Delta C \cong 4\frac{\varepsilon_r - 1}{\varepsilon_r + 2} \pi\varepsilon_0 a \left(\frac{aE_1}{V}\right)^2.$$

If the sphere is a conductor we can let $\varepsilon_r \to \infty$ and obtain

$$\Delta C \cong 4\pi\varepsilon_0 a \left(\frac{aE_1}{V}\right)^2. \tag{5–21}$$

We can find the justification for this by solving Problem 4–7. The polarization surface charge density on the dielectric sphere is equal to the surface charge density on the spherical conductor, so that the external fields are the same. The internal fields are not the same, since we have an electric flux density

$D_2 = 3D_1$ in the dielectric sphere (see Eq. 5–20).   However, the energy
density within the dielectric sphere is, as $\varepsilon \to \infty$,

$$\tfrac{1}{2}\mathbf{D}_2 \cdot \mathbf{E}_2 = \frac{3D_1}{2}\frac{3D_1}{\varepsilon} \to 0,$$

and thus contributes nothing to the final result.

Note that Eq. (5–21) gives us a relation between E_1 and ΔC.   Thus we
could measure the field intensity at P_1 by measuring the change in capacitance.
Practical measurements of this kind are performed at microwave frequencies
to determine the electric field intensities within cavities (see Section 10–10).

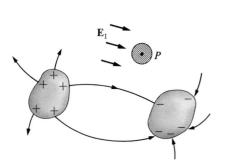

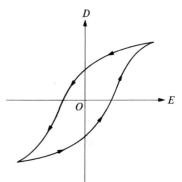

Fig. 5–8. Perturbation of an electric
field due to a small dielectric sphere.

Fig. 5–9. Hysteresis loop for a
dielectric.

5–5 HYSTERESIS IN DIELECTRICS

We have assumed up until now that permittivity is a function of position
but that it is independent of the electric field intensity.   This is a good approximation for many dielectric materials.   However, in general, permittivity is a
function of $\mathbf{E}$.   Figure 5–9 illustrates a typical functional relationship between
D and E for a periodic variation of E.   The loop shown in the figure is known
as a *hysteresis loop* and a consequence of this type of behavior is that the
dielectric absorbs energy from the field in an irreversible manner.

To discuss the energy absorption, let us consider the parallel-plate
capacitor of area A shown in Fig. 5–10.   The work done by a battery in trans-
ferring a charge dq from the lower plate to the upper plate is $dW = v\,dq$,

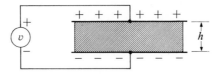

Fig. 5–10. A parallel-plate capacitor for which $D = D(E)$ is given by Fig. 5–9.

where $v = Eh$ is the potential difference. The magnitude of the electric flux density is $D = q/A$. Thus $dW = AhE \cdot dD$. Integrating over one cycle yields

$$w/Ah = \oint_C E \cdot dD,$$

which is equal to the energy dissipation per unit volume per cycle. The integral is equal to the area of the hysteresis loop shown in Fig. 5–9.

PROBLEMS

5–1 Let $P_1 = Qx$ represent the magnitude of the dipole moment of two charges Q and $-Q$ which are a small distance x apart. Show that the work done in moving Q a distance dx in a field E is $dW_1 = E \cdot dP_1$. Determine W_1 for the case in which P_1 is proportional to E. Apply this result to the case of a dielectric in which there is a continuous distribution of dipoles and show that the work done on the dielectric as the field is gradually increased from $E = 0$ to its final value is given by

$$W_d = \tfrac{1}{2} \int_v P \cdot E \, dv.$$

The work done in moving free charges from infinity to their final position is given by Eq. (5–8), where $D = \varepsilon_0 E$. Combine this result with W_d and show that Eq. (5–8) is applicable to a field containing dielectrics where $D = \varepsilon E$.

5–2 Determine the force between the conductors of an infinitely long straight two-wire transmission line. The potential difference is V, both radii are equal to a, and the distance between centers is d. Take $a \ll d$.

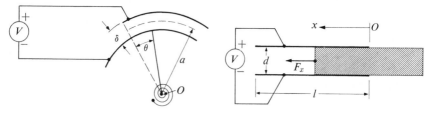

Figure 5–11   **Figure 5–12**

5–3 Figure 5–11 illustrates the cross-sectional view of a simple electrostatic voltmeter. Two cylindrical plates of width h have a small radial distance δ between them. A potential difference V is applied and the inner plate rotates about the axis O until a state of equilibrium is reached between the electrical torque and the mechanical torque, $T_{\text{mech}} = -k\theta$, resulting from a spring. Given that $\delta = 0.2$ cm, $a = 5$ cm, $h = 1$ cm, $V = 1000$ volts, and $\theta = 45°$, determine the spring constant k.

5–4 A parallel-plate capacitor has plates of width w and length l, and the spacing between plates is d. A dielectric slab with the same dimensions has a permittivity of ε and is introduced into the capacitor as shown in Fig. 5–12. Determine the force F_x for a potential difference of V. Take $d \ll x$ so that edge effects can be neglected.

5–5 A coaxial cable has an inner radius of a and outer radius of b and the dielectric has a permittivity of ε. An infinitely long straight conducting wire of radius $c \ll a$ is placed in the dielectric parallel to the cable axis. The distance between centers is r. Determine the change in capacitance per unit length due to the wire.

5–6 Consider an electric field which has the direction of the x-axis and in which $E_x = E_0 + fx$. A dielectric sphere of radius a and permittivity ε is placed at $x = 0$. Assume that $|af| \ll |E_0|$, and determine an approximate expression for the force acting on the sphere. [*Hint:* Apply Eqs. (5–18) and (5–20) when the center of the sphere is at $x = 0$ and at $x = \Delta x$. Determine the change in field energy due to the displacement Δx, and from this determine the force.]

5–7 The parallel-plate capacitor discussed in Problem 3–6 has a permittivity which is a linear function of the distance to the lower plate. Use Eq. (5–8) to determine the field energy and the capacitance. Evaluate the force of attraction between the plates.

CHAPTER 6

THE MAGNETOSTATIC FIELD

6–1 INTRODUCTION

The equations for static electric and magnetic fields are obtained by neglecting the derivatives with respect to time in Eqs. (2–46), and in conjunction with Eqs. (2–47) they lead to the following set of equations.

Electrostatics: $\text{curl } \mathbf{E} = 0,$

$\text{div } \mathbf{D} = \rho.$

Magnetostatics: $\text{curl } \mathbf{H} = \mathbf{J},$ (6–1a)

$\text{div } \mathbf{B} = 0.$ (6–1b)

Static electric and magnetic fields can be discussed separately, since there is no interaction between them. Equations (6–1) do not have to be restricted to zero frequency and can be used even at high frequencies. The condition, discussed briefly in Section 3–1, is that the physical dimensions of the system must be small compared with the wavelength (see Eq. 3–1). We have seen in Section 3–2 that the circulation of the electric field intensity $\mathbf{E}$ is zero and that $\mathbf{E}$ can be expressed as the negative gradient of a scalar electric potential. The scalar source for the electric flux density $\mathbf{D}$ is the charge density ρ. Equations (6–1) show that there is a fundamental difference between electric and magnetic fields. In general, the circulation of the magnetic field intensity $\mathbf{H}$ is nonzero and the vector source of the circulation is the current density $\mathbf{J}$. The scalar source for the magnetic flux density $\mathbf{B}$ is zero. We shall see that the vector $\mathbf{B}$ can be expressed as the curl of a vector potential. In a source-free region of space, $\mathbf{J} = 0$, $\rho = 0$, and the electrostatic and magnetostatic equations become similar. We can then express $\mathbf{H}$ as the negative gradient of a magnetic scalar potential. We shall see, therefore, that there are two possible representations for the magnetic field: one is in terms of a vector potential and the second in terms of a scalar potential. Both representations are useful. We shall discuss the vector potential formulation first, since it is of fundamental significance.

6–2 THE VECTOR POTENTIAL

When the current density $\mathbf{J}$ is a known function of position, we can solve Eqs. (6–1) to obtain $\mathbf{H}$ and $\mathbf{B}$. To find the solution, we first note that Eq.

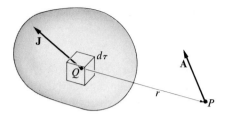

Fig. 6–1. The vector potential of a current distribution.

(6–1b) is satisfied if we choose (see Eq. 1–62)

$$\mathbf{B} = \operatorname{curl} \mathbf{A}. \tag{6–2}$$

The vector $\mathbf{A}$ is called the *vector potential*. Let us assume that the medium in which $\mathbf{J}$ exists has the permeability of free space. Thus $\mathbf{H} = \mathbf{B}/\mu_0$, and Eq. (6–1a) yields $\mathbf{\nabla} \times (\mathbf{\nabla} \times \mathbf{A}) = \mu_0 \mathbf{J}$. Thus (see Eq. 1–116)

$$\mathbf{\nabla}(\mathbf{\nabla} \cdot \mathbf{A}) - \mathbf{\nabla}^2 \mathbf{A} = \mu_0 \mathbf{J}. \tag{6–3}$$

Equation (6–3) is a formidable-looking partial differential equation for $\mathbf{A}$. However, the vector $\mathbf{A}$ is not uniquely defined by Eq. (6–2) and we can impose a further condition on $\mathbf{A}$. In order to simplify Eq. (6–3), let us try to choose $\mathbf{A}$ so that

$$\mathbf{\nabla} \cdot \mathbf{A} = 0. \tag{6–4}$$

It then follows that $\mathbf{A}$ must satisfy the vector form of Poisson's equation,

$$\mathbf{\nabla}^2 \mathbf{A} = -\mu_0 \mathbf{J}.$$

The x-component of this equation is

$$\mathbf{\nabla}^2 A_x = -\mu_0 J_x,$$

which is Poisson's equation, the solution of which (see Eq. 1–75) is

$$A_x = \frac{\mu_0}{4\pi} \int_v \frac{J_x}{r}\, dv.$$

For the y- and z-components, we find similar expressions. Thus, in vector form, we have

$$\mathbf{A} = \frac{\mu_0}{4\pi} \int_v \frac{\mathbf{J}}{r}\, dv. \tag{6–5}$$

We can see that the condition (6–4) allows us to solve for $\mathbf{A}$ in a relatively simple manner. However, we must now verify that the vector $\mathbf{A}$ given by Eq. (6–5) does satisfy this condition. Let us consider Fig. 6–1, in which P is the field point at which $\mathbf{A}$ is evaluated and Q is a source point. (The vector source for the field is the current density **J**, which is a function of Q.) We have

$$r^2 = (x_P - x_Q)^2 + (y_P - y_Q)^2 + (z_P - z_Q)^2.$$

The divergence operation in Eq. (6–4) is taken with respect to the coordinates of the point P. To distinguish between differentiations with respect to P and Q we introduce a subscript on ∇ which corresponds to that on the coordinates. This was discussed in Section 1–16, where it was shown that

$$\nabla_P U = -\nabla_Q U, \tag{6–6}$$

where $U = U(r)$. If we apply $\nabla_P \cdot$ to Eq. (6–5) we can carry out the differentiations under the integral sign. In the integrand Q and therefore **J** are fixed so that $\nabla_P \cdot$ operates only on $1/r$. Thus

$$\nabla_P \cdot \mathbf{A} = \frac{\mu_0}{4\pi} \int_v \mathbf{J} \cdot \nabla_P (1/r)\, dv = -\frac{\mu_0}{4\pi} \int_v \mathbf{J} \cdot \nabla_Q (1/r)\, dv. \tag{6–7}$$

We shall now apply the divergence theorem to Eq. (6–7); it is for this reason that we introduced Eq. (6–6). To apply the divergence theorem requires introducing the vector identity

$$\nabla_Q \cdot (\mathbf{J}/r) = \mathbf{J} \cdot \nabla_Q (1/r) + (1/r)\nabla_Q \cdot \mathbf{J}. \tag{6–8}$$

Since $\partial \rho / \partial t = 0$, it follows from the equation of continuity that $\nabla_Q \cdot \mathbf{J} = 0$. Substituting Eq. (6–8) into Eq. (6–7) and applying the divergence theorem yields

$$\nabla_P \cdot \mathbf{A} = -\frac{\mu_0}{4\pi} \int_S \frac{\mathbf{J} \cdot \mathbf{n}}{r}\, ds. \tag{6–9}$$

In all physical situations the current is limited to flow in a finite region of space. Thus, if we choose the infinite sphere for S, we have $\mathbf{J} = 0$ on S and condition (6–4) is fulfilled. We can also consider the ideal case of a transmission line extending to infinity or of surface currents on conductors. In the case of a transmission line the integral (6–9) vanishes because of the $1/r$ term in the integrand. In the case of surface currents we have $\mathbf{J} \cdot \mathbf{n} = 0$. Thus we see that, whatever physical situation we wish to consider, condition (6–4) is fulfilled.

In many practical situations the current is constrained to flow along thin conducting wires. We designate this type of current flow as a *current filament*. Let a be the cross-sectional area of the conducting wire and i be the total current (Fig. 6–2). We have

$$i = Ja, \qquad i\, d\mathbf{r} = \mathbf{J}\, dv,$$

where $dv = a\, dr$ is the volume element. The volume integral in Eq. (6–5)

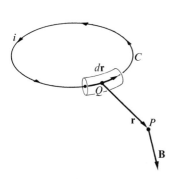

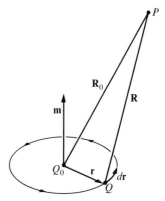

Fig. 6–2. A current filament.

Fig. 6–3. The vector potential of a small current loop.

can now be replaced by a contour integral taken along the filament axis C:

$$\mathbf{A} = \frac{\mu_0 i}{4\pi} \oint_C \frac{d\mathbf{r}}{r}. \tag{6–10}$$

As an example of Eq. (6–10), let us determine an expression for the vector potential of a current distribution which forms small closed loops. We can consider the current distribution as consisting of elementary current filaments, one of which is illustrated in Fig. 6–3. Since we take the dimensions of the filament to be small compared with R (see Eq. 1–6, where we assume that $U = 1/R$ and replace $d\mathbf{r}$ by $\mathbf{r}$), we have

$$\frac{1}{R} \cong \frac{1}{R_0} + \operatorname{grad} \frac{1}{R_0} \cdot \mathbf{r},$$

where $R^2 = (x_P - x_Q)^2 + (y_P - y_Q)^2 + (z_P - z_Q)^2$ and where Q_0 is an arbitrary fixed point within the current distribution. The gradient is to be taken with respect to Q. Thus

$$\operatorname{grad} \frac{1}{R_0} = \frac{\mathbf{R}_0}{R_0^3}.$$

Substituting into Eq. (6–10) and noting that for a closed filament $\oint_C d\mathbf{r} = 0$, we obtain

$$\mathbf{A} = \frac{\mu_0 i}{4\pi R_0^3} \oint_C (\mathbf{R}_0 \cdot \mathbf{r}) \, d\mathbf{r}.$$

We now make use of the vector identity

$$-\mathbf{R}_0 \times (\mathbf{r} \times d\mathbf{r}) = -(\mathbf{R}_0 \cdot d\mathbf{r})\mathbf{r} + (\mathbf{R}_0 \cdot \mathbf{r}) \, d\mathbf{r}$$

$$= -d[(\mathbf{R}_0 \cdot \mathbf{r})\mathbf{r}] + 2(\mathbf{R}_0 \cdot \mathbf{r}) \, d\mathbf{r}.$$

If this expression is integrated along C, the first term on the right-hand side yields zero, since the initial and final values are identical. Thus we obtain the result that

$$\mathbf{A} = \frac{\mu_0}{4\pi R_0^3} \mathbf{m} \times \mathbf{R}_0, \tag{6–11}$$

where

$$\mathbf{m} \triangleq \tfrac{1}{2} \oint_C \mathbf{r} \times (i \, d\mathbf{r}) \tag{6–12}$$

is defined as the *magnetic dipole moment*. When the filament lies in a plane, m is equal to the product of the area enclosed by the contour and the current. The vector $\mathbf{m}$ is normal to the plane and forms a right-handed system with respect to the direction of current flow.

Having obtained the dipole moment of a single current filament, we can now obtain the dipole moment of a volume distribution of current. The volume is considered to be composed of n tubes of current of cross-sectional area a. Each tube of current is replaced by a current filament defined by a contour C_k which forms a streamline for the current density $\mathbf{J}$. We assume that $i \, d\mathbf{r} = \mathbf{J} \, \Delta v$, where $\Delta v = a \, dr$, and obtain

$$\mathbf{m} = \lim_{\Delta v \to 0} \sum_{k=1}^{n} \tfrac{1}{2} \oint_{C_k} \mathbf{r} \times \mathbf{J} \, \Delta v = \tfrac{1}{2} \int_v \mathbf{r} \times \mathbf{J} \, dv.$$

Note that, when we are computing the limit, we first form the sum of all volume elements along a tube of current and then form the sum of all current tubes. The summation is therefore over all volume elements and the limit of the sum is, by definition, the volume integral.

6–3 THE BIOT-SAVART LAW

The magnetic flux density can be determined from Eq. (6–2), where $\mathbf{A}$ is given by Eq. (6–5), and in the case of current filaments by Eq. (6–10). In the case of a current filament, the resulting equation for $\mathbf{B}$ in terms of $\mathbf{J}$ yields an expression which, for historical reasons, is called the *Biot-Savart law*. We have

$$\mathbf{B} = \nabla_P \times \frac{\mu_0 i}{4\pi} \oint_C \frac{d\mathbf{r}}{r} = \frac{\mu_0 i}{4\pi} \oint_C \nabla_P \frac{1}{r} \times d\mathbf{r} = \frac{\mu_0 i}{4\pi} \oint_C d\mathbf{r} \times \frac{\mathbf{r}}{r^3}, \tag{6–13}$$

where $\mathbf{r}$ is a vector directed from the source point Q to the field point P. Equation (6–13) allows us to define the differential of $\mathbf{B}$ by the following form:

$$d\mathbf{B} \triangleq \frac{\mu_0 i}{4\pi} \frac{d\mathbf{r} \times \mathbf{r}_1}{r^2}, \tag{6–14}$$

where $\mathbf{r}_1 \triangleq \mathbf{r}/r$ is a unit vector. The expression given by Eq. (6–14) is the Biot-Savart law. It states that the vectors $d\mathbf{r}$, $\mathbf{r}_1$ and $d\mathbf{B}$ form a right-handed system (the so called right-hand rule) and that the magnitude of the magnetic flux density resulting from a current element $i\,d\mathbf{r}$ is given by (Fig. 6–4)

$$dB = \frac{\mu_0 i}{4\pi}\frac{dr\sin\theta}{r^2}.$$

An isolated current element of the form referred to by the Biot-Savart law can be considered to result from the movement of charge along a line segment. Since the ends of the segment become charged (due to the charge transport), a current element cannot exist in the steady dc state. Thus the Biot-Savart law in its differential form applies to a nonphysical element. In Section 7–6 we shall see that, as a consequence, the computed forces between two current elements are not equal in magnitude and oppositely directed (see Eq. 7–35). However, in the case of static fields, currents always form closed loops. The Biot-Savart law applied to a closed loop results in the integral from (6–13), from which it can be shown that the computed forces are equal in magnitude and oppositely directed, as required by Newton's third law. Thus we may apply Eq. (6–14) only in the case of static fields of closed current loops.

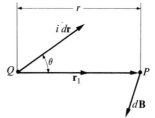

Fig. 6–4. The Biot-Savart law.

6–4 THE MAGNETIC SCALAR POTENTIAL

In a region of space in which the permeability μ is uniform and in which $\mathbf{J} = 0$, Eqs. (6–1) are satisfied if

$$\mathbf{H} = -\mathrm{grad}\,U, \tag{6–15}$$

where $\nabla^2 U = 0$. Thus the magnetic field intensity can be obtained from the negative gradient of a scalar magnetic potential U. The function U is a solution of Laplace's equation. However, since the magnetic field has no scalar sources, the evaluation of U is, in general, not as simple as it is in the case of an electric field. We must relate U in some manner to the vector source of the field, the current density $\mathbf{J}$. For this reason, to find U, we must work backward, starting with the known solution for $\mathbf{B}$ given by Eq. (6–13). There is no loss of generality in considering a current filament, since a volume distribution of current can be considered to be composed of an infinitely large number of elemental current filaments. If we substitute Eq. (6–15) into Eq.

(6–13), we see that U must satisfy the equation

$$\text{grad } U = -\frac{i}{4\pi}\oint_C \frac{d\mathbf{r} \times \mathbf{r}}{r^3}.$$

For a displacement $d\mathbf{R}$ of the field point P the change in potential is

$$dU = \text{grad } U \cdot d\mathbf{R} = -\frac{i}{4\pi}\oint_C \frac{\mathbf{r} \cdot (d\mathbf{R} \times d\mathbf{r})}{r^3}. \tag{6–16}$$

It is possible to determine U from Eq. (6–16) if we consider the geometric significance of the integrand (Fig. 6–5). Since the displacement is relative, the displacement $d\mathbf{R}$ of the field point P with Q fixed is equivalent to the displacement $-d\mathbf{R}$ of the point Q with P fixed. We find it more convenient to consider P as fixed. The vector $-d\mathbf{R} \times d\mathbf{r}$ has a magnitude which is the area of an elemental parallelogram formed by $-d\mathbf{R}$ and $d\mathbf{r}$, and the projection of this area onto a plane having a normal $-\mathbf{r}/r$ is

$$(-\mathbf{r}/r) \cdot (-d\mathbf{R} \times d\mathbf{r}) = a \cos \theta.$$

The integrand of the integral in Eq. (6–16) is therefore

$$\frac{\mathbf{r} \cdot (d\mathbf{R} \times d\mathbf{r})}{r^3} = \frac{a \cos \theta}{r^2},$$

and represents the projection of the elemental parallelogram onto a unit sphere centered at P. The integration over the complete filament results in an elemental solid angle $d\Omega$ on the unit sphere. Thus

$$dU = -\frac{i}{4\pi}\, d\Omega,$$

where $d\Omega$ is the change in the solid angle Ω caused by the vector displacement $d\mathbf{R}$. It follows that

$$U = -\frac{i\Omega}{4\pi}. \tag{6–17}$$

Substituting into Eq. (6–15) yields

$$\mathbf{H} = \frac{i}{4\pi}\,\text{grad } \Omega. \tag{6–18}$$

Equation (6–18) gives the desired relation between the magnetic potential U and the source of the magnetic field. We see that U can be determined by finding the solid angle of the contour which defines the filament.

So that we may become familiar with the concept of a solid angle of a current filament, let us consider Fig. 6-6, which illustrates two current filaments defined by the contours C_1 and C_2. The direction of current flow is indicated by the arrows. The contours C_1 and C_2 are projected radially onto

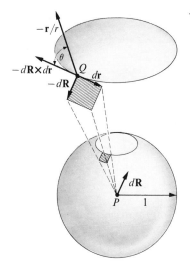

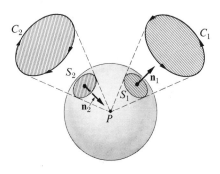

◀Fig. 6–5. The projection of an elemental parallelogram on a unit sphere.

Fig. 6–6. The solid angle of current filaments.

a unit sphere centered at P, which results in solid angles given by the areas S_1 and S_2, respectively. To account for the direction of current flow, we assume that the areas on the unit sphere have algebraic values which are determined by the direction of the normals n_1 and n_2, respectively. The normals are taken so that they form a right-handed system with respect to the direction of current flow. If the normal is outwardly directed, as is the case with n_1, we take the solid angle as positive. If the normal is inwardly directed, the solid angle is taken as negative. Thus, as shown in Fig. 6-6, we have $S_1 > 0$ and $S_2 < 0$.

6-5 MAGNETIC CHARGES AND DIPOLES

Since the magnetic flux density is given by Eq. (6-13), one might ask why we introduce the scalar magnetic potential and the solid angle. The answer is that we then obtain an analogy with the electrostatic field and thus it becomes possible for us to use all the methods discussed in Chapter 4 for solving magnetic-field problems. In this section we shall develop this analogy and show that the scalar magnetic potential can be interpreted as resulting from fictitious magnetic charges.

To develop this analogy in a simple case, let us consider a small coil of area a which has N turns. The direction of current flow is chosen so that the solid angle of the coil on a unit sphere centered at a field point P is negative (Fig. 6–7). When we project the area a onto a plane normal to the radius vector we obtain the area $a \cos \theta$. Thus the solid angle for the N turns is

$$\Omega = -\frac{aN \cos \theta}{r^2}$$

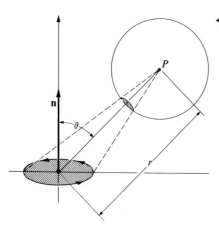

◄**Fig. 6–7.** The solid angle of a small coil.

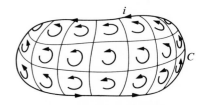

Fig. 6–8. A magnetic dipole sheet.

and the scalar potential is

$$U = \frac{m \cos \theta}{4\pi r^2} ,$$

where

$$m \triangleq aiN \tag{6–19}$$

is defined as the magnitude of the dipole moment (see Eq. 6–12).

When we compare the expression derived for U with Eq. (3–13), we see that a small coil has the same type of potential as that of an electric dipole. We can therefore replace the coil by an equivalent *magnetic dipole*, where m is given by Eq. (6–19) and where $\mathbf{m}$ has the direction of the normal $\mathbf{n}$ of the coil.

We must be careful when we make analogies between the electric and magnetic fields. In a static electric field (see Eq. 2–48a)

$$v_e \triangleq \oint_C \mathbf{E} \cdot d\mathbf{r} = 0,$$

while in a static magnetic field (see Eq. 2–48b),

$$v_m \triangleq \oint_C \mathbf{H} \cdot d\mathbf{r} = i, \tag{6–20}$$

where i is the current linked by the contour C. The necessity for satisfying Eq. (6–20) makes the interpretation of the scalar magnetic potential less straightforward.

In order to discuss the nature of the scalar magnetic potential, let us consider a surface S bounded by a contour C along which a current i flows (Fig. 6–8). We can divide the surface into elemental cells and let a current i flow around the boundary of each cell. In the interior of S the currents on the cell boundaries cancel each other, while on the contour C an effective

MAGNETIC CHARGES AND DIPOLES

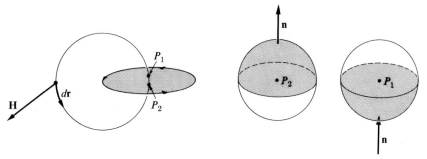

Fig. 6–9. The change in potential as the field point passes through a dipole sheet.

current i remains. Each of the elemental cells forms a current loop which can be replaced by a magnetic dipole. Thus we see that a current filament can be replaced by a uniform distribution of dipoles over an arbitrary surface S which is bounded by the filament.

It is because of the equivalence of a small current loop with a fictitious magnetic dipole that we have two possible representations for the magnetic field. If we consider the current filament we are led to the vector potential formulation. If we replace the current filament by a distribution of magnetic dipoles we are led to the scalar potential formulation, which is often very convenient for the solution of field problems because of the analogy with electrostatics. Since it is associated with a dipole sheet, the magnetic scalar potential is not, in general, a single-valued function of position. For example, let us consider a current filament which has been replaced by an equivalent dipole sheet (Fig. 6–9). Let P_1 and P_2 be points that are just above and below the dipole sheet, respectively. Let the solid angle at P_2 be Ω_2, and let us take this as positive. The solid angle at P_1 is then

$$\Omega_1 = -(4\pi - \Omega_2).$$

(Note that at P_1 the normal is directed toward the center of the unit sphere at P_1, so that the solid angle is negative and that $\Omega_2 + |\Omega_1| = 4\pi$ is the area of the unit sphere.) Thus the scalar potential changes by

$$U_2 - U_1 = -\frac{i}{4\pi}(\Omega_2 - \Omega_1) = -i$$

as we pass through the dipole sheet. We can see the reason for this jump in potential if we integrate the tangential component of **H** along a path connecting P_1 and P_2, as shown in Fig. 6–9. We find that

$$\int_{P_1}^{P_2} \mathbf{H} \cdot d\mathbf{r} = -(U_2 - U_1) = i.$$

Since P_1 and P_2 are taken to be infinitesimally close together, we can consider

the path to be a closed contour. This yields Eq. (6–20). When we trace
through a closed path which links a current the scalar magnetic potential
changes by multiples of i. The multi-valuedness of the scalar magnetic
potential is essential to account for Eq. (6–20). On the other hand, the
single-valuedness of the scalar electric potential shows that an electric
dipole sheet cannot exist.

Since we can consider a dipole to be composed of two point charges of
equal magnitude and of opposite polarity separated by a small distance, the
question now arises as to the possibility of introducing the concept of a
magnetic charge. We shall now show that the external magnetic field of a
long thin straight coil can be determined from the scalar potential of two
magnetic charges located at the ends of the coil (Fig. 6–10). Let i be the
current in the coil, n the number of turns per unit length, and a the cross-
sectional area of the coil. The equivalent magnetic charges used to represent
the field of the coil can be evaluated with the aid of Eq. (6–17). The projection
of the area a onto a plane normal to the radius vector gives an area $a \cos \theta$.

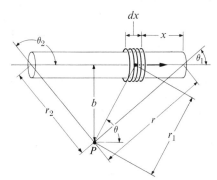

Fig. 6–10. The magnetic potential of a long thin coil.

Thus the elemental solid angle for the $n \, dx$ turns in an interval dx at x is

$$d\Omega = \frac{an \, dx \cos \theta}{r^2}. \qquad (6\text{–}21)$$

It can be seen from the figure that

$$r \sin \theta = b, \qquad r \, d\theta = \sin \theta \, dx.$$

Thus

$$\frac{dx}{r^2} = \frac{r \, d\theta}{r^2 \sin \theta} = \frac{d\theta}{b}.$$

Substituting into Eq. (6–21) and integrating yields the total solid angle for
all turns of the coil,

$$\Omega = \frac{an}{b} (\sin \theta_2 - \sin \theta_1) = an \left(\frac{1}{r_2} - \frac{1}{r_1} \right).$$

Thus the scalar potential (see Eq. 6–17) is

$$U = \frac{M_p}{4\pi}\left(\frac{1}{r_1} - \frac{1}{r_2}\right),$$

where

$$M_p \triangleq ani. \tag{6–22}$$

The form of the scalar potential is similar to that for two point electric charges. By analogy we can therefore define the *magnetic charge* by the quantity M_p. Magnetic charges are fictitious but are often useful for describing the magnetic field and its interaction with magnetic materials. The magnetic dipole moment **m** of a small coil may be considered to result from two magnetic charges M_p and $-M_p$ situated on the coil axis a distance l apart. Thus

$$m = \lim_{l \to 0} M_p l = aiN,$$

where $N = nl$ is the total number of turns of the coil (see Eq. 6–19).

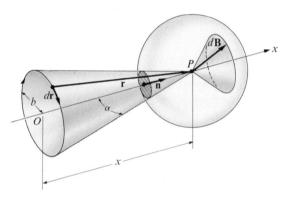

Fig. 6–11. The solid angle of a plane circular coil.

When the dimensions of a coil are not small, it is usually more convenient to use the Biot-Savart law or the solid angle of the coil to determine **H**. As an illustration of Eq. (6–18), let us consider a plane circular coil of radius b which has N closely wound turns (Fig. 6–11). The solid angle for one turn at a point P on the axis is the area enclosed on the unit sphere by a right circular cone of half-angle α. This area is

$$S = \int_0^\alpha 2\pi \sin\theta \, d\theta = 2\pi(1 - \cos\alpha).$$

The direction of the current i is chosen so that the normal **n** is directed toward the center of the unit sphere at P. The solid angle for the N turns is

$$\Omega = -2\pi N(1 - \cos\alpha).$$

Thus the scalar potential is

$$U = \frac{iN}{2}(1 - \cos \alpha) = \frac{iN}{2}\left(1 - \frac{x}{\sqrt{x^2 + b^2}}\right)$$

and the x-component of the magnetic field intensity is

$$H_x = -\frac{\partial U}{\partial x} = \frac{iNb^2}{2(x^2 + b^2)^{3/2}}. \tag{6-23}$$

We can obtain the same result by using the Biot-Savart law. Since the x-axis is an axis of symmetry, it follows from Eq. (6–14) that the vectors $d\mathbf{B}$ form a cone of half-angle $(\pi/2) - \alpha$. The resultant $\mathbf{B}$ is directed along the x-axis. Using Eq. (6–14) and accounting for the N turns, we obtain

$$B_x = \frac{\mu_0 iN \sin \alpha}{4\pi r^2} \oint_C dr = \frac{\mu_0 iNb^2}{2r^3},$$

where $r^2 = x^2 + b^2$.

We can determine the magnetic field for points off the x-axis in the same manner. However, the integrations to be performed are no longer elementary.

6-6 AMPERE'S CIRCUITAL LAW

The expression (6–20) is known as *Ampère's circuital law*, and is often the simplest means for determining the magnetic field if it is known that $\mathbf{H}$ is piecewise uniform along the path and has the direction of the path. This is the case if the current distribution has a high degree of symmetry. In electrostatics we have often made use of Gauss' law to determine the electric field in cases in which the charge distribution possessed a sufficient degree of symmetry. In magnetostatics we shall now make similar use of Ampère's circuital law. Several examples will be given to illustrate problems that can be solved by the use of Eq. (6–20).

Example 1. Let us determine the magnetic field due to a current i in an infinitely long straight conductor of circular cross section with a radius b (Fig. 6–12). The current density $\mathbf{J} = \mathbf{i}_z(i/\pi b^2)$ is uniform. Due to symmetry, H is constant along the circular path shown in the figure and $\mathbf{H}$ is tangent to the path. Thus, if the path is outside the conductor, we have

$$\oint_C \mathbf{H} \cdot d\mathbf{r} = H2\pi r = i, \qquad r \geqq b.$$

If the path is inside the conductor, only part of the current i is linked by the path. Thus

$$H2\pi r = i\frac{\pi r^2}{\pi b^2}, \qquad r \leqq b.$$

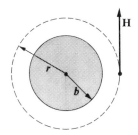

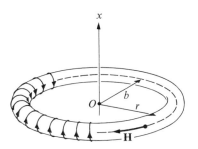

Fig. 6–12. A cross-sectional view of an infinitely long straight conductor with a circular cross section.

Fig. 6–13. A toroidal coil.

The magnetic field intensity is given by

$$H = \frac{1}{2}\left(\frac{b}{r}\right)^2 J \times r, \quad r \geqq b, \qquad H = \tfrac{1}{2}J \times r, \quad r \leqq b. \quad (6\text{–}24)$$

Example 2. Figure 6–13 illustrates a toroidal coil of N uniformly wound turns and of uniform cross-sectional area a. Choosing the circular path of radius r shown in the figure and applying Ampère's circuital law yields

$$H_t 2\pi r = iN,$$

where H_t is the component of **H** tangent to the path. If the cross-sectional dimensions are small compared with r, the transverse component of **H** is negligible, and we obtain

$$H \cong H_t = iN/2\pi r. \quad (6\text{–}25)$$

For a field point outside the toroid the coil will appear to be approximately equivalent to a single turn along the axis. The x-component of the magnetic field intensity (see Eq. 6–23) is then

$$H_x = \frac{ib^2}{2(x^2 + b^2)^{3/2}},$$

where b is the radius for the equivalent single turn. At $x = 0$, the ratio $H_x/H = \pi r/bN$ shows that the order of magnitude of the external field is smaller than that of the internal field by a factor of N.

Example 3. Let us determine an approximate expression for the magnetic field intensity due to a transmission line consisting of two infinitely long parallel conducting plates of width l and spaced a distance d apart (Fig. 6–14). The current in the plates is i and $-i$, respectively, and is assumed to be uniformly distributed over each plate. At a field point between the conductors the magnetic field intensity will be approximately constant and directed as shown in the figure. At a field point such as P_1 the field is negligible if $d/l \ll 1$, since the effects of the currents tend to cancel each other. As a

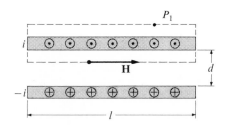

Fig. 6–14. A transmission line consisting of two infinitely long parallel conducting plates.

first approximation we take the field to be zero. Thus, applying Ampère's circuital law to the path shown in the figure, we obtain

$$\oint_C \mathbf{H} \cdot d\mathbf{r} = i \cong Hl. \qquad (6\text{–}26)$$

6–7 MAGNETIZATION AND MAGNETIZATION CURRENTS

Up to this point our discussion has been restricted to the magnetic field of conduction currents in free space. In the presence of a magnetic field a magnetic medium can become magnetized or magnetically polarized. Within the medium, on an atomic scale, we have electrons moving on orbits bound to atoms and spinning about their axes (electron spins). The motion of the electrons results in an effective macroscopic current which must be accounted for. We shall introduce a vector **M**, the *dipole moment per unit volume* (also called the *magnetization*) to account for this current. We consider the motion of electrons in a magnetic material to be equivalent to elemental current loops. Let n be the density of the current loops per unit volume, a the area, and i_C the circulating current in a loop. The current loops can be considered equivalent to magnetic dipoles and the dipole moment per unit volume is

$$\mathbf{M} = \mathbf{k} a n i_C,$$

where the unit vector **k** is normal to the plane of the loop and forms a right-handed system with respect to the direction of current flow. Let us consider an elemental cylinder of length dx along the x-axis formed by the current loops (Fig. 6–15). The current loops result in a surface current on the cylinder which is given by

$$n i_C a \cos \theta \, dx = M_x \, dx, \qquad (6\text{–}27)$$

where M_x is the x-component of **M**. Similar expressions can be obtained for the y- and z-components. Let us now consider Fig. 6–16, which shows a surface element $ds = dx \, dy$ of a section of the interior of the magnetic material. Due to the current loops along the edge of ds, there are electrons

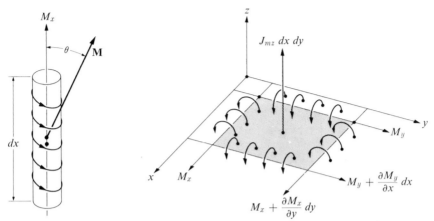

Fig. 6–15. The magnet-   **Fig. 6–16.** The magnetization current density $\mathbf{J}_m$.
ization vector **M**.

moving through ds in both directions. If, in a unit time interval, more electrons move up through the surface than down, an effective current density
$\mathbf{J}_m$ must exist and the current through ds is given by $J_{mz} \, dx \, dy$. This current
can be determined by using Eq. (6–27) to evaluate the contribution of each
of the four edges of ds:

$$J_{mz}\,dx\,dy = M_x\,dx + \left(M_y + \frac{\partial M_y}{\partial x}\,dx\right)dy - M_y\,dy - \left(M_x + \frac{\partial M_x}{\partial y}\,dy\right)dx.$$

Thus

$$J_{mz} = \frac{\partial M_y}{\partial x} - \frac{\partial M_x}{\partial y}.$$

Similar expressions can be obtained for the y- and z-components of $\mathbf{J}_m$.
We therefore define the *magnetization current density* by the equation

$$\mathbf{J}_m \triangleq \operatorname{curl} \mathbf{M}. \tag{6–28}$$

For the case in which **M** is uniform, $\mathbf{J}_m = 0$. This result can be seen by
noting that the current loops within the medium cancel each other. If **M**
is not uniform, there is an effective current density $\mathbf{J}_m$ within the medium.
The current density $\mathbf{J}_m$ sets up a magnetic field in the same manner as the
conduction current density **J**.

The magnetization current density $\mathbf{J}_m$ given by Eq. (6–28) is in the interior
of the material. At the surface, the current loops result in an effective
surface magnetization current density $\mathbf{J}_{sm}$, which can be determined by
considering Fig. 6–17. The current loops in a segment of length h of the
surface result in an effective surface current

$$J_{sm}h = ni_Cah \sin\theta = hMi_C \sin\theta.$$

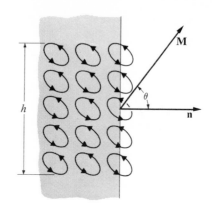

Fig. 6–17. The surface magnetization current density.

Noting the direction of the current, we obtain

$$\mathbf{J}_{sm} \triangleq \mathbf{M} \times \mathbf{n}. \tag{6–29}$$

Let us consider a general case in which we have a conduction current density $\mathbf{J}$ in a volume v which sets up a magnetic field magnetizing a magnetic medium of volume v_m which is bounded by the surface S_m. From a fundamental point of view we do not distinguish between the kinds of current densities. All currents set up a magnetic field in the same manner and the resulting vector potential is

$$\mathbf{A} = \frac{\mu_0}{4\pi} \int_v \frac{\mathbf{J}}{r} \, dv + \frac{\mu_0}{4\pi} \int_{v_m} \frac{\mathbf{J}_m}{r} \, dv + \frac{\mu_0}{4\pi} \int_{S_m} \frac{\mathbf{J}_{sm}}{r} \, ds. \tag{6–30}$$

The current densities $\mathbf{J}_m$ and $\mathbf{J}_{sm}$ are induced in the magnetic medium by the primary magnetic field set up by $\mathbf{J}$. In the case of *magnetically soft materials* (so-called *soft iron*), the magnetization is related to the magnetic field intensity by the equation

$$\mathbf{M} = \chi_m \mathbf{H}, \tag{6–31}$$

where χ_m is the *magnetic susceptibility*. In the case of permanent magnets the functional relationship is more complicated, since the material remains magnetized after the externally applied field is removed. For soft iron, $\mathbf{J}_m$ and $\mathbf{J}_{sm}$ are not known until $\mathbf{H}$ has been determined. Thus Eq. (6–30), even though it is of fundamental significance, is not very useful for the practical solution of field problems. However, we shall see that by properly defining $\mathbf{H}$ in Eq. (6–31) we can use this vector as a very convenient means for the solution of field problems. The magnetic field intensity $\mathbf{H}$ in a magnetic medium is defined by the equation

$$\mathbf{H} \triangleq \frac{\mathbf{B}}{\mu_0} - \mathbf{M}. \tag{6–32}$$

Substituting Eq. (6–31) into Eq. (6–32) yields

$$\mathbf{B} = \mu_0(1 + \chi_m)\mathbf{H} = \mu\mathbf{H}, \tag{6–33}$$

where $\mu \triangleq \mu_0(1 + \chi_m)$ is the *permeability*. By introducing μ and $\mathbf{H}$ in this manner we can eliminate any explicit consideration of the magnetization current. With the aid of Eq. (6–31), we can write the magnetization current density and the surface magnetization current density in a region where μ is uniform in the form

$$\mathbf{J}_m = \chi_m \operatorname{curl} \mathbf{H} = \chi_m \mathbf{J}, \tag{6–34a}$$

$$\mathbf{J}_{sm} = \chi_m \mathbf{H} \times \mathbf{n}. \tag{6–34b}$$

Here we have made use of Eq. (6–1a).

In order to illustrate Eqs. (6–34), let us consider once more Example 1 of Section 6–6. We shall now assume that the conductor is an iron wire of permeability μ. Using Ampère's circuital law in the form (6–20), we obtain Eqs. (6–24) as before. However, the magnetic flux density now has a magnitude given by

$$B = \mu_0 H = \frac{\mu_0 J b^2}{2r}, \quad r > b, \qquad B = \mu H = \frac{\mu J r}{2}, \quad r < b. \tag{6–35}$$

(Note that there is a discontinuity in B at $r = b$.) With the aid of Eqs. (6–34) we obtain the magnetization current density and the surface magnetization current density

$$\mathbf{J}_m = \chi_m \mathbf{J}, \qquad \mathbf{J}_{sm} = -\frac{\chi_m b \mathbf{J}}{2}.$$

We see that the use of the vector $\mathbf{H}$ and the scalar μ results in a relatively straightforward solution of the field problem. Once $\mathbf{H}$ has been found we are in a position to determine the magnetization currents.

Let us now derive Eqs. (6–35) using Ampère's circuital law in the form given by Eq. (2–25), where we take $d\phi_e/dt = 0$. We have

$$\oint_C \frac{\mathbf{B}}{\mu_0} \cdot d\mathbf{r} = i_T. \tag{6–36}$$

Here C is a contour which links the total current i_T. We are here adopting the fundamental point of view expressed by Eq. (6–30), but we find it more convenient to solve the problem using Ampère's circuital law. When $r < b$, we have, using Eq. (6–34a) and noting that both $\mathbf{J}$ and $\mathbf{J}_m$ contribute to the total current,

$$\frac{B}{\mu_0} 2\pi r = \pi r^2 (J + J_m) = \pi r^2 (1 + \chi_m) J.$$

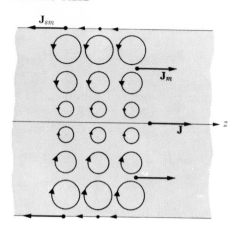

Fig. 6–18. The conduction current density **J**, the magnetization current density **J**$_m$, and the surface magnetization current density **J**$_{sm}$ for an iron wire.

Thus

$$B = \frac{\mu r J}{2}, \quad r < b.$$

When $r > b$, the surface current due to **J**$_{sm}$ is also linked and we have

$$\frac{B}{\mu_0} 2\pi r = \pi b^2 (J + J_m) + J_{sm} 2\pi b = \pi b^2 J.$$

Thus

$$B = \frac{\mu_0 b^2 J}{2r}, \quad r > b.$$

The effect of the permeability of the iron wire is to increase the magnetic flux density within the wire. We can understand the increase by noting that the magnetic field due to **J** magnetizes the iron, resulting in a magnetization current density which increases the effective current density to the value

$$\mathbf{J} + \mathbf{J}_m = (1 + \chi_m)\mathbf{J} = \mu_r \mathbf{J}.$$

Outside the iron wire the magnetic flux density has the same value as for a conductor of permeability μ_0. This is a consequence of the fact that the magnetization results in a surface current which flows in a direction opposite to that of **J**. The surface current accounts for the discontinuity in B. These effects are illustrated in Fig. 6–18. We note that the magnetization increases as r increases (this is depicted in the figure by the increasing size of the current loops). At the surface where $r = a$, the current loops result in an effective surface current density **J**$_{sm}$ which is directed oppositely to **J**. Within the conductor the increasing strength of the current loops with r results in an effective current density **J**$_m$ which has the same direction as **J**.

Comparing the two methods of solving this problem clearly illustrates the advantage in using the vector **H**, which in Ampère's circuital law is associated only with the conduction current, thus eliminating any explicit consideration of the magnetization current. However, the vector **B**, which in the form (2–25) of Ampère's circuital law is associated with the total current, is of more fundamental significance and in this problem results in a clearer visualization of the magnetization phenomena occurring within the wire.

Because of its fundamental significance we shall now derive Eq. (6–30) in a different manner. We have shown that the vector potential of a small current loop is given by Eq. (6–11) (see Fig. 6–3). Let us write Eq. (6–11) in the form

$$\mathbf{A} = \frac{\mu_0}{4\pi r^3}\, \mathbf{m} \times \mathbf{r} = \frac{\mu_0}{4\pi}\, \mathbf{m} \times \nabla \frac{1}{r},$$

where the gradient is to be taken with respect to the source point Q. If we apply the above expression to a continuous distribution of current loops in a magnetic medium we have

$$\mathbf{A}_m = \frac{\mu_0}{4\pi} \int_{v_m} \mathbf{M} \times \nabla \frac{1}{r}\, dv,$$

where the magnetization **M** is interpreted as the dipole moment per unit volume. With the aid of the vector identity

$$\nabla \times \left(\frac{\mathbf{M}}{r}\right) = \left(\nabla \frac{1}{r}\right) \times \mathbf{M} + \frac{1}{r} \nabla \times \mathbf{M},$$

we obtain

$$\mathbf{A}_m = \frac{\mu_0}{4\pi} \int_{v_m} \frac{\nabla \times \mathbf{M}}{r}\, dv - \frac{\mu_0}{4\pi} \int_{v_m} \nabla \times \left(\frac{\mathbf{M}}{r}\right) dv.$$

The second volume integral can be transformed into a surface integral (see Eq. 1–37) and we find that

$$\mathbf{A}_m = \frac{\mu_0}{4\pi} \int_{v_m} \frac{\mathbf{J}_m}{r}\, dv + \frac{\mu_0}{4\pi} \int_{S_m} \frac{\mathbf{J}_{sm}}{r}\, ds,$$

where $\mathbf{J}_m$ and $\mathbf{J}_{sm}$ are the magnetization current density and the surface magnetization current density, respectively. Combining $\mathbf{A}_m$ with the vector potential of the conduction current yields Eq. (6–30).

Experimental evidence indicates that magnetism is a consequence of coupling between electron spins. This is essentially the point of view we have adopted in describing magnetization in terms of elemental current loops. However, there is an alternative method for describing magnetic phenomena in terms of fictitious magnetic charges. In Section 6–5 it was shown that a small current loop is equivalent to a magnetic dipole. This fact makes it

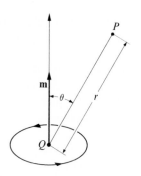

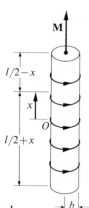

Fig. 6–19. A magnetic dipole.

Fig. 6–20. A permanently magnetized rod.

possible to represent the magnetization of a medium in terms of a scalar potential. The potential of a single dipole (Fig. 6–19) is

$$U = \frac{m \cos \theta}{4\pi r^2} = \frac{1}{4\pi} \mathbf{m} \cdot \nabla \frac{1}{r}.$$

Applying the above expression to a continuous distribution of dipoles which replace the current loops of a magnetized medium yields

$$U_m = \frac{1}{4\pi} \int_{v_m} \mathbf{M} \cdot \nabla \frac{1}{r} \, dv.$$

With the aid of the vector identity

$$\nabla \cdot \left(\frac{\mathbf{M}}{r} \right) = \mathbf{M} \cdot \nabla \frac{1}{r} + \frac{1}{r} \nabla \cdot \mathbf{M},$$

we obtain

$$U_m = \frac{1}{4\pi} \int_{v_m} \operatorname{div} \left(\frac{\mathbf{M}}{r} \right) dv + \frac{1}{4\pi} \int_{v_m} \frac{-\operatorname{div} \mathbf{M}}{r} \, dv$$

$$= \frac{1}{4\pi} \int_{S_m} \frac{\mathbf{M} \cdot \mathbf{n}}{r} \, ds + \frac{1}{4\pi} \int_{v_m} \frac{-\operatorname{div} \mathbf{M}}{r} \, dv.$$

If we let

$$\rho_m \triangleq -\operatorname{div} \mathbf{M}, \qquad \sigma_m \triangleq \mathbf{M} \cdot \mathbf{n} \qquad (6\text{–}37)$$

represent a fictitious *magnetic charge density* and a *magnetic surface charge density*, respectively, we find that

$$U_m = \frac{1}{4\pi} \int_{v_m} \frac{\rho_m}{r} \, dv + \frac{1}{4\pi} \int_{S_m} \frac{\sigma_m}{r} \, ds. \qquad (6\text{–}38)$$

The above expression corresponds to the expression (3–30) for electrostatic fields.

To illustrate the two possible methods for representing a magnetic field, let us discuss the magnetic field of a long thin permanently magnetized circular rod of length l and radius b (Fig. 6-20). From a fundamental point of view, the permanent magnetism is due to a self-induced alignment of electron spins. We consider the aligned electron spins to be represented on a macroscopic scale by a magnetization $\mathbf{M}$. As a first approximation we assume that $\mathbf{M}$ is uniform throughout the rod. It then follows from Eqs. (6-28) and (6-29) that $J_m = 0$ and $J_{sm} = M$. Thus there is a uniform surface current circulating on the rod. The permanently magnetized rod is therefore equivalent to an air-core coil of the same dimensions having an excitation of M ampere turns per unit length. The axial component of $\mathbf{B}$ (see Problem 6-5b) is then

$$B_x = \frac{M}{2}\left[\frac{l/2 - x}{\sqrt{b^2 + (l/2 - x)^2}} + \frac{l/2 + x}{\sqrt{b^2 + (l/2 + x)^2}}\right].$$

We can then find the axial component of $\mathbf{H}$ from Eq. (6-32), which yields

$$-H_x/M = 1 - \frac{1}{2}\left[\frac{l/2 - x}{\sqrt{b^2 + (l/2 - x)^2}} + \frac{l/2 + x}{\sqrt{b^2 + (l/2 + x)^2}}\right]. \quad (6\text{-}39)$$

Within the permanent magnet we see that $\mathbf{H}$ is directed oppositely to $\mathbf{B}$ so that the magnetic field intensity $\mathbf{H}$ tends to demagnetize the original magnetization $\mathbf{M}$. Thus we see that the assumption of a uniform $\mathbf{M}$ can be only an approximation.

The magnetic field of a permanent magnet can also be described in terms of magnetic charges, and the evaluation of $\mathbf{H}$ will again yield Eq. (6-39). However, we are now in a position to give a "physical" interpretation to the negative sign in Eq. (6-39). It follows from Eq. (6-37) that over the faces of the magnet a magnetic surface charge density, $\sigma_m = \pm M$, is present. It is left to the reader as an exercise (see Problem 6-8) to derive the magnetic scalar potential at an axial point and to obtain Eq. (6-39) from this potential. It follows from the polarity of the magnetic charge on the two faces that the magnetic field intensity $\mathbf{H}$ due to these charges is directed oppositely to $\mathbf{B}$ within the magnet. The field external to the magnet can be approximately determined by using the scalar potential of two magnetic charges located at either end of the coil (see Eq. 6-22). The magnetic charge is given by

$$M_p = \pi b^2 \sigma_m.$$

6-8 BOUNDARY CONDITIONS; SOLUTION OF MAGNETOSTATIC FIELD PROBLEMS

Through the use of the scalar magnetic potential, we can obtain the solution of magnetic field problems in the same manner as we obtain the solution of electrostatic field problems (see Chapter 4). Given that U_1, $\mathbf{B}_1$, $\mathbf{H}_1$ and

U_2, $\mathbf{B}_2$, $\mathbf{H}_2$ are the potentials and field vectors in two magnetic media which have an interface S_b, then the Maxwell equations relate these quantities over S_b (Fig. 6–21). These relations are known as *boundary conditions*. One boundary condition arises from Eq. (6–1b), which is a consequence of Maxwell's first equation. It follows from Eq. (6–1b) and the divergence theorem that

$$\int_S \mathbf{B} \cdot \mathbf{n} \, ds = 0 \qquad (6\text{–}40)$$

for any closed surface. Let us choose a small flat cylinder, as shown in Fig. 6–21, so that $\mathbf{B}_1$ and $\mathbf{B}_2$ are nearly uniform over the cylinder faces. Equation (6–40) yields

$$\mathbf{B}_1 \cdot \mathbf{n}_1 a + \mathbf{B}_2 \cdot \mathbf{n}_2 a + O(h) = 0,$$

where a is the area of the face and $O(h)$ indicates terms of the order of h which arise due to the magnetic flux through the sides of the cylinder. If we let $\mathbf{n} = \mathbf{n}_1 = -\mathbf{n}_2$ and let $h \to 0$, we find that $\mathbf{B}_1 \cdot \mathbf{n} = \mathbf{B}_2 \cdot \mathbf{n}$ and

$$-\mu_1 \frac{\partial U_1}{\partial n} = -\mu_2 \frac{\partial U_2}{\partial n}. \qquad (6\text{–}41)$$

Equation (6–41) states that the normal component of the magnetic flux density is continuous over the interface S_b.

In general, we must consider the case in which a surface current density $\mathbf{J}_s = J_s \mathbf{n} \times \mathbf{t}$ is present on S_b. Here $\mathbf{n}$ is a unit normal to S_b and $\mathbf{t}$ is a unit tangent vector taken so that $\mathbf{n} \times \mathbf{t}$ has the direction of $\mathbf{J}_s$. When we apply Ampère's circuital law to the path illustrated in Fig. 6–21, we obtain

$$\mathbf{H}_1 \cdot \mathbf{t}l + \mathbf{H}_2 \cdot (-\mathbf{t}l) + O(h) = J_s.$$

Thus, as $h \to 0$, we find that $(\mathbf{H}_1 - \mathbf{H}_2) \cdot \mathbf{t} = J_s$. Thus

$$-\frac{\partial U_1}{\partial t} + \frac{\partial U_2}{\partial t} = J_s. \qquad (6\text{–}42)$$

Given that $J_s = 0$, Eq. (6–42) is satisfied if $U_1 = U_2$, and the equation then states that the tangential component of $\mathbf{H}$ is continuous over S_b.

Equations (6–41) and (6–42) are the boundary conditions which must be satisfied by U_1 and U_2 over the interface S_b. We shall now discuss several examples illustrating typical problems in magnetostatics.

Example 1. A spherical shell of outer and inner radii a and b, respectively, has a permeability μ and is placed in a uniform magnetic field $\mathbf{H}_0$. We wish to determine the magnetic field inside the shell (Fig. 6–22). The primary potential for the uniform field is $U_p = -H_0 r \cos \theta$. In each of the regions 1, 2, and 3, the permeability is uniform and the scalar potential satisfies Laplace's equation. The primary field $\mathbf{H}_0$ magnetizes the sphere and in

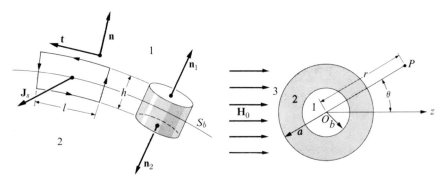

Fig. 6–21. The boundary between two magnetic media.

Fig. 6–22. A spherical magnetic shell in a uniform magnetic field.

region 3 the magnetized sphere appears as a dipole. Thus we assume that

$$U_3 = -H_0 r \cos \theta + \frac{C}{r^2} \cos \theta, \qquad r \geqq a.$$

In region 1 we assume that the field is uniform so that the potential is

$$U_1 = -H_i r \cos \theta, \qquad r \leqq b.$$

In order to satisfy the boundary conditions, the potential in region 2 must have the form

$$U_2 = -Ar \cos \theta + \frac{B}{r^2} \cos \theta, \qquad b \leqq r \leqq a.$$

In each of the regions the potential chosen satisfies Laplace's equation. The problem is solved if we can determine constants A, B, C, and H_i so that the boundary conditions are satisfied. At the inner boundary ($r = b$), the condition $U_1 = U_2$ yields

$$-H_i = -A + B/b^3. \tag{6-43}$$

The continuity of the normal component of magnetic flux density yields the condition (see Eq. 6–41)

$$\frac{1}{\mu_r} H_i = A + \frac{2B}{b^3}. \tag{6-44}$$

Solving Eqs. (6–43) and (6–44) for A and B in terms of H_i yields

$$A = \frac{2\mu_r + 1}{3\mu_r} H_i, \qquad B = \frac{1 - \mu_r}{3\mu_r} b^3 H_i. \tag{6-45}$$

At the outer boundary ($r = a$), the condition $U_2 = U_3$ yields

$$-H_0 + C/a^3 = -A + B/a^3, \tag{6-46}$$

and Eq. (6–41) yields

$$\frac{1}{\mu_r}\left(H_0 + \frac{2C}{a^3}\right) = A + \frac{2B}{a^3}.$$ (6–47)

If we eliminate C from Eqs. (6–46) and (6–47), we find that

$$H_0 = \frac{\mu_r + 2}{3} A + \frac{\mu_r - 1}{3}\frac{2B}{a^3}.$$

Substituting A and B from Eqs. (6–45), and rearranging terms yields

$$\frac{H_i}{H_0} = \frac{1}{1 + \frac{2}{9}(\mu_r - 1)^2[1 - (b/a)^3]/\mu_r}.$$

As a numerical application of this equation, let us consider the case of a spherical shell of thickness $\delta \triangleq a - b \ll a$, so that

$$\left(\frac{b}{a}\right)^3 \cong 1 - 3\frac{\delta}{a}$$

and take $\mu_r = 10^4$, $a = 2.5$ cm, and $\delta = 0.03$ cm. We find that

$$\frac{H_i}{H_0} = \frac{B_i}{B_0} = \frac{1}{81}.$$

It is evident that even a thin shell can be an effective shield against an external magnetic field, provided that $\mu_r \gg 1$. However, as B_0 is increased, the magnetic material becomes saturated (see Section 7–5) and the ratio B_i/B_0 then increases rapidly with further increase of B_0. In order to evaluate the maximum value of B_0 that can be effectively shielded for a given material, we note that the maximum flux density B_M in medium 2 occurs at $\theta = \pi/2$. We can determine B_M from the continuity of the tangential component of H. Thus

$$B_M = \mu H_i = \mu_r B_i.$$

If the magnetic material under consideration saturates at $B_M = 0.5$ Wb/m², we find that the maximum value of external field which can be effectively shielded is given by

$$B_0 = \frac{B_0}{B_i}\frac{B_M}{\mu_r} = 0.405 \times 10^{-2} \text{ Wb/m}^2.$$

Example 2. Let us determine the field of a uniformly magnetized spherical permanent magnet of radius a (Fig. 6–23). The magnetization is $\mathbf{M} = \mathbf{i}_z M$. We shall first solve this problem by means of an indirect approach by considering a soft-iron sphere, of the same radius and permeability μ, magnetized by a uniform magnetic field $\mathbf{H}_0 = \mathbf{i}_z H_0$. The solution of this

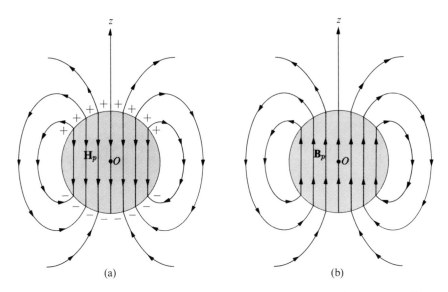

Fig. 6–23. Magnetic field of a spherical permanent magnet. (a) The streamlines for the magnetic field intensity $\mathbf{H}_p$. (b) The streamlines for the magnetic flux density $\mathbf{B}_p$.

latter problem (the proof is left as an exercise) is given by

$$U_1 = - \frac{3H_0}{2 + \mu_r} r \cos \theta, \qquad r < a, \tag{6–48a}$$

$$U_2 = -H_0 r \cos \theta + \frac{\mu_r - 1}{\mu_r + 2} a^3 H_0 \frac{\cos \theta}{r^2}, \qquad r > a. \tag{6–48b}$$

Within the sphere we have the relation

$$\frac{\mathbf{B}_i}{\mu_0} = \mathbf{H}_i + \mathbf{M} = \mu_r \mathbf{H}_i. \tag{6–49}$$

After the sphere has been magnetized, we imagine the magnetization $\mathbf{M}$ to be frozen so that it remains constant as we remove the external field; that is, we hold $\mathbf{M}$ constant and let $H_0 \to 0$. In the limit we obtain the permanently magnetized sphere which has in its interior a magnetic flux density $\mathbf{B}_p$ and a magnetic field intensity $\mathbf{H}_p$. From Eq. (6–48a) we can find $\mathbf{H}_i$ and then evaluate the limit,

$$\mathbf{H}_p = \lim_{H_0 \to 0} \mathbf{H}_i = \lim_{H_0 \to 0} \frac{3H_0}{2 + \mu_r}.$$

The existence of this limit requires that $\lim_{H_0 \to 0} \mu_r = -2$. Equation (6–49) yields, as $H_0 \rightarrow 0$,

$$\frac{\mathbf{B}_p}{\mu_0} = \mathbf{H}_p + \mathbf{M} = -2\mathbf{H}_p.$$

Thus

$$\mathbf{H}_p = -\tfrac{1}{3}\mathbf{M}, \tag{6–50a}$$

$$\mathbf{B}_p = \tfrac{2}{3}\mu_0\mathbf{M}. \tag{6–50b}$$

It should be noted that $\mathbf{B}_p$ and $\mathbf{H}_p$ are directed oppositely within a permanent magnet. Equations (6–48) yield, as $H_0 \rightarrow 0$,

$$U_1 = \frac{M}{3}\, r \cos \theta, \qquad r < a, \tag{6–51a}$$

$$U_2 = \frac{m}{4\pi}\frac{\cos \theta}{r^2}, \qquad r > a, \tag{6–51b}$$

where $\mathbf{m} = (4\pi a^3/3)\mathbf{M}$ is the dipole moment of the uniformly magnetized sphere. With the aid of Eqs. (6–37) we can evaluate the magnetic charge densities:

$$\rho_m = -\mathrm{div}\,\mathbf{M} = 0, \qquad \sigma_m = \mathbf{M} \cdot \mathbf{n} = M \cos \theta. \tag{6–52}$$

We may consider that the magnetic field intensity $\mathbf{H}$ results from a magnetic surface charge density σ_m on the sphere. It is evident from the polarity of the charge distribution given by Eq. (6–52) that $\mathbf{H}$ and $\mathbf{M}$ are directed oppositely within the magnet. Since $U_1 = U_2$ for $r = a$, we see that the tangential component of $\mathbf{H}$ is continuous on the boundary. We interpret the discontinuity in the normal component of $\mathbf{H}$ as a consequence of the surface charge density. This is seen from Eqs. (6–51), which yield

$$(\mathbf{H}_2 - \mathbf{H}_1) \cdot \mathbf{i}_r = \left(-\frac{\partial U_2}{\partial r} + \frac{\partial U_1}{\partial r}\right)_{r=a} = \frac{2M}{3}\cos \theta + \frac{M}{3}\cos \theta = \sigma_m.$$

Since $\mathbf{B}_2 = \mu_0\mathbf{H}_2$ for $r > a$, we see from Eqs. (6–50b) and (6–51b) that the normal component of $\mathbf{B}$ is continuous:

$$\frac{1}{\mu_0}(\mathbf{B}_2 - \mathbf{B}_1) \cdot \mathbf{i}_r = -\frac{\partial U_2}{\partial r}\bigg]_{r=a} - \tfrac{2}{3}M \cos \theta = 0.$$

There is a discontinuity in the tangential component of $\mathbf{B}$. To discuss this discontinuity, we shall solve the problem by a direct approach using $\mathbf{M}$. Since $\mathbf{M}$ is uniform we have

$$\mathbf{J}_{sm} = \mathbf{i}_z \times \mathbf{i}_r M = \mathbf{i}_\phi M \sin \theta \tag{6–53}$$

and $J_m = 0$. Because of Eq. (6–53) we can consider the magnetized sphere to be equivalent to an air-core spherical coil with the same radius and the same surface current density. Let $\mathbf{H}_{c1}$, $\mathbf{H}_{c2}$ represent the magnetic field intensities of the spherical coil in the regions $r < a$ and $r > a$, respectively. We can express the magnetic field intensity as the negative gradient of a scalar potential which must satisfy Laplace's equation. Since we anticipate a uniform field for $r < a$ and a dipole field for $r > a$, we take

$$U_{c1} = -H_{c1}r \cos \theta, \qquad r < a, \qquad \text{(6–54a)}$$

$$U_{c2} = A \frac{\cos \theta}{r^2}, \qquad r > a, \qquad \text{(6–54b)}$$

where A is a constant. Since $\mu_1 = \mu_2 = \mu_0$, the boundary condition (6–41) yields

$$H_{c1} = \frac{2A}{a^3}. \qquad \text{(6–55)}$$

Taking $\mathbf{t} = \mathbf{i}_\theta$, $U_1 = U_{c2}$, and $U_2 = U_{c1}$ in the boundary condition (6–42) and using $\mathbf{J}_s = \mathbf{J}_{sm}$, where $\mathbf{J}_{sm}$ is given by Eq. (6–53), we find that (note that $\partial t = a \, \partial\theta$)

$$H_{c1} + \frac{A}{a^3} = M. \qquad \text{(6–56)}$$

Solving Eqs. (6–55) and (6–56) for A and H_{c1} yields

$$H_{c1} = \tfrac{2}{3}M, \qquad \text{(6–57a)}$$

$$A = \frac{a^3M}{3}. \qquad \text{(6–57b)}$$

Comparing Eqs. (6–51b) and (6–57b), we see that the external fields of the spherical coil and the permanent magnet are identical. Some care must be taken in comparing the internal fields. For the spherical coil we have

$$\mathbf{B}_{c1} = \mu_0\mathbf{H}_{c1} = \tfrac{2}{3}\mu_0\mathbf{M},$$

and we can take $\mathbf{B}_p = \mathbf{B}_{c1}$, since the current distribution is the same in both cases. Having found $\mathbf{B}_p$, we determine $\mathbf{H}_p$ inside the permanent magnet by the defining equation

$$\mathbf{H}_p \triangleq \frac{\mathbf{B}_p}{\mu_0} - \mathbf{M} = -\tfrac{1}{3}\mathbf{M}.$$

These results are the same as those obtained by the first method. We see from the boundary condition (6–56) that the discontinuity in the tangential component of $\mathbf{B}$ is a consequence of the surface current density. This example illustrates that it can be convenient to consider fictitious magnetic charges as the scalar source for the magnetic field intensity. We can consider the total current density as the vector source for the magnetic flux density.

Example 3. A closely wound circular coil of radius b which has N turns is located a distance $d \gg b$ from a semi-infinite plane magnetic medium of permeability μ (Fig. 6–24). The current i in the coil has a right-handed sense with respect to the unit vector $\mathbf{i}_z$. To determine the field potential in regions 1 and 2 we can consider the coil as equivalent to a dipole whose dipole moment is

$$\mathbf{m} = \mathbf{i}_z \pi b^2 i N.$$

The primary potential due to this dipole is

$$U_p = \frac{m}{4\pi} \frac{z - d}{r_1^3}, \qquad (6\text{–}58)$$

where $r_1^2 = x^2 + y^2 + (z - d)^2$. The primary field magnetizes the magnetic medium, giving rise to a secondary potential. When the field point P is in region 1 we can use the method of images and replace the magnetized medium by an equivalent dipole located at $z = -d$. Thus we set

$$U_s = \frac{A}{4\pi} \frac{z + d}{r_2^3},$$

where $r_2^2 = x^2 + y^2 + (z + d)^2$. The potential in medium 1 is

$$U_1 = U_p + U_s, \qquad z \geqq 0.$$

When the field point is in region 2, we can consider the magnetized medium as a shield screening the effect of the original dipole. Thus we set

$$U_2 = \frac{C}{4\pi} \frac{z - d}{r_1^3}, \qquad z \leqq 0.$$

At $z = 0$ the condition $U_1 = U_2$ yields $A - m = -C$, and the condition for the continuity of the normal component of **B** yields $A + m = \mu_r C$. Thus

$$A = \frac{\mu_r - 1}{\mu_r + 1} m, \qquad C = \frac{2}{\mu_r + 1} m.$$

When $\mu_r \to \infty$, one can see that $A = m$, $C = 0$. Thus the magnetic field intensity in region 2 is zero and the image, as seen from points in region 1, is the same as the original dipole. In magnetostatics, the magnetic medium with infinite permeability has a property which corresponds to that of a perfect conductor in electrostatics.

Example 4. Let us determine the magnetic field in the air gap of a cylindrical machine which has smooth stator and rotor surfaces. To a good approximation we can consider a sector of the stator and rotor surfaces as parallel when their spacing a is small compared with their radii, so that the field is two-dimensional (Fig. 6–25). The rotor winding is accounted for by a

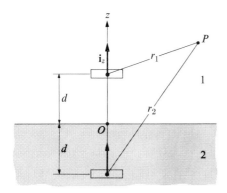

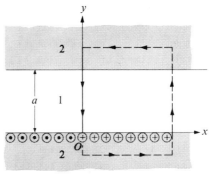

Fig. 6–24. A small coil near a semi-infinite magnetic medium.

Fig. 6–25. Air gap between a smooth stator and a smooth rotor.

surface current density $\mathbf{J}_s$ on the rotor surface. We take $\mathbf{J}_s$ to have a sinusoidal form:

$$\mathbf{J}_s = -\mathbf{i}_z J_0 \sin \frac{\pi x}{b} .$$

The relative permeabilities of the rotor and stator surfaces are very large compared with unity, so that we can consider the limiting case of infinite permeability in which the magnetic field intensity in region 2 is zero. The boundary condition (6–42), evaluated at $y = 0$, requires that

$$-\frac{\partial U}{\partial x} = J_0 \sin \frac{\pi x}{b} . \tag{6–59}$$

At $y = a$ there is no surface current and

$$-\frac{\partial U}{\partial x} = H_x = 0. \tag{6–60}$$

The latter condition requires that $\mathbf{H}$ be normal to the surface at $y = a$. In order to satisfy Eq. (6–59), we take the potential to have the form

$$U = \frac{J_0 b}{\pi} f(y) \cos \frac{\pi x}{b} .$$

The conditions (6–59) and (6–60) are satisfied if

$$f(0) = 1, \quad f(a) = 0. \tag{6–61}$$

Laplace's equation for the two-dimensional case is

$$\frac{\partial^2 U}{\partial x^2} + \frac{\partial^2 U}{\partial y^2} = 0.$$

Substituting for U yields

$$\frac{d^2f}{dy^2} - \left(\frac{\pi}{b}\right)^2 f = 0,$$

which has the solution

$$f = c_1 \cosh\frac{\pi y}{b} + c_2 \sinh\frac{\pi y}{b}.$$

The conditions (6–61) yield

$$c_1 = 1, \qquad c_2 = -\cotanh\frac{\pi a}{b}.$$

It is usually the case that $(a/b) \ll 1$. A Taylor expansion then yields the approximation $f \cong 1 - y/a$, and we obtain

$$H_x = -\frac{\partial U}{\partial x} \cong J_0\left(1 - \frac{y}{a}\right)\sin\frac{\pi x}{b},$$

$$H_y = -\frac{\partial U}{\partial y} \cong \frac{J_0}{\pi}\frac{b}{a}\cos\frac{\pi x}{b}.$$

Note that H_y is considerably larger than H_x except for a small range in values of x for which $\cos(\pi x/b) \cong 0$.

In elementary machine theory the component H_y is usually determined from the mmf. Let us consider the path illustrated in Fig. 6–25. Using Ampère's circuital law, we have

$$v_m = \oint_C \mathbf{H} \cdot d\mathbf{r} = \int_0^x - J_0 \sin(\pi x/b)\, dx,$$

$$H_y(x) = H_y(0) + \frac{J_0}{\pi}\frac{b}{a}[\cos(\pi x/b) - 1].$$

When we assume that $H_y = 0$ where J is a maximum, which occurs at $x = b/2$, we obtain the expression for H_y given previously.

6–9 MAGNETIC FIELD AND VECTOR POTENTIAL OF INFINITELY LONG STRAIGHT TRANSMISSION LINES

Long straight transmission lines find widespread use in communication and electrical power systems. An analysis of the electromagnetic properties of these lines by means of Maxwell's equations is therefore of considerable technical significance. At low frequencies, the electric and magnetic fields do not interact. In Section 3–8 we studied the electric field of transmission lines. We shall now investigate the magnetic field. The vector potential due to a uniform axial distribution of current over the cross-sectional area of an infinitely long straight transmission line can be determined by means of Eq. (6–5). This method of solution in the case of a circular cross section of

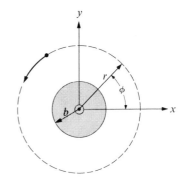

Fig. 6–26. Cross section of an infinitely long circular conductor.

radius b is left as an exercise for the student. Here we shall use Ampère's circuital law to find **H**, and then we shall use Eq. (6–2) to find **A** (Fig. 6–26). The magnitude of the magnetic field intensity (see Eqs. 6–24) is given by

$$H = \frac{i}{2\pi r}, \qquad r \geqq b, \tag{6–62a}$$

$$H = \frac{ir}{2\pi b^2}, \qquad 0 \leqq r \leqq b. \tag{6–62b}$$

Since $\mathbf{A} = \mathbf{i}_z A$, where A is a function of r only, we have (see Eq. 1–102)

$$\mathbf{B} = \text{curl } \mathbf{A} = -\mathbf{i}_\phi \frac{\partial A}{\partial r}.$$

Thus

$$B = \mu_0 H = -\frac{\partial A}{\partial r}.$$

When $r \geqq b$, we substitute Eq. (6–62a) and obtain

$$\frac{\partial A}{\partial r} = -\frac{\mu_0 i}{2\pi r}, \qquad A = -\frac{\mu_0 i}{2\pi} \cdot \ln r + c_1.$$

When $0 \leqq r \leqq b$, we substitute Eq. (6–62b) and obtain

$$\frac{\partial A}{\partial r} = -\frac{\mu_0 ir}{2\pi b^2}, \qquad A = -\frac{\mu_0 i}{4\pi} \left(\frac{r}{b}\right)^2 + c_2.$$

The vector potential is continuous at $r = b$. Thus if we let $c = c_2$ we find that

$$A = \left(-\frac{\mu_0 i}{4\pi} - \frac{\mu_0 i}{2\pi} \ln \frac{r}{b} + c\right), \qquad r \geqq b, \tag{6–63a}$$

$$A = -\frac{\mu_0 i}{4\pi} \left(\frac{r}{b}\right)^2 + c, \qquad 0 \leqq r \leqq b. \tag{6–63b}$$

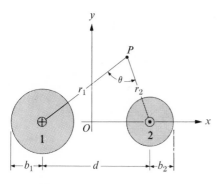

Fig. 6–27. Cross section of a two-wire transmission line.

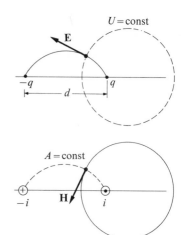

Fig. 6–28. Static electric and magnetic fields of a two-wire transmission line.

Let us now consider a two-wire transmission line, as illustrated in Fig. 6–27. We can determine the vector potential by superimposing the vector potentials of the individual conductors. For conductor 1 we must change the sign of i if we use the previously derived equations. Thus, if the field point is outside both conductors, we use Eq. (6–63a) and obtain

$$A = \left(-\frac{\mu_0 i}{4\pi} - \frac{\mu_0 i}{2\pi} \ln \frac{r_2}{b_2} + c_2\right)$$

$$+ \left(\frac{\mu_0 i}{4\pi} + \frac{\mu_0 i}{2\pi} \ln \frac{r_1}{b_1} + c_1\right) = \frac{\mu_0 i}{2\pi} \ln \frac{r_1}{r_2}. \qquad (6\text{–}64)$$

In the final step we have taken

$$-\frac{\mu_0 i}{2\pi} \ln \frac{b_1}{b_2} + c_2 + c_1 = 0,$$

so that $A \to 0$ as r_1 and r_2 become infinite. If the field point is inside conductor 2 we use Eq. (6–63a) for the vector potential of conductor 1 and Eq. (6–63b) for the vector potential of conductor 2:

$$A = \left[-\frac{\mu_0 i}{4\pi}\left(\frac{r_2}{b_2}\right)^2 + c_2\right] + \left(\frac{\mu_0 i}{4\pi} + \frac{\mu_0 i}{2\pi} \ln \frac{r_1}{b_1} + c_1\right)$$

$$= \frac{\mu_0 i}{4\pi}\left[1 - \left(\frac{r_2}{b_2}\right)^2\right] + \frac{\mu_0 i}{2\pi} \ln \frac{r_1}{b_2}. \qquad (6\text{–}65)$$

In the region outside both conductors A has the same form as the electrostatic potential of a charged two-wire transmission line (see Example 2, Section 4–4). When we choose a constant c, so that $\mu_0 i = cq/\varepsilon_0$, we see that

$A = cU$, where U is the electric scalar potential. The magnetic flux density is given by

$$\mathbf{B} = \mathbf{i}_x \frac{\partial A}{\partial y} - \mathbf{i}_y \frac{\partial A}{\partial x} = -\mathbf{i}_z \times \operatorname{grad} A = c\mathbf{i}_z \times \mathbf{E}, \qquad (6\text{–}66)$$

where $\mathbf{E} = -\operatorname{grad} U$. Thus we see that the $\mathbf{E}$ and $\mathbf{B}$ fields differ in that the role of the field vector and equipotential are interchanged (Fig. 6–28).

6–10 ANISOTROPIC MAGNETIC MEDIA

In an isotropic magnetic medium $\mathbf{M}$ and $\mathbf{H}$ are collinear and an equation of the type

$$\mathbf{M} = \chi\mathbf{H}$$

holds. In general, however, this need not be the case and we then speak of an *anisotropic magnetic medium*. For an anisotropic magnetic medium $\mathbf{M}$ changes its orientation with respect to $\mathbf{H}$ as the direction of $\mathbf{H}$ changes, and in a cartesian coordinate system we have relations of the form

$$M_x = a_{11}H_x + a_{12}H_y + a_{13}H_z,$$

$$M_y = a_{21}H_x + a_{22}H_y + a_{23}H_z,$$

$$M_z = a_{31}H_x + a_{32}H_y + a_{33}H_z.$$

These equations can be expressed (see Section 1–22) in a tensor form,

$$\mathbf{M} = \mathbf{\chi} \cdot \mathbf{H},$$

where

$$\mathbf{\chi} \triangleq \begin{pmatrix} a_{11} & a_{12} & a_{13} \\ a_{21} & a_{22} & a_{23} \\ a_{31} & a_{32} & a_{33} \end{pmatrix}$$

is defined as the *tensor magnetic susceptibility*.

Many important technical applications of anisotropic magnetic media occur in microwave engineering. If a dc magnetic field is used to magnetize a ferrite, it can exhibit anisotropic effects at very high frequencies (see Chapter 12). We shall discuss the case of a small ferrite sphere of radius a situated in a high-frequency sinusoidally time-varying field (Fig. 6–29). If the radius is sufficiently small we can use static field methods to compute the internal high-frequency field. In the case of sinusoidally time-varying fields we introduce phasor quantities to represent the field vectors and scalar potentials. The physically observed field vectors are then given by*

$$\operatorname{Re}\,[\mathbf{H}e^{j\omega t}], \qquad \operatorname{Re}\,[\mathbf{M}e^{j\omega t}],$$

---

* Re $[\mathring{f}]$ denotes the real part of f. For a further discussion of phasors see Section 7–8.

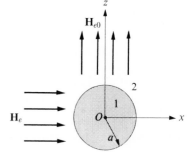

Fig. 6–29. A small ferrite sphere in a combined dc field $\mathbf{H}_{e0}$ and a time-varying field with an amplitude $\mathbf{H}_e$.

where $\mathbf{H}$ and $\mathbf{M}$ are the field phasors. The analysis of the problem will be carried out using phasors. An applied dc magnetic field $\mathbf{H}_{e0} = \mathbf{i}_z H_{e0}$ results in a tensor magnetic susceptibility,

$$\boldsymbol{\chi} = \begin{pmatrix} \chi & -j\kappa & 0 \\ j\kappa & \chi & 0 \\ 0 & 0 & 0 \end{pmatrix} = \mathbf{i}_x(\mathbf{i}_x\chi - \mathbf{i}_y j\kappa) + \mathbf{i}_y(\mathbf{i}_x j\kappa + \mathbf{i}_y\chi),$$

and the phasors $\mathbf{H}$ and $\mathbf{M}$ are related by the equation $\mathbf{M} = \boldsymbol{\chi} \cdot \mathbf{H}$. It should be noted that the elements of $\boldsymbol{\chi}$ are functions of the angular frequency ω. The phasor magnetic flux density is given by the equation

$$\mathbf{B} = \mu_0\mathbf{H} + \mu_0\boldsymbol{\chi} \cdot \mathbf{H}.$$

In region 1 inside the sphere we represent the magnetic field intensity as the negative gradient of a scalar potential: $\mathbf{H}_1 = -\text{grad } U_1$. We then have

$$-\boldsymbol{\chi} \cdot \mathbf{H}_1 = \mathbf{i}_x\left(\chi\frac{\partial U_1}{\partial x} - j\kappa\frac{\partial U_1}{\partial y}\right) + \mathbf{i}_y\left(j\kappa\frac{\partial U_1}{\partial x} + \chi\frac{\partial U_1}{\partial y}\right). \quad (6\text{–}67)$$

The condition div $\mathbf{B}_1 = 0$ yields

$$\nabla^2 U_1 + \chi\left(\nabla^2 U_1 - \frac{\partial^2 U_1}{\partial z^2}\right) = 0,$$

which can be written as

$$\mu_r \nabla^2 U_1 - \chi\frac{\partial^2 U_1}{\partial z^2} = 0, \quad (6\text{–}68)$$

where

$$\mu_r \overset{\triangle}{=} 1 + \chi. \quad (6\text{–}69)$$

In region 2 outside the sphere the potential satisfies Laplace's equation

$$\nabla^2 U_2 = 0. \quad (6\text{–}70)$$

We can determine U_1 and U_2 by a generalization of the method discussed in Example 3, Section 4–4. Thus for a field point in medium 2 we assume that the sphere will appear as a dipole whose axis is in the xy-plane, and we set

$$U_2 = -H_e x - D_1 \frac{x}{r^3} - D_2 \frac{y}{r^3}, \qquad r \geq a,$$

where

$$\mathbf{H}_e = \mathbf{i}_x H_e$$

is the externally applied phasor magnetic field intensity.

Inside the sphere we expect that the amplitude of the field will be uniform. Since the field potential must satisfy Eq. (6–68) (note that Eq. 6–68 is not Laplace's equation), we set

$$U_1 = -A_1 x - A_2 y, \qquad r \leq a.$$

The assumed potentials U_1 and U_2 satisfy Eqs. (6–68) and (6–70), respectively. We must now determine the unknown constants so that the boundary conditions are satisfied. We set

$$x = r \cos \theta_x, \qquad y = r \cos \theta_y.$$

The condition that $U_1 = U_2$ at $r = a$ is satisfied if we equate like coefficients of $\cos \theta_x$ and $\cos \theta_y$ on both sides of the equation. This yields

$$D_2 = a^3 A_2, \qquad D_1 = a^3(A_1 - H_e).$$

The normal component of $\mathbf{B}$ must be continuous at $r = a$. This requires that

$$\mu_0 \mathbf{n} \cdot \mathbf{H}_2 = \mu_0 \mathbf{n} \cdot (\mathbf{H}_1 + \boldsymbol{\chi} \cdot \mathbf{H}_1),$$

$$\frac{\partial U_2}{\partial r} = \frac{\partial U_1}{\partial r} - \mathbf{n} \cdot (\boldsymbol{\chi} \cdot \mathbf{H}_1)$$

$$= \frac{\partial U_1}{\partial r} + \left(\chi \frac{\partial U_1}{\partial x} - j\kappa \frac{\partial U_1}{\partial y} \right) \cos \theta_x + \left(j\kappa \frac{\partial U_1}{\partial x} + \chi \frac{\partial U_1}{\partial y} \right) \cos \theta_y.$$

In the final step we have made use of Eq. (6–67). Equating like coefficients of $\cos \theta_x$ and $\cos \theta_y$ on both sides of the equation yields

$$(3 + \chi)A_1 - j\kappa A_2 = 3H_e, \qquad j\kappa A_1 + (3 + \chi)A_2 = 0.$$

Solving the above equations, we obtain (see Eq. (6–69) for the definition of μ_r)

$$A_1 = \frac{3(2 + \mu_r)}{(2 + \mu_r)^2 - \kappa^2} H_e, \qquad A_2 = -\frac{j3\kappa}{(2 + \mu_r)^2 - \kappa^2} H_e.$$

The phasor representation for the internal magnetic field is

$$\mathbf{H}_i = -\mathbf{i}_x \frac{\partial U_1}{\partial x} - \mathbf{i}_y \frac{\partial U_1}{\partial y} = \mathbf{i}_x A_1 + \mathbf{i}_y A_2, \tag{6–71}$$

and the real time-varying magnetic field intensity is given by

$$\text{Re } [\mathbf{H}_i e^{j\omega t}].$$

PROBLEMS

6–1 Use the Biot-Savart law and show that the magnetic field intensity of a straight current filament of length l at a field point P (Fig. 6–30) is

$$\mathbf{H} = \mathbf{i}_z \frac{i}{4\pi R} (\cos \alpha_1 - \cos \alpha_2).$$

In a static field the current must flow in closed loops. Thus the above expression is applicable only to segments of a closed filament. The next two problems illustrate this.

6–2 A current filament has the shape of a uniform plane polygon of n sides (Fig. 6–31). Use the result of Problem 6–1 and show that the magnetic field intensity at the center O is given by

$$\mathbf{H} = \mathbf{i}_z \frac{in}{2\pi a} \sin \frac{\pi}{n},$$

where i is the current. Use this expression to determine the magnetic field intensity at the center of a circular current filament.

6–3 A rectangular current filament has its center on the x-axis at a distance x from the origin (Fig. 6–32). The plane of the rectangle is parallel to the yz-plane and the current is i. (a) Use the result of Problem 6–1 and show that for a field point at O,

$$B_x = \frac{\mu_0 iab}{4\pi} \frac{1}{\sqrt{x^2 + (a/2)^2 + (b/2)^2}} \left[\frac{1}{x^2 + (b/2)^2} + \frac{1}{x^2 + (a/2)^2} \right].$$

(b) Given that the interval x contains a uniformly distributed rectangular winding of n turns per unit length, show that

$$B_x = \frac{\mu_0 in}{\pi} \left[\arcsin \frac{2ax}{\sqrt{(a^2 + b^2)(b^2 + 4x^2)}} + \arcsin \frac{2bx}{\sqrt{(a^2 + b^2)(a^2 + 4x^2)}} \right].$$

[*Hint:* To perform the integration, use the substitutions $x = (a/2) \tan \theta$ and $u = a \sin \theta / \sqrt{a^2 + b^2}$.]

6–4 An infinitely long plane conducting strip has negligible thickness, a width w, and the current i is uniformly distributed (Fig. 6–33). Determine the magnetic field intensity at the point P which is opposite one edge, as shown in the figure.

6–5 A uniformly wound coil of length l has n turns per unit length, a circular cross section of radius a, and carries a current i. The direction of current flow forms a right-handed system with respect to the x-axis (Fig. 6–34). Determine the component H_x on the x-axis using Eq. (6–15), for a case in which: (a) the point P is outside the coil, (b) the point P is inside the coil. [*Hint:* Use the result of part (a) with $x = 0$ and apply it to the two sections of the coil on either side of P.]

6–6 Consider an infinitely long circular cylindrical conductor of radius a which has a uniform axial current density $\mathbf{J}$ (Fig. 6–35). The conductor has an off-centered hole of radius b. Show that the magnetic field intensity inside the hole is given by $\mathbf{H} = (\mathbf{J} \times \mathbf{C})/2$, where $\mathbf{C}$ is the vector defined by the centers of the circles. [*Hint:*

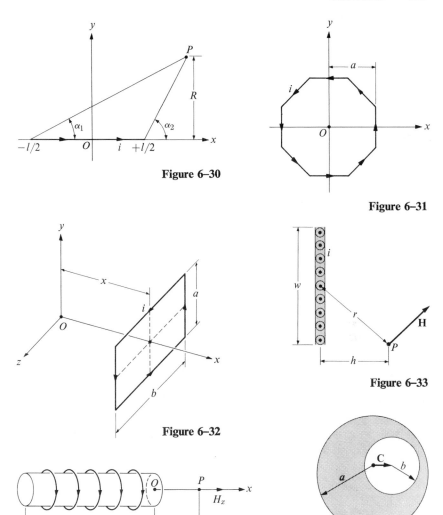

Figure 6–30

Figure 6–31

Figure 6–32

Figure 6–33

Figure 6–34

Figure 6–35

Consider the resultant field of two circular conductors of radii a and b which have current densities of $\mathbf{J}$ and $-\mathbf{J}$, respectively.]

6–7 Two infinitely long straight current filaments are parallel at a distance d apart. The currents in the filaments are i and $-i$, respectively (see Fig. 6–27). Determine the solid angle resulting from the projection of the filaments on a unit sphere centered at a field point P. With the aid of Eq. (6–10), determine the vector potential at P. What is the relation between A and the scalar magnetic potential U given by Eq.(6–17)?

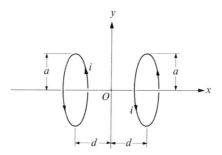

Figure 6–36

6–8 Consider the permanent magnet illustrated in Fig. 6–20. It follows from Eq. (6–37) that we can consider a uniform surface charge density $\sigma_m = \pm M$ to exist over the magnet faces. Use Eq. (6–38) and prove Eq. (6–39).

6–9 Figure 6–36 illustrates two Helmholz coils which can be used to obtain a uniform magnetic field in the neighborhood of the origin O. Given that a is the coil radius and $2d$ the distance between coils, determine the relationship between a and d which gives a maximally uniform field at O.

6–10 Show that the boundary condition (6–42) can be written in the form

$$(\mathbf{H}_2 - \mathbf{H}_1) \times \mathbf{n} = \mathbf{J}_s.$$

6–11 A coil is wound on the surface of a sphere of radius a. Let $n(\theta)$ be the winding density, so that $an(\theta)\, d\theta$ is the number of turns enclosed by the angle $d\theta$, and let i be the current. Here θ is the polar angle of a spherical coordinate system centered at the origin of the sphere. Determine $n(\theta)$ for a case in which the magnetic field intensity $\mathbf{H}_i$ inside the sphere is to be uniform.

6–12 A perfectly conducting sphere of radius a is placed in a uniform magnetic field $\mathbf{H}_0 = \mathbf{i}_z H_0$. Use spherical coordinates and show that the surface current density

$$\mathbf{J}_s = -\mathbf{i}_\phi \frac{3H_0}{2} \sin \theta$$

results in perfect shielding, where $\mathbf{H} = 0$ for $0 \leqq r \leqq a$.

6–13 A soft-iron sphere of radius a and permeability μ is placed in a uniform magnetic field $\mathbf{H}_0 = \mathbf{i}_z H_0$. Prove that the potential U_1 inside the sphere and the potential U_2 outside the sphere are given by Eqs. (6–48). Evaluate the magnetization current densities $\mathbf{J}_m$ and $\mathbf{J}_{sm}$.

6–14 If we let $\mu \to 0$ in Problem 6–13 we have a case in which no magnetic flux can penetrate the sphere. The situation is then similar to the case of the perfectly conducting sphere discussed in Problem 6–12. Show that the surface magnetization current density is equal to the surface current density of the conducting sphere and that the external fields are the same. Are the internal fields the same?

6–15 Consider an infinitely long circular cylindrical shell of permeability μ and of outer and inner radii a and b, respectively. The cylinder is placed in a uniform magnetic field $\mathbf{H}_0$ which is perpendicular to the axis of the cylinder. Determine the field $\mathbf{H}_i$ inside the cylinder.

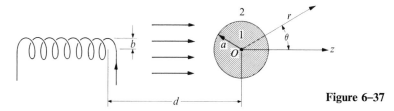

Figure 6–37

6–16 A soft-iron sphere of radius a and permeability μ is placed at a distance d from one end of a semi-infinitely long uniform coil of circular cross section, as shown in Fig. 6–37. The cross section has a radius b, the coil is uniformly wound with n turns per unit length, and the current is i. Given that $a \ll d$, $b \ll d$, the field H_0 due to the coil in the vicinity of the sphere can be considered to be uniform, so that the potentials in regions 1 and 2 are given approximately by

$$U_1 = -H_0 r \cos \theta + \frac{A \cos \theta}{r^2}, \qquad U_2 = -H_i r \cos \theta.$$

Show that

$$H_0 = M_p / 4\pi d^2, \qquad M_p = \pi b^2 in,$$

$$H_i = \frac{3}{2 + \mu_r} H_0, \qquad \frac{A}{a^3} = \frac{\mu_r - 1}{\mu_r + 2} H_0.$$

6–17 A small closely wound circular coil of radius c and N turns is located at the center of a soft-iron spherical shell of permeability μ. The current in the coil is i and the outer and inner radii of the shell are a and b, respectively. Given that $c \ll a$, determine an expression for the effectiveness of the shell in shielding the exterior region $(r > a)$ from the magnetic field of the coil. [*Hint:* Assume that the field inside the shell consists of the dipole field of the coil and a uniform field due to the magnetic shell.]

6–18 Show that the magnetization current density $\mathbf{J}_m$ and the surface magnetization current density $\mathbf{J}_{sm}$ satisfy the relation

$$\int_{v_m} \mathbf{J}_m \, dv + \int_{S_m} \mathbf{J}_{sm} \, ds = 0,$$

where S_m is the surface of a magnetic medium of volume v_m.

6–19 A plane current filament is at a distance d from a semi-infinite plane magnetic medium of permeability μ (Fig. 6–38). Show that for $z > 0$ the magnetic flux density can be considered to be due to the original filament carrying a current i and an image filament located as shown in the figure and carrying a current

$$i' = \frac{\mu_r - 1}{\mu_r + 1} i,$$

and that for $z < 0$ the magnetic flux density can be considered to be due to the

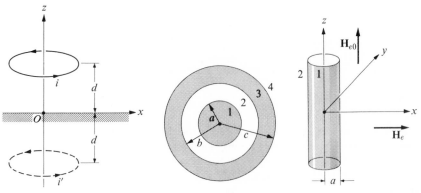

Figure 6–38   **Figure 6–39**   **Figure 6–40**

original filament alone, but carrying a current

$$i'' = \frac{2\mu_r}{\mu_r + 1} i.$$

[*Hint:* Replace the current filament by a distribution of dipoles and use the results given in Example 3, Section 6–8.]

6–20 An infinitesimally thin conducting spherical shell of radius a is charged to a potential V with respect to infinity and is rotated with an angular velocity ω about the z-axis passing through its center. Show that there exists within the shell a uniform magnetic field intensity which is given by

$$\mathbf{H}_i = \mathbf{i}_z \tfrac{2}{3}\omega\varepsilon_0 V,$$

and that for $r > a$ the rotating shell appears as a dipole with a dipole moment

$$\mathbf{m} = \mathbf{i}_z \frac{4\pi a^3}{3} \omega\varepsilon_0 V.$$

6–21 Consider the infinitely long coaxial cable shown in Fig. 6–39. The currents i and $-i$ are uniformly distributed over the cross-sectional areas of the inner and outer conductors, respectively. Determine the magnetic field intensity in the regions 1, 2, 3, and 4.

6–22 A surface current density

$$\mathbf{J}_s = \mathbf{i}_y J_0 \sin\frac{\pi x}{b}$$

exists on the surface $z = 0$ defined in a cartesian coordinate system. Determine the magnetic field intensity at any field point by solving Laplace's equation for a suitable potential function. The surface is situated in free space.

6–23 A long thin circular ferrite cylinder of radius a is placed in a dc magnetic field $\mathbf{H}_{e0} = \mathbf{i}_z H_{e0}$ which has the direction of the cylinder axis (Fig. 6–40). A high-frequency sinusoidally time-varying magnetic field is applied which has a phasor representation $\mathbf{H}_e = \mathbf{i}_x H_e$. Use the method discussed in Section 6–10 and show that

$$U_2 = -H_e x - \frac{D_1 x}{r^2} - \frac{D_2 y}{r^2}, \qquad r \geqq a, \qquad\qquad U_1 = -A_1 x - A_2 y, \qquad r \leqq a,$$

where

$$A_1 = \frac{2(\mu_r + 1)}{(\mu_r + 1)^2 - \kappa^2} H_e, \qquad A_2 = \frac{-j2\kappa}{(\mu_r + 1)^2 - \kappa^2} H_e$$

are the phasor potentials from which the phasor magnetic field intensity can be found.

CHAPTER 7

THE QUASI-STATIC ELECTROMAGNETIC FIELD

7-1 INTRODUCTION

In Chapters 4 and 6 we treated the electric and magnetic fields independently of each other. In this chapter we shall begin to account for the interaction between **E** and **B** if the current density **J** is time-varying. We define the *quasi-static electromagnetic field* by the equations (see Eqs. 2–42, 2–46, and 2–47)

$$\text{curl } \mathbf{E} = -\frac{\partial \mathbf{B}}{\partial t}, \qquad \text{curl } \mathbf{H} = \mathbf{J},$$

$$\text{div } \mathbf{B} = 0, \qquad \text{div } \mathbf{D} = \rho, \qquad \text{div } \mathbf{J} = 0.$$

In a quasi-static electromagnetic field we allow **J** to be time-varying but consider $\partial \rho / \partial t$ to be negligible so that $\partial \mathbf{D}/\partial t$ is also negligible. In Section 11–11 it will be shown that $\partial \rho / \partial t$ is negligible when the frequency is sufficiently low or when the circuit dimensions are sufficiently small. We may then neglect $d\phi_e/dt$ in Eq. (2–54b), so that for the quasi-static electromagnetic field we use the integral forms

$$\oint_C \mathbf{E} \cdot d\mathbf{r} = -\frac{d\phi}{dt}, \tag{7–1a}$$

$$\oint_C \mathbf{H} \cdot d\mathbf{r} = i. \tag{7–1b}$$

Here we have set $\phi \triangleq \phi_m$ since we need not distinguish between ϕ_e and ϕ_m. We shall discuss the application of Eqs. (7–1) to coils composed of current filaments in which the cross-sectional area is negligible. When a coil has N closely wound turns we have

$$\oint_C \mathbf{E} \cdot d\mathbf{r} = -N\frac{d\phi}{dt}, \tag{7–2}$$

where C is the contour for the complete N-turn filament and ϕ is the magnetic flux linked by one turn. (Thus $N\phi$ is the magnetic flux linked by the contour C.) Equation (7–1b) is Ampère's circuital law. Thus we see that the quasi-static magnetic field can be determined by the methods developed in Chapter 6 for the static magnetic field. However, the magnetic field will now be con-

198

sidered to be time-varying, and associated with the time-varying magnetic field is an electric field intensity $\mathbf{E}'$ which satisfies Eq. (7–1a). Associated with the charge density ρ is an electric field intensity $\mathbf{E}''$ which can be determined by the methods discussed in Chapter 4. However, $\mathbf{E}''$ does not interact with the magnetic field. Thus, without loss of generality for magnetic fields satisfying the quasi-static conditions, we can consider ρ to be zero, so that we may take $\mathbf{E} = \mathbf{E}' + \mathbf{E}'' = \mathbf{E}'$.

7–2 THE CONCEPT OF VOLTAGE SOURCES AND EQUIVALENT CIRCUITS

Let us consider a fixed closely wound coil of N turns in a time-varying magnetic field. Associated with the time-varying magnetic field is an electric field intensity which causes a current i to flow. We have (see Eqs. 2–10 and 7–2)

$$iR + N\frac{\partial \phi}{\partial t} = 0, \qquad (7\text{–}3)$$

where the resistance R of the coil is given by Eq. (2–7). The current i sets up a magnetic field, and for the case in which ϕ is due to i alone we have a relation of the form

$$N\frac{\partial \phi}{\partial t} = L\frac{di}{dt}, \qquad (7\text{–}4)$$

where the parameter L is defined as the self-inductance of the coil. Equation (7–3) can then be written as

$$iR + L\frac{di}{dt} = 0, \qquad (7\text{–}5)$$

which can be interpreted in terms of an equivalent circuit (Fig. 7–1). We speak of a *voltage iR* between the terminals of the resistor R and of a *voltage* $L(di/dt)$ between the terminals of the inductor L. Equation (7–5) is then a special case of *Kirchhoff's law*, which states that the sum of the voltages between the terminals of network elements in a closed loop is zero.

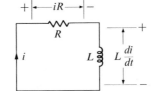

Fig. 7–1. Equivalent circuit for a coil.

In general, we have one or more coils interacting in some manner with sources of electromagnetic energy. Let us consider a coil driven by means of a long transmission line whose spacing h is infinitesimally small (Fig. 7–2a).

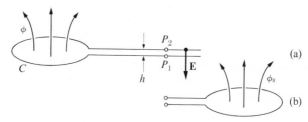

Fig. 7–2. Excitation of a coil (a) by (b) a transmission line and (c) a battery.

The infinitesimal gap at the terminals of the coil is important for physical reasons, since it is at the gap that we consider the coil to be excited. The transmission line can be excited by a second coil which is inductively coupled to a magnetic field, as illustrated in Fig. 7–2b. The coil can be fixed and be linked by a time-varying flux ϕ_s, as is the case in a transformer, or the coil may rotate with ϕ_s fixed, as is the case in a rotating machine. The transmission line can also be driven from a battery, as shown in Fig. 7–2c.

We find it convenient to consider the driving source and the coil separately. Thus we consider only that portion of the network to the left of the transmission-line terminals P_1 and P_2. For simplicity we take the transmission line to be a perfect conductor, so that $\mathbf{E} \cdot d\mathbf{r} = 0$ along the transmission-line surface. The electric field intensity $\mathbf{E}$ at the terminals is taken to have the direction shown in the figure. We now apply Eq. (7–2) to the path consisting of the coil, the transmission line, and the path from P_1 to P_2 and obtain

$$\oint_C \mathbf{E} \cdot d\mathbf{r} + (-Eh) = -N \frac{\partial \phi}{\partial t} .$$

The above equation can be written in the form (see Eq. 7–3)

$$iR + N \frac{\partial \phi}{\partial t} = v, \tag{7–6}$$

where $v = Eh$ is defined as the *applied voltage* at the terminals P_1 and P_2. In computing R, we evaluate the line integral along the coil axis C. Since we take $h \to 0$, we consider the limit of C to be a closed contour. Figure 7–3 illustrates the equivalent circuit associated with Eq. (7–6), where we consider the circuit to be driven by the voltage source v.

Network theory can be developed independently of physical considerations, while field theory is the means by which physical elements can be represented by the ideal elements of network theory. Considerable care must be taken in the interpretation of field equations in terms of equivalent circuits. In the subsequent discussions we shall consider that coils are driven

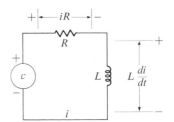

Fig. 7–3. Equivalent circuit for a coil driven by a voltage source.

by voltage sources and the figures will indicate this accordingly. However, it must be kept in mind that the physical situation corresponds to that shown in Fig. 7–2, where each coil is driven from a source of electromagnetic energy through a closely spaced transmission line. (At low frequencies the transmission line often takes the form of twisted conducting leads.)

Given that $R = 0$, we can write Eq. (7–6) as

$$N \frac{\partial \phi}{\partial t} = v = L \frac{di}{dt}. \tag{7–7}$$

Equation (7–7) is a special case of Faraday's law of electromagnetic induction, and the vector $\mathbf{E}$ in Eq. (7–1a) is often referred to as the *induced electric field intensity*.

Since we can determine the quasi-static magnetic field by the methods discussed in Chapter 6, we need only determine $\mathbf{E}$ to find the complete quasi-static electromagnetic field. We shall now show that $\mathbf{E}$ may be expressed in terms of the vector potential $\mathbf{A}$. Let us consider an arbitrary coil of one turn which has a contour C_1. The magnetic flux linked by C_1 is

$$\phi = \int_{S_1} \mathbf{B} \cdot \mathbf{n} \, ds,$$

where S_1 is an arbitrary surface bounded by C_1. With the aid of Stokes' theorem and the equation $\mathbf{B} = \text{curl } \mathbf{A}$, we find that

$$\phi = \oint_{C_1} \mathbf{A} \cdot d\mathbf{r}. \tag{7–8}$$

Equation (7–1a) yields

$$\oint_C \mathbf{E} \cdot d\mathbf{r} = - \oint_{C_1} \frac{\partial \mathbf{A}}{\partial t} \cdot d\mathbf{r},$$

where the partial derivative indicates that the contour is fixed. Since C_1 is arbitrary, it follows that

$$\mathbf{E} = - \frac{\partial \mathbf{A}}{\partial t}. \tag{7–9}$$

Thus in a quasi-static magnetic field the electric field intensity is equal to the negative time rate of change of the vector potential.

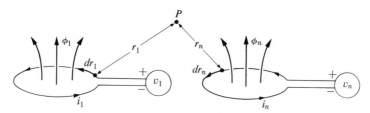

Fig. 7–4. Diagram of n separate coils driven by n voltage sources.

7–3 THE SELF AND MUTUAL INDUCTANCE OF COILS

Figure 7–4 illustrates a situation in which n coils are driven by n voltage sources v_j. We are interested in determining the relationships which exist between the voltages v_j, the currents i_j, and the magnetic fluxes ϕ_j linked by the coils. It follows from Eq. (7–8) that the flux linked by the contour C_j of one turn is

$$\phi_j = \oint_{C_j} \mathbf{A} \cdot d\mathbf{r}. \tag{7–10}$$

The vector potential at a field point P (see Eq. 6–10) is

$$\mathbf{A} = \frac{\mu_0}{4\pi} \sum_{k=1}^{n} i_k N_k \oint_{C_k} \frac{d\mathbf{r}_k}{r_k(P)},$$

where N_k is the number of closely wound turns of the kth coil. Substituting into Eq. (7–10) yields the flux linked by the N_j turns of the jth coil,

$$\phi_j N_j = \sum_{k=1}^{n} L_{jk} i_k. \tag{7–11}$$

Here we have set

$$L_{jk} \triangleq \frac{\mu_0 N_j N_k}{4\pi} \oint_{C_k} \oint_{C_j} \frac{d\mathbf{r}_j \cdot d\mathbf{r}_k}{r_{jk}}, \tag{7–12}$$

where r_{jk} is the distance between the line elements $d\mathbf{r}_j$ and $d\mathbf{r}_k$. Equation (7–7) applied to the jth coil yields

$$v_j = \sum_{k=1}^{n} L_{jk} \frac{di_k}{dt}. \tag{7–13}$$

We can interpret the parameter L_{jk} by considering the special case in which all currents are constant with the exception of i_m. We then have

$$v_j = L_{jm} \frac{di_m}{dt}, \quad i_j = \text{const for all } j \neq m.$$

A rate of change of current in the mth coil induces an electric field in the jth coil which must be compensated for by an applied voltage v_j, if the current i_j is to remain constant. The parameter L_{jk} is defined as the *mutual inductance* between the jth and kth coils and can be determined from Eq. (7–12), which is known as *Neumann's formula*. It follows from $r_{jk} = r_{kj}$ that $L_{jk} = L_{kj}$.

We shall now give two examples to illustrate the use of Eqs. (7–4) and (7–12) for computing the inductance of coils.

Example 1. Let us determine the inductance of the toroidal winding discussed in Example 2, Section 6–6. The component of magnetic field intensity normal to the cross-sectional area is given by Eq. (6–25). Given that μ is the permeability of the core material, the normal component of the magnetic flux density is

$$\mathbf{B} \cdot \mathbf{n} = \frac{\mu i N}{2\pi r}.$$

When we make the substitution (see Fig. 7–5) $r = b - \rho \cos \theta$, we find that the flux linked by one turn is

$$\phi = \frac{\mu i N}{2\pi} \int_0^a \int_0^{2\pi} \frac{\rho \, d\rho \, d\theta}{b - \rho \cos \theta}.$$

To perform the integration, we make use of the formula

$$\int_0^{2\pi} \frac{d\theta}{b - \rho \cos \theta} = \frac{2\pi}{\sqrt{b^2 - \rho^2}}, \qquad b > \rho. \tag{7–14}$$

Thus

$$\phi = \mu i N \int_0^a \frac{\rho \, d\rho}{\sqrt{b^2 - \rho^2}} = \mu i N (-\sqrt{b^2 - \rho^2})\Big]_0^a = \mu i N (b - \sqrt{b^2 - a^2}).$$

Equation (7–4), which defines the inductance, can be integrated with respect to time. This yields

$$L = \frac{\phi N}{i}. \tag{7–15}$$

Equation (7–15) is useful for finding L once we have expressed ϕ in terms of i. We find that

$$L = \mu N^2 (b - \sqrt{b^2 - a^2}).$$

(The inductance can also be determined from the magnetic field energy, as given by Eq. 7–22.)

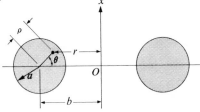

Fig. 7–5. Cross section of a toroidal coil.

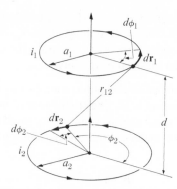

Fig. 7–6. Two coaxial circular coils.

Example 2. Figure 7–6 illustrates two closely wound circular coils which
have N_1 and N_2 turns and radii a_1 and a_2, respectively. The planes of the
coils are parallel and a distance d apart. To determine the mutual inductance
we use Neumann's formula (7–12). We note that

$$d\mathbf{r}_1 \cdot d\mathbf{r}_2 = (a_1 \, d\phi_1)(a_2 \, d\phi_2) \cos \phi_2$$

and that the law of cosines gives

$$r_{12}^2 = d^2 + a_1^2 + a_2^2 - 2a_1 a_2 \cos \phi_2.$$

Thus

$$L_{12} = \frac{\mu_0 N_1 N_2 a_1 a_2}{4\pi} \int_0^{2\pi} \int_0^{2\pi} \frac{\cos \phi_2}{r_{12}} \, d\phi_2 \, d\phi_1.$$

Let f denote the integrand of the above integral, and let

$$I \triangleq \int_0^{2\pi} f \, d\phi_2.$$

By means of the substitution $\phi_2 = \pi - 2\beta$, we find that

$$I = 4 \int_0^{\pi/2} f \, d\beta$$

and that

$$\cos \phi_2 = 2 \sin^2 \beta - 1, \qquad r_{12}^2 = \frac{4a_1 a_2}{k^2} (1 - k^2 \sin^2 \beta)$$

where

$$k^2 \triangleq \frac{4a_1 a_2}{d^2 + (a_1 + a_2)^2}.$$

The function f can be written as

$$f = \frac{k}{2\sqrt{a_1 a_2}} \left[\frac{2}{k^2} - 1 - \frac{2}{k^2} (1 - k^2 \sin^2 \beta) \right] \frac{1}{\sqrt{1 - k^2 \sin^2 \beta}}.$$

Thus

$$I = \frac{2}{\sqrt{a_1 a_2}}\left[\left(\frac{2}{k} - k\right)F - \frac{2E}{k}\right]$$

where

$$F \triangleq \int_0^{\pi/2} \frac{d\beta}{\sqrt{1 - k^2 \sin^2 \beta}}, \qquad E \triangleq \int_0^{\pi/2} \sqrt{1 - k^2 \sin^2 \beta}\; d\beta$$

are the complete elliptic integrals of the first and second kinds, respectively (see Eq. 4–75). Since I is independent of ϕ_1, the integration with respect to ϕ_1 yields 2π. Thus

$$L_{12} = \mu_0 N_1 N_2 \sqrt{a_1 a_2}\left[\left(\frac{2}{k} - k\right)F - \frac{2E}{k}\right]. \tag{7–16}$$

7–4 MAGNETIC FIELD ENERGY

We shall now determine an expression for the magnetic field energy of a system of n conducting coils (Fig. 7–4). For reasons of simplicity, we consider the coils to be perfect conductors, so that we need not consider the dissipative losses. The field energy is supplied by the n voltage sources and the input power is the rate of change of field energy:

$$P = \frac{\partial W}{\partial t} = v_1 i_1 + \cdots + v_n i_n$$

$$= i_1 N_1 \frac{\partial \phi_1}{\partial t} + \cdots + i_n N_n \frac{\partial \phi_n}{\partial t}. \tag{7–17}$$

For the special case in which all currents i_k are constant with the exception of i_j ($j \neq k$), Eq. (7–17) yields

$$\frac{\partial W}{\partial i_j} = i_1 N_1 \frac{\partial \phi_1}{\partial i_j} + \cdots + i_n N_n \frac{\partial \phi_n}{\partial i_j}$$

$$= i_1 L_{j1} + \cdots + i_n L_{jn} = \phi_j N_j. \tag{7–18}$$

In the second step of the above derivation we have used the relation

$$N_j \frac{\partial \phi_j}{\partial i_k} = L_{jk} = L_{kj},$$

which is obtained by differentiating Eq. (7–11) with respect to i_k. In the final step of the derivation we have made direct use of Eq. (7–11).

In order to determine W we must integrate Eq. (7–17) with respect to t. However, the right-hand side of the equation cannot, as it stands, be integrated. We therefore first consider W as a function of the currents:

$$W = W(i_1, i_2, \ldots, i_n).$$

Differentiating with respect to t, we obtain

$$\frac{\partial W}{\partial t} = \frac{\partial W}{\partial i_1}\frac{\partial i_1}{\partial t} + \cdots + \frac{\partial W}{\partial i_n}\frac{\partial i_n}{\partial t} = \phi_1 N_1 \frac{\partial i_1}{\partial t} + \cdots + \phi_n N_n \frac{\partial i_n}{\partial t}, \quad (7\text{–}19)$$

where we have used Eq. (7–18). Adding Eqs. (7–17) and (7–19) yields

$$2\frac{\partial W}{\partial t} = \frac{\partial}{\partial t}(i_1 N_1 \phi_1 + \cdots + i_n N_n \phi_n)$$

which can be integrated with respect to t. Thus

$$W = \tfrac{1}{2}\sum_{j=1}^{n} i_j N_j \phi_j, \quad (7\text{–}20)$$

where $N_j \phi_j$ is the flux linked by the current i_j. We speak of the product $i_j N_j \phi_j$ as a *flux-current linkage*. The magnetic field energy is equal to one-half the sum of all flux-current linkages. Substituting Eq. (7–11) into Eq. (7–20) yields

$$W = \tfrac{1}{2}\sum_{j=1}^{n}\sum_{k=1}^{n} L_{jk} i_j i_k. \quad (7\text{–}21)$$

For the special case of a single coil, Eqs. (7–20) and (7–21) reduce to

$$W = \tfrac{1}{2}Li^2 = \tfrac{1}{2}iN\phi. \quad (7\text{–}22)$$

In the case of two coils we have

$$W = \tfrac{1}{2}i_1 N_1 \phi_1 + \tfrac{1}{2}i_2 N_2 \phi_2 = \tfrac{1}{2}L_{11}i_1^2 + Mi_1 i_2 + \tfrac{1}{2}L_{22}i_2^2, \quad (7\text{–}23)$$

where $M = L_{12} = L_{21}$ is the mutual inductance between the two coils.

Equation (7–20) can be used to determine the magnetic field energy of a continuous distribution of current within a volume v. We consider the current distribution to consist of elemental current filaments of cross-sectional area a and of one turn, so that $N_k = 1$. Equation (7–20) yields

$$W = \tfrac{1}{2}\sum_{j=1}^{n} i_j \oint_{C_j} \mathbf{A}\cdot d\mathbf{r}_j = \tfrac{1}{2}\int_v \mathbf{A}\cdot \mathbf{J}\, dv. \quad (7\text{–}24)$$

Here we have used the relation

$$i_j\, d\mathbf{r}_j = a\mathbf{J}(P_j)\, dr = \mathbf{J}\,\Delta v,$$

where Δv is the volume element associated with the field point P_j. The volume integral is obtained by noting that the summation is over all volume elements of v and that we take the limit of the sum as $\Delta v \to 0$.

We can find an alternative expression for W in terms of the field vectors $\mathbf{B}$ and $\mathbf{H}$. We make use of the vector identity

$$\mathbf{V}\cdot(\mathbf{A}\times\mathbf{H}) = \mathbf{H}\cdot(\mathbf{V}\times\mathbf{A}) - \mathbf{A}\cdot(\mathbf{V}\times\mathbf{H}) = \mathbf{H}\cdot\mathbf{B} - \mathbf{A}\cdot\mathbf{J}.$$

Substituting into Eq. (7–24) and applying the divergence theorem yields

$$W = \tfrac{1}{2} \int_v \mathbf{H} \cdot \mathbf{B} \, dv - \tfrac{1}{2} \int_S (\mathbf{A} \times \mathbf{H}) \cdot \mathbf{n} \, ds,$$

where S is the surface which bounds v. For any given physical situation the currents in the field flow in a finite region of space. If the field point is at a sufficiently large distance r from this region the vector $\mathbf{A}$ will vanish at least as $1/r$, while $\mathbf{H}$ will vanish at least as $1/r^2$ (see Eqs. 6–5 and 6–13). If we choose the infinite sphere for S so that $r \to \infty$, we find that

$$\left| \int_S (\mathbf{A} \times \mathbf{H}) \cdot \mathbf{n} \, ds \right| \leqq \frac{c}{r^3} 4\pi r^2 = \frac{4\pi c}{r}, \qquad (7\text{--}25)$$

where c is a constant. Thus the surface integral vanishes when $r \to \infty$, and we obtain

$$W = \tfrac{1}{2} \int_v \mathbf{H} \cdot \mathbf{B} \, dv, \qquad (7\text{--}26)$$

where the volume v, in general, extends over all of space. Equation (7–26) can be shown to be applicable to magnetic media where $\mathbf{B} = \mu\mathbf{H}$ (see Problem 7–4).

Equation (7–26) is of fundamental importance and it is of interest to give an alternative derivation. Let us consider an elemental charge dQ moving with a velocity $\mathbf{u}$ in an electromagnetic field. The electromagnetic force acting on the charge is given by the Lorentz force

$$d\mathbf{F} = dQ(\mathbf{E} + \mathbf{u} \times \mathbf{B}).$$

We consider the Lorentz force to be balanced by an external mechanical force applied to the charge so that

$$d\mathbf{F}_{\text{mech}} = - d\mathbf{F}.$$

The elemental mechanical work done for a displacement $d\mathbf{r}$ of the charge is

$$d\mathbf{F}_{\text{mech}} \cdot d\mathbf{r} = -dQ\mathbf{E} \cdot d\mathbf{r}.$$

(Note that $\mathbf{u} \times d\mathbf{r} = (d\mathbf{r}/dt) \times d\mathbf{r} = 0$ so that the magnetic field does not affect the work done.) The motion of the charge results in a current density $\mathbf{J}$ which is defined by the equation

$$dQ \frac{d\mathbf{r}}{dt} = \mathbf{J} \, dv,$$

where dv is the volume of the charge dQ. Summing over all elements of charge and dividing by the time interval dt yields the power input due to all mechanical sources

$$\frac{\partial W_{\text{mech}}}{\partial t} = \int_v (-\mathbf{E} \cdot \mathbf{J}) \, dv. \qquad (7\text{--}27)$$

Here the partial derivative is used to indicate that the volume v is considered fixed. The mechanical energy is transformed into magnetic field energy, so that we can set $W = W_{\text{mech}}$. We now make use of the vector identity

$$\nabla \cdot (\mathbf{E} \times \mathbf{H}) = \mathbf{H} \cdot (\nabla \times \mathbf{E}) - \mathbf{E} \cdot (\nabla \times \mathbf{H}) = -\mathbf{H} \cdot \frac{\partial \mathbf{B}}{\partial t} - \mathbf{E} \cdot \mathbf{J}.$$

Substituting into Eq. (7-27) and applying the divergence theorem yields

$$\frac{\partial W}{\partial t} = \int_v \mathbf{H} \cdot \frac{\partial \mathbf{B}}{\partial t} \, dv + \int_S (\mathbf{E} \times \mathbf{H}) \cdot \mathbf{n} \, ds. \qquad (7\text{-}28)$$

If we choose the infinite sphere for S, the surface integral vanishes since $\mathbf{E}$, considered as a function of r, behaves like $\mathbf{A}$ (see Eq. 7-9) and we can therefore derive an inequality similar to (7-25). For the integrand of the volume integral we have

$$\mathbf{H} \cdot \frac{\partial \mathbf{B}}{\partial t} = \mu \mathbf{H} \cdot \frac{\partial \mathbf{H}}{\partial t} = \frac{\mu}{2} \frac{\partial}{\partial t} (\mathbf{H} \cdot \mathbf{H}).$$

Substituting into Eq. (7-28) and integrating with respect to t yields Eq. (7-26).

With the aid of Eq. (7-22) we can give a simple and informative derivation of Eq. (7-26). Equation (7-22) can be derived in an elementary manner by noting that the applied voltage at the terminals of the coil is $v = L(di/dt)$, and that the power input is

$$\frac{\partial W}{\partial t} = vi = Li \frac{di}{dt}.$$

Integration with respect to t yields Eq. (7-22). Let us now consider a section of length h of the parallel-plate transmission line discussed in Example 3, Section 6-6 (see Fig. 6-14). The magnitude of the magnetic flux density is determined by $B = \mu i/l$ and the magnetic flux by $\phi = \mu ihd/l$. The inductance is given by Eq. (7-15): $L = \mu hd/l$. With the aid of these relations we can express the field energy in the form

$$W = \tfrac{1}{2} L i^2 = \frac{1}{2} \frac{\mu i}{l} \left(\frac{i}{l}\right)(hld) = \tfrac{1}{2} BH(hld).$$

Dividing by the volume yields the *magnetic energy density*, $\tfrac{1}{2}\mathbf{B} \cdot \mathbf{H}$.

With the aid of the above expression for the magnetic energy density in a parallel-plate transmission line, we can now determine the field energy of a general magnetic field. We divide the field region into elemental cells of volume $\Delta v = hld$, as shown in Fig. 7-7, where the cell walls are either parallel to or normal to $\mathbf{H}$. On the cell walls parallel to $\mathbf{H}$ we assume a surface current density $\mathbf{J}_s = \mathbf{n} \times \mathbf{H}$ to be present, where $\mathbf{n}$ is a unit inwardly directed normal to the cell walls. Within the field the assumed surface

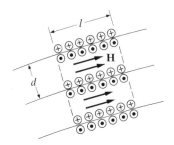

Fig. 7–7. A magnetic field considered as resulting from elemental cells with surface currents.

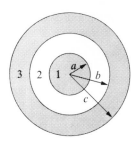

Fig. 7–8. Cross section of a coaxial cable.

currents on adjacent cell walls cancel each other, so that the original field is in no way altered. Each cell appears as an elemental parallel-plate transmission line and has a magnetic energy

$$\Delta W = \tfrac{1}{2}\mathbf{B} \cdot \mathbf{H}\, \Delta v.$$

Letting $\Delta v \to 0$ and summing over all cells yields Eq. (7–26).

We shall now illustrate the usefulness of Eqs. (7–24) and (7–26) by deriving the inductance per unit length for two types of transmission line.

Example 1. Figure 7–8 illustrates a coaxial cable. Due to symmetry the magnetic field intensity in regions 1, 2, and 3 can be found by Ampère's circuital law, and we obtain (see Problem 6–21)

$$H_\phi = \frac{ir}{2\pi a^2}, \qquad 0 \leqq r \leqq a,$$

$$H_\phi = \frac{i}{2\pi r}, \qquad a \leqq r \leqq b,$$

$$H_\phi = \frac{i}{2\pi r}\frac{c^2 - r^2}{c^2 - b^2}, \qquad b \leqq r \leqq c.$$

Let us assume that regions 1 and 3 have a permeability μ and that region 2 has a permeability μ_0. For a unit length of cable the volume element can be taken as

$$dv = (2\pi r\, dr)(1).$$

We can now evaluate the magnetic field energy per unit length by using Eq. (7–26). For region 1 we have

$$W_1 = \frac{\mu}{2} \int_0^a H_\phi^2 (2\pi r\, dr) = \frac{\mu i^2}{16\pi}.$$

For regions 2 and 3 we find that

$$W_2 = \frac{\mu_0 i^2}{4\pi} \ln(b/a), \qquad W_3 = \frac{\mu i^2}{4\pi}\left[\frac{c^4}{(c^2 - b^2)^2}\ln(c/b) - \frac{3c^2 - b^2}{4(c^2 - b^2)}\right].$$

The inductance per unit length is given by

$$L = \frac{2(W_1 + W_2 + W_3)}{i^2}$$

$$= \frac{\mu_0}{2\pi}\ln\frac{b}{a} + \frac{\mu}{2\pi}\left[\frac{1}{4} + \frac{c^4}{(c^2 - b^2)^2}\ln\frac{c}{b} - \frac{3c^2 - b^2}{4(c^2 - b^2)}\right].$$

Example 2. We shall now determine the self-inductance per unit length of the two-wire transmission line shown in Fig. 6–27. The permeability of the conductors is taken to be μ_0. It is convenient to use Eq. (7–24) to determine the field energy, since the range of integration is restricted to the cross-sectional areas S_1 and S_2 of the conductors. The volume element for a unit length is $dv = (1)\, ds$. Since $\mathbf{A} \cdot \mathbf{J}_2 = iA/S_2$, $\mathbf{A} \cdot \mathbf{J}_1 = -iA/S_1$, the magnetic field energy per unit length is given by

$$W = \tfrac{1}{2}Li^2 = \frac{i}{2}\left(\frac{1}{S_2}\int_{S_2} A\, ds - \frac{1}{S_1}\int_{S_1} A\, ds\right).$$

Thus we find that

$$L = \frac{\bar{A}_2 - \bar{A}_1}{i}, \tag{7–29}$$

where

$$\bar{A}_k \triangleq \frac{1}{S_k}\int_{S_k} A\, ds$$

is the average value of A over the area S_k. Let us consider A_2. With the aid of Eq. (6–65) we obtain

$$S_2 A_2 = \frac{\mu_0 i}{4\pi}\int_{S_2}\left[1 - \left(\frac{r_2}{b_2}\right)^2 + 2\ln\frac{r_1}{b_2}\right] ds.$$

To evaluate the integral we use polar coordinates, so that $ds = r_2\, dr_2\, d\theta$. Thus

$$\int_{S_2}\left(\frac{r_2}{b_2}\right)^2 ds = \frac{S_2}{2}.$$

The law of cosines yields

$$r_1^2 = r_2^2 + d^2 + 2r_2 d\cos\theta = d^2 f^2,$$

where

$$f^2 \triangleq 1 + \left(\frac{r_2}{d}\right)^2 + 2\left(\frac{r_2}{d}\right)\cos\theta.$$

To perform the integration we make use of the formula

$$\int_0^{2\pi} \ln f \, d\theta = 0, \qquad r_2/d < 1.$$

Thus

$$\int_{S_2} \ln \frac{r_1}{b_2} \, ds = \int_{S_2} \ln \frac{d}{b_2} \, ds = S_2 \ln \frac{d}{b_2}$$

and we find that

$$S_2 \bar{A}_2 = \frac{\mu_0 i S_2}{4\pi} \left(\frac{1}{2} + 2 \ln \frac{d}{b_2} \right).$$

We can determine $\bar{A}_1$ by changing the sign of i in the above expression and replacing b_2 by b_1. Substituting into Eq. (7–29) yields the self-inductance per unit length:

$$L = \frac{\mu_0}{\pi} \left(\frac{1}{4} + \ln \frac{d}{\sqrt{b_1 b_2}} \right).$$

7–5 HYSTERESIS IN MAGNETIC MATERIALS

In the previous discussions of magnetic materials we have assumed that the permeability is piecewise uniform and independent of **H**. This is a reasonable first-order approximation for many magnetic materials. However, in general, **B** is a nonlinear function of **H**. The functional relationship is further complicated by the fact that **B** also depends on the past history of the material. Let **i** be a constant unit vector which is collinear with **B** at a field point within the material and let B and H be defined by the equations $\mathbf{B} = \mathbf{i}B$ and $\mathbf{H} = \mathbf{i}H$, respectively. Given that the initial magnetization is zero and that H is increasing, the function $B = B(H)$ will have the form shown by the dashed curve connecting the points P_0 and P_s in Fig. 7–9. The maximum value of the slope $(1/\mu_0)(dB/dH)$ determines the *maximum relative permeability*

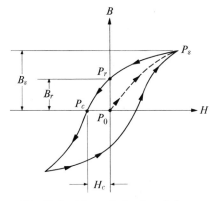

Fig. 7–9. Magnetic hysteresis loop.

μ_{rm}. The magnetic field tends to align the current loops (the electron spins) in the material in the direction of the field.* When all the loops are aligned with their axes parallel, saturation sets in. This starts to occur at the saturation value $B = B_s$, after which the increments ΔB and ΔH tend to satisfy the free-space relation

$$\lim_{H \to \infty} \frac{\Delta B}{\Delta H} = \mu_0.$$

If after reaching the point P_s the magnetic field is reduced to zero, the path P_sP_r is traced out. The magnetic flux density B_r at P_r is called the *remanence*. It results from the fact that some of the current loops remain oriented in the direction of the previously applied magnetic field. (A large remanence is important for permanent magnets.) If the magnetic field intensity is now reversed in direction, the path P_rP_c is traced out and B is reduced to zero. The magnitude of the magnetic field intensity H_c at P_c is known as the *coercive force*. It represents the magnetic field intensity required to compensate for the oriented current loops in the material in order to reduce B to zero. If H is varied in a periodic manner, a steady-state hysteresis loop will result after the transient effects due to the initial magnetization have vanished. Table 7–1 gives some typical values for various materials.

Table 7–1

Material	μ_{rm}	B_s, Wb/m^2	H_c, ampere-turns/m
Cold rolled steel	2×10^3	2.1	1.4×10^2
4% Silicon iron	7×10^3	2	0.4×10^2
78 Permalloy	10^5	1.1	4×10^2
Supermalloy	10^6	0.8	0.2

Let us now consider a long straight coil of length l and cross-sectional area a which has N uniformly wound turns. The voltage applied to the coil terminals is taken to be a periodic function of time, so that a hysteresis loop is traced out when B is plotted against H. To a good approximation we can take the magnetic field inside the core to be uniform. Thus, applying Ampère's circuital law to the dashed path shown in Fig. 7–10 (see Eq. 6–26), we find that

$$Hl \cong iN.$$

The magnetic flux linking one turn is $\phi = aB$. Thus $v = aN(dB/dt)$ and the

---

* In the case of ferrites some of the spins are parallel (ferromagnetic) and some are antiparallel (anti-ferromagnetic). However, the resultant effect is due to uncompensated parallel spins.

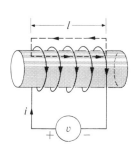

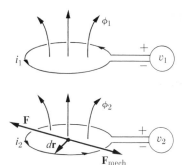

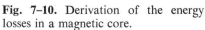

Fig. 7–10. Derivation of the energy losses in a magnetic core.

Fig. 7–11. Forces between two coils.

power input is

$$\frac{\partial W}{\partial t} = vi = \left(aN\frac{dB}{dt}\right)\left(\frac{Hl}{N}\right) = H\frac{dB}{dt}\,v,$$

where $v = al$ is the volume of the magnetic material. The energy dissipated per unit volume per cycle is

$$W/v = \oint_C \mathbf{H}\cdot d\mathbf{B},$$

which is equal to the area of the hysteresis loop.

7–6 FORCES AND TORQUES ON CONDUCTING COILS IN MAGNETIC FIELDS

A current is composed of moving charges. Due to the Lorentz force on the moving charges, current-carrying coils experience forces when situated in a magnetic field. Let us determine the force $\mathbf{F}$ acting on a coil 2 of N_2 closely wound turns due to the magnetic field of a coil 1 of N_1 closely wound turns (Fig. 7–11). A mechanical force, $\mathbf{F}_{\text{mech}} = -\mathbf{F}$, is required to hold the coil at rest. (In general, a mechanical torque is also required, but this does not enter into the following relations and will not be considered.) Let us suppose that the voltage sources are automatically adjusted to compensate for the induced electric field intensity when the coils are moved, so that the currents i_1 and i_2 are maintained constant. If all elements of coil 2 are given a displacement $d\mathbf{r}$, the mechanical work done is

$$dW_{\text{mech}} = \mathbf{F}_{\text{mech}}\cdot d\mathbf{r} = -\mathbf{F}\cdot d\mathbf{r}.$$

The displacement $d\mathbf{r}$ results in a change in the fluxes ϕ_1 and ϕ_2 and the electrical work done by the voltage sources is given by

$$dW_{\text{elec}} = v_1 i_1\,dt + v_2 i_2\,dt = i_1 N_1\,d\phi_1 + i_2 N_2\,d\phi_2.$$

The change in magnetic field energy is

$$dW = dW_{\text{mech}} + dW_{\text{elec}}. \tag{7-30}$$

Using Eq. (7-20) for the case of two coils and noting that both i_1 and i_2 are constant, we obtain

$$dW = \tfrac{1}{2}i_1 N_1\, d\phi_1 + \tfrac{1}{2}i_2 N_2\, d\phi_2 = 2\, dW_{\text{elec}}.$$

Substituting into Eq. (7-30) yields $-dW = dW_{\text{mech}}$ and we obtain

$$\mathbf{F} \cdot d\mathbf{r} = dW = \text{grad}\, W \cdot d\mathbf{r}. \tag{7-31}$$

Since $d\mathbf{r}$ is arbitrary, it follows from Eq. (7-31) that

$$\mathbf{F} = \text{grad}\, W, \qquad i_k = \text{const}. \tag{7-32}$$

Let us now consider a different situation, in which the fluxes ϕ_k are held constant. We can visualize this condition by inserting a resistor in series with each voltage source to obtain a current source and adjusting the current sources automatically so that the ϕ_k remain constant. Since ϕ_k is constant, the voltage between the coil terminals is zero and no electrical energy is supplied to the field. Thus Eq. (7-30) now has the form $dW = dW_{\text{mech}}$, so that

$$\text{grad}\, W \cdot d\mathbf{r} = -\mathbf{F} \cdot d\mathbf{r},$$

which yields

$$\mathbf{F} = -\text{grad}\, W, \qquad \phi_k = \text{const}. \tag{7-33}$$

We shall now derive Eq. (7-32) by an alternative method, which is of interest since it illustrates more clearly the origin of the magnetic forces between current-carrying coils. Let us consider a volume element dv. Let the total charge of all electrons in dv be dq_e and let their average velocity be $\mathbf{u}$. The elemental force acting on the electrons is given by the Lorentz force

$$d\mathbf{F}_e = dq_e(\mathbf{E} + \mathbf{u} \times \mathbf{B}).$$

Let the charge of the fixed protons in dv be dq_p. The elemental force acting on the fixed protons is given by

$$d\mathbf{F}_p = dq_p\mathbf{E}.$$

In a quasi-static field we consider the charge density to be zero. Thus the total charge $dq_e + dq_p$ within dv is zero and the elemental resultant force is

$$d\mathbf{F} = d\mathbf{F}_e + d\mathbf{F}_p = dq_e\mathbf{u} \times \mathbf{B}.$$

We now introduce the electron charge density ρ_e and let $dq_e = \rho_e\, dv$. The motion of the electrons results in a current density $\mathbf{J}$, defined by the equation

$$\mathbf{J} \triangleq \rho_e\mathbf{u} = \rho_e \frac{d\mathbf{r}}{dt}.$$

In the case of a current filament we have $\rho_e \mathbf{u}\, dv = \mathbf{J}\, dv = i\, d\mathbf{r}$, and the elemental force acting on the current filament is

$$d\mathbf{F} = i(d\mathbf{r} \times \mathbf{B}). \tag{7-34}$$

Let us now apply Eq. (7-34) to determine the forces between two current filaments located at points P_1 and P_2, respectively. We can obtain the elemental magnetic flux density at P_2 due to the current element at P_1 with the aid of the Biot-Savart law (see Eq. 6-14). Given that coil 1 has N_1 closely wound turns, we must introduce the factor N_1 into Eq. (6-14). Thus

$$d\mathbf{B}_1 = \frac{\mu_0 i_1 N_1}{4\pi r_{12}^3}(d\mathbf{r}_1 \times \mathbf{r}_{12}).$$

We can obtain the second-order differential force $d^2\mathbf{F}_2$ acting on the N_2 current elements of coil 2 at P_2 from Eq. (7-34):

$$d^2\mathbf{F}_2 = i_2 N_2 (d\mathbf{r}_2 \times d\mathbf{B}_1) = \frac{\mu_0 i_1 i_2 N_1 N_2}{4\pi r_{12}^3}\, d\mathbf{r}_2 \times (d\mathbf{r}_1 \times \mathbf{r}_{12}). \tag{7-35}$$

In a similar manner we can compute the elemental force $d^2\mathbf{F}_1$ which acts on the current elements at P_1. In general, we shall find that

$$d^2\mathbf{F}_1 \neq -d^2\mathbf{F}_2,$$

so that it would appear that the forces of action and reaction are not equal in magnitude and directed oppositely. This apparent paradox results from the fact that the Biot-Savart law in differential form applies to a nonphysical element. (See Section 6-3.) Let us now integrate Eq. (7-35) over the contours C_1 and C_2 of a single turn of coils 1 and 2, respectively. We find that the total force on coil 2 is

$$\mathbf{F}_2 = \frac{\mu_0 i_1 i_2 N_1 N_2}{4\pi} \oint_{C_1} \oint_{C_2} \frac{d\mathbf{r}_2 \times (d\mathbf{r}_1 \times \mathbf{r}_{12})}{r_{12}^3}.$$

The integrand contains the term

$$d\mathbf{r}_2 \times (d\mathbf{r}_1 \times \mathbf{r}_{12}) = (\mathbf{r}_{12} \cdot d\mathbf{r}_2)\, d\mathbf{r}_1 - (d\mathbf{r}_1 \cdot d\mathbf{r}_2)\mathbf{r}_{12},$$

and when we consider P_1 as fixed and P_2 as variable and let $r_{12} = r$, we see that $\mathbf{r}_{12} \cdot d\mathbf{r}_2 = r\, dr$. Thus

$$\oint_{C_2} r^{-2}\, dr = 0,$$

since the initial and final values of r are identical. Using the above result, we find that

$$\mathbf{F}_2 = -\frac{\mu_0 i_1 i_2 N_1 N_2}{4\pi} \oint_{C_1} \oint_{C_2} \frac{\mathbf{r}_{12}(d\mathbf{r}_1 \cdot d\mathbf{r}_2)}{r_{12}^3}. \tag{7-36}$$

Since $\mathbf{r}_{12} = -\mathbf{r}_{21}$, it follows from Eq. (7–36) that $\mathbf{F}_1 = -\mathbf{F}_2$. Thus the Biot-Savart law yields correct results if we restrict its application to closed current loops.

Equation (7–32) is equivalent to Eq. (7–36). We can see this if we use Eq. (7–23) and Neumann's formula (7–12). Thus

$$\mathbf{F} = i_1 i_2 \operatorname{grad} L_{12} = \frac{\mu_0 i_1 i_2 N_1 N_2}{4\pi} \oint_{C_1} \oint_{C_2} \operatorname{grad} \frac{1}{r_{12}} \, d\mathbf{r}_1 \cdot d\mathbf{r}_2. \quad (7\text{–}37)$$

Here we take the gradient with respect to $P_2(x_2, y_2, z_2)$, considering $P_1(x_1, y_1, z_1)$ as fixed. Since

$$r_{12}^2 = (x_2 - x_1)^2 + (y_2 - y_1)^2 + (z_2 - z_1)^2,$$

we find that

$$\operatorname{grad} \frac{1}{r_{12}} = -\frac{1}{r_{12}^2} \operatorname{grad} r_{12} = -\frac{\mathbf{r}_{12}}{r_{12}^3},$$

and thus Eq. (7–37) is identical to Eq. (7–36).

In general, both a mechanical force and a mechanical torque are required to hold a coil at rest in a magnetic field. We can find the torque $\mathbf{T}$ acting on the coil about any axis in a manner similar to that which we used to find the force $\mathbf{F}$. A mechanical torque, $\mathbf{T}_{\text{mech}} = -\mathbf{T}$, is required to prevent the coil from rotating. When the coil is given an elemental angular displacement $d\theta$ about an axis, the mechanical work done is $dW_{\text{mech}} = -T \, d\theta$. Equation (7–31) now has the form $T \, d\theta = (\partial W / \partial \theta) \, d\theta$, which yields

$$T = \frac{\partial W}{\partial \theta}, \qquad i_k = \text{const.} \quad (7\text{–}38)$$

Similarly, we find that

$$T = -\frac{\partial W}{\partial \theta}, \qquad \phi_k = \text{const.} \quad (7\text{–}39)$$

We can also find the torque with the aid of Eq. (7–34). The elemental torque on a current element (see Fig. 7–12) is

$$\mathbf{r} \times d\mathbf{F} = i\mathbf{r} \times (d\mathbf{r} \times \mathbf{B}).$$

Let the coil have N closely wound turns. Integrating the above expression around the contour C_1 of one turn and multiplying by N yields the torque on the coil,

$$\mathbf{T} = iN \oint_{C_1} \mathbf{r} \times (d\mathbf{r} \times \mathbf{B}). \quad (7\text{–}40)$$

Given that $\mathbf{B}$ is uniform over the contour C_1, we can simplify the integral by means of the vector identities,

$$\mathbf{r} \times (d\mathbf{r} \times \mathbf{B}) = (\mathbf{r} \cdot \mathbf{B}) \, d\mathbf{r} - (\mathbf{r} \cdot d\mathbf{r})\mathbf{B},$$

$$\tfrac{1}{2}\mathbf{B} \times (d\mathbf{r} \times \mathbf{r}) = \tfrac{1}{2}(\mathbf{r} \cdot \mathbf{B}) \, d\mathbf{r} - \tfrac{1}{2}(\mathbf{B} \cdot d\mathbf{r})\mathbf{r}.$$

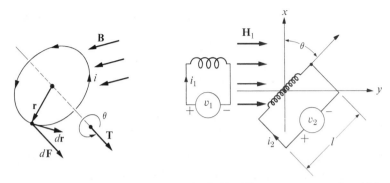

Fig. 7–12. The torque on a coil in a uniform magnetic field.

Fig. 7–13. The torque on a solenoid in a uniform magnetic field.

Subtracting the two equations and noting that **B** is uniform yields

$$\mathbf{r} \times (d\mathbf{r} \times \mathbf{B}) - \tfrac{1}{2}\mathbf{B} \times (d\mathbf{r} \times \mathbf{r}) = \tfrac{1}{2}d[(\mathbf{r} \cdot \mathbf{B})\mathbf{r}] - \tfrac{1}{2}\mathbf{B}\, d(\mathbf{r} \cdot \mathbf{r}).$$

The right-hand terms of the above expression vanish when they are integrated around a closed contour. Thus we obtain

$$\mathbf{T} = \mathbf{m} \times \mathbf{B}, \qquad (7\text{–}41)$$

where

$$\mathbf{m} = \tfrac{1}{2}iN \oint_{C_1} \mathbf{r} \times d\mathbf{r}$$

is the magnetic dipole moment of the coil. For a plane coil, m is equal to the product aiN, where a is the area of the coil.

We shall now give several examples illustrating various methods for evaluating the force and torque on conducting coils in a magnetic field.

Example 1. A long thin straight coil of length l and cross-sectional area a has N turns and carries a current i_2. We wish to determine the torque on the coil when it is placed in a uniform magnetic field $\mathbf{H}_1$ (Fig. 7–13). We consider the field $\mathbf{H}_1$ to result from a current i_1 in a coil 1. The magnetic field energy is then

$$W = \tfrac{1}{2}L_{11}i_1^2 + Mi_1i_2 + \tfrac{1}{2}L_{22}i_2^2.$$

Since the self inductances L_{11} and L_{22} do not depend on θ, we find from Eq. (7–38) that

$$T = i_1i_2 \frac{\partial M}{\partial \theta}.$$

In order to determine the mutual inductance M, we can assume that $i_2 = 0$

and consider the open-circuit voltage between the terminals of coil 2:

$$v_2 = M \frac{di_1}{dt} = N \frac{d\phi_{21}}{dt}. \qquad (7\text{–}42)$$

Here $\phi_{21} = \mu_0 a H_1 \sin \theta$ is the magnetic flux linking one turn of coil 2. Integrating Eq. (7–42) with respect to t, we find that $M = N\phi_{21}/i_1$. Thus

$$T = i_2 N_2 \frac{\partial \phi_{21}}{\partial \theta} = \mu_0 a i_2 N_2 H_1 \cos \theta. \qquad (7\text{–}43)$$

In Eq. (7–43) we have used the field $\mathbf{H}_1$ due to i_1 to determine T. There is also a torque on the coil elements due to the field of the current i_2. However, this torque is compensated for by the mechanical constraints which hold the turns in place.

The torque can also be found with the aid of Eq. (7–41). The magnitude of $\mathbf{m}$ is $m = a_2 i_2 N_2$. Thus

$$T = m B_1 \cos \theta,$$

which is identical to Eq. (7–43).

It is interesting to note that we can also obtain Eq. (7–43) by replacing the coil by magnetic charges $M_p = \pm aiN/l$ situated at the ends of the coil (see Eq. 6–22) and by taking the force on a magnetic charge M_p in a magnetic field $\mathbf{B}_1$ to be given by

$$\mathbf{F} = M_p \mathbf{B}_1. \qquad (7\text{–}44)$$

The torque on the rigidly connected magnetic charges is then

$$T = M_p B_1 l \cos \theta,$$

which is identical to Eq. (7–43).

Example 2. In this example we shall determine the force on the coil shown in Fig. 6–24 and discussed in Example 3, Section 6–8. The potential along the z-axis due to the magnetized medium is

$$U_s = \frac{A}{4\pi(z + d)^2}, \qquad z \geqq 0,$$

where

$$A = \frac{\mu_r - 1}{\mu_r + 1} m,$$

and where $m = \pi b^2 i N$ is the magnitude of the dipole moment of the coil. We can consider the dipole to consist of two magnetic charges M_p and $-M_p$ separated by an infinitesimal distance h, where

$$m = \lim_{h \to 0} h M_p.$$

The field due to U_s produces forces on the magnetic charges which can be

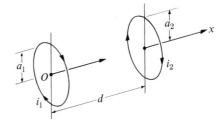

Fig. 7-14. The force between two coaxial circular coils.

found with the aid of Eq. (7–44). The resultant force on the coil is given by

$$F_z = \mu_0 M_p[H_{sz}(d + h) - H_{sz}(d)] \cong \mu_0 h M_p \left[\frac{\partial H_{sz}}{\partial z}\right]_{z=d}$$

$$= -\mu_0 m\left[\frac{\partial^2 U_s}{\partial z^2}\right]_{z=d} = -\frac{3\pi\mu_0}{32} \cdot \frac{\mu_r - 1}{\mu_r + 1}\left(\frac{b}{d}\right)^4 (iN)^2.$$

Example 3. Let us determine the force between two coaxial circular coils of radii a_1 and a_2 which have N_1 and N_2 closely wound turns and carry currents i_1 and i_2, respectively (Fig. 7–14). Let d be the distance between the parallel planes of the coils. As a first approximation, we assume that $a_1 \ll d$, $a_2 \ll d$, and replace the coils by magnetic dipoles. The magnitude of the dipole moment for coil 1 is

$$m_1 = \pi a_2^2 i_1 N_1$$

and the potential along the x-axis due to coil 1 is

$$U_1 = \frac{m_1}{4\pi x^2}.$$

We consider dipole 2 to consist of two magnetic charges, M_p and $-M_p$, separated by an infinitesimal distance h. Thus

$$m_2 = a_2^2 i_2 N_2 = \lim_{h \to 0} h M_p.$$

The force on dipole 2 due to the field of dipole 1 (see Eq. 7–44) is given by

$$F_x = \mu_0 M_{p2}[H_{1x}(d + h) - H_{1x}(d)] \cong \mu_0 h M_{p2}\left[\frac{\partial H_{1x}}{\partial x}\right]_{x=d}$$

$$= -\mu_0 m_2\left[\frac{\partial^2 U_1}{\partial x^2}\right]_{x=d} = -\frac{3\mu_0}{2\pi} \cdot m_1 m_2 \frac{1}{d^4}.$$

As a second approximation let us consider the dimensions of coil 1 to be finite. The magnetic field intensity on the x-axis (see Eq. 6–23) is given by

$$H_{x1} = \frac{i_1 N_1 a_1^2}{2(a_1^2 + x^2)^{3/2}}. \tag{7-45}$$

In order to evaluate F_x, we first determine an expression for the mutual inductance, considering the dimensions of coil 2 to be small compared with d. The flux due to coil 1, which links one turn of coil 2, is

$$\phi_{21} \cong \pi a_2^2 \mu_0 H_{x1},$$

where we have assumed that the field is uniform over the area of coil 2. The mutual inductance can be found by taking $i_2 = 0$ and using the relation

$$v_2 = N_2 \frac{d\phi_{21}}{dt} = M \frac{di_1}{dt}.$$

Integrating with respect to t yields

$$M = \frac{N_2 \phi_{21}}{i_1} \cong \frac{\mu_0}{2} N_1 N_2 \frac{\pi a_1^2 a_2^2}{(a_1^2 + x^2)^{3/2}}.$$

(Note that the above expression for M is only an approximation and is not symmetrical in the subscripts.)

The force is given by

$$F_x = \left[\frac{\partial W}{\partial x} \right]_{x=d} = i_1 i_2 \left[\frac{\partial M}{\partial x} \right]_{x=d} \cong -\frac{3\mu_0}{2\pi} m_1 m_2 \frac{d}{(a_1^2 + d^2)^{5/2}}.$$

The exact expression for the force can be obtained from Eqs. (7–16) and (7–23). Thus, using the notation of Example 2, Section 7–3, we obtain

$$F_x = i_1 i_2 \frac{\partial L_{12}}{\partial k} \frac{\partial k}{\partial d} = -i_1 i_2 \frac{k^3 d}{4 a_1 a_2} \frac{\partial L_{12}}{\partial k}.$$

With the aid of the formulas

$$\frac{\partial E}{\partial k} = \frac{E - F}{k}, \qquad \frac{\partial F}{\partial k} = \frac{E}{k(1 - k^2)} - \frac{F}{k},$$

we find that

$$\frac{\partial L_{12}}{\partial k} = 2\mu_0 N_1 N_2 \frac{\sqrt{a_1 a_2}}{k^2} \left(\frac{2 - k^2}{1 - k^2} \frac{E}{2} - F \right).$$

Thus

$$F_x = -\frac{\mu_0 i_1 i_2 N_1 N_2 d}{\sqrt{d^2 + (a_1 + a_2)^2}} \left[\frac{a_1^2 + a_2^2 + d^2}{(a_1 - a_2)^2 + d^2} E - F \right]. \qquad (7\text{–}46)$$

Equation (7–46) plays an important role in the definition of the absolute ampere. In the mks system of units we choose $\mu_0 \triangleq 4\pi \times 10^{-7}$ henry/meter (H/m). Thus, by taking $i_1 = i_2 = i$, and by measuring the dimensions of the coils and the force between the coils, we can measure i.

7-7 PERTURBATION OF MAGNETIC FIELD ENERGY

In Section 5–4 we discussed the perturbation of the electrostatic field energy due to the introduction of small material bodies into the field. In general, a body perturbs both the electric and magnetic field energies. In this section we shall discuss the perturbation of the magnetic field energy.

Let us consider two magnetic fields $\mathbf{B}_1$, $\mathbf{H}_1$, U_1 and $\mathbf{B}_2$, $\mathbf{H}_2$, U_2 resulting from the same current distribution $\mathbf{J}_1 = \mathbf{J}_2 = \mathbf{J}$ and in which $\mu_1 = \mu_2$ everywhere, with the exception of a volume v_m where $\mu_1 \neq \mu_2$. We wish to determine an expression for the change in magnetic field energy resulting from changing the permeability of the volume v_m from μ_1 to μ_2 under the condition that all conduction currents remain constant. The change in field energy is

$$\Delta W = W_2 - W_1 = \tfrac{1}{2} \int_v (\mathbf{B}_2 \cdot \mathbf{H}_2 - \mathbf{B}_1 \cdot \mathbf{H}_1)\, dv$$

$$= \tfrac{1}{2} \int_v (\mathbf{B}_2 + \mathbf{B}_1) \cdot (\mathbf{H}_2 - \mathbf{H}_1)\, dv$$

$$+ \tfrac{1}{2} \int_v (\mathbf{B}_2 \cdot \mathbf{H}_1 - \mathbf{B}_1 \cdot \mathbf{H}_2)\, dv.$$

We shall show that under the assumed condition the first integral I on the right-hand side of the above expression is zero. Thus we obtain the desired result,

$$\Delta W = \tfrac{1}{2} \int_{v_m} (\mu_2 - \mu_1)\mathbf{H}_1 \cdot \mathbf{H}_2\, dv = \tfrac{1}{2} \int_{v_m} (1/\mu_1 - 1/\mu_2)\mathbf{B}_1 \cdot \mathbf{B}_2\, dv. \quad (7\text{–}47)$$

(We can restrict the integration to the volume v_m, since $\mu_1 = \mu_2$ for points outside v.) To prove that I is zero, we set

$$\mathbf{A} \triangleq \mathbf{A}_1 + \mathbf{A}_2, \qquad \mathbf{B} \triangleq \mathbf{B}_1 + \mathbf{B}_2 = \operatorname{curl} \mathbf{A}, \qquad \mathbf{H} \triangleq \mathbf{H}_1 - \mathbf{H}_2,$$

and note that under the assumed condition we have

$$\operatorname{curl} \mathbf{H} = \mathbf{J}_2 - \mathbf{J}_1 = 0.$$

By introducing the vector identity

$$\nabla \cdot (\mathbf{A} \times \mathbf{H}) = \mathbf{H} \cdot (\nabla \times \mathbf{A}) - \mathbf{A} \cdot (\nabla \times \mathbf{H})$$

and applying the divergence theorem, we find that

$$I = \int_v \mathbf{H} \cdot \mathbf{B}\, dv = \int_S (\mathbf{A} \times \mathbf{H}) \cdot \mathbf{n}\, ds. \quad (7\text{–}48)$$

The surface integral will vanish if we choose the infinite sphere for S (see Eq. 7–25).

In the above derivation we have assumed that $\mathbf{J}$ is a piecewise continuous function of position. However, we can also treat the case of a surface current density $\mathbf{J}_s$ on a surface S_c, in which case $\mathbf{J}$ is infinite on the surface. The relation (7–48) remains valid for S_c and the integrand (see Problem 6–10) is

$$-\mathbf{n} \cdot (\mathbf{H} \times \mathbf{A}) = -\mathbf{A} \cdot (\mathbf{n} \times \mathbf{H}) = -\mathbf{A} \cdot (\mathbf{J}_{s1} - \mathbf{J}_{s2}) = 0.$$

Since we have fixed the surface currents, the surface integral vanishes and Eq. (7–47) remains the same.

We shall now illustrate the usefulness of Eq. (7–47) by means of an example. Let us determine the change in inductance ΔL of a coil in free space due to the introduction of a small soft-iron sphere of radius a and permeability μ at a field point P (Fig. 7–15). Since the sphere is small we can consider it to be situated in a uniform primary field $\mathbf{H}_1(P)$ which is due to the current i in the coil. The sphere becomes magnetized, resulting in a uniform field $\mathbf{H}_2$ inside the sphere. Provided that we hold i constant there will be no change in $\mathbf{J}$, since it is constrained by the windings of the coil. We may therefore apply Eq. (7–47), which yields

$$\Delta W = \frac{2\pi a^3}{3}(\mu - \mu_0)H_1 H_2.$$

The field within the sphere can be found by the method of images discussed in Chapter 4:

$$\mathbf{H}_2 = \frac{3}{2 + \mu_r}\mathbf{H}_1. \tag{7–49}$$

Thus

$$\Delta W = 2\pi\mu_0 a\frac{\mu_r - 1}{\mu_r + 2}(aH_1)^2.$$

The change in inductance can be found from the equation (note that $i = \text{const}$)

$$W_2 = \tfrac{1}{2}(L + \Delta L)i^2 = W_1 + \Delta W,$$

which yields

$$\Delta L \cong \frac{2\,\Delta W}{i^2} = 4\pi\mu_0 a\frac{\mu_r - 1}{\mu_r + 2}\left(\frac{aH_1}{i}\right)^2. \tag{7–50}$$

If the sphere is a perfect conductor and if the field is time-varying but quasi-static, surface currents are set up which prevent the magnetic field from penetrating the sphere. We can obtain the change in inductance for the case of a conducting sphere by taking the limit as $\mu_r \to 0$ in Eq. (7–50). Thus

$$\Delta L = -2\pi\mu_0 a\left(\frac{aH_1}{i}\right)^2.$$

The justification for this is given in Problem 6–14, where the discussion shows that, as $\mu_r \to 0$, the surface magnetization current density on the

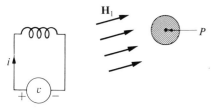

Fig. 7–15. The change in inductance of a coil due to the presence of a small soft-iron sphere.

Fig. 7–16. A section of a current filament.

soft-iron sphere is equal to the surface current density on the spherical conductor, so that the external fields of both spheres are identical. The internal fields are not the same, since we have a magnetic field intensity (see Eq. 7–49) of $H_2 = \frac{3}{2}H_1$ within the soft-iron sphere. However, the energy density within the soft-iron sphere is, as $\mu_r \to 0$,

$$\tfrac{1}{2}B_2H_2 = \frac{\mu}{2}\left(\frac{3H_1}{2}\right)^2 \to 0,$$

and thus contributes nothing to the final result.

7–8 INDUCED CURRENTS IN A QUASI-STATIC ELECTROMAGNETIC FIELD

Associated with a time-varying magnetic flux density **B** is an induced electric field intensity **E**. When a conductor is present in the field, the induced electric field intensity produces a current density **J**. Given that σ is the conductivity of the conductor, we have

$$\mathbf{J} = \sigma\mathbf{E}. \tag{7–51}$$

The current density **J** contributes to the magnetic field and this complicates the solution of quasi-static field problems. The solution of such problems is of considerable technical interest. The distribution of current throughout a conductor is important in determining the dissipated power. The dissipation due to ohmic losses is usually undesired in sharply tuned network elements. In other applications, however, such as induction heating, the dissipation of power finds a useful application.

   In order to determine the dissipated power in a conductor we shall consider a section of a current filament of cross-sectional area a and length l (Fig. 7–16). The voltage difference between the ends of the filament is defined by

$$V \triangleq \int_{P_1}^{P_2} \mathbf{E} \cdot d\mathbf{r}.$$

Substituting Eq. (7–51) yields $V = iR$, where

$$R \triangleq \int_{P_1}^{P_2} \frac{1}{\sigma a} \, dr \qquad (7\text{–}52)$$

is the resistance of the filament and where $i = aJ$ is the current. When a charge Q moves from P_1 to P_2, it absorbs an energy, $W = QV$, from the field, which is dissipated as heat in the filament. The instantaneous rate of energy dissipation is then

$$P_{D_i} = Vi = i^2R, \qquad (7\text{–}53)$$

where $i = dQ/dt$ is the current. Equation (7–53) is known as *Joule's law*. By means of Eqs. (7–51) and (7–52), we can write Eq. (7–53) in the form

$$P_{D_i} = \int_v \mathbf{E} \cdot \mathbf{J} \, dv, \qquad (7\text{–}54)$$

where $v = al$ is the volume of the filament. Equations (7–53) and (7–54) apply for instantaneous values of i, V, $\mathbf{E}$, and $\mathbf{J}$. However, in many technical applications the field excitation varies sinusoidally with time. For the sinusoidal steady state, the solution of field and network problems is best carried out through phasor analysis. It will be assumed that the reader has a working knowledge of phasor analysis, since it is extensively covered in elementary circuit analysis courses. Here this text will present a brief discussion of phasor analysis so that the reader may become acquainted with the notation that will be used when we are dealing with sinusoidally time-varying field vectors.

In phasor analysis we consider that all quantities are in a sinusoidal steady state. Thus, given that P is a field point, we represent a vector at P in the complex exponential form

$$\mathbf{F}(P, t) = \mathbf{F}e^{j\omega t},$$

where $\mathbf{F} \triangleq \mathbf{F}(P)$ is the *phasor representation* of the field vector at P. We take

$$\mathrm{Re} \, [\mathbf{F}e^{j\omega t}]$$

as the real (physically observable) field vector. Similar considerations apply for scalar quantities. From a mathematical point of view, the representation of vectors and scalars in exponential form is of interest, since it results in what is essentially the *Fourier transform* of these quantities. The importance of the exponential representation is that the ratio of complex field quantities is then independent of time. (Note that only for the exponential and for no other function is this generally the case.) The time independence of such ratios follows from the fact that

$$\frac{\partial \mathbf{F}(P, t)}{\partial t} = j\omega \mathbf{F}(P, t).$$

Thus the complex exponential representation allows us to write the operational equivalence, $\partial/\partial t = j\omega$, and since $e^{j\omega t}$ occurs as a common factor, it drops out. The field equations then reduce to algebraic equations between the field phasors.

For sinusoidally time-varying currents we are usually interested in the average power dissipated. If we take the phasors $\mathbf{E}$ and $\mathbf{J}$ in the form

$$\mathbf{E} = \mathbf{E}_r e^{j\phi}, \qquad \mathbf{J} = \mathbf{J}_r e^{j\theta},$$

where $\mathbf{E}_r$ and $\mathbf{J}_r$ are real, we find that the real electric field intensity and the real current density are given by

$$\text{Re}\,[\mathbf{E}e^{j\omega t}] = \mathbf{E}_r \cos(\omega t + \phi),$$

$$\text{Re}\,[\mathbf{J}e^{j\omega t}] = \mathbf{J}_r \cos(\omega t + \theta).$$

Substituting the real field vectors into Eq. (7–54) yields the instantaneous dissipated power

$$P_{D_i} = \int_v \mathbf{E}_r \cdot \mathbf{J}_r \cos(\omega t + \phi)\cos(\omega t + \theta)\,dv.$$

The average dissipated power is

$$P_D \triangleq \frac{\omega}{2\pi}\int_0^{2\pi/\omega} P_{D_i}\,dt = \tfrac{1}{2}\int_v \mathbf{E}_r \cdot \mathbf{J}_r \cos(\phi - \theta)\,dv.$$

A very convenient way of obtaining P_D is to note that

$$\text{Re}\,[\mathbf{E} \cdot \mathbf{J}^*] = \mathbf{E}_r \cdot \mathbf{J}_r \cos(\phi - \theta).$$

Thus

$$P_D = \text{Re}\left[\tfrac{1}{2}\int_v \mathbf{E} \cdot \mathbf{J}^*\,dv\right]. \tag{7–55}$$

To illustrate these concepts, we shall now discuss two examples of sinusoidally time-varying quasi-static electromagnetic fields for which an analytic solution is possible.

Example 1. A lossless circular coil of radius c has N closely wound turns. The current in the coil has a phasor representation of $I = I_0 e^{j\omega t}$. We shield the coil by placing it at the center of a spherical shell of radius $a \gg c$, conductivity σ, and thickness $\delta \ll a$. We wish to determine the induced current density in the shell, the average power dissipated in the shell, and the equivalent resistor to be used in a network representation of the coil and surrounding field.

Since $a \gg c$, we may replace the coil by a magnetic dipole and represent the field inside the sphere as a superposition of a dipole field due to the coil and a uniform field due to the induced currents in the shell. We therefore assume that the phasor scalar magnetic potential has the form

$$U_1 = A_1 r \cos \theta + \frac{m}{4\pi} \frac{\cos \theta}{r^2}, \qquad r < a, \qquad (7\text{–}56)$$

where $m = \pi c^2 IN$ is the magnitude of the dipole moment of the coil. Here we have taken a spherical coordinate system with the origin at the center of the sphere and the coil axis as the z-axis. For $r > a$, we anticipate that the field will appear as a dipole field, and we take

$$U_2 = A_2 \frac{\cos \theta}{r^2}, \qquad r > a. \qquad (7\text{–}57)$$

Let $\mathbf{J} = \mathbf{i}_\phi J$ be the phasor current density. Since $\delta \ll a$, we can introduce a phasor surface current density $\mathbf{J}_s \triangleq \delta \mathbf{J}$. To find A_1, A_2, and $\mathbf{J}_s$, we must first express J_s in terms of A_1 and m. The z-component of the phasor magnetic field intensity within the sphere (see Eq. 7–56) is

$$H_{z1} = -\frac{\partial U_1}{\partial z} = -A_1 - \frac{m}{4\pi}\left(\frac{1}{r^3} - \frac{3z^2}{r^5}\right). \qquad (7\text{–}58)$$

The phasor magnetic flux linked by the circle C on the sphere defined by $r = a$ and the angle θ is given by

$$\Phi = \mu_0 \int_0^{a \sin \theta} H_{z1}(2\pi\rho \, d\rho),$$

where $r^2 = \rho^2 + z^2$. Integration yields

$$\Phi = -\mu_0 \pi a^2 \sin^2 \theta \left(A_1 - \frac{m}{2\pi} \frac{1}{a^3}\right). \qquad (7\text{–}59)$$

The induced electric field intensity along the circle C can be found from Eq. (7–1a). Introducing phasor representation yields

$$\oint_C \mathbf{E} \cdot d\mathbf{r} = E_\phi 2\pi a \sin \theta = -j\omega\Phi. \qquad (7\text{–}60)$$

Equations (7–59) and (7–60) can be used to obtain J_s:

$$J_s = \delta\sigma E_\phi = \frac{j\omega\mu_0 \, \delta\sigma a \sin \theta}{2}\left(A_1 - \frac{m}{2\pi a^3}\right). \qquad (7\text{–}61)$$

We are now in a position to evaluate A_1 and A_2 from the boundary conditions (see Eqs. 6–41 and 6–42 and note the direction chosen here for $\mathbf{J}$):

$$H_{\theta 2} - H_{\theta 1} = \left[-\frac{1}{a}\frac{\partial U_2}{\partial \theta} + \frac{1}{a}\frac{\partial U_1}{\partial \theta}\right]_{r=a} = J_s, \qquad \left[-\frac{\partial U_1}{\partial r} + \frac{\partial U_2}{\partial r}\right]_{r=a} = 0.$$

Substituting Eqs. (7–56), (7–57), and (7–61) into the above equation yields

$$A_1 = j \frac{\omega\mu_0 \, \delta\sigma a}{3 + j\omega\mu_0 \, \delta\sigma a} \frac{m}{2\pi a^3}, \qquad (7\text{–}62\text{a})$$

$$A_2 = \frac{3}{3 + j\omega\mu_0 \, \delta\sigma a} \frac{m}{4\pi}. \qquad (7\text{–}62\text{b})$$

The average power dissipated in the shell (see Eq. 7–55) is given by

$$P_D = \frac{1}{2} \int_v \frac{|J|^2}{\sigma} \, dv,$$

where v is the volume of the shell. We take $dv = (2\pi a \sin \theta)(a \, d\theta)(\delta)$ and obtain

$$P_D = \frac{\pi a^2}{\sigma\delta} \int_0^\pi |J_s|^2 \sin \theta \, d\theta.$$

Substituting Eqs. (7–61) and (7–62a) into the integrand of the above integral yields $P_D = \frac{1}{2} |I|^2 R$, where

$$R \triangleq \frac{3\pi}{2} \frac{1}{\delta\sigma} \left(\frac{c^2 N}{a^2}\right)^2 \frac{1}{1 + (3/\omega\mu_0 \, \delta\sigma a)^2} \qquad (7\text{–}63)$$

is the equivalent resistor which accounts for the power dissipated in the shell.

It is instructive to derive Eq. (7–63) in a different manner. Given that V is the phasor voltage applied at the terminals of the coil, we can show that

$$P_D = \frac{1}{2} \text{Re} \, [VI^*]. \qquad (7\text{–}64)$$

The proof is identical to the proof used for Eq. (7–55). The phasor magnetic flux linked by the coil is

$$\Phi = \pi c^2 \mu_0 H_{z1}(P_0).$$

Here P_0 is a field point which can be taken arbitrarily close to the origin O. The reason for not allowing P_0 to coincide with O is that H_{z1} becomes infinite at the origin. This is a consequence of our representation of the coil as a dipole. Since the coil is lossless, we anticipate that the singularity of the dipole field will not affect P_D. Since $v = N(d\phi/dt)$, where v is the voltage applied at the coil terminals, we have

$$V = j\omega N\Phi = j\omega\pi c^2 N\mu_0 H_{z1}(P_0). \qquad (7\text{–}65)$$

Substituting

$$I = m/\pi c^2 N \qquad (7\text{–}66)$$

and Eq. (7–65) into Eq. (7–64) yields

$$P_D = \frac{\mu_0\omega}{2} \text{Re} \, [jH_{z1}(P_0)m^*].$$

From Eq. (7–56) we obtain, for any $P_0 \neq 0$,

$$\text{Re}\,[jH_{z1}(P_0)m^*] = \text{Re}\,[-jA_1m^*].$$

Thus we see that the singularity of the dipole field does not affect P_D as we had anticipated. Substituting Eq. (7–62a) into

$$P_D = \frac{\mu_0\omega}{2}\,\text{Re}\,[-jA_1m^*] = \tfrac{1}{2}\,|I|^2\,R$$

and using Eq. (7–66) to eliminate m, we find that R is again given by Eq. (7–63).

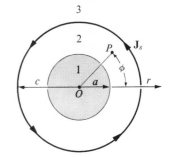

Fig. 7–17. Cross section of a circular cylindrical induction heater.

Example 2. Figure 7–17 illustrates the cross section of a circular cylindrical induction heater. The heating element is an infinitely long circular shell of radius c and negligible thickness, with a sinusoidally time-varying surface current density $\mathbf{J}_s = \mathbf{i}_\phi J_s$. The element to be heated is considered to be an infinitely long circular rod of radius a, permeability μ, and conductivity σ. The time-varying current in the shell sets up a time-varying magnetic field intensity $\mathbf{H} = \mathbf{i}_z H_z$ which induces an electric field intensity $\mathbf{E} = \mathbf{i}_\phi E_\phi$, which in turn causes a current density $\mathbf{J} = \mathbf{i}_\phi J_\phi$. The power dissipation associated with $\mathbf{J}$ heats the rod. We wish to determine the quasi-static field and find J_ϕ. In region 1 within the rod the Maxwell equations for the quasi-static field take the form

$$\nabla \times \mathbf{H} = \mathbf{J}, \qquad \nabla \times \mathbf{E} = \frac{1}{\sigma}\nabla \times \mathbf{J} = -\frac{\partial \mathbf{B}}{\partial t}.$$

Introducing phasor notation and using Eq. (1–102) to find the components of curl, we obtain

$$-\frac{dH_z}{dr} = J_\phi, \tag{7–67a}$$

$$\frac{1}{r}\frac{d}{dr}(rJ_\phi) = -j\omega\mu\sigma H_z. \tag{7–67b}$$

(Note that, due to symmetry, H_z and J_ϕ are functions of r only.) Eliminating

H_z from Eqs. (7–67) yields

$$\frac{d^2 J_\phi^*}{dr^2} + \frac{1}{r}\frac{dJ_\phi^*}{dr} + \left(k^2 - \frac{1}{r^2}\right)J_\phi^* = 0, \qquad (7\text{–}68)$$

where

$$k \triangleq \sqrt{j\omega\mu\sigma}. \qquad (7\text{–}69)$$

A solution of Eq. (7–68) which remains finite at the origin is

$$J_\phi^* = CJ_1(kr), \qquad (7\text{–}70)$$

where $J_n(u)$ is the *Bessel function of the first kind of order n* (see Appendix A–2). The constant C is obtained from the boundary condition at $r = a$. For simplicity we take $a = c$. In region 3 we can obtain the magnetic field from a scalar potential which satisfies Laplace's equation in cylindrical coordinates. We can obtain the desired solution by separating variables. The solution meeting the boundary conditions of this problem would result in $\mathbf{H} = 0$ for region 3. We can see this by noting that the cylindrical shell forms an infinitely long circular coil and that the surface current constrains the magnetic flux to flow within the coil. Anticipating that the magnetic field intensity in region 3 is zero, we can now attempt to satisfy the boundary conditions. If we can satisfy the boundary conditions the uniqueness theorem assures us that we have the correct solution. In region 1, $B_r = 0$; hence the normal component of the magnetic flux density is continuous, as required. The condition (6–42) yields $H_{1z}(a) = J_s$. If we use the formula

$$\frac{d}{du}(uJ_1(u)) = uJ_0(u)$$

and substitute Eqs. (7–67b) and (7–70), we obtain $C = kJ_s^*/J_0(ka)$. The current distribution within the rod is given by†

$$J_\phi^* = kJ_s^* \frac{J_1(kr)}{J_0(kr)}. \qquad (7\text{–}71)$$

PROBLEMS

7–1 Consider the coil shown in Fig. 6–34 (Problem 6–5). (a) If $a \ll l$, determine a first approximation for the inductance L of the coil by assuming that the magnetic field intensity $\mathbf{H}$ is uniform inside the coil and zero outside. (b) Use the axial field component H_x determined in Problem 6–5 and find a second approximation for L. Assume that $H_x(x)$ is uniform over the cross section at x. Compare this result with that obtained in part (a).

---

† The functions $J_0(kr)$ and $J_1(kr)$ are tabulated. See E. Jahnke and F. Emde, *Tables of Functions*, Dover Publications, New York, 1945.

7-2 Determine the inductance per unit length of the parallel-plate transmission line illustrated in Fig. 6–14, given that $l = 10$ cm and $d = 0.25$ cm. Determine the force per unit length if $i = 1000$ A. Are the plates attracted or repelled by each other?

7-3 An infinitely long straight current filament lies in the plane of a circular current filament of radius a (Fig. 7–18). The perpendicular distance between the center of the circle and the line is d. The currents are i_1 and i_2, respectively, and are directed as shown. Determine the mutual inductance between the filaments and determine the force **F** acting on the line.

7-4 The magnetization of a magnetic medium can be explained on the basis of elemental current loops. The energy required to create an elemental current loop of area a and circulating current i (see Eq. 7–20) is

$$W_1 = \tfrac{1}{2}i\phi = \tfrac{1}{2}\mathbf{B} \cdot \mathbf{m},$$

where $\mathbf{m} = \mathbf{n}ai$ is the magnetic dipole moment of the current loop. Extend this result to the case of a uniform distribution of current loops which are used to represent a soft-iron magnetic medium and show that the energy of magnetization is

$$W_m = \tfrac{1}{2}\int_{v_m} \mathbf{B} \cdot \mathbf{M}\, dv,$$

where v_m is the volume of the magnetic medium. Consider now the case in which the magnetic medium is magnetized by a distribution of current-carrying coils. If we consider the coils and magnetization current loops to be excited directly by external sources, the energy input W_T is given by Eq. (7–26), where $\mathbf{B} = \mu_0 \mathbf{H}$:

$$W_T = \frac{1}{2}\int_v \frac{\mathbf{B}}{\mu_0} \cdot \mathbf{H}\, dv.$$

Here v extends over all of space. However, the excitation of the magnetization current loops does not come directly from external sources, but arises out of coupling with the field. Given that W is the energy input to the coils from the external sources, we have $W + W_m = W_T$. Use this relation to prove the general validity of Eq. (7–26), where we can now take $\mathbf{B} = \mu \mathbf{H}$.

7-5 Determine the force on the soft-iron sphere considered in Problem 6–16. [*Hint:* Replace the coil by a point magnetic charge M_p and evaluate the force on M_p.]

7-6 A spherical conducting shell of radius a, conductivity σ, and thickness $\delta \ll a$ is placed in a sinusoidally time-varying magnetic field which has the phasor representation $\mathbf{i}_z B_0 e^{j\omega t}$. Determine the scalar potential for the magnetic field. Evaluate the power dissipated in the shell. Determine the value of $\delta\sigma$ which results in a maximum power dissipation for a fixed ωa.

7-7 Consider Example 1, Section 7–8. Determine the value of $\delta\sigma$ which results in a maximum power dissipation in the shell for a fixed ωa.

7-8 Assume that the quasi-static conditions given in Section 7–1 are satisfied, and show that the current density **J** in a medium of uniform permeability μ and conductivity σ satisfies the equation

$$\nabla \cdot (\nabla \mathbf{J}) = \mu\sigma\, \frac{\partial \mathbf{J}}{\partial t}.$$

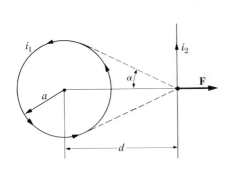

Figure 7–18	Figure 7–19

What form does this equation take in cylindrical coordinates, given that $\mathbf{J} = \mathbf{i}_z J(r)e^{j\omega t}$?

7-9 A thin circular coil of radius a and resistance R rotates with an angular velocity $\boldsymbol{\omega} = \mathbf{i}_y \omega_1$ about a radial axis in a uniform time-varying magnetic field $\mathbf{B} = \mathbf{i}_x B_0 \sin \omega_2 t$. Find expressions for the instantaneous power dissipated and the driving torque.

7-10 Consider Fig. 7–19, which illustrates four infinitely long parallel cylindrical conductors of circular cross section. The conductors are grouped into two transmission line pairs (1, 2) and (3, 4), carrying axially directed currents of i_1, $-i_1$, i_2 and $-i_2$, respectively. Show that the mutual inductance per unit length is

$$M = \frac{\mu_0}{2\pi} \ln \frac{d_{13}d_{24}}{d_{23}d_{14}},$$

and that the result is independent of whether the conductors are solid or hollow, as shown in the figure.

7-11 Determine the inductance of the spherical coil discussed in Problem 6–11.

7-12 A soft-iron sphere of permeability μ which has a radius a is situated at the origin of a spherical coordinate system in a uniform time-varying magnetic field $\mathbf{B} = \mathbf{i}_z B_0 \sin \omega t$. The magnetic material is ferrite, which has a high resistivity, so that the induced currents can be neglected. A closely wound coil of N turns is wound over the surface at $z = 0$. Show that the open-circuit voltage at the coil terminals is given by

$$V = \pi a^2 \frac{3\mu_r}{2 + \mu_r} N\omega B_0 \cos \omega t.$$

[*Hint:* Use Eq. (7–49) to determine the field inside the sphere.] If the coil terminals are short-circuited, what change, if any, would you anticipate in the magnetic field?

7-13 A circular coil of radius c which has N closely wound turns is placed at the center of a ferrite shell of permeability μ, radius a, and thickness $\delta \ll a$. Compute the change in inductance of the coil (see Problem 6–17).

7-14 Consider Problem 5-4 and Fig. 5-12 and suppose that the figure now illustrates the cross section of a parallel-plate transmission line carrying a current i and $-i$ in the upper and lower plates, respectively. Determine the force F_x acting on a soft-iron slab introduced between the slabs, as shown in the figure.

7-15 An infinite conducting sheet of thickness δ and conductivity σ moves with a velocity $\mathbf{u}$ at right angles to a magnetic field $\mathbf{B}_0$ which is normal to the sheet. Show that the force per unit area of the sheet opposing the motion has a magnitude given by $F = \sigma \delta u B_0^2$. Neglect the effect of the induced current on $\mathbf{B}_0$ and the effect of the displaced charges on the induced electric field intensity within the sheet.

CHAPTER 8

MAGNETIC CIRCUITS

8-1 INTRODUCTION

Magnetic devices consisting of permanent magnets and conducting coils wound on soft-iron cores are of considerable practical importance. The design of inductors, electromagnets, and linear stroke and torque motors are examples in which the dimensions of coils and magnetic cores must be evaluated. Permanent magnets are important because they eliminate the need for current-carrying coils and the sources of excitation for such coils. They are used in moving-coil instruments, loudspeakers, and for obtaining focusing fields for a variety of electronic devices in which a relatively large magnetic flux must be economically maintained within a gap. Technical details of many electromagnetic and permanent-magnet devices are given in references 1, 2, and 3.

Determining the magnetic fields of the devices mentioned above by solving boundary-value problems is so complex that very few practical cases can be solved analytically. However, methods are available for obtaining relatively simple approximate solutions. We shall concern ourselves in this chapter with the development of approximate methods of solution and their application to a variety of magnetic devices.

8-2 EQUIVALENT MAGNETIC CIRCUITS

Figure 8–1 shows a simple toroidal magnetic circuit. We wish to establish a relation between the core and gap dimensions, the ampere turns, and the magnetic flux in the core and air gap. Let us first discuss a case in which there is no air gap, so that $l_g = 0$. The magnetic core is assumed to have a permeability μ. The cross-sectional area is A_m, the average radius is r_m, and the coil is uniformly wound over a section of length l_c with N turns. The magnetic field intensity must satisfy the field equations inside and outside the core and also satisfy the boundary conditions on the surface of the core. An approximate solution can be obtained by applying Ampère's circuital law to the circular path shown in the figure. We find that

$$H = \frac{iN}{2\pi r} \cdot \tag{8-1}$$

The average value of H can be taken as

$$H_m = iN/l_m, \tag{8-2}$$

where $l_m \triangleq 2\pi r_m$ is the estimated average path length of the magnetic flux in the core. It is interesting to note that we can interpret $\mathbf{H}$ as resulting from a current iN flowing in an infinitely long straight filamentary conductor centered at the origin O and normal to the plane of the figure. Thus $\mathbf{H}$ is an exact solution to the field equation curl $\mathbf{H} = 0$, provided that $r \neq 0$. The question then arises as to whether the boundary conditions are met by this solution. It follows from the equation

$$\lim_{\mu \to \infty} \mathbf{H} = \lim_{\mu \to \infty} \mathbf{B}/\mu = 0$$

that the magnetic field intensity inside the core is negligible if μ_r is large compared with unity. As a first approximation, we can therefore take the field components to be zero outside the core. The tangential component of $\mathbf{H}$ is continuous, since it is zero (or nearly so) on either side of the boundary. The normal component of $\mathbf{B}$ is continuous, since $\mathbf{B}$ is parallel to the surface within the core and zero outside. Thus we see that the boundary conditions are satisfied in the limit as $\mu \to \infty$. A good approximation is therefore obtained by using Eq. (8–1) to determine H within the core and taking $H = 0$ outside the core.

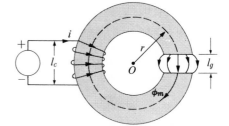

Fig. 8–1. A toroidal magnetic circuit.

It is of interest to discuss briefly the physical reason for the fact that the magnetic flux is constrained to flow within the core when $\mu \to \infty$. From Eq. (6–34b) we see that the surface magnetization current density has a magnitude

$$J_{sm} = (\mu_r - 1)H.$$

Applying Ampère's circuital law in the form given by Eq. (6–36), we find that

$$\frac{B_m}{\mu_0} 2\pi l_m = iN + (\mu_r - 1)iN = \mu_r iN,$$

which again yields Eq. (8–2). In effect the surface magnetization current density $\mathbf{J}_{sm}$ results in the magnetic core being equivalent to a uniformly wound toroidal core in free space which has $\mu_r iN$ ampere turns. We know

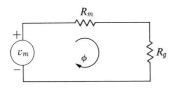

Fig. 8–2. An equivalent circuit for the magnetic circuit of Fig. 8–1.

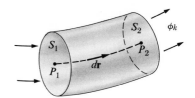

Fig. 8–3. A tube of magnetic flux.

that for a uniformly wound toroidal coil the flux is constrained to flow nearly entirely within the coil (see Eq. 6–25 and note that it is identical to Eq. 8–1).

In most technical applications a gap is present in the magnetic circuit, as is the case, for example, in a moving-coil instrument. The average magnitude B_g of the magnetic flux density in the central region of the air gap is of interest. Let the area of the air gap be A_g. In general, the flux spreads out in the gap so that $A_g > A_m$. We can find an approximate value for A_g in terms of A_m by assuming a circular path for the flux at the edges. It follows that A_g is determined by increasing the linear dimensions of the cross section of the core by the amount l_g. Considering the magnetic flux ϕ within the core as a tube of magnetic flux which spreads out in the air gap, we can write $\phi = B_g A_g = B_m A_m$. Equation (8–2) now has the form

$$H_m l_m + H_g l_g = v_m,$$

where $v_m = iN$ is the magnetomotive force (see Eq. 2–50). Since

$$H_k = B_k/\mu_k = \phi/\mu_k A_k, \qquad k = g, m,$$

we find that

$$\phi(R_m + R_g) = v_m, \tag{8–3}$$

where

$$R_k \triangleq l_k/\mu_k A_k \tag{8–4}$$

is defined as the *reluctance* of the gap ($k = g$) and core ($k = m$), respectively. Equation (8–3) can be interpreted in terms of an equivalent circuit (Fig. 8–2). In analogy with the voltage and current relations of a resistive network, we can speak of a flux ϕ flowing through a reluctance R under the action of a mmf v_m.

In general, the reluctance of a tube of magnetic flux bounded by two terminal surfaces S_1 and S_2 (Fig. 8–3) is defined by $R_k \triangleq v_k/\phi_k$, where

$$v_k \triangleq \int_{P_1}^{P_2} \mathbf{H} \cdot d\mathbf{r}$$

is defined as the *magnetic potential difference* between the end faces of the tube of flux and where ϕ_k is the magnetic flux within the tube.

The *permeance* P_k for a tube of flux is defined as the reciprocal of the reluctance of the tube: $P_k \triangleq \phi_k/v_k$. The concept of permeance is convenient for numerical computations when there are many flux tubes in parallel.

In most cases we can obtain sufficient accuracy by assuming that the average flux path in a tube of flux is defined by the centroids of the cross sections. We shall now give two examples to illustrate the approximate solution of magnetic circuit problems.

Example 1. A toroidal type of magnetic core of rectangular cross section has the following parameter values:

$$l_m = 20 \text{ cm}, \qquad A_m = (2 \text{ cm})(1 \text{ cm}) = 2 \text{ cm}^2,$$

$$l_g = 0.1 \text{ cm}, \qquad \mu_r = 4000.$$

We wish to determine the ampere turns iN required to realize a magnetic flux density in the air gap of magnitude $B_g = 0.1$ Wb/m². The air-gap area is taken as $A_g = (2 + 0.1)(1 + 0.1) \text{ cm}^2 = 2.31 \text{ cm}^2$. The magnetic flux in the air gap is

$$\phi = B_g A_g = 2.31 \times 10^{-5} \text{ Wb}.$$

Since $\mu_0 = 4\pi \times 10^{-7}$, we find from Eq. (8–4) that the numerical value of the core reluctance is given by $R_m = 1.99 \times 10^5$. To eliminate the need for conversion factors, it is convenient to evaluate the ratio

$$\frac{R_g}{R_m} = \mu_r \left(\frac{A_m}{A_g}\right) \left(\frac{l_g}{l_m}\right) = 17.3.$$

The required number of ampere turns is given by the mmf:

$$v_m = \phi R_m (1 + R_g/R_m) = 84.1 \text{ ampere turns}.$$

Assume that the coil has 200 turns and that the inductance is to be found. We can use Eq. (7–15) and obtain

$$L = \phi N^2/iN = 1.1 \times 10^{-2} \text{ H}.$$

Example 2. Let us consider the magnetic circuit illustrated in Fig. 8–4. The magnetic field intensities and the average path lengths in the various core sections are designated by H_1, H_2, H_3 and l_1, l_2, and l_3, respectively. We can apply Ampère's circuital law to the two paths C_2 and C_3 shown in the figure and obtain

$$H_1 l_1 + H_g l_g + H_2 l_2 = v_m, \tag{8–5a}$$

$$H_1 l_1 + H_g l_g + H_3 l_3 = v_m. \tag{8–5b}$$

Each term on the left-hand sides of Eqs. (8–5) represents the magnetic potential difference for the corresponding part of the magnetic circuit. These potential differences will now be expressed in terms of the corresponding

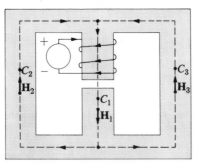

Fig. 8–4. A magnetic circuit with parallel paths for the magnetic flux.

fluxes and reluctances. Let ϕ_1 represent the magnetic flux in the center section and ϕ_2 and ϕ_3 represent the magnetic fluxes in the respective outside legs. We then have

$$H_k = \phi_1/\mu_k A_k, \qquad k = 1, g,$$

$$H_k = \phi_k/\mu_k A_k, \qquad k = 2, 3.$$

Substituting into Eqs. (8–5) yields

$$\phi_1 R_1 + \phi_2 R_2 = v_m, \qquad (8\text{–}6a)$$

$$\phi_1 R_1 + \phi_3 R_3 = v_m, \qquad (8\text{–}6b)$$

where

$$R_1 \triangleq l_1/\mu_1 A_1 + l_g/\mu_0 A_g, \qquad R_k \triangleq l_k/\mu_k A_k, \qquad k = 2, 3.$$

Equations (8–6) in conjunction with the equation of continuity for the magnetic flux, $\phi_1 = \phi_2 = \phi_3$, results in the equivalent circuit illustrated in Fig. 8–5. We can interpret Eqs. (8–6) by stating that the sum of the magnetic potential differences in a closed loop is equal to the applied mmf. We then have a direct analogy with Kirchhoff's law for electrical circuits.

Fig. 8–5. An equivalent circuit for the magnetic circuit of Fig. 8–3.

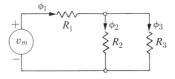

Consider now the problem of determining the ampere turns required to realize a magnetic flux density in the air gap of magnitude $B_g = 0.2$ Wb/m², given that

$$l_1 = 10 \text{ cm}, \qquad A_1 = A_2 = A_3$$

$$l_2 = l_3 = 25 \text{ cm}, \qquad A_1 = (2.5)(2.5) \text{ cm}^2 = 6.25 \text{ cm}^2,$$

$$l_g = 0.3 \text{ cm}, \qquad \mu_r = 4000.$$

The air-gap area is taken as

$$A_g = (2.5 + 0.3)(2.5 + 0.3) \text{ cm}^2 = 7.84 \text{ cm}^2,$$

and the required magnetic flux in the center section is $\phi_1 = 1.57 \times 10^{-4}$ Wb. We have $R_2 = R_3 = 7.96 \times 10^4$ and

$$R_1 = \frac{l_1}{l_2}\left[1 + \mu_r\left(\frac{A_m}{A_g}\right)\left(\frac{l_g}{l_1}\right)\right]R_2 = 38.7R_2.$$

For the parallel branches the combined permeance is given by $P_c = P_2 + P_3$, and the reluctance is given by the reciprocal of P_c:

$$R_c = \frac{R_2R_3}{R_2 + R_3} = 0.5R_2.$$

The total reluctance is

$$R = R_1 + R_c = 39.2R_2,$$

and the number of required ampere turns is given

$$v_m = \phi_1 R = 490 \text{ ampere turns.}$$

8-3 ELECTROMAGNETS, LINEAR-STROKE, AND TORQUE MOTORS

Electromagnets find important applications in devices for converting an electrical signal into a mechanical force. A wide variety of magnetic circuits can be used. To discuss the principles used in determining inductance, force, and torque, we shall first consider the magnetic circuit illustrated in Fig. 8-6. Both magnetic cores are assumed to have the same permeability μ, and we let l_m represent the average path length of the magnetic flux in the core. Ampère's circuital law applied to the average path yields

$$\phi(R_m + R_g) = iN = \phi R, \tag{8-7}$$

where

$$R_m = l_m/\mu A_m, \qquad R_g = 2x/\mu_0 A_g, \qquad R \triangleq R_m + R_g.$$

The air-gap area A_g is, in general, a function of the air-gap spacing x. However, when x is small we can assume that $A_g \cong A_m$. The magnetic field energy is given by Eq. (7-22):

$$W = \tfrac{1}{2}iN\phi = \tfrac{1}{2}Li^2.$$

With the aid of Eq. (8-7), we obtain the following expression for the inductance:

$$L = N^2/R. \tag{8-8}$$

Assuming that i is constant, we can write W in the form $W = (iN)^2/2R$, from

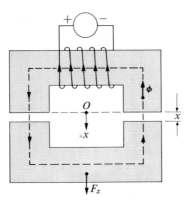

Fig. 8–6. A lifting electromagnet.

which we obtain (see Eq. 7–32) the force

$$F_x = -\frac{\phi^2}{2}\frac{\partial R}{\partial x}.$$ (8–9)

Equations (8–7), (8–8), and (8–9) apply to magnetic circuits in general. For the particular case shown in Fig. 8–6 we find that

$$F_x = -\frac{\phi^2}{\mu_0 A_g}\left(1 - \frac{x}{A_g}\frac{\partial A_g}{\partial x}\right).$$

For small x we can use the approximation

$$\frac{\partial A_g}{\partial x} \simeq \frac{A_g - A_m}{x}$$

and we obtain

$$F_x = -\frac{B_g^2 A_m}{\mu_0} = -B_g H_g A_m.$$ (8–10)

Equation (8–10) can also be derived by taking the flux ϕ to be constant and considering a differential displacement dx. The change in magnetic energy is then entirely due to the change in the air-gap volume. Thus, assuming as a first approximation that $A_g \simeq A_m$, we obtain

$$dW = 2(\tfrac{1}{2}B_g H_g)A_m\,dx.$$

Since ϕ is constant, we must use Eq. (7–33) to determine the force. The result is identical to Eq. (8–10). We can easily generalize the above derivation by noting that if ϕ is constant, we can write W in the form $W = \tfrac{1}{2}\phi^2 R$, from which Eq. (8–9) follows when we apply Eq. (7–33).

We shall now give several examples illustrating the methods that can be used to determine forces and torques in electromechanical devices.

Example 1. The negative sign in Eq. (8–10) indicates that the force between the two magnetic cores is attractive. Let us determine the force of attraction $F = -F_x$ for a magnetic circuit whose parameters are such that

$$B_g = 0.2 \text{ Wb/m}^2, \qquad A_m = 10^{-2} \text{ m}^2.$$

Substituting into Eq. (8–10) yields

$$F = 318 \text{ N} = 71.6 \text{ lbf}.$$

Example 2. Figure 8–7 illustrates the cross section of an electromagnetic circuit breaker which has circular symmetry about the center axis. The magnetic core and plunger are taken to have the same permeability μ. Let H_m represent the average magnitude of magnetic field intensity in the plunger and central section of the core. We define an equivalent path length l_e by means of the equation

$$H_m(l_e - x) + H_g x = H_m(l - x) + H_g x + \int_b^a H_r \, dr + H_a l = iN, \quad (8\text{–}11)$$

which is obtained by applying Ampère's circuital law to the dashed path shown in the figure. The relationship between H_m, H_g, H_r and H_a is obtained from the equations expressing the continuity of magnetic flux:

$$\phi = \mu \pi b^2 H_m = \mu_0 A_g H_g = \mu_0 \pi (b + x)^2 H_g$$

$$= \mu 2\pi r c H_r = \mu \pi [(a + c/2)^2 - (a - c/2)^2] H_a = \mu \pi 2 a c H_a.$$

Solving the above equations for H_g, H_r, and H_a in terms of H_m, we obtain

$$H_g = \mu_r \left(\frac{b}{b + x}\right)^2 H_m, \qquad H_r = \frac{b^2}{2cr} H_m, \qquad H_a = \frac{b^2}{2ac} H_m.$$

Substituting into Eq. (8–11) yields

$$l_e = l\left(1 + \frac{1}{2}\frac{b^2}{ac} + \frac{b^2}{2cl}\ln\frac{a}{b}\right).$$

The reluctance of the magnetic circuit is

$$R = \frac{l_e - x}{\mu \pi b^2} + \frac{x}{\mu_0 \pi (b + x)^2},$$

and the force can be found from Eq. (8–9).

Example 3. An electromagnetic linear-stroke motor is often used in control systems to actuate hydraulic valves. Figure 8–8 illustrates the cross section of such a device, which has circular symmetry about the center axis. The current i_1 in the center coil sets up flux paths such as C_1 which link all three coils. The current i_2 in coil 2 sets up flux paths such as C_2 which link coil 2. For coil 3 we choose $i_3 = i_2$ and take the winding sense opposite to that of

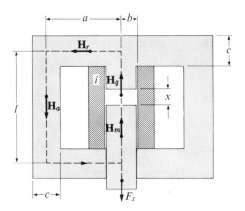

Fig. 8–7. A circuit-breaker electromagnet.

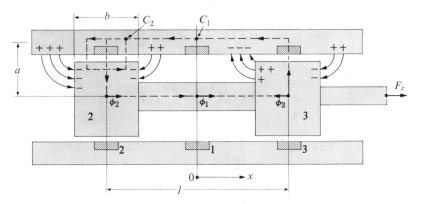

Fig. 8–8. A linear-stroke motor.

coil 2. We can understand the operation of the device by considering section 2 of the movable plunger. With the polarities as shown in the figure, the magnetic fields of coils 1 and 2 are additive on the left-hand side and subtractive on the right-hand side. The induced magnetic charges (indicated in the figure by the polarity signs) are stronger on the left, resulting in a force of attraction to the left. Section 3 also contributes to the resultant force, and thus for the polarities chosen we have $F_x < 0$. Let us now derive an expression for F_x. The magnetic flux linking coil 2 is

$$\phi_2 = \phi_{22} + \phi_{21},$$

where ϕ_{22} is the magnetic flux linking coil 2 due to i_2 and ϕ_{21} is the magnetic flux linking coil 2 due to i_1. For small displacements from the center, ϕ_{22} remains constant. Thus, since ϕ_{21} decreases as x increases,

$$d\phi_2 = d\phi_{21} = -B_{g1}2\pi a \, dx,$$

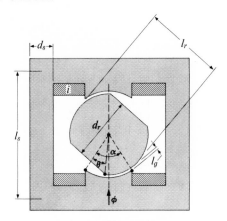

Fig. 8–9. A torque motor.

where $\mathbf{B}_{g1}$ is the air-gap magnetic flux density due to i_1. For coil 3 we have

$$d\phi_3 = d\phi_{31} = -B_{g1}2\pi a\,dx.$$

The magnetic field energy is

$$W = \tfrac{1}{2}i_1 N_1 \phi_1 + \tfrac{1}{2}i_2 N_2 \phi_2 + \tfrac{1}{2}i_3 N_3 \phi_3.$$

Noting that $i_2 = i_3$, $N_2 = N_3$, we obtain $F_x = -i_2 N_2 (2\pi a)B_{g1}$.

In order to determine B_{g1}, we define an equivalent path length l_m by the equation

$$H_m l_m + H_g l_g = \oint_C \mathbf{H} \cdot d\mathbf{r} = i_1 N_1,$$

where the mmf is evaluated along the average flux path and where $\mathbf{H}_m = (1/\mu)\mathbf{B}_{g1}$. We find that

$$B_{g1} = \frac{\mu_0 i_1 N_1}{l_g(1 + l_m/\mu_r l_g)}.$$

Thus

$$F_x = -(i_1 i_2 N_1 N_2)\left(\frac{a}{l_g}\right)\frac{2\pi\mu_0}{1 + l_m/\mu_r l_g}.$$

Note that the direction of the force can be reversed by reversing the direction of i_1 or i_2.

Example 4. Figure 8–9 illustrates the cross section (taken perpendicular to the axis) of a magnetic device which can supply a mechanical torque proportional to the current. We can understand the operation of the device by noting that the magnetic field due to the current i induces magnetic surface charges on the rotor and stator surfaces. The force of attraction between the induced magnetic charges results in a torque $\mathbf{T}$. Let us determine an expression for T.

Ampère's circuital law applied to the average flux path yields

$$H_r l_r + H_g 2l_g + H_s l_s = iN,$$

where H_r, H_g, and H_s are the average magnitudes for the magnetic field intensities in the rotor, air gap, and stator, respectively. The equation for the continuity of magnetic flux yields

$$\phi = \mu_0 H_g A_g = \mu H_r l \, d_r = 2\mu H_s l \, d_s,$$

where l is the axial length of the rotor. The reluctance is given by $R = R_g + R_r + R_s$, where

$$R_g \triangleq 2l_g / \mu_0 A_g, \qquad R_r \triangleq l_r / \mu l \, d_r, \qquad R_s \triangleq l_s / 2\mu l \, d_s,$$

and where the air-gap area is $A_g = l l_r (\alpha - \theta)/2$. When we take i to be constant, we can write the magnetic field energy in the form

$$W = \tfrac{1}{2} iN\phi = \frac{1}{2}\left(\frac{iN}{R}\right)^2.$$

Thus (see Eq. 7–38)

$$T = \frac{\partial W}{\partial \theta} = -\tfrac{1}{2}\phi^2 \frac{\partial R}{\partial \theta} = -\tfrac{1}{4}\phi^2 R_g \frac{l_r l_g}{A_g}.$$

If the relative permeability is very large compared with unity and if l_g / l_r is not excessively small, the reluctance is mainly due to the air gap. Thus $\phi \cong iN/R_g$, and we find that $T \cong -C(iN)^2$, where $C \triangleq \mu_0 l l_r / 8 l_g$.

The torque can be made bidirectional by adding a second pole group to the stator, a group which is situated at right angles with respect to the first pole group. The two stator windings are wound so that the ampere turns are additive for pole group 1, resulting in a torque

$$T = -C(i_1 N_1 + i_2 N_2)^2,$$

and so that the ampere turns are subtractive for pole group 2. This results in a torque

$$T_2 = C(i_1 N_1 - i_2 N_2)^2.$$

The resultant torque is then

$$T = T_2 - T_1 = -4C(i_1 i_2 N_1 N_2).$$

8–4 PERMANENT MAGNETS

In permanent magnets the mutual coupling between electron spins results in a permanent alignment of the spins. Macroscopically we describe such a state by a permanent magnetization vector $\mathbf{M}_p$. The magnetization results in a magnetization current density $\mathbf{J}_m$ and a surface magnetization current

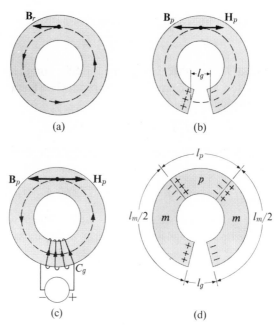

Fig. 8-10. Permanent magnet circuits.

density $\mathbf{J}_{sm}$, which in turn results in a magnetic flux density

$$\mathbf{B}_r = \mu_0 \mathbf{M}_p. \tag{8-12}$$

The magnetic field intensity within a permanent magnet is defined by the equation

$$\mathbf{H}_p \triangleq \frac{\mathbf{B}_p}{\mu_0} - \mathbf{M}_p, \tag{8-13}$$

and we note that $\mathbf{H}_p = 0$ when $\mathbf{B}_p = \mathbf{B}_r$. This is the case when the permanent magnet forms a closed toroidal path, as shown in Fig. 8-10(a). It follows from the symmetry and from Ampère's circuital law that $\mathbf{H}_p = 0$, since no conduction current is linked by a closed path in the magnet.

When $l_g \neq 0$, it is convenient to consider that $\mathbf{H}_p$ results from magnetic charges (Fig. 8-10b). We can obtain the magnetic charge density and magnetic surface charge density from the magnetization $\mathbf{M}_p$ by use of Eqs. (6-37). Due to these charges $\mathbf{H}_p$ has a direction opposite to that of $\mathbf{B}_p$ within the magnet. We can interpret the effect of $\mathbf{H}_p$ in a different manner by using Eq. (8-13). We consider that the magnetic flux density $\mu_0 \mathbf{H}_p$ associated with the magnetic charges combines with the magnetic flux density $\mathbf{B}_r$ due to the permanent magnetization to yield a resultant magnetic flux density

$$\mathbf{B}_p = \mu_0 \mathbf{H}_p + \mathbf{B}_r. \tag{8-14}$$

Since $\mathbf{B}_r$ and $\mathbf{H}_p$ are oppositely directed, we see that the effect of the magnetic charges is to decrease the magnitude of the resultant magnetic flux density. A gap, therefore, results in a demagnetization of the magnet.

An alternative description in terms of the surface magnetization current can also be given (Fig. 8–10c). We can interpret the field in the gap region in the following manner. We first consider that no gap is present and that the magnetization is uniform. This results in a uniform surface current density $\mathbf{J}_{sm}$. The gap can be accounted for by means of a coil C_g which has a uniform surface current density of $-\mathbf{J}_{sm}$ and which is superimposed on the magnet surface in the gap region. The resultant surface current density in the gap region is then zero. The magnetic field intensity inside the coil in free space is equivalent to $\mathbf{H}_p$, and we note that $\mathbf{H}_p$ has a direction opposite to that of $\mathbf{B}_p$. It is interesting to note that we can consider the external field of C_g as the leakage field of the gap. This provides a simple means for estimating the leakage flux in the gap field.

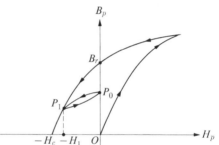

Fig. 8–11. The B–H characteristic of a permanent magnet.

A permanent magnet is often used in conjunction with soft-iron pole pieces (Fig. 8–10d). The polarities shown in the figure indicate the induced magnetic surface charges at the gap. It should be noted that $\mathbf{H}$ has the same direction as $\mathbf{B}$ within the soft-iron and air-gap regions, while $\mathbf{H}$ has a direction opposite to that of $\mathbf{B}$ within the permanent magnet.

Let us now consider the permanent magnet illustrated in Fig. 8–10(c). A coil is wound on the magnet surface and is excited by a current i. The magnetic field intensity $\mathbf{H}_p$ of the coil will result in a magnetic flux density $\mathbf{B}_p$ given by Eq. (8–14). Let $\mathbf{i}$ be a constant unit vector which is collinear with $\mathbf{B}_p$ at a field point within the magnet and let B_p and H_p be defined by the equations $\mathbf{B}_p = \mathbf{i}B_p$ and $\mathbf{H}_p = \mathbf{i}H_p$, respectively. In general, B_p is a nonlinear function of H_p; a typical functional relationship is illustrated in Fig. 8–11. When the current i is reduced to zero after the magnet has been in saturation, there remains a *remanent magnetic flux density* $\mathbf{B}_r$, which is the permanent magnetization. If i is reversed, the direction of $\mathbf{H}_p$ is reversed, and when $H_p = -H_c$ we have $\mathbf{B}_p = 0$ (H_c is known as the *coercive force*). If at some intermediate point such as P_1 we increase i to zero, the path P_1P_0 is followed. As H_p varies thereafter in the range $-H_1 \leqq H_p \leqq 0$, minor hysteresis loops are traced out. These loops are often so narrow that they can be represented accurately enough by a straight line.

Instead of obtaining $\mathbf{H}_p$ by means of a coil, we can also obtain it by introducing an air gap. The portion of the B–H characteristic in the second quadrant where $B_p > 0$ and $H_p < 0$ is known as the *demagnetization curve*.

For the magnetic circuit shown in Fig. 8–10(d) we can apply Ampère's circuital law to an average flux path, and since no conduction current is linked we obtain

$$H_p l_p + H_m l_m + H_g l_g = 0. \tag{8-15}$$

From a practical point of view it is important to estimate the leakage flux from the permanent magnet and soft iron. Most methods for estimating leakage flux depend on estimating flux paths and require considerable experience with magnetic fields [1]. For reasons of simplicity, we shall neglect leakage fluxes for all parts of the magnetic circuit with the exception of the air gap. If we neglect the leakage flux from both the permanent magnet and soft iron, the equation for the continuity of magnetic flux yields

$$H_m = \frac{B_m}{\mu} = \frac{A_p}{A_m} \frac{B_p}{\mu}, \tag{8-16}$$

where A_p and A_m are the respective cross-sectional areas.

To account for the leakage flux in the air gap, we consider the gap closed by the soft iron and a coil C_g to be wound over the soft iron in the gap region. We assume that the surface current density in the coil is $-\mathbf{J}_{sm}$, where $\mathbf{J}_{sm}$ is the surface current density of the soft iron. When $\mu_r \gg 1$, the magnitude of $\mathbf{J}_{sm}$ (see Eq. 6–34b) is given by

$$J_{sm} \cong \mu_r H_m = B_m/\mu_0. \tag{8-17}$$

The superposition of the magnetic flux density $\mathbf{B}_c$ of the coil in free space and the magnetic flux density $\mathbf{B}_m$ of the soft iron gives a useful approximation of the magnetic flux density $\mathbf{B}_g$ in the air gap. Since $\mathbf{B}_c$ is directed oppositely to $\mathbf{B}_m$, we obtain, by using Eq. (8–17),

$$B_g = B_m - B_c = (1 - f)B_m, \tag{8-18}$$

where

$$f \triangleq B_c/\mu_0 J_{sm}.$$

Here $\mathbf{B}_c$ is the magnetic flux density at the center of the coil C_g in free space. In the case of a rectangular cross section we can determine the factor f by substituting $iN = J_{sm}$ into the result given in Problem 6–3(b) and introducing a factor of two to account for the two sections of coil on either side of the center. Thus

$$f = \frac{2}{\pi}\left[\arcsin \frac{al}{\sqrt{(a^2 + b^2)(b^2 + l^2)}} + \arcsin \frac{bl}{\sqrt{(a^2 + b^2)(a^2 + l^2)}} \right], \tag{8-19}$$

where $2x = l$ is the length of the coil. Given that $l \ll a$ and $l \ll b$, we have

$$f \simeq \frac{2}{\pi} \frac{l}{\sqrt{a^2 + b^2}} \left(\frac{a}{b} + \frac{b}{a} \right). \qquad (8\text{–}20)$$

Since

$$H_g = B_g/\mu_0, \qquad H_m = B_m/\mu = A_p B_p/\mu A_m,$$

we obtain with the aid of Eqs. (8–15), (8–16), and (8–18) the result

$$\frac{-\mu_0 H_p}{B_p} = \frac{A_p}{A_m} \left[\frac{l_m}{l_p \mu_r} + \frac{l_g}{l_p} (1 - f) \right] \simeq \left(\frac{A_p}{A_m} \right) \left(\frac{l_g}{l_p} \right) (1 - f), \qquad (8\text{–}21)$$

where we have taken $(l_m/l_p \mu_r) \ll 1$. The plot of B_p against H_p is known as the *shearing line* and its intersection with the B–H curve determines the average state or operating point for the permanent magnet. (Since the magnetization is not uniform, the volume elements of the magnet are in different magnetic states. We can therefore compute only an average magnetic state.)

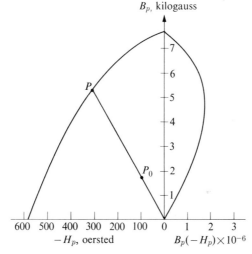

Fig. 8–12. The demagnetization curve for Alnico II.

To illustrate the principles involved in the solution of a permanent magnet circuit problem, we shall take the following parameter values for the circuit illustrated in Fig. 8–10(d):

$$l_m = 2l_p = 10 \text{ cm}, \qquad A_p = A_m = 1 \text{ cm}^2,$$
$$l_g = 0.5 \text{ cm}, \qquad \mu_r = 4000.$$

The cross-sectional area is taken to be square, so that $a = b = 1$ cm. The problem here will be to determine the magnetic flux density in the air gap, given that the permanent magnet material is Alnico II (see Fig. 8–12 for the demagnetization curve). Equations (8–20) and (8–21) yield $f = 0.45$ and

$$B_p/-\mu_0 H_p = 18.2. \tag{8–22}$$

It is customary to use cgs units to describe the properties of magnetic materials. In cgs units we have 1 oersted (Oe) $= (\frac{1}{4}\pi) \times 10^3$ ampere turns/m and 1 gauss (G) $= 10^{-4}$ Wb/m². To determine the shearing line we can take $-H_p = 100$ Oe $= (\frac{1}{4}\pi) \times 10^5$ ampere turns/m. We then have

$$-\mu_0 H_p = 10^{-2} \text{ Wb/m}^2,$$

and Eq. (8–22) yields $B_p = 1.82 \times 10^{-1}$ Wb/m² $= 1.82$ kilogauss (kG). The point $(B_p, -H_p)$ is indicated by P_0 in Fig. 8–11. The intersection of the shearing line through P_0 and the demagnetization curve yields the operating point P at which the flux density is $B_p = 5.3$ kG. The flux density in the air gap is given by Eq. (8–18):

$$B_g = B_p(1 - f) = 2.9 \text{ kG.}$$

Here we have taken $B_m = B_p$.

REFERENCES

1. H. C. ROTERS, *Electromagnetic Devices*, London: Chapman & Hall, 1941
2. D. HADFIELD, *Permanent Magnets and Magnetism*, New York: John Wiley & Sons, 1962
3. R. J. PARKER and R. J. STUDDERS, *Permanent Magnets and Their Application*, New York: John Wiley & Sons, 1962

PROBLEMS

8–1 Consider the transformer illustrated in Fig. 8–13. The cross section is square and the parameter values are:

$$l_1 = 10 \text{ cm}, \quad N_1 = 1000, \quad l_2 = 7 \text{ cm},$$

$$N_2 = 100, \quad a = 3 \text{ cm}, \quad \mu_r = 3000.$$

(a) Neglect the leakage flux and determine the self-inductances L_1 and L_2. Determine i_1 for a case in which $i_2 = 0$ and the flux density in the core has a magnitude of $B = 0.3$ Wb/m². (b) The secondary is connected to a resistance of one ohm and a sinusoidal voltage $v_1 = V_m \sin 400t$ is applied at the primary terminals. Given that the maximum allowable flux density in the core has a magnitude of 0.3 Wb/m², determine V_m, i_1, and i_2.

8–2 Consider Example 2, Section 8–3 (see Fig. 8–7). Given that $a = 10$ cm, $b = c = 3$ cm, $l = 10$ cm, $\mu_r = 3000$, determine the maximum attractive force for a case in which the flux density in the plunger has a magnitude of 0.35 Wb/m².

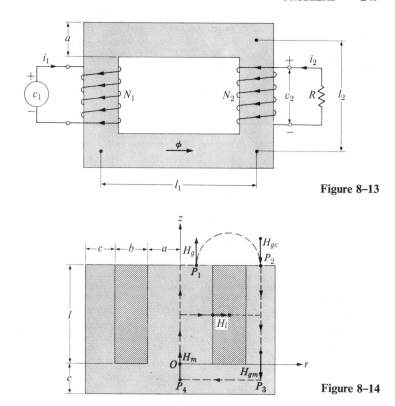

Figure 8–13

Figure 8–14

Suppose that $N = 2500$; determine the current required to realize the given flux density and evaluate the inductance of the coil.

8–3 Figure 8–14 illustrates the cross section of a lifting electromagnet which has circular symmetry about the z-axis. Apply Ampère's circuital law to the paths shown in the figure and determine the relationship between the ampere turns iN, the core flux $\phi_m = B_m \pi a^2$, the air-gap flux $\phi_g = B_g \pi a^2$ and the leakage flux $\phi_l = \phi_m - \phi_g$. Note that suitable assumptions must be made concerning the flux paths. Take the average flux path of ϕ_g to be the dashed semicircle shown. For the average value of H along this path use the arithmetic average $\frac{1}{2}(H_g + H_{gc})$. For the leakage flux paths of ϕ_l, take a straight line as shown. Assume that $\mu_r \gg 1$.

8–4 A permanent magnet of square cross section and of the type illustrated in Fig. 8–10(d) is to have an air-gap flux density of magnitude $B_g = 3.3$ kG. The minimum volume of the magnetic material Alnico II is obtained if $B_p = 4.5$ kG (see Problem 8–5 and Fig. 8–12). The air-gap width is $l_g = 0.3$ cm. Account approximately for the spreading of the flux in the air gap, but otherwise neglect the leakage flux and determine the length l_p and cross-sectional area A_p of the permanent magnet.

8–5 Consider the permanent magnet illustrated in Fig. 8–10(b). Show that if the air-gap flux density $\mathbf{B}_g$ is fixed, the permanent magnet volume is a minimum when the energy density $\frac{1}{2}(-H_p B_p)$ is a maximum.

8–6 Figure 8–15 illustrates a simple magnetic relay. The movable relay arm of permeability μ_1 has a rectangular cross section of dimensions $w \times b$ and is situated as shown in the air gap of an electromagnet. The electromagnet is of permeability μ_2 and has a rectangular cross section of dimensions $a \times b$. The length of the average flux path in the electromagnet is l_m. Determine an expression for the force F on the relay arm, given that the coil has iN ampere turns. Take $l_g \cong w$.

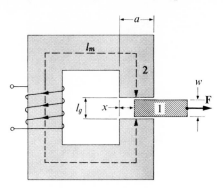

Figure 8–15

8–7 Consider a spherical permanent magnet of radius a made of Alnico II (see Fig. 8–12). Determine the operating point on the demagnetization curve and find B_p and H_p. What is the numerical value of the magnetization and the surface current density given by Eq. (6–53)?

CHAPTER 9

ELECTROMAGNETIC FIELD ENERGY; PLANE ELECTROMAGNETIC WAVES

9-1 INTRODUCTION

In Chapters 3 and 6 we discussed electrostatic and magnetostatic fields in which electric field intensity and magnetic flux density are independent of each other. In Chapter 7, which dealt with the quasi-static electromagnetic field, it was shown that electric field intensity was dependent on magnetic flux density, and that it could be obtained from the vector potential. In general, both $\mathbf{E}$ and $\mathbf{B}$ are related to each other and to the sources of the field through the Maxwell equations

$$\text{curl } \mathbf{E} = -\frac{\partial \mathbf{B}}{\partial t}, \tag{9-1a}$$

$$\text{curl } \mathbf{H} = \mathbf{J} + \frac{\partial \mathbf{D}}{\partial t}. \tag{9-1b}$$

The sources of the field are related to each other through the equation of continuity,

$$\text{div } \mathbf{J} = -\frac{\partial \rho}{\partial t}. \tag{9-2}$$

For material media we have the constitutive equations,

$$\mathbf{D} = \varepsilon \mathbf{E}, \tag{9-3a}$$

$$\mathbf{B} = \mu \mathbf{H}, \tag{9-3b}$$

$$\mathbf{J} = \sigma \mathbf{E}. \tag{9-3c}$$

It follows from Eqs. (9–1) and (9–2) that (see Eqs. 2–47)

$$\text{div } \mathbf{D} = \rho, \tag{9-4a}$$

$$\text{div } \mathbf{B} = 0. \tag{9-4b}$$

A general solution of the above group of equations will be discussed in Chapter 11, which deals with antennas.

In order to generate electromagnetic waves, we must have moving charges in some region of space v_g. In v_g we then have a current density $\mathbf{J}$

and a charge density ρ which are both time-varying and which set up the electromagnetic field. It is, however, often convenient to consider electromagnetic waves in a source-free region of space in which we need not be explicitly concerned with the sources of the field. We shall see that in a source-free region of space, Maxwell's equations reduce to a wave equation. A simple and important solution of the wave equation is a plane wave. Besides its mathematical simplicity, a plane wave has further significance. The distant electromagnetic field of a radiating antenna can be approximately represented by a plane electromagnetic wave, and we are often interested in the transmission and reflection of the wave in both dielectric and conducting media. Important concepts of transmission lines can be developed for the case of a plane wave, concepts which are applicable to more complex electromagnetic fields.

9–2 THE WAVE EQUATION IN CARTESIAN COORDINATES

In a region of space in which ε and μ are both uniform and in which $\mathbf{J} = 0$, we can take the curl of Eq. (9–1a), and with the aid of Eqs. (9–1b) and (9–3a) we can eliminate $\mathbf{B}$ and $\mathbf{D}$. Thus

$$\mathbf{V} \times (\mathbf{V} \times \mathbf{E}) = -\mu\varepsilon \frac{\partial^2 \mathbf{E}}{\partial t^2}.$$

If in addition $\rho = 0$, it follows from Eq. (9–4a) and the uniformity of ε that div $\mathbf{E} = 0$. With the aid of the vector identity (1–116), we obtain the *wave equation*,

$$\mathbf{V}^2\mathbf{E} = \frac{\partial^2 \mathbf{E}}{\partial x^2} + \frac{\partial^2 \mathbf{E}}{\partial y^2} + \frac{\partial^2 \mathbf{E}}{\partial z^2} = \mu\varepsilon \frac{\partial^2 \mathbf{E}}{\partial t^2}. \tag{9–5}$$

Here we have expressed the operator $\mathbf{V}^2$ in a cartesian coordinate system. In a similar manner we can show that the vector $\mathbf{H}$ satisfies the wave equation.

We obtain a simple solution of Eq. (9–5) if $\mathbf{E}$ has the form $\mathbf{E} = \mathbf{i}_x E(z, t)$. The x-component of Eq. (9–5) then yields the one-dimensional wave equation

$$\frac{\partial^2 E}{\partial z^2} = \frac{1}{u^2} \frac{\partial^2 E}{\partial t^2}, \tag{9–6}$$

where

$$u \triangleq 1/\sqrt{\mu\varepsilon}. \tag{9–7}$$

We can readily see by direct substitution that

$$E = f(z - ut) \tag{9–8}$$

is a solution of Eq. (9–6) in which the function $f(z')$ must have a second derivative with respect to z', but is otherwise arbitrary. The vector $\mathbf{H}$ is related to $\mathbf{E}$ through Eq. (9–1a):

$$-\mu \frac{\partial \mathbf{H}}{\partial t} = \mathbf{i}_y \frac{\partial E}{\partial z}.$$

Noting that $\partial f / \partial t = -u(\partial f / \partial z)$, we obtain

$$\mathbf{H} = \mathbf{i}_y \frac{f}{u\mu} = \frac{1}{u\mu} \mathbf{i}_z \times \mathbf{E}. \tag{9–9}$$

It follows from Eq. (9–9) that $\mathbf{E}$ and $\mathbf{H}$ are orthogonal to each other. In order to discuss the significance of the quantity u we consider the function $f(z')$ as seen in a frame of reference $\mathscr{F}'(x', y', z')$, where $x' = x$, $y' = y$, and $z' = ut - z$. We note that the waveform f is fixed in $\mathscr{F}'$ and moves in the positive z-direction with a velocity $\mathbf{u}$ relative to the frame of reference $\mathscr{F}(x, y, z)$ (Fig. 9–1). The quantity u given by Eq. (9–7) thus represents the velocity of propagation of the waveform (the so-called *phase-velocity*) of the electromagnetic wave. In free space $\mu_0 = 4\pi \times 10^{-7}$, $\varepsilon_0 = (\frac{1}{36}\pi) \times 10^{-9}$, and we find that the phase velocity of a plane electromagnetic wave in free space is $c = 3 \times 10^8$ m/sec.

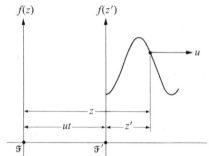

Fig. 9–1. A waveform $f(z')$ fixed in $\mathscr{F}'$ and moving relative to $\mathscr{F}$.

Since u occurs in Eq. (9–6) as u^2, we can change the sign of u in Eqs. (9–8) and (9–9) and obtain a second solution which represents a plane electromagnetic wave moving in the negative z-direction. In general we can have both types of wave present. Thus

$$f(z, t) = f_1(z - ut) + f_2(z + ut)$$

is a general solution of the one-dimensional wave equation.

9–3 PLANE WAVES AND THE SINUSOIDAL STEADY STATE

In most engineering applications dealing with plane waves we consider the field to be in a sinusoidal steady state. It is then very convenient to use phasor analysis to solve field problems. Using the notation discussed in

Section 7–8, we now assume that the **E** and **H** field vectors have the complex form

$$\mathbf{E}(P, t) = \mathbf{E}e^{j\omega t}, \qquad \mathbf{H}(P, t) = \mathbf{H}e^{j\omega t},$$

and that the real field vectors are given by

$$\mathrm{Re}\,[\mathbf{E}e^{j\omega t}], \qquad \mathrm{Re}\,[\mathbf{H}e^{j\omega t}].$$

The phasor form of Maxwell's equations are

$$\mathrm{curl}\ \mathbf{E} = -j\omega\mathbf{B}, \tag{9–10a}$$

$$\mathrm{curl}\ \mathbf{H} = \mathbf{J} + j\omega\mathbf{D}. \tag{9–10b}$$

In cartesian coordinates we obtain, taking $\mathbf{J} = 0$, $\mathbf{E} = \mathbf{i}_x E(z)$ and $\mathbf{H} = \mathbf{i}_y H(z)$,

$$\frac{\partial E}{\partial z} = -j\omega\mu H, \tag{9–11a}$$

$$-\frac{\partial H}{\partial z} = j\omega\varepsilon E. \tag{9–11b}$$

A solution of these equations can be obtained if we let

$$E = E_+ e^{-j\beta z}, \qquad H = H_+ e^{-j\beta z}.$$

Substituting into Eqs. (9–11), we obtain

$$E_+/H_+ = \omega\mu/\beta = \beta/\omega\varepsilon = Z_w, \tag{9–12}$$

where Z_w is defined as the *wave impedance* of the medium. It is often referred to as the *intrinsic impedance*. The parameter β, which is called the *phase function*, satisfies the equation $\beta = \omega\sqrt{\mu\varepsilon} = \omega/u$. Thus

$$Z_w = \sqrt{\mu/\varepsilon}. \tag{9–13}$$

It follows from Eq. (9–13) that the intrinsic impedance of free space is $Z_0 = 120\pi$ ohms (Ω).

The complex form for the electric field intensity is

$$\mathbf{E}(P, t) = \mathbf{i}_x E_+ e^{j(\omega t - \beta z)},$$

and the real electric field intensity, taking E_+ to be real, is

$$\mathbf{i}_x E_+ \cos(\omega t - \beta z).$$

Comparing this result with Eq. (9–8), we note that the electromagnetic field has a sinusoidal waveform which moves in the positive z-direction. By changing the sign of β, we obtain a solution which represents a sinusoidal waveform moving in the negative z-direction. Thus the general form for the

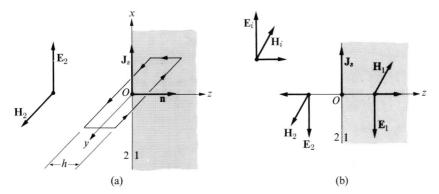

Fig. 9–2. A plane electromagnetic wave normally incident on a perfectly conducting plane.

electromagnetic field phasors is given by

$$\mathbf{E} = \mathbf{i}_x[E_+e^{-j\beta z} + E_-e^{j\beta z}],$$

$$\mathbf{H} = \mathbf{i}_y \frac{1}{Z_w}[E_+e^{-j\beta z} - E_-e^{j\beta z}].$$

(9–14)

As an example of a plane electromagnetic wave we shall discuss the case illustrated in Fig. 9–2(a), in which a plane electromagnetic wave is normally incident on a plane perfect conductor. The boundary condition for $\mathbf{E}$ requires that the tangential component of $\mathbf{E}$ vanish on the surface of the perfect conductor. Thus $E_+ = -E_-$ and the field phasors, taking E_+ to be real, are

$$\mathbf{E} = \mathbf{i}_x E_+[e^{-j\beta z} - e^{j\beta z}] = -\mathbf{i}_x j2E_+ \sin \beta z,$$

$$\mathbf{H} = \mathbf{i}_y \frac{E_+}{Z_w}[e^{-j\beta z} + e^{j\beta z}] = \mathbf{i}_y \frac{2E_+}{Z_w} \cos \beta z.$$

The real field vectors are given by

$$\text{Re}[\mathbf{E}e^{j\omega t}] = \mathbf{i}_x 2E_+ \sin \beta z \sin \omega t,$$

$$\text{Re}[\mathbf{H}e^{j\omega t}] = \mathbf{i}_y \frac{2E_+}{Z_w} \cos \beta z \cos \omega t.$$

(9–15)

It should be noted that the waveform represented by Eqs. (9–15) does not move with respect to the z-axis. We refer to the waveform as a *standing wave*.

A surface current density $\mathbf{J}_s$ which exists in the conductor surface can be determined from the boundary condition for $\mathbf{H}$. The condition is obtained by applying Stokes' theorem to Eq. (9–1b), where the path of integration for the contour is chosen as shown in Fig. 9–2(a). We let $h \to 0$, and since

$\partial \mathbf{D}/\partial t$ is a continuous function of position, we obtain the same result as for the case of a static magnetic field (see Problem 6–10):

$$(\mathbf{H}_2 - \mathbf{H}_1) \times \mathbf{n} = \mathbf{J}_s. \qquad (9\text{–}16)$$

In the above example $\mathbf{H}_1 = 0$; thus the phasor surface current density is

$$\mathbf{J}_s = \mathbf{i}_x \frac{2E_+}{Z_w}. \qquad (9\text{–}17)$$

The solution to the problem can be interpreted in the following manner. An incident wave with a phasor electric field intensity given by $\mathbf{E}_i = \mathbf{i}_x E_+ e^{-j\beta z}$ is completely reflected by the conductor. The reflected wave has a phasor electric field intensity given by $\mathbf{E}_r = -\mathbf{i}_x E_+ e^{j\beta z}$, and combines with the incident wave to give a resultant field which is a standing wave in region 2 and is zero in region 1.

An alternative interpretation of the physical situation is possible. We can consider the incident wave to propagate through the conductor. At the conductor surface the electric field intensity $\mathbf{E}_i$ of the incident wave gives rise to a surface current density $\mathbf{J}_s$. Associated with $\mathbf{J}_s$ is a plane electromagnetic wave in region 1 with a phasor electric field intensity given by $\mathbf{E}_1 = \mathbf{i}_x E_s e^{-j\beta z}$, which propagates in the positive z-direction and, due to symmetry, there is a plane electromagnetic wave in region 2 with a phasor electric field intensity given by $\mathbf{E}_2 = -\mathbf{i}_x E_s e^{j\beta z}$, which propagates in the negative z-direction. The phasor magnetic field intensities associated with these waves are given, respectively, by

$$\mathbf{H}_1 = \mathbf{i}_y \frac{E_s}{Z_w} e^{-j\beta z}, \qquad \mathbf{H}_2 = -\mathbf{i}_y \frac{E_s}{Z_w} e^{j\beta z}.$$

Equation (9–17) and the boundary condition for $\mathbf{H}$ give $E_s = -E_+$. In region 1 the electric field intensities $\mathbf{E}_i$ and $\mathbf{E}_1$ combine to yield a zero electric field intensity, while in region 2 the electric field intensities $\mathbf{E}_i$ and $\mathbf{E}_2$ combine to form the electric field intensity $\mathbf{E}$ of the standing wave.

9-4 ENERGY RELATIONS IN AN ELECTROMAGNETIC FIELD; THE POYNTING VECTOR

We now wish to generalize the concept of electric and magnetic field energies developed in Sections 5–2 and 7–4, so that we may define the energy content of an electromagnetic field. Consider an electromagnetic field in a lossy region v_d bounded by a surface S, and suppose that no electromagnetic energy enters v_d through S. In order for the electromagnetic field to be sustained, there must be a mechanism present in a volume v_g which can move charges against the opposing forces due to the electromagnetic field and thus supply energy to the field. (In batteries and semiconductors the mechanism is one of diffusion.) However, so long as we are concerned only with the conservation of energy, we need not be concerned with the internal structure of the generator region v_g. In many cases it is convenient to consider that the energy input is due to mechanical sources distributed throughout the generator region. From a mathematical point of view this is extremely convenient, since we can then postulate the existence of current filaments in free space which are held together by mechanical forces. Thus we can avoid the complications arising from the solution of boundary-value problems associated with real conductors.

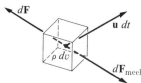

Fig. 9–3. The forces on a moving charge element.

Consider now Fig. 9–3. The elemental force acting on an element of charge $\rho\,dv$ moving with a velocity **u** is given by the Lorentz force,

$$d\mathbf{F} = \rho\,dv[\mathbf{E} + \mathbf{u} \times \mathbf{B}].$$

In the generator region this force is balanced by an elemental mechanical force $d\mathbf{F}_{\text{mech}} = -d\mathbf{F}$. The elemental mechanical power input is

$$dP_{\text{mech}} = -\rho\,dv\mathbf{E} \cdot \mathbf{u} = -\mathbf{E} \cdot \mathbf{J}\,dv,$$

where $\mathbf{J} \triangleq \rho\mathbf{u}$ is the current density. The total mechanical power input is

$$P_{\text{mech}} = \int_{v_g} (-\mathbf{E} \cdot \mathbf{J})\,dv. \tag{9–18}$$

In order to express the above integral in a form suitable for obtaining the desired energy relation, we make use of the vector identity (see Eqs. 9–1)

$$\nabla \cdot (\mathbf{E} \times \mathbf{H}) = -\mathbf{E} \cdot (\nabla \times \mathbf{H}) + \mathbf{H} \cdot (\nabla \times \mathbf{E}) = -\mathbf{E} \cdot (\nabla \times \mathbf{H}) - \mathbf{H} \cdot \frac{\partial \mathbf{B}}{\partial t} \tag{9–19}$$

and obtain

$$-\mathbf{E} \cdot \mathbf{J} = \mathbf{E} \cdot \frac{\partial \mathbf{D}}{\partial t} + \mathbf{H} \cdot \frac{\partial \mathbf{B}}{\partial t} + \operatorname{div}(\mathbf{E} \times \mathbf{H}). \tag{9–20}$$

Integrating the above expression over the volume $v = v_g + v_d$ and applying the divergence theorem to the last term yields

$$P_{\text{mech}} = \frac{\partial}{\partial t}(W_m + W_e) + P_R + P_D. \tag{9–21}$$

Here v_d is a lossy region in which Eq. (9–3c) is valid so that we have a power dissipation per unit volume given by $\mathbf{E} \cdot \mathbf{J} = J^2/\sigma$. The quantities in Eq. (9–21) are defined as follows: The instantaneous magnetic and electric field energy in v are defined, respectively, by

$$W_{mi} \triangleq \frac{1}{2} \int_v \mathbf{H} \cdot \mathbf{B} \, dv, \qquad W_{ei} \triangleq \frac{1}{2} \int_v \mathbf{E} \cdot \mathbf{D} \, dv.$$

The instantaneous power dissipated in v_d is defined by

$$P_{D_i} \triangleq \int_{v_d} \frac{J^2}{\sigma} \, dv.$$

We consider the instantaneous rate of flow of electromagnetic energy out of the volume v to be defined by

$$P_{R_i} \triangleq \int_S (\mathbf{E} \times \mathbf{H}) \cdot \mathbf{n} \, ds. \tag{9–22}$$

Here S is the surface bounding v and $\mathbf{n}$ is the outwardly directed normal to S. The vector

$$\mathbf{P} \triangleq \mathbf{E} \times \mathbf{H}, \tag{9–23}$$

which has the dimensions of watts/meter^2, is defined as the *Poynting vector*.

When the normal component of $\mathbf{P}$ is integrated over a closed surface we obtain the outward flow of energy per unit time. It is therefore convenient to consider $\mathbf{P}$ as representing a rate of flow of energy per unit area. Consider, for example, the case of a plane electromagnetic wave propagating in the direction of the z-axis. If the field varies sinusoidally with time, the phasor field vectors are

$$\mathbf{E} = \mathbf{i}_x E_+ e^{-j\beta z}, \qquad \mathbf{H} = \mathbf{i}_y \frac{E_+}{Z_w} e^{-j\beta z},$$

and the real field vectors, taking E_+ to be real, are

$$\text{Re}\,[\mathbf{E}e^{j\omega t}] = \mathbf{i}_x E_+ \cos(\omega t - \beta z), \qquad \text{Re}\,[\mathbf{H}e^{j\omega t}] = \mathbf{i}_y \frac{E_+}{Z_w} \cos(\omega t - \beta z).$$

The Poynting vector is given by

$$\mathbf{P} = \mathbf{i}_z \frac{E_+^2}{Z_w} \cos^2(\omega t - \beta z).$$

We consider $\mathbf{P}$ to represent the rate of flow of energy through a unit area in the xy-plane in the direction of the positive z-axis. The justification for this point of view can be found if we consider the *electromagnetic energy density*

$$f \triangleq \tfrac{1}{2}(\mathbf{H} \cdot \mathbf{B} + \mathbf{E} \cdot \mathbf{D}) = \frac{E_+^2}{2} \left(\frac{\mu}{Z_w^2} + \varepsilon \right) \cos^2(\omega t - \beta z)$$

to propagate with the velocity $\mathbf{u}$ of the electromagnetic wave. The rate of flow of energy per unit area is then $f\mathbf{u}$, and with the aid of Eqs. (9–7) and (9–13) we can readily see that $\mathbf{P} = f\mathbf{u}$. Thus in the case of a sinusoidally time-varying plane wave, we can take $\mathbf{P}$ as the rate of flow of energy per unit area. We shall find it convenient to consider $\mathbf{P}$ in this manner, even for a general type of electromagnetic field. This point of view results in a correct physical description of energy relations in an electromagnetic field, with the exception of special cases of static fields.

In most practical applications no mechanical sources are present and $P_{\text{mech}} = 0$. If the electromagnetic field within a volume v is to be sustained, it follows from Eq. (9–22) that there must be an energy input over a part S_i of the surface S. Equation (9–21), in which we take $P_{\text{mech}} = 0$, shows that part of the energy input changes the field energy within v, part of it is dissipated, and the remainder is scattered out of v through the part $S - S_i$ of the surface S.

We have seen that in the case of the sinusoidal steady state it is preferable to use phasors. We can define a complex power in terms of phasors, and when we apply this definition to Eqs. (9–10) (see Eq. 7–55), we obtain

$$P_{\text{mech}} = \tfrac{1}{2}\int_{v_g} (-\mathbf{E} \cdot \mathbf{J}^*)\, dv, \qquad (9\text{--}24)$$

where all quantities are now phasors. The real average power input is Re $[P_{\text{mech}}]$ and the peak stored energy can be found from the magnitude of Im $[P_{\text{mech}}]$. The distinction between the complex power represented by Eq. (9–24) and the instantaneous power represented by Eq. (9–18) should be carefully noted. In order to transform the integral in Eq. (9–24), we must use the phasor form of Maxwell's equations (9–10) and express Eqs. (9–19) and (9–20) in a corresponding form. Thus

$$-\mathbf{E} \cdot \mathbf{J}^* = j\omega(\mathbf{B} \cdot \mathbf{H}^* - \mathbf{E} \cdot \mathbf{D}^*) + \operatorname{div}(\mathbf{E} \cdot \mathbf{H}^*).$$

Substituting the above expression into Eq. (9–24) yields

$$P_{\text{mech}} = j\omega(W_m - W_e) + P_D + P_C, \qquad (9\text{--}25a)$$

where the peak stored magnetic and electric field energy in v are defined, respectively, by

$$W_m \triangleq \tfrac{1}{2}\int_v \mathbf{B} \cdot \mathbf{H}^*\, dv, \qquad (9\text{--}25b)$$

$$W_e \triangleq \tfrac{1}{2}\int_v \mathbf{E} \cdot \mathbf{D}^*\, dv. \qquad (9\text{--}25c)$$

The average power dissipated in v_d is defined by

$$P_D \triangleq \frac{1}{2}\int_{v_d} \frac{|J|^2}{\sigma}\, dv, \qquad (9\text{--}25d)$$

and the rate of flow of complex energy through S is defined by

$$P_C \triangleq \frac{1}{2} \int_S (\mathbf{E} \times \mathbf{H}^*) \cdot \mathbf{n} \, ds. \tag{9–25e}$$

The vector

$$\mathbf{P} \triangleq \frac{1}{2} \mathbf{E} \times \mathbf{H}^* \tag{9–26a}$$

is defined as the *complex Poynting vector*, and the quantity

$$\mathbf{P}_a = \text{Re} \, [\mathbf{P}] = \frac{1}{2} \, \text{Re} \, [\mathbf{E} \times \mathbf{H}^*] \tag{9–26b}$$

defines the average rate of flow of energy per unit area.

To illustrate these concepts, let us consider the real and complex Poynting vectors for the plane electromagnetic wave discussed in Section 9–3. Equation (9–15) gives the components of the **E** and **H** fields. Thus (see Eq. 9–23)

$$\mathbf{P} = \mathbf{i}_z \frac{E_+^2}{Z_w} \sin 2\beta z \sin 2\omega t.$$

From this expression we see that the average rate of flow of energy is zero and that the peak instantaneous rate of flow of energy per unit area is

$$P_{\max} = \frac{E_+^2}{Z_w} \cdot \sin 2\beta z.$$

The complex Poynting vector is given by

$$\mathbf{P} = -\mathbf{i}_z j \frac{E_+^2}{Z_w} \cdot \sin 2\beta z,$$

and we see that the average rate of flow of energy per unit area, Re [**P**], is zero and that the magnitude of Im [**P**] gives the peak instantaneous rate of flow of energy per unit area.

9–5 PLANE ELECTROMAGNETIC WAVES IN CONDUCTING MEDIA

In a conducting medium the electric field intensity **E** results in a current density **J** which is related to **E** by Eq. (9–3c). The phasor form of Maxwell's equations in a conducting medium is given by (see Eqs. 9–10)

$$\text{curl } \mathbf{E} = -j\omega\mathbf{B}, \tag{9–27a}$$

$$\text{curl } \mathbf{H} = \sigma\mathbf{E} + j\omega\varepsilon\mathbf{E} = j\omega\varepsilon_c\mathbf{E}, \tag{9–27b}$$

where $\varepsilon_c \triangleq \varepsilon + (\sigma/j\omega)$ can be considered as an *equivalent permittivity* for the conductor. Thus the considerations of Section 9–3 apply, provided that ε is replaced by ε_c. A sinusoidally time-varying plane wave can therefore propagate in a conducting medium and the field phasors are given by Eqs. (9–14), where the propagation function and the wave impedance for the conductor are given, respectively, by

$$\beta_c = \omega\sqrt{\mu\varepsilon_c}, \qquad Z_c = \frac{\omega\mu}{\beta_c}. \qquad (9\text{–}28)$$

Let us consider a sinusoidally time-varying plane wave in free space which is normally incident on a semi-infinite plane conductor. The incident wave has an **E** field given by

$$\mathbf{E}_i = \mathbf{i}_x E_+ e^{-j\beta z}$$

and the reflected and transmitted plane waves have **E** fields given, respectively, by

$$\mathbf{E}_r = \mathbf{i}_x \Gamma E_+ e^{j\beta z}, \qquad \mathbf{E}_t = \mathbf{i}_x T E_+ e^{-j\beta_c z}.$$

(See Fig. 9–4, where the arrows indicate the direction of propagation of the waves.) The parameters Γ and T are called the *reflection coefficient* and *transmission coefficient*, respectively. The magnetic fields associated with the incident, reflected, and transmitted waves are given, respectively, by

$$\mathbf{H}_i = \mathbf{i}_y \frac{E_+}{Z_0} e^{-j\beta z}, \qquad \mathbf{H}_r = -\mathbf{i}_y \frac{\Gamma E_+}{Z_0} e^{j\beta z}, \qquad \mathbf{H}_t = \mathbf{i}_y \frac{T E_+}{Z_c} e^{-j\beta_c z}.$$

The boundary conditions at $z = 0$ require that

$$E_i + E_r = E_t, \qquad H_i + H_r = H_t.$$

(Note that **J** is a continuous function of z for $z \geqq 0$, and thus there is no surface current density.) These conditions yield the relations

$$T = \frac{2}{1 + Z_0/Z_c}, \qquad (9\text{–}29\text{a})$$

$$\Gamma = \frac{Z_c - Z_0}{Z_c + Z_0}. \qquad (9\text{–}29\text{b})$$

The current density in the conducting medium is given by

$$\mathbf{J} = \mathbf{i}_x \sigma T E_+ e^{-j\beta_c z}. \qquad (9\text{–}30)$$

Note that β_i is complex and that $\mathrm{Re}\,[j\beta_c] > 0$, so that the transmitted wave is attenuated.

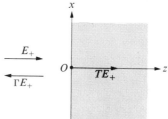

Fig. 9–4. A plane electromagnetic wave normally incident on a semi-infinite plane conductor.

The complex Poynting vector at $z = 0$ is given by

$$\mathbf{P} = \mathbf{i}_z \frac{1}{2} \frac{|TE_+|^2}{Z_c^*},$$

and the average rate of flow of energy per unit area at $z = 0$ is

$$P_a = \tfrac{1}{2} |TE_+|^2 \operatorname{Re}\left[\frac{1}{Z_c^*}\right]. \tag{9–31}$$

This expression gives the average power dissipated in an infinite cylindrical volume of the conductor of unit cross-sectional area in the xy-plane. Let us verify this by direct computation of the average power dissipated in the cylindrical volume. We let

$$dv = (1)(1)(dz), \qquad \alpha \triangleq (j/2)(\beta_c - \beta_c^*),$$

and obtain

$$P_D = \tfrac{1}{2} \int_0^\infty \sigma |E_t|^2 \cdot dz = \frac{\sigma |TE_+|^2}{4\alpha}. \tag{9–32}$$

To prove the equality of Eqs. (9–31) and (9–32), it is sufficient to note that (see Eqs. 9–28)

$$\frac{1}{\alpha} = \frac{2}{j}\left(\frac{\beta_c + \beta_c^*}{\beta_c^2 - \beta_c^{*2}}\right) = \frac{\beta_c + \beta_c^*}{\omega\mu\sigma}, \qquad \operatorname{Re}\left[\frac{1}{Z_c^*}\right] = \frac{1}{2}\left(\frac{1}{Z_c} + \frac{1}{Z_c^*}\right) = \frac{\beta_c + \beta_c^*}{2\omega\mu}.$$

We therefore obtain $P_a = P_D$. The dissipated power within the conductor is supplied by the flow of electromagnetic energy through the conductor surface.

For good conductors such as copper ($\sigma = 5.8 \times 10^7$ mhos/m and $\varepsilon \cong \varepsilon_0$) and for all practical frequencies we have $\omega\varepsilon/\sigma \ll 1$. Thus $\varepsilon_C \cong (\sigma/j\omega)$, and from Eq. (9–28) we obtain

$$\beta_c \cong \sqrt{\omega\mu\sigma}\, e^{-j\pi/4} = (1 - j)/\delta,$$
$$Z_c \cong \sqrt{\omega\mu/\sigma}\, e^{j\pi/4} = \sqrt{2}\, R_c e^{j\pi/4}, \tag{9–33}$$

where

$$R_c \triangleq \operatorname{Re}[Z_c] = \sqrt{\omega\mu/2\sigma}, \tag{9–34}$$

and where

$$\delta \triangleq \sqrt{2/\omega\mu\sigma} = \frac{1}{\sigma R_c} \tag{9–35}$$

is defined as the *penetration depth* of the wave. (The field is attenuated by a factor of $e^{-z/\delta}$ in an interval of length z.)

When we express the average rate of flow of energy per unit area at $z = 0$ in terms of the tangential component of $\mathbf{H}$, we obtain an expression which will prove useful when we are discussing wave-guide losses. With the aid of Eq. (9–26b) we obtain

$$P_a = \tfrac{1}{2} |H_t|^2 \operatorname{Re} [Z_c] = \tfrac{1}{2} R_c |H_t|^2. \tag{9–36}$$

Since the depth of penetration of the wave is negligible for good conductors, it is of interest to compute the total current flowing in the conductor and consider this to flow at the surface as a surface current density. The current density $\mathbf{J}'_s$ which flows across a section of the y-axis of unit length is (see Eq. 9–30)

$$\mathbf{J}'_s = \mathbf{i}_x \int_0^\infty J \, dz = \mathbf{i}_x \frac{TE_+}{j\beta_c} = \mathbf{i}_x \frac{\sigma H_t Z_c}{j\beta_c} = \mathbf{i}_x H_t.$$

Comparing this result with that obtained from Eq. (9–16), we see that, if the depth of penetration is small, we can replace the current density $\mathbf{J}'_s$ by a surface current density $\mathbf{J}_s$ on the surface. The field inside the conductor is then taken as zero. This is an approximation to the physical situation. However, it results in a considerable mathematical simplification of the problem.

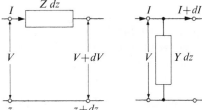

Fig. 9–5. Equivalent circuits for a section of length dz of a transmission line.

9-6 TRANSMISSION LINE EQUATIONS

In many problems dealing with wave propagation it is convenient to introduce a transmission line analog for the field equations. We then consider a phasor voltage $V = V(z)$ and a phasor current $I = I(z)$ which are related by the so-called *transmission-line equations*,

$$dV/dz = -ZI, \tag{9–37a}$$

$$dI/dz = -YV, \tag{9–37b}$$

where Z is the *impedance per unit length* and Y is the *admittance per unit length*. We can derive Eqs. (9–37) by interpreting $Z \, dz$ and $Y \, dz$ as the series impedance and shunt admittance for a section of the line of length dz (Fig. 9–5). It follows from Eqs. (9–37) that

$$d^2V/dz^2 = \gamma^2 V, \tag{9–38}$$

where $\gamma \triangleq \sqrt{ZY}$ is defined as the propagation function. Equation (9–38) has the solution

$$V = V_+ e^{-\gamma z} + V_- e^{\gamma z}. \tag{9–39}$$

When we define $Z_0 \triangleq Z/\gamma = \sqrt{Z/Y}$ as the *characteristic impedance*, it follows from Eq. (9–37a) that

$$I = \frac{1}{Z_0}(V_+ e^{-\gamma z} - V_- e^{\gamma z}). \tag{9–40}$$

If the line is lossless we have

$$Z = j\omega L, \qquad Y = j\omega C, \qquad \gamma = j\beta,$$

where L is the *series inductance per unit length* and C is the *shunt capacitance per unit length*. Thus, for a lossless line,

$$Z_0 = \sqrt{L/C}, \qquad \beta = \omega\sqrt{LC}. \tag{9–41}$$

Let us now compare Eqs. (9–11) with Eqs. (9–37). We see that a transmission line analog is obtained by multiplying E and H by a unit length and taking

$$V \triangleq E \times 1, \qquad I \triangleq H \times 1,$$

$$L \triangleq \mu \times 1, \qquad C \triangleq \varepsilon \times 1.$$

Equations (9–14) then correspond to Eqs. (9–39) and (9–40) and the complex power for the transmission line corresponds to the amplitude of the complex Poynting vector:

$$\tfrac{1}{2}VI^* = \tfrac{1}{2}EH^* \times (1 \text{ m})^2.$$

The characteristic impedance of the transmission line is then identical to the wave impedance:

$$Z_0 = \sqrt{\mu/\varepsilon} = Z_w.$$

We have seen in the discussion of Eq. (9–14) that $V_+ e^{-j\beta z}$ is associated with the electromagnetic wave propagating in the positive z-direction and that $V_- e^{j\beta z}$ is associated with the electromagnetic wave propagating in the negative z-direction. The ratio

$$\Gamma \triangleq \frac{V_- e^{j\beta z}}{V_+ e^{-j\beta z}} \tag{9–42}$$

is defined as the *reflection coefficient* and the ratio

$$Z \triangleq \frac{V}{I} = Z_0 \frac{1 + \Gamma}{1 - \Gamma} \tag{9–43}$$

is defined as the *impedance*. Note that both Γ and Z are functions of z.

For a transmission line of length l terminated in a load impedance Z_l, Eq. (9–43) (see Fig. 9–6) yields

$$Z_l = Z_0 \frac{1 + \Gamma_l}{1 - \Gamma_l},$$

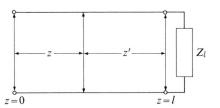

Fig. 9–6. A transmission line of length l terminated in a load impedance Z_l.

where

$$\Gamma_l \triangleq \frac{V_-}{V_+} \cdot e^{j2\beta l}$$

is the reflection coefficient at $z = l$. The reflection coefficient at a position z (see Eq. 9–42) is given by

$$\Gamma = \Gamma_l e^{-j2\beta(l-z)}. \tag{9-44}$$

Note that for a lossless line $|\Gamma| = |\Gamma_l|$ everywhere along the line. Thus the phase of Γ varies, while its magnitude remains constant. When we substitute for Γ in Eq. (9–43) and then multiply the numerator and denominator by $e^{j\beta(l-z)}$, we obtain

$$Z = Z_0 \frac{Z_l \cos \beta z' + jZ_0 \sin \beta z'}{Z_0 \cos \beta z' + jZ_l \sin \beta z'}, \tag{9-45}$$

where $z' \triangleq l - z$ is the distance along the line between the point z and the load.

We shall now discuss the practical significance of the transmission-line analog. Let

$$V_+ = |V_+| \, e^{j\phi_+}, \qquad V_- = |V_-| \, e^{j\phi_-},$$

and let us consider

$$|V|^2 = |V_+|^2 + |V_-|^2 + 2 |V_+V_-| \cos (2\beta z - \phi_+ + \phi_-).$$

We note that $|V|$ has a maximum and a minimum given by

$$|V|_{\max} = |V_+| + |V_-|, \qquad 2\beta z - \phi_+ + \phi_- = 2\pi n,$$

$$|V|_{\min} = |V_+| - |V_-|, \qquad 2\beta z - \phi_+ + \phi_- = \pi(2n + 1).$$

Here n is either zero or an integer. The ratio

$$r \triangleq \frac{|V|_{\max}}{|V|_{\min}} = \frac{1 + |\Gamma|}{1 - |\Gamma|} = \frac{1 + |\Gamma_l|}{1 - |\Gamma_l|} \tag{9-46}$$

is defined as the *voltage standing-wave ratio*. Note that at a maximum of $|V|$ we have, using Eqs. (9–42) and (9–43),

$$\Gamma = \frac{|V_-|}{|V_+|} = |\Gamma|, \qquad Z = rZ_0, \tag{9-47}$$

and that at a minimum of $|V|$ we have

$$\Gamma = -\frac{|V_-|}{|V_+|} = -|\Gamma|, \qquad Z = Z_0/r. \qquad (9\text{-}48)$$

Equations (9–46), (9–47), and (9–48) are of considerable practical significance. In the measurement of electromagnetic fields, a probe is moved along the axis of wave propagation and the positions and relative values of the maximum and minimum electric field intensities are observed. These measurements determine the voltage standing-wave ratio and the reflection coefficient. If a minimum of E occurs at a distance z' from the load, we can use Eqs. (9–44) and (9–48) to obtain

$$\Gamma_l = -|\Gamma|\, e^{j2\beta z'}.$$

We can then use Eq. (9–43) to determine the load impedance Z_l. If we need to determine the impedance at any position z, we can use Eq. (9–45).

It is common practice to measure distances along the transmission line in terms of wavelengths. The wavelength is defined by the distance λ which satisfies the equation

$$e^{j\beta z} = e^{j\beta(z+\lambda)}.$$

Hence

$$\lambda \triangleq 2\pi/\beta = u/f,$$

where $f = 2\pi\omega$ is the frequency. The field is therefore a periodic function of z with a period λ. For a standing wave, the distance between a maximum of $|V|$ and a minimum of $|V|$ is a quarter wavelength.

The complex power at any point along the transmission line is given by

$$P = \tfrac{1}{2}VI^* = \frac{|V_+|^2}{2Z_0}[1 - |\Gamma|^2 + j2\,|\Gamma|\sin(2\beta z - \phi_+ + \phi_-)].$$

At a position z at which $|V|$ is a maximum or a minimum we have

$$P = \frac{|V_+|^2}{2Z_0}(1 - |\Gamma|^2) = \frac{|V|_{\max}^2}{2Z_0}\frac{1 - |\Gamma|}{1 + |\Gamma|}. \qquad (9\text{-}49)$$

This expression also gives the real power at any position along the transmission line. In the case of a wave which is nearly a standing wave, so that $V_+ \cong V_-$, we have $|\Gamma_l| \cong 1$. It follows from Eq. (9–46) that we then have a large standing-wave ratio and from Eq. (9–49) we see that the complex power is almost purely imaginary. For the case in which there is no reflected wave ($V_- = 0$), we have $r = 1$ and $\Gamma_l = 0$. The transmission line is said to be *matched* to the load if $\Gamma_l = 0$. From Eq. (9–49) we see that the complex power is real for the matched case and from Eq. (9–43) we see that the impedance at any position is the characteristic impedance. Thus we obtain the matched case by choosing $Z_0 = Z_l$. We shall now give two examples illustrating the applications of these concepts.

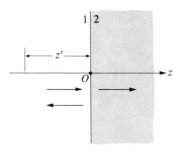

Fig. 9–7. A plane electromagnetic wave normally incident on a semi-infinite dielectric.

Example 1. A plane electromagnetic wave is normally incident on a plane semi-infinite dielectric (Fig. 9–7). The standing-wave ratio in the free-space medium 1 is $r = 1.73$ and there is an average rate of flow of energy in the z-direction of 1 W/m². The problem here is to determine the relative permittivity of the dielectric, the maximum and minimum electric field intensities in medium 1, and the electric field intensity in medium 2. We can represent medium 1 by a transmission line analog. This is terminated at $z = 0$ in the characteristic impedance of medium 2, which is considered to be the load. Thus

$$Z_l = Z_0/\sqrt{\varepsilon_r}.$$

When we use Eq. (9–45) and Eq. (9–47), we see that at the first maximum of $|V|$ we have

$$\beta z' = \pi/2, \qquad Z = Z_0^2/Z_l = Z_0\sqrt{\varepsilon_r} = rZ_0,$$

and that at the first minimum of $|V|$ away from the load we have

$$\beta z' = \pi, \qquad Z = Z_l = Z_0/\sqrt{\varepsilon_r} = Z_0/r.$$

Thus $\varepsilon_r = r^2 = 3$ and

$$\Gamma_l = \frac{1 - \sqrt{\varepsilon_r}}{1 + \sqrt{\varepsilon_r}} = -0.268.$$

Equation (9–49) yields the average rate of flow of energy per unit area:

$$\frac{|V_+|^2}{2Z_0} [1 - |\Gamma|^2] = 1 \text{ W/m}^2.$$

Since $Z_0 = 120\pi$ ohms we obtain $|V_+| = 28.5$ V. Thus

$$|V_-| = |\Gamma V_+| = 7.6 \text{ V},$$

and in medium 1 we have

$$|E|_{\text{max}} = 36.1 \text{ V/m}, \qquad |E|_{\text{min}} = 20.9 \text{ V/m}.$$

At $z = 0$ we have a minimum of $|E|$ and it follows from the continuity of the tangential component of $\mathbf{E}$ that in medium 2 we have $|E| = 20.9$ V/m. Note that the rate of flow of energy per unit area in medium 2 is

$$P = \frac{1}{2}\frac{|E|^2}{Z_l} = 1 \text{ W/m}^2,$$

as required by the conservation of energy.

Suppose now that the frequency is 10 GHz* and that the wavelengths in medium 1 and 2 are to be found. The wavelength in medium 1 is given by

$$\lambda_1 = c/f = 3 \text{ cm}.$$

The velocity of propagation in medium 2 is given by

$$u = c/\sqrt{\varepsilon_r} = 1.73 \times 10^8 \text{ m/sec}$$

and the wavelength is given by

$$\lambda_2 = u/f = 1.73 \text{ cm}.$$

Example 2. The reflected wave in medium 1 for the previous example can be eliminated by a quarter-wave matching section (Fig. 9–8). Consider a medium of characteristic impedance Z_m and of width d where $\beta_m d = \pi/2$. It follows from Eq. (9–45) that

$$Z = Z_m^2/Z_l. \tag{9–50}$$

Since $\beta_m = 2\pi/\lambda_m$, where λ_m is the wavelength in m, we have $d = \lambda_m/4$. Thus a quarter-wave section of medium m can transform a load impedance Z_l according to Eq. (9–50) into an impedance Z. It is possible to choose Z_m so that the transmission line analog of medium 1 is terminated in a matched load. This requires that

$$Z_m = \sqrt{Z_0 Z_l} = Z_0(\varepsilon_r)^{-1/4}. \tag{9–51}$$

Equation (9–51) yields

$$\varepsilon_{rm} = \sqrt{\varepsilon_r} = 1.73.$$

The characteristic impedance of the quarter-wave matching section is

$$Z_m = \frac{120\pi}{\sqrt{\varepsilon_{rm}}} = 287 \text{ ohms},$$

and its width is

$$d = \lambda_m/4 = c/4f\sqrt{\varepsilon_{rm}} = 0.57 \text{ cm}.$$

---

* 1 Hz = 1 cps, 1 kHz = 10^3 cps, 1 MHz = 10^6 cps, 1 GHz = 10^9 cps, where 1 Hz = one Hertz.

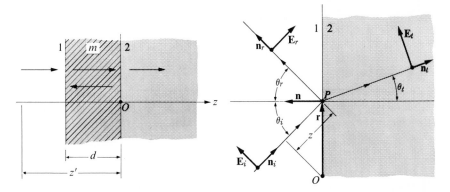

Fig. 9–8. A plane wave normally incident on a semi-infinite dielectric coated with a $\lambda/4$ matching section.

Fig. 9–9. A plane electromagnetic wave incident at an angle θ_i on a semi-infinite dielectric.

When the average rate of flow of energy is the same as in Example 1, we find from the equation

$$\frac{1}{2}\frac{|E|^2}{Z_0} = 1 \text{ W/m}^2$$

that $|E| = 27.5$ V/m in medium 1. Note that in the matching section there are both incident and reflected waves. In mediums 1 and 2, however, there are no reflected waves.

9–7 REFLECTION AND REFRACTION OF PLANE ELECTROMAGNETIC WAVES

Figure 9–9 illustrates an electromagnetic wave in free space incident on a semi-infinite plane dielectric where θ_i, θ_r, and θ_t are the angles of incidence, reflection, and transmission, respectively. Let $\mathbf{n}_i$, $\mathbf{n}_r$, and $\mathbf{n}_t$ be unit normals for the direction of propagation of the incident, reflected, and transmitted waves, respectively. We shall discuss the case in which the electric field intensity $\mathbf{E}_i$ for the incident wave is parallel to the plane of incidence formed by $\mathbf{n}_i$ and the surface normal $\mathbf{n}$. Let $\mathbf{r}$ be a radial vector from a point O in the boundary surface between medium 1 and 2. The coordinate of a field point P with respect to O in the direction of $\mathbf{n}_i$ is given by $z = \mathbf{n}_i \cdot \mathbf{r}$. We can therefore express the incident $\mathbf{E}$ field at P in the form

$$\mathbf{E}_i = \mathbf{E}_{i0}e^{-\gamma_1 \mathbf{n}_i \cdot \mathbf{r}}.$$

Similarly,

$$\mathbf{E}_r = \mathbf{E}_{r0}e^{-\gamma_1 \mathbf{n}_r \cdot \mathbf{r}}, \qquad \mathbf{E}_t = \mathbf{E}_{t0}e^{-\gamma_2 \mathbf{n}_t \cdot \mathbf{r}}.$$

Here γ_1 and γ_2 are the propagation functions for medium 1 and 2, respectively. The boundary condition requires that the tangential component of $\mathbf{E}$ be continuous at the boundary. Thus

$$(\mathbf{n}_i - \mathbf{n}_r) \cdot \mathbf{r} = 0, \tag{9–52a}$$

$$(\gamma_1 \mathbf{n}_i - \gamma_2 \mathbf{n}_t) \cdot \mathbf{r} = 0. \tag{9–52b}$$

Equation (9–52a) requires that $\theta_i = \theta_r$. Furthermore, Eq. (9–52a) states that $\mathbf{n}_i - \mathbf{n}_r$ is perpendicular to $\mathbf{r}$. Thus $\mathbf{n}_i - \mathbf{n}_r$ is parallel to $\mathbf{n}$ and therefore the vectors $\mathbf{n}_i$, $\mathbf{n}_r$, and $\mathbf{n}$ are coplanar. When we substitute $\gamma_k = j\omega/u_k$ ($k = 1, 2$) into Eq. (9–52b), we obtain *Snell's law*,

$$n_1 \sin \theta_i = n_2 \sin \theta_t. \tag{9–53}$$

Here $n_k \triangleq c/u_k$ is defined as the *index of refraction* for medium k. Equation (9–52b) requires that $\gamma_1 \mathbf{n}_i - \gamma_2 \mathbf{n}_t$ be parallel to $\mathbf{n}$. Thus $\mathbf{n}_i$, $\mathbf{n}_t$, and $\mathbf{n}$ must be coplanar. We then have the result that $\mathbf{n}_i$, $\mathbf{n}_r$, $\mathbf{n}_t$ and $\mathbf{n}$ are all coplanar, as shown in Fig. 9–9.

From Eqs. (9–14) we obtain, by taking $E_- = 0$,

$$\mathbf{H} = \frac{\mathbf{i}_z \times \mathbf{E}}{Z_w},$$

where $\mathbf{i}_z$ is a unit vector in the direction of propagation. Applying this result to the incident, reflected, and transmitted wave in our present discussion, we obtain

$$\mathbf{H}_i = \frac{\mathbf{n}_i \times \mathbf{E}_i}{Z_1}, \qquad \mathbf{H}_r = \frac{\mathbf{n}_r \times \mathbf{E}_r}{Z_1}, \qquad \mathbf{H}_t = \frac{\mathbf{n}_t \times \mathbf{E}_t}{Z_2}.$$

The boundary conditions for the continuity of the tangential $\mathbf{H}$ and $\mathbf{E}$ fields yield the two equations,

$$\frac{E_{i0}}{Z_1} - \frac{E_{r0}}{Z_1} = \frac{E_{t0}}{Z_2}, \qquad E_{i0} \cos \theta_i + E_{r0} \cos \theta_i = E_{t0} \cos \theta_t.$$

Here the subscript zero is used to indicate that the quantities are to be evaluated at the boundary. Solving for E_{t0} and E_{r0} in terms of E_{i0} yields

$$E_{t0} = E_{i0} \frac{2n_1 \cos \theta_i}{n_1 \cos \theta_t + n_2 \cos \theta_i},$$

$$E_{r0} = E_{i0} \frac{n_1 \cos \theta_t - n_2 \cos \theta_i}{n_1 \cos \theta_t + n_2 \cos \theta_i}. \tag{9–54}$$

Here we have introduced the indexes of refraction by means of the equation

$$Z_1/Z_2 = \sqrt{\mu_0 \varepsilon_2 / \mu_0 \varepsilon_0} = n_2/n_1.$$

From Eq. (9–54) we see that there is no reflected wave when the angle of incidence is equal to the *Brewster angle* θ_B, which is defined by the condition

$$n_1 \cos \theta_t = n_2 \cos \theta_B. \tag{9–55}$$

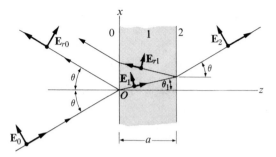

Fig. 9–10. A plane electromagnetic wave incident at an angle θ on a dielectric slab.

Equation (9–55) together with Snell's law (9–53) yields $\theta_t = (\pi/2) - \theta_B$. Using this relation to eliminate θ_t in Eq. (9–55) yields

$$\tan \theta_B = n_2/n_1.$$

At the Brewster angle of incidence the sum of the angle of incidence and the angle of transmission is 90°.

Plane electromagnetic waves are often used in a variety of technical measurements. For example, it is possible to determine the thickness and permittivity of sections of a dielectric slab by measuring the change in phase of an electromagnetic wave when the slab is inserted in the field. Figure 9–10 shows a situation in which a plane electromagnetic wave is incident at an angle θ on a dielectric slab of permittivity ε and thickness a. We shall now determine expressions relating ε, a, and the phase change ϕ. The incident **E** field is assumed to be parallel to the plane of incidence and the vector components of the **E** field are assumed to have the directions shown in the figure. We can obtain the vector components of the **H** field by noting that in a plane wave **E**, **H**, and **n** form a right-handed system. Here **n** is a unit vector in the direction of propagation. The scalar components of the field are of the form:

Incident wave in 0, $E_0 = e^{-j\beta_0 r_0}, \qquad H_0 = \dfrac{1}{Z_0} e^{-j\beta_0 r_0}.$

Reflected wave in 0, $E_{r0} = \Gamma_0 e^{-j\beta_0 r_0'}, \qquad H_{r0} = \dfrac{\Gamma_0}{Z_0} e^{-j\beta_0 r_0'}.$

Transmitted wave in 1, $E_1 = T_1 e^{-j\beta_1 r_1}, \qquad H_1 = \dfrac{T_1}{Z_1} e^{-j\beta_1 r_1}.$

Reflected wave in 1, $E_{r1} = T_1 \Gamma_1 e^{-j\beta_1 r_1'}, \qquad H_{r1} = \dfrac{T_1 \Gamma_1}{Z_1} e^{-j\beta_1 r_1'}.$

Transmitted wave in 2, $E_2 = T_2 e^{-j\beta_0 r_0}, \qquad H_2 = \dfrac{T_2}{Z_2} e^{-j\beta_0 r_0}.$

Here we have assumed that

$$r_0 = z \cos \theta + x \sin \theta, \qquad r_0' = -z \cos \theta + x \sin \theta;$$

$$r_1 = z \cos \theta_1 + x \sin \theta_1, \qquad r_1' = -z \cos \theta_1 + x \sin \theta_1.$$

The boundary conditions at $z = 0$ are

$$E_0 \cos \theta + E_{r0} \cos \theta = E_1 \cos \theta_1 + E_{r1} \cos \theta_1,$$

$$H_0 - H_{r0} = H_1 - H_{r1},$$

and yield the two equations

$$T_1 = \frac{Z_1}{Z_0} \frac{1 - \Gamma_0}{1 - \Gamma_1}, \tag{9–56}$$

$$\frac{1 + \Gamma_0}{1 - \Gamma_0} = f \frac{1 + \Gamma_1}{1 - \Gamma_1}, \tag{9–57}$$

where

$$f \triangleq \frac{Z_1 \cos \theta_1}{Z_0 \cos \theta}. \tag{9–58}$$

Eliminating Γ_0 in Eq. (9–56) with the aid of Eq. (9–57) yields

$$\frac{Z_0}{Z_1} T_1 = \frac{2}{1 - \Gamma_1 + f(1 + \Gamma_1)}. \tag{9–59}$$

The boundary conditions at $z = a$ are

$$E_1 \cos \theta_1 + E_{r1} \cos \theta_1 = E_2 \cos \theta,$$

$$H_1 - H_{r1} = H_2,$$

and yield the two equations

$$\frac{1 + \Gamma_1 e^{j\psi}}{1 - \Gamma_1 e^{j\psi}} = \frac{1}{f}, \tag{9–60}$$

$$T_2 = \left(\frac{2f}{1 + f} \right) \left(\frac{Z_0 T_1}{Z_1} \right) e^{-j\psi/2} e^{j\beta_0 a \cos \theta}, \tag{9–61}$$

where

$$\psi \triangleq 2\beta_1 a \cos \theta_1. \tag{9–62}$$

Solving Eq. (9–60) for Γ_1 yields

$$\Gamma_1 e^{j\psi} = \frac{1 - f}{1 + f}. \tag{9–63}$$

Substituting Eqs. (9–59) and (9–63) into Eq. (9–61) yields

$$T_2 = \frac{4f e^{j\beta_0 a \cos \theta}}{(1 + f)^2 e^{j\psi/2} - (1 - f)^2 e^{-j\psi/2}}. \tag{9–64}$$

Now let ϕ be the phase shift caused by the slab when it is inserted in the electromagnetic field. Since

$$E_2 = |T_2| e^{-j(\beta_0 r_2 + \phi)},$$

we see that

$$\phi = -\arg [T_2] = \alpha - \beta_0 a \cos \theta, \qquad (9\text{–}65)$$

where α is the phase angle of the denominator term of Eq. (9–64) which is determined by (see Eq. 9–58)

$$\tan \alpha = \frac{1 + f^2}{2f} \tan \frac{\psi}{2} = \frac{\varepsilon_r^2 \cos^2 \theta + \varepsilon_r - \sin^2 \theta}{2\varepsilon_r \cos \theta \sqrt{\varepsilon_r - \sin^2 \theta}} \tan \frac{\psi}{2}. \qquad (9\text{–}66)$$

Equations (9–62), (9–65), and (9–66) express the desired relations between ε, a, and ϕ.

For the special case in which θ is equal to the Brewster angle defined by Eq. (9–55), we see from Eq. (9–58) that $f = 1$. Thus (see Eqs. 9–63, 9–57, and 9–56)

$$\Gamma_1 = \Gamma_0 = 0, \qquad T_1 = Z_1/Z_0,$$

and Eq. (9–61) yields the phase shift

$$\phi = \beta_1 a \cos \theta_1 - \beta_0 a \cos \theta_B. \qquad (9\text{–}67)$$

9–8 POLARIZATION OF PLANE WAVES

If the electric field intensity of a plane wave is always parallel to a given direction, the wave is said to be *linearly polarized*. By combining two linearly polarized waves of the same frequency but of different phase and orientation we obtain an *elliptically polarized wave*. Let us assume that the two linearly polarized waves have the phasor representation

$$\mathbf{E}_1 = \mathbf{i}_x E_1 e^{-j\beta z}, \qquad \mathbf{E}_2 = j\mathbf{i}_y E_2 e^{-j\beta z}.$$

The resultant real electric field intensity is then given by

$$\text{Re} [(\mathbf{E}_1 + \mathbf{E}_2)e^{j\omega t}] = \mathbf{i}_x E_1 \cos (\omega t - \beta z) - \mathbf{i}_y E_2 \sin (\omega t - \beta z).$$

The x- and y-components of the electric field intensity are

$$E_x = E_1 \cos \phi, \qquad E_y = -E_2 \sin \phi, \qquad (9\text{–}68)$$

where

$$\phi \triangleq \omega t - \beta z.$$

From Eqs. (9–68) we see that for a fixed z the terminus of $\mathbf{E}$ describes an ellipse in the xy-plane. Given that $E_1 = E_2 = E$, we have

$$\mathbf{E}_1 = \mathbf{i}_x E e^{-j\beta z}, \qquad \mathbf{E}_2 = j\mathbf{i}_y E e^{-j\beta z}, \qquad (9\text{–}69)$$

and the wave is said to be *negatively circularly polarized*, since the terminus of

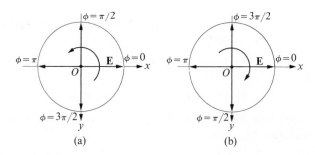

Fig. 9–11. The **E** vector for a circularly polarized plane wave propagating in the direction of the positive z-axis. (a) Negative circular polarization. (b) Positive circular polarization.

E rotates in a counterclockwise direction when viewed in the direction of propagation (Fig. 9–11a). If we choose

$$\mathbf{E}_1 = \mathbf{i}_x E e^{-j\beta z}, \qquad \mathbf{E}_2 = -j\mathbf{i}_y E e^{-j\beta z}, \tag{9–70}$$

we obtain

$$E_x = E \cos \phi, \qquad E_y = E \sin \phi.$$

Equation (9–70) gives the phasor representation for the vector components of a *positively circularly polarized wave* in which the **E** vector rotates in a clockwise direction when viewed in the direction of propagation (Fig. 9–11b).

9–9 GEOMETRIC OPTICS

In material media in which ε or μ are functions of position it becomes difficult to obtain solutions of Maxwell's equations. In the case of very high frequencies an approximate solution can be obtained by the method of *geometric optics*, in which a wave is described by a geometric curve or ray. The tangent to the ray gives the direction of propagation for the wave. In the geometric optics approximation the solution of Maxwell's equation takes the form of a plane wave:

$$\mathbf{E} = \mathbf{E}_0 e^{-j\phi}, \qquad \mathbf{H} = \mathbf{H}_0 e^{-j\phi}.$$

Here $\mathbf{E}_0$, $\mathbf{H}_0$, and L are functions of position and the phase ϕ of the wave is defined by

$$\phi \triangleq \omega L/c, \tag{9–71}$$

where c is the velocity of light in free space. Substituting into Eqs. (9–10) (where we take $\mathbf{J} = 0$) yields

$$\frac{j}{\omega\mu} \nabla \times \mathbf{E}_0 - \frac{1}{\mu c} \mathbf{E}_0 \times \nabla L = \mathbf{H}_0,$$

$$-\frac{j}{\omega\varepsilon} \nabla \times \mathbf{H}_0 + \frac{1}{\varepsilon c} \mathbf{H}_0 \times \nabla L = \mathbf{E}_0.$$

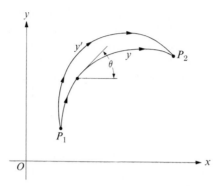

Fig. 9–12. Illustration of Fermat's principle.

If we let $\omega \to \infty$ in the above equations, we obtain the geometric optics approximation

$$\mathbf{H}_0 \cong \frac{1}{Z_w} \mathbf{i} \times \mathbf{E}_0, \qquad \mathbf{E}_0 \cong Z_w \mathbf{H}_0 \times \mathbf{i}, \qquad (9\text{–}72)$$

where $Z_w = \sqrt{\mu/\varepsilon}$ is the wave impedance of the medium which, in general, is a function of position. The unit vector $\mathbf{i}$ is defined by the equation

$$\nabla L = n\mathbf{i}, \qquad (9\text{–}73)$$

where $n = c/u$ is the index of refraction. Equations (9–72) represent a plane electromagnetic wave propagating in the direction of the vector $\mathbf{i}$ (see Problem 9–1). Equation (9–73) yields the following partial differential equation for L:

$$(\nabla L)\cdot(\nabla L) = \left(\frac{\partial L}{\partial x}\right)^2 + \left(\frac{\partial L}{\partial y}\right)^2 + \left(\frac{\partial L}{\partial z}\right)^2 = n^2. \qquad (9\text{–}74)$$

The solutions of Eq. (9–74) yield surfaces $L(x, y, z) = \text{const}$, which are known as *wave fronts*. It follows from Eq. (9–71) that the phase of the electromagnetic wave is uniform over a wave front. A wave front is therefore also known as an *equiphase surface*.

We shall not undertake the solution of Eq. (9–74) for equiphase surfaces. Instead we shall make use of Eq. (9–73), which can be used to determine the difference in phase between two terminal points P_1 and P_2 on a ray (Fig. 9–12). We have

$$L_2 - L_1 = \int_{P_1}^{P_2} \text{grad } L \cdot d\mathbf{r} = \int_{P_1}^{P_2} n \, dr. \qquad (9\text{–}75)$$

The value of this integral for a given path is known as the *optical path length*. The difference in phase (see Eq. 9–71) is given by

$$\phi_2 - \phi_1 = \frac{\omega}{c}(L_2 - L_1).$$

To determine the differential equation describing a ray, we make use of *Fermat's principle*, which states that along a ray the phase change is stationary. To understand this principle, we can consider the case of a thin beam of monochromatic light. The axis of the beam defines the ray. Now consider Fig. 9–12. The electromagnetic field over the cross section of the beam can be resolved into elementary plane waves which travel over slightly different paths to the point P_2 on a ray. These waves arrive at P_2 with the same change in phase, and are therefore additive. For points not on the ray, there is destructive interference due to the phase differences in the elementary plane waves. Consequently, the elementary plane waves are focused and travel along a ray. The unit vector **i** in Eq. (9–73) is a tangential vector of the ray and the equiphase surfaces are normal to the rays. Locally, at any point, we consider that the electromagnetic field is like a plane wave for which the field vectors are given by Eqs. (9–72).

For simplicity we shall apply Fermat's principle to a two-dimensional case (again see Fig. 9–12). Let $y = y(x)$ represent the ray which passes through P_1 and P_2 and let $y' = y + a\eta$ be a neighboring path. Here a is a parameter and η is an arbitrary function of x which meets the end conditions, $\eta(x_1) = \eta(x_2) = 0$. Stated in mathematical terms, Fermat's principle of stationary phase requires that if we substitute y' into Eq. (9–75) we must have

$$\left[\frac{d}{da}(L_2 - L_1)\right]_{a=0} = 0. \tag{9–76}$$

To determine y from Fermat's principle we let $dr = \sqrt{1 + p'^2}\, dx$, where $p' \triangleq dy'/dx$. Since $dp'/da = d\eta/dx$, Eq. (9–76) yields

$$\int_{x_1}^{x} \frac{np}{\sqrt{1 + p^2}} \frac{d\eta}{dx}\, dx = 0. \tag{9–77}$$

Integrating Eq. (9–77) by parts and using the terminal conditions for η, we obtain

$$\int_{x_1}^{x_2} \eta \frac{d}{dx}\left(\frac{np}{\sqrt{1 + p^2}}\right) dx = 0. \tag{9–78}$$

Since η is an arbitrary function, we must have

$$\frac{d}{dx}\left(\frac{np}{\sqrt{1 + p^2}}\right) = 0, \tag{9–79}$$

since otherwise we could choose

$$\eta = \frac{d}{dx}\left(\frac{np}{\sqrt{1 + p^2}}\right) \neq 0,$$

which would result in a contradiction with Eq. (9–78). Integrating Eq.

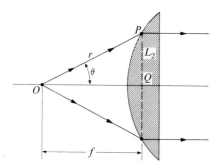

Fig. 9–13. A hyperbolic lens.   **Fig. 9–14.** The path of a ray through a dielectric slab.

(9–79) yields $np/\sqrt{1 + p^2} =$ const.   Substituting $p = \tan \theta$ yields the general form of Snell's law,

$$n \sin \theta = \text{const.} \tag{9–80}$$

Since n is a given function of position, Eq. (9–80) defines the ray.

It is often possible to obtain simple solutions in geometric optics by the use of the *law of the optical path*. This law states that the optical path lengths between two equiphase surfaces are equal. As an example of this law, let us consider Fig. 9–13. A source of electromagnetic radiation is at the origin O, which we surround by a spherical equiphase surface of infinitesimally small radius. The spherical wave front from O is to be converted to a plane wave front by means of a lens of uniform index of refraction n. We wish to determine the equation for the shape of the rear surface of the lens. Points P and Q are on the plane equiphase surface L_2. Equating the optical path length of the path $\overline{OP}$ to the optical path length of the path $\overline{OQ}$ yields (note that $n = 1$ in free space)

$$r = f + n(r \cos \theta - f).$$

Solving for r yields the equation of a hyperbola:

$$r = \frac{(n - 1)f}{n \cos \theta - 1}.$$

As a final example, let us treat the case of a plane electromagnetic wave incident at the Brewster angle θ_B on a dielectric slab by the method of geometric optics (Fig. 9–14). At the Brewster angle of incidence there are no reflected rays and the path of the incident ray is determined by Snell's law. The phase difference ϕ_0 for the path $\overline{OP'}$ along the incident ray in free space is

$$\phi_0 = \frac{\beta_0 a}{\cos \theta_B}.$$

To determine the phase difference for the path $\overline{OQ} + \overline{QP}$ we note that

$$\overline{QP} = a(\tan \theta_B - \tan \theta_1) \sin \theta_B = a \frac{\sin^2 \theta_B}{\cos \theta_B} - a\sqrt{\bar{\varepsilon}_r} \frac{\sin^2 \theta_1}{\cos \theta_1},$$

where we have made use of Snell's law. Thus the phase difference between the two paths is

$$\phi = \beta_1 \overline{OQ} + \beta_0 \overline{QP} - \phi_0 = \beta_1 a \cos \theta_1 - \beta_0 a \cos \theta_B.$$

The above result is identical to Eq. (9–67).

PROBLEMS

9–1 Show that Maxwell's equations for the case of a sinusoidally time-varying plane electromagnetic wave in a uniform medium take the form

$$\nabla \times \mathbf{E} = -\gamma \mathbf{n} \times \mathbf{E} = -j\omega \mathbf{B}, \qquad \nabla \times \mathbf{H} = -\gamma \mathbf{n} \times \mathbf{H} = j\omega \mathbf{D},$$

where $\mathbf{n}$ is a unit vector in the direction of propagation and where $\gamma = j\omega\sqrt{\mu\varepsilon}$ is the propagation function. Show that

$$\mathbf{H} = \frac{1}{Z_w} \mathbf{n} \times \mathbf{E}, \qquad \mathbf{E} = Z_w \mathbf{H} \times \mathbf{n},$$

where $Z_w = \sqrt{\mu/\varepsilon}$.

9–2 A sinusoidally time-varying plane electromagnetic wave in free space is normally incident on a plane semi-infinite dielectric medium of permittivity ε (Fig. 9–15). Determine the reflection and transmission coefficients and evaluate the Poynting vector.

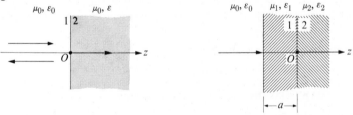

Figure 9–15   **Figure 9–16**

9–3 It is desired to match the wave impedance of free space to the wave impedance of a medium of permittivity ε_2 and permeability μ_2 so that there is no reflection of a normally incident sinusoidally time-varying plane electromagnetic wave in the free-space region (Fig. 9–16). Determine the required permittivity ε_1 and thickness a of the dielectric matching slab.

9–4 A sinusoidally time-varying plane electromagnetic wave in free space is normally incident on a plane dielectric slab of thickness a (Fig. 9–17). The slab has a perfectly conducting sheet coated on its back. Determine the electromagnetic field in regions 1 and 2.

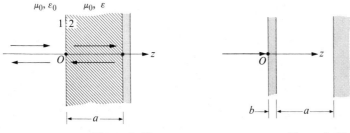

Figure 9–17   **Figure 9–18**

9–5 A plane lossy conductor of thickness b is placed at a distance $a = \lambda/4$ from a parallel perfectly conducting plane (Fig. 9–18). Determine the conductivity of the lossy conductor, given that $b \ll a$ and that it is desired to have negligible reflection of a normally incident sinusoidally time-varying plane electromagnetic wave. Can you explain why the choice $a = \lambda/4$ is made?

9–6 Consider Fig. 9–7. Suppose that the conductor is made of brass of conductivity $\sigma = 1.45 \times 10^7$ mhos/m, and determine the penetration depth of the incident plane wave at frequencies of 1 MHz, 1 GHz, and 10 GHz.

9–7 Consider Fig. 9–7. Suppose that the conductor is made of aluminum of conductivity $\sigma = 3.43 \times 10^7$ mhos/m, and determine the minimum and maximum electric field intensities of the plane wave in medium 1, given that one watt is dissipated per unit area of conductor surface and that the frequency is 1 GHz. Show that the effective surface current density satisfies the equation $J_s = E_c/Z_c$, where E_c is the electric field intensity just inside the conductor surface and where Z_c is defined by Eq. (9–33). Evaluate E_c and J_s.

9–8 Consider Fig. 9–10. Show that if the incident **E** field is normal to the plane of incidence, then the angle α in Eq. (9–65) is given by

$$\tan \alpha = \frac{\varepsilon_r + \cos^2 \theta - \sin^2 \theta}{2 \cos \theta \sqrt{\varepsilon_r - \sin^2 \theta}} \tan \frac{\psi}{2}.$$

9–9 A sinusoidally time-varying plane electromagnetic wave in free space is incident at an angle θ on a semi-infinite medium of permittivity ε and permeability μ. Determine the reflection coefficient $\Gamma = E_{r0}/E_{i0}$ and the transmission coefficient $T = E_{t0}/E_{i0}$, given that the incident **E** field is normal to the plane of incidence (see Fig. 9–9).

9–10 A sinusoidally time-varying plane electromagnetic wave in free space is incident at an angle θ on a dielectric slab of permittivity ε and width a which is coated with a perfectly conducting sheet on its rear surface (Fig. 9–19). The incident **E** field is parallel to the plane of incidence. Prove that the relative phase shift between the reflected and incident waves at the surface $z = 0$ is given by $\phi = \pi - \alpha$, where

$$\tan \alpha = \frac{2\varepsilon_r \cos \theta \tan (\psi/2)\sqrt{\varepsilon_r - \sin^2 \theta}}{\varepsilon_r^2 \cos^2 \theta - (\varepsilon_r - \sin^2 \theta) \tan^2 (\psi/2)},$$

and where $\psi = 2\beta_1 a \cos \theta_1$.

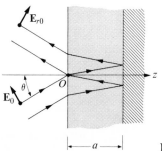

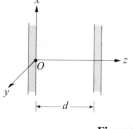

Figure 9-19   **Figure 9-20**

9-11 A Fabry-Perot resonator is often used in laser applications to obtain a highly resonant electromagnetic cavity. In its simplest form it consists of two parallel conducting plates in which a plane standing wave is sustained by a suitable source of energy (Fig. 9-20). (a) Assume that the distance between the perfectly conducting plates is d and that the field components are

$$E_x = E_0 \sin \beta z, \qquad H_y = j \frac{E_0}{Z_0} \cos \beta z,$$

where $\beta = \omega/c$, show that the possible values of β are given by

$$\beta = \pi n/d, \qquad n = 1, 2, \ldots,$$

and determine the frequencies of oscillation for each n. (b) Show that the peak electric and magnetic field energies in a volume v of the cavity of unit base area in the xy-plane and of height d are given for all n by

$$W_e = W_m = \frac{\varepsilon_0 |E_0| d}{4}.$$

(c) Determine the value of n and the frequency, given that the wavelength in the air-filled cavity is $\lambda = 10^{-4}$ and that $d = 4$ cm. Determine the value of R_c (see Eq. 9-34) at this frequency if the plates are coated with silver of conductivity $\sigma = 6.14 \times 10^7$ mhos/m. Given that $E_0 = 100$ V/m, compute the maximum magnitude of the effective surface current density in the plates. Compute the average power dissipated, P_D, in the base areas of the volume v. (d) A parameter of considerable importance in resonator studies (see Eq. 10-69) is $Q = \omega W_e/P_D$. Compute the Q associated with the volume v, using the data of part (c).

9-12 A Fabry-Perot interferometer can be used to resolve spectral lines. In its simplest form it consists of a coated plane slab, as illustrated in Fig. 9-21. Let a plane sinusoidally time-varying electromagnetic wave be incident on the slab at an angle θ and let the E field be parallel to the plane of incidence. In the geometric optics approximation the incident, reflected, and transmitted waves are considered as rays. The transmitted ray can be considered to be the sum of an infinite number of rays which are due to a succession of reflected waves in the slab, as shown in the figure. Each internal reflection results in a reduction in the amplitude associated with the ray by a factor $k < 1$ and a phase shift Δ. (a) Prove that the resultant

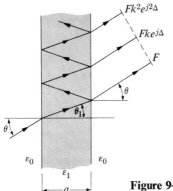

Figure 9–21

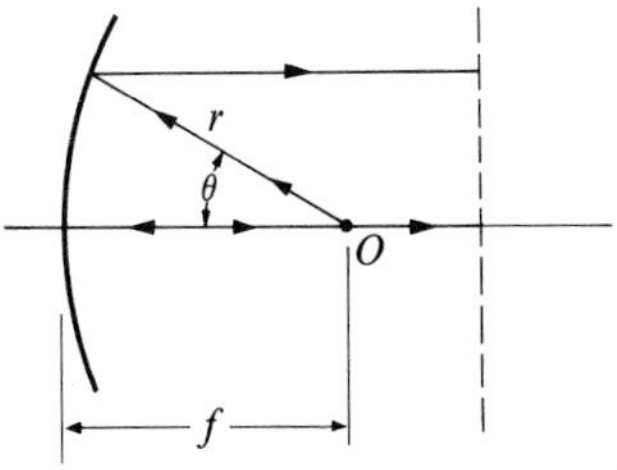

Figure 9–22

transmitted wave has an amplitude

$$T_2 = \frac{F}{1 - ke^{j\Delta}}$$

and that

$$|T_2|^2 = \frac{|F|^2}{(1 - k)^2 + 4k \sin^2 (\Delta/2)}.$$

Plot $|T_2|^2$ for $k = 0.9$, taking $0 \leqq \Delta \leqq \pi$. (b) With the aid of Eq. (9–64), determine expressions for F, k, and Δ in terms of a, ε_1, θ and θ_1. Can you obtain these expressions from the principle of geometric optics? On the basis of your results in parts (a) and (b), explain the resolution ability of the Fabry-Perot interferometer, given that several incident waves arrive at different angles of incidence and at different frequencies.

9–13 A spherical electromagnetic wave front from a point source O is to be converted to a plane wave front by an ideal reflector (Fig. 9–22). Apply the method of geometric optics and show that the equation for the reflector surface is the parabola

$$r = \frac{2f}{1 + \cos \theta}.$$

9–14 Given that R is the radius of curvature of a ray and that **N** is a unit normal of the ray directed toward the center of curvature, prove that

$$\frac{1}{R} = \frac{1}{n} \mathbf{N} \cdot \text{grad } n.$$

Note that the ray tends to bend toward the region of high index of refraction. *Hint:* From Fig. 1–25 one can see that $d\mathbf{i}/dr = \mathbf{N}/R$. Use Eq. (9–73) and show that

$$\mathbf{N} \cdot \frac{d\mathbf{i}}{dr} = \frac{\mathbf{N}}{n} \cdot \nabla \frac{dL}{dr} = \frac{\mathbf{N}}{n} \cdot \nabla n.$$

CHAPTER 10

WAVE GUIDES AND CAVITY RESONATORS

10-1 INTRODUCTION

One can guide an electromagnetic wave by confining it to a region bounded by conducting surfaces. Conductor systems capable of guiding electromagnetic waves are called *wave guides*, and are extensively used in communication and antenna systems. Sections of a wave guide can be used to form cavity resonators which find applications in various measurement techniques and in microwave oscillators and filters. In this chapter we shall discuss the solution of Maxwell's equations in regions that are partly or completely bounded by perfectly conducting surfaces. Unless otherwise stated, the regions under consideration will be assumed to be source-free ($\mathbf{J} = 0$, $\rho = 0$) and to have piecewise uniform permeability μ and permittivity ε.

10-2 SOLUTION OF MAXWELL'S EQUATIONS IN GENERAL COORDINATES

For sinusoidally time-varying fields Maxwell's equations can be expressed in the phasor form given by Eqs. (9–10). When we express the scalar components of the curl in an orthogonal curvilinear coordinate system (see Eqs. 1–84), we obtain:

$$\frac{1}{h_2 h_3}\left[\frac{\partial}{\partial u_2}(h_3 E_3) - \frac{\partial}{\partial u_3}(h_2 E_2)\right] = -j\omega\mu H_1, \tag{10-1a}$$

$$\frac{1}{h_3 h_1}\left[\frac{\partial}{\partial u_3}(h_1 E_1) - \frac{\partial}{\partial u_1}(h_3 E_3)\right] = -j\omega\mu H_2, \tag{10-1b}$$

$$\frac{1}{h_1 h_2}\left[\frac{\partial}{\partial u_1}(h_2 E_2) - \frac{\partial}{\partial u_2}(h_1 E_1)\right] = -j\omega\mu H_3, \tag{10-1c}$$

$$\frac{1}{h_2 h_3}\left[\frac{\partial}{\partial u_2}(h_3 H_3) - \frac{\partial}{\partial u_3}(h_2 H_2)\right] = j\omega\varepsilon E_1, \tag{10-1d}$$

$$\frac{1}{h_3 h_1}\left[\frac{\partial}{\partial u_3}(h_1 H_1) - \frac{\partial}{\partial u_1}(h_3 H_3)\right] = j\omega\varepsilon E_2, \tag{10-1e}$$

$$\frac{1}{h_1 h_2}\left[\frac{\partial}{\partial u_1}(h_2 H_2) - \frac{\partial}{\partial u_2}(h_1 H_1)\right] = j\omega\varepsilon E_3 + J_3. \tag{10-1f}$$

Here we have taken a component J_3 of the current density to be nonzero so that the equations will have a form suitable for the discussion of traveling-wave tubes, which will be given in Chapter 13. The system of equations (10–1) admittedly appears very formidable. To discuss the theory of commonly used wave guides, we must obtain solutions of Eqs. (10–1) in cartesian, cylindrical, and spherical coordinates. By specializing Eqs. (10–1) to a particular coordinate system and restricting the discussion to certain wave types, we can achieve some simplification. However, the technique of solution to be used for these coordinate systems is a general one and we would be introducing unnecessary repetition if we were to solve Eqs. (10–1) for each special coordinate system. We shall therefore obtain a general solution.

In the case of electrostatic and magnetostatic fields, we have seen the convenience of expressing the field vectors as the gradient of a scalar potential. We shall now attempt a similar kind of representation in which the phasor field components are expressed in terms of the derivatives of a scalar function. In order to obtain the desired representation we must restrict the class of coordinate systems to those which satisfy the conditions

$$h_3 = 1, \qquad \frac{\partial}{\partial u_3}\left(\frac{h_1}{h_2}\right) = 0, \tag{10–2}$$

and where we take u_3 to be the coordinate corresponding to the direction of propagation. Cartesian, cylindrical, and spherical coordinate systems are among the class of coordinate systems satisfying conditions (10–2). We shall see that there are two possible kinds of solutions. One is obtained by setting $H_3 = 0$ and the second by setting $E_3 = 0$. In the first case the magnetic field intensity has no component in the direction of propagation and we designate the wave as a *transverse magnetic* (*TM*) *wave*. Similarly the wave with $E_3 = 0$ is designated as a *transverse electric* (*TE*) *wave*.

We shall first discuss the case of *TM* waves. Equation (10–1c) is satisfied if we let

$$h_1 E_1 = \frac{\partial f_1}{\partial u_1}, \qquad h_2 E_2 = \frac{\partial f}{\partial u_2}, \tag{10–3}$$

where f is a function of position. Substituting into Eqs. (10–1d) and (10–1e) and noting conditions (10–2), we obtain

$$j\omega\varepsilon\,\frac{\partial f}{\partial u_1} = -\frac{h_1}{h_2 h_3}\frac{\partial}{\partial u_3}(h_2 H_2) = -\frac{\partial}{\partial u_3}(h_1 H_2),$$

$$j\omega\varepsilon\,\frac{\partial f}{\partial u_2} = \frac{h_2}{h_3 h_1}\frac{\partial}{\partial u_3}(h_1 H_1) = \frac{\partial}{\partial u_3}(h_2 H_1).$$

For convenience we now let $z \triangleq u_3$. Since the right-hand sides of the above equations are partial derivatives with respect to z, we choose

$$f = \frac{\partial}{\partial z}(Ue^{-\gamma z}) = -\gamma Ue^{-\gamma z},$$

where U is a function of u_1 and u_2. Substituting for f, we see that

$$H_1 = j\frac{\omega\varepsilon}{h_2}\frac{\partial U}{\partial u_2}e^{-\gamma z}, \qquad H_2 = -j\frac{\omega\varepsilon}{h_1}\frac{\partial U}{\partial u_1}e^{-\gamma z}, \qquad H_3 = 0. \quad (10\text{–}4)$$

Equations (10–4) have the desired form, in which the phasor components of $\mathbf{H}$ are expressed in terms of partial derivatives of a scalar function U. We must now express the phasor components of $\mathbf{E}$ in terms of partial derivatives of U and obtain a partial differential equation for the function U. These equations are obtained from the remaining equations of the system of equations (10–1) which have not as yet been accounted for. Substituting Eqs. (10–3) and (10–4) into Eqs. (10–1a) and (10–1b) yields the equations

$$\omega^2\mu\varepsilon\frac{\partial U}{\partial u_2}e^{-\gamma z} = \frac{\partial}{\partial u_2}[E_z - \gamma^2 Ue^{-\gamma z}], \qquad \omega^2\mu\varepsilon\frac{\partial U}{\partial u_1}e^{-\gamma z} = \frac{\partial}{\partial u_1}[E_z - \gamma^2 Ue^{-\gamma z}],$$

which are satisfied if

$$E_z = (\gamma^2 + \omega^2\mu\varepsilon)Ue^{-\gamma z}.$$

Thus the phasor components of the electric field intensity are given by

$$E_1 = -\frac{\gamma}{h_1}\frac{\partial U}{\partial u_1}e^{-\gamma z}, \qquad E_2 = -\frac{\gamma}{h_2}\frac{\partial U}{\partial u_2}e^{-\gamma z}, \qquad E_z = (\gamma^2 + \omega^2\mu\varepsilon)Ue^{-\gamma z}.$$

$$(10\text{–}5)$$

Equations (10–4) and (10–5) give the desired representation for the phasor components of the field vectors in terms of a scalar function U. The function U satisfies the equation obtained by substituting Eqs. (10–4) and (10–5) into Eq. (10–1f):

$$\frac{1}{h_1 h_2}\left[\frac{\partial}{\partial u_1}\left(\frac{h_2}{h_1}\frac{\partial U}{\partial u_1}\right) + \frac{\partial}{\partial u_2}\left(\frac{h_1}{h_2}\frac{\partial U}{\partial u_2}\right)\right] + (\gamma^2 + \omega^2\mu\varepsilon)U = \frac{j}{\omega\varepsilon}J. \quad (10\text{–}6)$$

Here we have taken $J_3 = Je^{-\gamma z}$. It is interesting to note that when $J = 0$ Eq. (10–6) is the scalar wave equation in phasor form and in general coordinates. In this chapter we shall restrict ourselves to the case of $J = 0$.

We take the perfectly conducting surfaces to be represented by the coordinate surfaces $u_1 = \text{const}$ and $u_2 = \text{const}$. From Eqs. (10–5) we see that we must have

$$U = 0 \qquad\qquad (10\text{–}7)$$

on the conducting surfaces in order for the tangential components of $\mathbf{E}$ to vanish.

In a similar manner we can express the phasor components of a *TE* wave in terms of a scalar function V. We find that

$$E_1 = -j\omega\mu\frac{1}{h_2}\frac{\partial V}{\partial u_2}e^{-\gamma z}, \qquad H_1 = -\frac{\gamma}{h_1}\frac{\partial V}{\partial u_1}e^{-\gamma z},$$

$$E_2 = j\omega\mu\frac{1}{h_1}\frac{\partial V}{\partial u_1}e^{-\gamma z}, \qquad H_2 = -\frac{\gamma}{h_2}\frac{\partial V}{\partial u_2}e^{-\gamma z}, \qquad (10\text{–}8)$$

$$E_3 = 0, \qquad\qquad H_3 = (\gamma^2 + \omega^2\mu\varepsilon)Ve^{-\gamma z}.$$

The function V is a solution of Eq. (10–6) for the case of $J = 0$. In order that the tangential components of **E** will vanish on the conducting walls defined by $u_1 = c_1$ and $u_2 = c_2$, we must have

$$\frac{\partial V}{\partial u_2}\bigg]_{u_2=c_2} = 0, \qquad \frac{\partial V}{\partial u_1}\bigg]_{u_1=c_1} = 0. \qquad (10\text{–}9)$$

A special case occurs when $E_3 = 0$, $H_3 = 0$, which results in a *transverse electromagnetic (TEM) wave*. For this case it follows from Eq. (10–5) that $\gamma^2 + \omega^2\mu\varepsilon = 0$. Thus $\gamma = \pm j\beta$, where $\beta = \omega/\sqrt{\mu\varepsilon}$, and if we compare this result with the case of a plane wave (see Section 9–3), we see that a *TEM* wave propagates with the velocity of a plane wave in an unbounded medium having the same permeability μ and permittivity ε as that of the wave guide:

$$u = 1/\sqrt{\mu\varepsilon}.$$

In the case of a *TEM* wave, the function U satisfies the equation

$$\frac{\partial}{\partial u_1}\left(\frac{h_2}{h_1}\frac{\partial U}{\partial u_1}\right) + \frac{\partial}{\partial u_2}\left(\frac{h_1}{h_2}\frac{\partial U}{\partial u_2}\right) = 0, \qquad (10\text{–}10)$$

which is Laplace's equation in the general two-dimensional coordinates u_1 and u_2. The boundary conditions for a *TEM* wave are satisfied if

$$U]_{u_1=c_1} = d_1, \qquad U]_{u_2=c_2} = d_2, \qquad (10\text{–}11)$$

are both constant over the wave-guide walls. When we choose a wave propagating in the positive z-direction, we have $\gamma = j\beta$ and Eqs. (10–4) and (10–5) yield

$$E_1 = -\frac{j\beta}{h_1}\frac{\partial U}{\partial u_1}e^{-j\beta z}, \qquad H_1 = \frac{j\omega\varepsilon}{h_2}\frac{\partial U}{\partial u_2}e^{-j\beta z},$$

$$E_2 = -\frac{j\beta}{h_2}\frac{\partial U}{\partial u_2}e^{-j\beta z}, \qquad H_2 = -\frac{j\omega\varepsilon}{h_1}\frac{\partial U}{\partial u_1}e^{-j\gamma z}. \qquad (10\text{–}12)$$

Equations (10–12) can be written in the vector form

$$\mathbf{E}_T = -j\beta e^{-j\beta z}\boldsymbol{\nabla}_T U, \qquad \mathbf{H}_T = j\omega\varepsilon e^{-j\beta z}\boldsymbol{\nabla}_T U \times \mathbf{i}_z, \qquad (10\text{–}13)$$

where $\mathbf{E}_T$ and $\mathbf{H}_T$ are the transverse field phasors and where

$$\nabla_T \triangleq \mathbf{i}_1 \frac{1}{h_1} \frac{\partial}{\partial u_1} + \mathbf{i}_2 \frac{1}{h_2} \frac{\partial}{\partial u_2} \tag{10–14}$$

is the transverse del operator (see Section 1–21). It is interesting to note that the vector components of a *TEM* wave are determined by equations which correspond very closely to the equations for the magnetostatic and electrostatic cases (see Eq. 6–66).

10–3 TRANSVERSE ELECTRIC
WAVES IN A RECTANGULAR WAVE GUIDE

In cartesian coordinates we have $u_1 = x$, $u_2 = y$, $u_3 = z$, $h_1 = h_2 = h_3 = 1$, and Eq. (10–6) takes the form

$$\frac{\partial^2 V}{\partial x^2} + \frac{\partial^2 V}{\partial y^2} + (\gamma^2 + \omega^2 \mu \varepsilon) V = 0.$$

We can determine a solution of this equation by the separation of variables. We set $V = f_1(x) f_2(y)$ and obtain

$$\frac{d^2 f_1}{dx^2} + \left(\frac{\pi m}{a}\right)^2 f_1 = 0, \qquad \frac{d^2 f_2}{dy^2} + \left(\frac{\pi n}{b}\right)^2 f_2 = 0. \tag{10–15}$$

Here $(\pi m/a)^2$ and $(\pi n/b)^2$ are separation constants which satisfy the relation

$$\gamma^2 + (\omega/u)^2 = (\pi m/a)^2 + (\pi n/b)^2, \tag{10–16}$$

and where a and b are the dimensions of the wave-guide cross section (see Fig. 10–1). We determine the function V and the parameters m and n by choosing solutions of Eqs. (10–15) which satisfy the boundary conditions (10–9) on the wave-guide walls. Thus

$$V = \cos\,(\pi m x/a) \cos\,(\pi n y/b), \tag{10–17}$$

where m and n are integers. The electromagnetic field which is determined by m and n is referred to as the *mn*th *mode*.

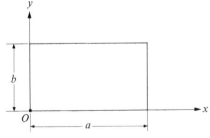

Fig. 10–1. The transverse cross section of a rectangular wave guide.

The quantity $\gamma = \alpha + j\beta$ is called the *propagation function*, α is the *attenuation function* and β is the *phase function*. When $\alpha > 0$, the electromagnetic field components are attenuated in the direction of the positive z-axis. A mode for which $\alpha > 0$ is called an *evanescent wave*. Evanescent waves are important in regions in which the field is perturbed by a probe or by a wave-guide discontinuity. In such regions a superposition of all modes is necessary to meet the boundary conditions. However, as we move away from the perturbed region, the evanescent waves are attenuated and only the propagating modes remain. If the wave is to propagate we must have $\alpha = 0$, and Eq. (10–16) yields

$$\beta = \beta_{mn} \triangleq \sqrt{(\omega/u)^2 - (\pi m/a)^2 - (\pi n/b)^2}. \qquad (10\text{–}18)$$

We see from Eq. (10–18) that the wave guide acts like a high-pass filter with a cutoff frequency

$$f_c = u\sqrt{(m/2a)^2 + (n/2b)^2}.$$

Below the cutoff frequency the modes are evanescent.

The wavelength λ_g of a propagating mode in the wave guide is the distance along the z-axis in which the field is periodic. Thus λ_g must satisfy the relation

$$e^{-j\beta z} = e^{-j\beta(z+\lambda_g)}$$

which yields $\beta\lambda_g = 2\pi$. Substituting Eq. (10–18), we obtain

$$\lambda/\lambda_g = \sqrt{1 - (m\lambda/2a)^2 - (n\lambda/2b)^2},$$

where $\lambda \triangleq 2\pi u/\omega$ is the wavelength in the unbounded medium. For a given frequency we see that the effect of the wave-guide boundaries is to increase the ratio λ_g/λ of the wavelengths. The phasor components of the *TE* wave can be found from Eqs. (10–8):

$$E_x = j\omega\mu \frac{\pi n}{b} \cos \frac{\pi m x}{a} \sin \frac{\pi n y}{b} e^{-j\beta_{mn}z},$$

$$E_y = -j\omega\mu \frac{\pi m}{a} \sin \frac{\pi m x}{a} \cos \frac{\pi n y}{b} e^{-j\beta_{mn}z},$$

$$E_z = 0, \qquad (10\text{–}19)$$

$$H_x = j\beta_{mn} \frac{\pi m}{a} \sin \frac{\pi m x}{a} \cos \frac{\pi n y}{b} e^{-j\beta_{mn}z},$$

$$H_y = j\beta_{mn} \frac{\pi n}{b} \cos \frac{\pi m x}{a} \sin \frac{\pi n y}{b} e^{-j\beta_{mn}z},$$

$$H_z = [(\pi m/a)^2 + (\pi n/b)^2] \cos (\pi m x/a) \cos (\pi n y/b) e^{-j\beta_{mn}z}.$$

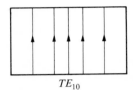 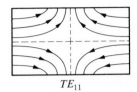 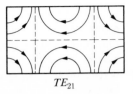

TE_{10} TE_{11} TE_{21}

Fig. 10–2. The electric field distribution in rectangular wave guides for TE_{mn} modes.

Figure 10–2 illustrates the E-field configuration for various modes. The subscripts m and n correspond to the number of half-periods of the field in the directions of the x- and y-axes, respectively.

Example. A standard X-band rectangular wave guide of dimensions $a = 0.9$ in. and $b = 0.4$ in. will be used to illustrate typical numerical values for the cutoff frequency and for operating frequencies and wavelengths. For an air-filled guide the cutoff frequency for the TE_{10} mode is

$$f_c = c/2a = 6.56 \text{ GHz.}$$

When we take a frequency higher than f_c, for example $f = 8.2$ GHz, the TE_{10} mode will propagate. The free-space wavelength at this frequency is $\lambda = c/f = 3.66$ cm, and the guide wavelength is $\lambda_g = 6.1$ cm. When we take a frequency lower than f_c, for example $f = 3$ GHz, the TE_{10} mode will be evanescent. The attenuation function is given by

$$\alpha = (2\pi/\lambda)\sqrt{(\lambda/2a)^2 - 1} = 122 \text{ nepers/meter (Np/m),}$$

and the field intensities decrease by a factor of e^{-1} in a distance of 0.82 cm. The cutoff frequency for the TE_{20} and TE_{11} modes are $f_c = 13.12$ GHz and $f_c = 16.14$ GHz, respectively. A suggested frequency range for propagating the TE_{10} mode is 8.2–12.4 GHz. In this frequency range only the TE_{10} mode will propagate and all other modes are evanescent. It is often important to avoid having more than one mode propagate at a given frequency and the wave-guide dimensions must be chosen so that this is the case.

**10–4 TRANSVERSE MAGNETIC
WAVES IN A CIRCULAR WAVE GUIDE**

To investigate TM waves in a circular wave guide of radius a, we use cylindrical coordinates where $u_1 = r$, $u_2 = \phi$, $h_1 = 1$, $h_2 = r$ (see Fig. 10–3). We substitute $U = f_1(r)f_2(\phi)$ into Eq. (10–6). Separation of variables yields

$$r\frac{d}{dr}\left(r\frac{df_1}{dr}\right) + (r^2k^2 - m^2)f_1 = 0, \qquad (10\text{–}20a)$$

$$\frac{d^2f_2}{d\phi^2} + m^2f_2 = 0, \qquad (10\text{–}20b)$$

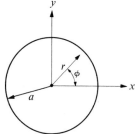

Fig. 10–3. The transverse cross section of a circular wave guide.

where m^2 is a separation constant and where

$$k^2 = \gamma^2 + (\omega/u)^2. \tag{10–21}$$

The field orientation in the guide is determined by the function f_2. Let us choose the orientation so that $f_2 = \cos m\phi$. A solution of Eq. (10–20a) which is finite at the origin is $f_1 = J_m(kr)$, where J_m is the Bessel function of the first kind of order m (see Appendix A–16). Thus

$$U = J_m(kr) \cos m\phi e^{-\gamma z},$$

and the boundary condition (10–7) requires that $J_m(ka) = 0$. The solution of this equation yields an infinite sequence of values $k = k_{mn}$ ($n = 1, 2, \ldots$) for each m. Table 10–1 gives the zeros of the Bessel functions

$$\frac{dJ_m(u)}{du} \triangleq J'_m$$

and $J_m(u)$ for small integer values of m and n.

For a propagating mode we have $\gamma = j\beta_{mn}$ (see Eq. 10–21), where

$$\beta_{mn} \triangleq \sqrt{(\omega/u)^2 - k_{mn}^2}$$

and the wavelength in the guide is determined by the equation

$$\lambda/\lambda_g = \sqrt{1 - [(ak_{mn}/2\pi)(\lambda/a)]^2},$$

where λ is the wavelength in the unbounded medium.

Table 10–1

Zeros of J_m				Zeros of J'_m			
n / m	1	2	3	n / m	1	2	3
0	2.405	5.520	8.654	0	3.832	7.016	10.173
1	3.832	7.016	10.173	1	1.841	5.331	8.536
2	5.136	8.417	11.620	2	3.054	6.706	9.969

Example. Consider a TM_{01} mode in an air-filled circular wave guide of radius $a = 5.1$ cm. From Table 10–1 we see that $ak_{01} = 2.405$. The cutoff frequency for the TM_{01} mode is therefore

$$f_c = \frac{1}{2\pi}\left(\frac{c}{a}\right)(ak_{01}) = 2.25 \text{ GHz.}$$

When we take a frequency higher than f_c, for example $f = 5$ GHz, the TM_{01} mode will propagate. The free-space wavelength at this frequency is $\lambda = c/f = 6$ cm, and the guide wavelength is $\lambda_g = 6.72$ cm.

The phasor components of the field are determined from Eqs. (10–4) and (10–5):

$$E_r = -j\beta_{mn}k_{mn}J'_m(k_{mn}r)\cos m\phi e^{-j\beta_{mn}z},$$

$$E_\phi = j\frac{\beta_{mn}m}{r}J(k_{mn}r)\sin m\phi e^{-j\beta_{mn}z},$$

$$E_z = k_{mn}^2 J_m(k_{mn}r)\cos m\phi e^{-j\beta_{mn}z},$$

$$H_r = -j\frac{\omega\varepsilon m}{r}J_m(k_{mn}r)\sin m\phi e^{-j\beta_{mn}z}, \tag{10-22}$$

$$H_\phi = -j\omega\varepsilon k_{mn}J'_m(k_{mn}r)\cos m\phi e^{-j\beta_{mn}z},$$

$$H_z = 0.$$

Equations (10–22) give the phasor field components for a TM_{mn} mode in a circular wave guide. The subscripts m and n correspond to the number of half-periods of the field in the directions of increasing r and ϕ, respectively.

For applications in which a relatively long wave guide is required, the circular wave guide has a disadvantage in that the field orientation is not stable. The choice $f_2 = \sin m\phi$ results in a field with the same mode numbers m and n. Initially we have made the choice $f_2 = \cos m\phi$. However, if there are small imperfections in the wave guide, the mode corresponding to $f_2 = \sin m\phi$ and evanescent modes can be excited. The field corresponding to $f_2 = \sin m\phi$ combines with the field corresponding to $f_2 = \cos m\phi$, causing a rotation of the resultant field.

10–5 WAVE GUIDES FOR TEM WAVES

In order for a wave guide to propagate a *TEM* wave, there must be at least two distinct conductors. If there were only one conductor it would follow from the boundary conditions (10–7) and the uniqueness of the solution of Laplace's equations that $U = 0$ everywhere. For two distinct conductors, the boundary conditions (10–11) apply and if $d_1 \neq d_2$ we can obtain a non-trivial solution. There is no cutoff frequency for the *TEM* mode and propagation is possible at all frequencies. Physically this can be seen from the fact that it is possible to reduce the frequency to zero and still maintain a potential difference between the two conductors.

Consider now the infinitely long cylindrical transmission line illustrated in Fig. 10–4. For the *TEM* mode, the scalar function U is a solution of Laplace's equation (10–10) and we have essentially an electrostatic and magnetostatic field configuration which propagates along the z-axis. To see that this is the case let us substitute $U' = j\beta U$ into Eqs. (10–13) and let us use the notation $f = f'e^{-j\beta z}$ for all other quantities where $f' = f'(x, y)$ is considered to be the static component of f. We obtain

$$\mathbf{E}' = -\nabla_T U', \tag{10–23a}$$

$$\mathbf{H}' = \frac{\omega\varepsilon}{\beta}\,\mathbf{i}_z \times \mathbf{E}'. \tag{10–23b}$$

Since U' is a solution of Laplace's equation, we see that $\mathbf{E}'$ can be obtained as the negative gradient of a potential function, as is the case with electrostatic fields. Equation (10–23b) corresponds to Eq. (6–66) in the special case of circular boundaries. However, for perfectly conducting boundaries, the current is constrained to flow in the surface of the conductor. Comparing Eq. (6–66) and Eq. (10–23b), we anticipate a relation of the form

$$I'/q' = \omega/\beta \tag{10–24}$$

to hold between the static current I' in the conductor and the static charge per unit length q'.

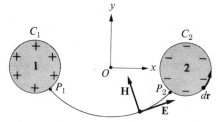

Fig. 10–4. A two-wire transmission line.

The field configuration can be derived by solving Laplace's equation for the potential function U' which meets the boundary conditions

$$U' = U_1' \text{ on } C_1, \qquad U' = U_2' \text{ on } C_2.$$

Here

$$V' = U_1' - U_2' = \int_{P_1}^{P_2} \mathbf{E}' \cdot d\mathbf{r} \tag{10–25}$$

is the static potential difference between the conductors. It follows from Eq. (10–25) that we can define a *phasor voltage* by the integral

$$V \triangleq \int_{P_1}^{P_2} \mathbf{E} \cdot d\mathbf{r} = V'e^{-j\beta z}. \tag{10–26}$$

Note that the integral is independent of the path, provided the path is taken in a transverse plane where z is constant. A *phasor current* can be defined by the equation

$$I \triangleq e^{-j\beta z} \oint_{C_1} \mathbf{J}'_s \cdot \mathbf{i}_z \, dr, \tag{10–27}$$

where C_1 is the contour bounding the cross-sectional area of conductor 1 and where J'_s is the static surface current density. To determine J'_s, we use the boundary condition given in Problem 6–10, where we take $\mathbf{H}_2 = 0$, $\mathbf{H}_1 = \mathbf{H}'$. Since $\mathbf{n}$ is an outwardly directed normal, we obtain with the aid of Eq. (10–23b)

$$\mathbf{J}'_s = \mathbf{n} \times \mathbf{H}' = \mathbf{i}_z \frac{\omega \varepsilon}{\beta} \mathbf{E}' \cdot \mathbf{n} = \mathbf{i}_z \frac{\omega \sigma'_s}{\beta}. \tag{10–28}$$

Here $\sigma'_s = \mathbf{E}' \cdot \mathbf{n}$ is the static surface charge density. We see that the static charge density per unit length and the static current are given, respectively, by

$$q' \triangleq \oint_{C_1} \sigma'_s \, dr, \qquad I' \triangleq \oint_{C_1} J'_s \, dr = \frac{\omega}{\beta} q'. \tag{10–29}$$

Here we have made use of Eq. (10–28) to relate I' and q'. Equation (10–29) is the anticipated equation (10–24). It is interesting to note that Eq. (10–29) is a consequence of the equation of continuity which in phasor form and for our case of surface current and charges is given by $dJ_s/dz = -j\omega\sigma_s$. Substituting $J_s = J'_s e^{-j\beta z}$ and $\sigma_s = \sigma'_s e^{-j\beta z}$ yields $\beta J'_s = \omega\sigma'_s$, from which we can obtain Eq. (10–29) by integrating over the contour C_1.

The *wave impedance* at any field point is defined by the ratio (see Eq. 10–23b)

$$Z_w \triangleq H/E = H'/E' = \omega\varepsilon/\beta. \tag{10–30}$$

For the *TEM* mode we see that the wave impedance is uniform over the field. The *characteristic impedance* is defined by the ratio

$$Z_0 \triangleq V/I = V'/I'.$$

Introducing the capacitance per unit length $C = q'/V'$ and Eq. (10–29), we see that

$$Z_0 = 1/uC, \tag{10–31}$$

where u is the velocity of propagation. It is important to note that in general $Z_w \neq Z_0$.

When the two-wire transmission line has the dimensions shown in Fig. 4–5, we can use the results of Example 2, Section 4–4, and choose

$$U' = \frac{q'}{2\pi\varepsilon_0} \ln \frac{r_1}{r_2} \tag{10–32}$$

as the static potential from which the *TEM* field components can be derived.

An important two-conductor wave guide is the coaxial cable (Fig. 10–5). Due to circular symmetry, it is convenient to use cylindrical coordinates where $u_1 = r$, $u_2 = \phi$, $h_1 = 1$, and $h_2 = r$. In cylindrical coordinates Eq. (10–10) takes the form

$$\frac{\partial}{\partial r}\left(r\frac{\partial U}{\partial r}\right) + \frac{1}{r}\frac{\partial^2 U}{\partial \phi^2} = 0, \qquad (10\text{–}33)$$

and by taking $U = f_1(r)f_2(\phi)$ and separating the variables, we obtain the equations:

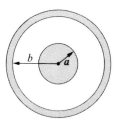

$$\frac{d^2 f_2}{d\phi^2} = c_1, \qquad (10\text{–}34a)$$

$$r\frac{d}{dr}\left(r\frac{df_1}{dr}\right) = -c_1 f_1, \qquad (10\text{–}34b)$$

Fig. 10–5. The transverse cross section of a coaxial cable.

where c_1 is the separation constant. Given that U is to be a periodic function of ϕ, it follows from Eq. (10–34a) that we must take $c_1 = 0$. Because of the symmetry it follows that f_2 must be a constant. For convenience we choose $f_2 = 1$. The solution of Eq. (10–34b) is $f_1 = c_0 \ln r$, where c_0 is a constant of integration. Thus $U = c_0 \ln r$. We see that U satisfies the boundary conditions (10–11) at $r = a$ and $r = b$ for all values of ω. As a consequence of this there is no cutoff frequency for a *TEM* wave. Since $\beta = \omega/\sqrt{\mu\varepsilon}$, it follows that the wavelength is the same as in the unbounded medium. The phasor components of the field (see Eqs. 10–12) are

$$E_r = -\frac{j\beta c_0}{r}e^{-j\beta z}, \qquad H_r = 0,$$

$$E_\phi = 0, \qquad H_\phi = -\frac{j\omega\varepsilon c_0}{r}e^{-j\beta z}, \qquad (10\text{–}35)$$

$$E_z = 0, \qquad H_z = 0.$$

10–6 THE TRANSMISSION LINE ANALOG FOR WAVE GUIDES

The surface current density $\mathbf{J}_s$ in a wave-guide surface can be found from the boundary conditions for $\mathbf{H}$ (see Eq. 9–16, where we take $\mathbf{H}_2 = \mathbf{H}$, $\mathbf{H}_1 = 0$),

$$\mathbf{J}_s = \mathbf{n} \times \mathbf{H}, \qquad (10\text{–}36)$$

and the surface charge density σ_s can be found from the boundary condition for the normal component of $\mathbf{E}$:

$$\sigma_s = \varepsilon\mathbf{n} \cdot \mathbf{E}. \qquad (10\text{–}37)$$

Here $\mathbf{n}$ is a unit normal to the wave-guide surface directed into the field.

The equations determining the field distribution within a wave guide and the distribution of $\mathbf{J}_s$ and σ_s over the conducting walls of a wave guide are very elaborate. Often we are interested only in the complex power and the standing-wave ratio as a function of the position z along the wave-guide axis. It is then very convenient to introduce a transmission-line analog of the wave guide; we no longer concern ourselves explicitly with the details of the field configuration and with the current-density and charge-density distributions.

We have seen that transmission-line equations, which were discussed in Section 9–6, proved useful in the analysis of the reflection and transmission of plane electromagnetic waves. There is no unique way of defining a phasor current I and a phasor voltage V for a wave guide. However, they must be chosen so that the equation for the complex power is satisfied:

$$P = \tfrac{1}{2}VI^*. \tag{10–38}$$

To illustrate how a transmission-line analog is obtained, we consider the case of an incident TEM wave in a coaxial cable. (Here we consider a wave propagating in the direction of the positive z-axis as an incident wave. A wave propagating in the direction of the negative z-axis is considered to be a reflected wave.) The current density on the surface of the inner conductor is determined by the boundary conditions (9–16), where we take $H_1 = 0$, $H_2 = H_\phi$. Thus $J_s = H_\phi]_{r=a}$ and the total phasor current is

$$I = 2\pi a J_s = -j2\pi\omega\varepsilon c_0 e^{-j\beta z}. \tag{10–39}$$

Let us define the phasor voltage by the equation

$$V \triangleq \int_a^b E_r \, dr = -j\beta c_0 \ln (b/a)e^{-j\beta z}. \tag{10–40}$$

We obtain an equation of the form (9–37b) if we choose

$$C = \frac{2\pi\varepsilon}{\ln (b/a)}, \tag{10–41}$$

which is the capacitance per unit length of the cable. It follows from Eqs. (9–41) that $LC = (\beta/\omega)^2 = 1/u^2$. Thus

$$Z_0 = \frac{1}{uC} = \frac{Z_w}{2\pi} \ln (b/a), \tag{10–42}$$

where $u = 1/\sqrt{\mu\varepsilon}$ and where (see Eqs. 10–35) $Z_w = E_r/H_\phi = \beta/\omega\varepsilon = \sqrt{\mu/\varepsilon}$ is the wave impedance.

In general we shall have both an incident and a reflected wave. In Eqs. (10–35) let us choose $c_0 = c_+$ for an incident wave, replace β by $-\beta$, and choose $c_0 = c_-$ for a reflected wave. The resultant phasor field components are

$$E_r = -\frac{j\beta}{r}(c_+e^{-j\beta z} - c_-e^{j\beta z}), \qquad H_\phi = -\frac{j\omega\varepsilon}{r}(c_+e^{-j\beta z} + c_-e^{j\beta z}),$$

and the phasor voltage and current are

$$V = -j\beta \ln (b/a)(c_+e^{-j\beta z} - c_-e^{j\beta z}), \qquad I = -j2\pi\omega\varepsilon(c_+e^{-j\beta z} + c_-e^{j\beta z}).$$

If we now choose

$$V_+ \triangleq -j\beta c_+ \ln (b/a), \qquad V_- \triangleq j\beta c_- \ln (b/a),$$

we obtain the transmission-line equations (see Eq. 10–42)

$$V = V_+e^{-j\beta z} + V_-e^{j\beta z}, \qquad I = \frac{1}{Z_0}(V_+e^{-j\beta z} - V_-e^{j\beta z}).$$

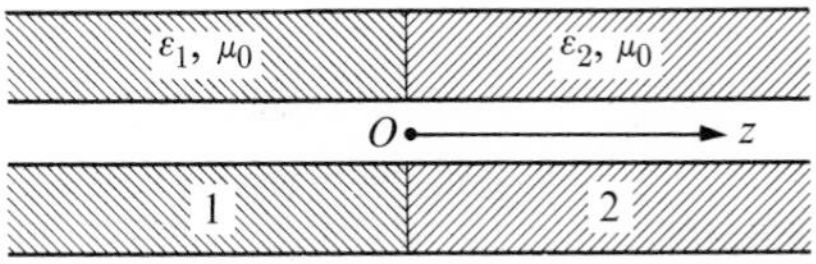

Fig. 10–6. The longitudinal cross section of a coaxial cable with an abrupt change in the permittivity.

Example. As a numerical example let us consider an air-filled coaxial cable in which $a = 1$ cm, $b = 3$ cm. The capacitance per unit length (see Eq. 10–41 where we take $\varepsilon = \varepsilon_0$) is $C = 5.06 \times 10^{-11}$ farad/meter (F/m). The velocity of propagation is $u = c = 3 \times 10^8$ m/sec and the characteristic impedance (see Eq. 10–42) is $Z_0 = 66$ ohms. When there is no reflected wave so that $\Gamma = 0$ and when the peak current is one ampere (1 A), so that $I_+ = V_+/Z_0 = 1$ A, we find that the average power and peak voltage are given, respectively, by

$$P = \tfrac{1}{2}Z_0I_+^2 = 33 \text{ W}, \qquad V_+ = Z_0I_+ = 66 \text{ V}.$$

Let us now discuss a case in which there is an abrupt change in the permittivity of the coaxial cable (Fig. 10–6). Let $\varepsilon_1 = \varepsilon_0$, $\varepsilon_2 = 2.9\,\varepsilon_0$. The boundary conditions at the interface of the two dielectrics require that the tangential components of the **E** and **H** fields be continuous, which in turn requires that V and I be continuous. Thus, if we have a transmitted wave represented by

$$V_2 = V_{2+}e^{-j\beta_2 z}, \qquad I_2 = (V_{2+}/Z_{02})e^{-j\beta_2 z}$$

in medium 2, we must have an incident and a reflected wave in medium 1:

$$V_1 = V_{1+}(e^{-j\beta_1 z} + \Gamma e^{j\beta_1 z}), \qquad I_1 = (V_{1+}/Z_{01})(e^{-j\beta_1 z} - \Gamma e^{j\beta_1 z}).$$

The boundary conditions at $z = 0$ yield

$$V_{2+} = V_{1+}(1 + \Gamma), \qquad V_{2+} = (Z_{02}/Z_{01})(1 - \Gamma)V_{1+}.$$

Since $Z_{01} = \sqrt{\varepsilon_r}Z_{02}$, we obtain

$$\Gamma = (1 - \sqrt{\varepsilon_r})/(1 + \sqrt{\varepsilon_r}) = -0.26.$$

It is also possible to obtain transmission-line analogs for TM and TE waves. We shall consider the case of TM waves. Equations (10–4) and (10–5) for the transverse field components can be written in a form similar to that which occurs in the case of TEM waves (see Eqs. 10–13 and 10–14):

$$\mathbf{E}_T = -\gamma e^{-\gamma z} \nabla_T U, \tag{10–43a}$$

$$\mathbf{H}_T = j\omega\varepsilon e^{-\gamma z} \nabla_T U \times \mathbf{i}_z. \tag{10–43b}$$

Substituting $\gamma = j\beta_{mn}$ yields

$$\mathbf{E}_T = Z_{mn}\mathbf{H}_T \times \mathbf{i}_z, \tag{10–44}$$

where $Z_{mn} \triangleq \beta_{mn}/\omega\varepsilon$ is defined as the *transverse wave impedance*. To obtain a transmission-line analog, we now introduce quantities V and I so that

$$\mathbf{E}_T = -V \nabla_T U, \tag{10–45a}$$

$$\mathbf{H}_T \times \mathbf{i}_z = -gI \nabla_T U, \tag{10–45b}$$

where g is an as-yet-undetermined real parameter. From Eq. (10–44) we see that we then obtain the transmission-line equation for an incident wave, $V = Z_0 I$, where we take $Z_0 \triangleq gZ_{mn}$ as the *characteristic impedance*. To obtain the transmission-line equations (9–37), we substitute Eq. (10–45a) into Eq. (10–43b). This yields the equation $V = \gamma e^{-\gamma z}$, from which we obtain

$$dV/dz = -\gamma V = -ZI, \tag{10–46}$$

where $Z \triangleq \gamma Z_0 = j\beta_{mn}Z_0$. Similarly, we find that

$$\frac{dI}{dz} = \frac{1}{Z_0}\frac{dV}{dz} = -YZ, \tag{10–47}$$

where $Y \triangleq \gamma/Z_0 = j\beta_{mn}/Z_0$. The parameter g is determined by equating the complex powers (see Eq. 9–25e)

$$P_C = \frac{1}{2}\int_S (\mathbf{E}_T \times \mathbf{H}_T^*) \cdot \mathbf{i}_z \, ds = \frac{gVI^*}{2}\int_S |\nabla_T U|^2 \, ds = \tfrac{1}{2}VI^*.$$

Here S is the cross-sectional area of the wave guide. Thus

$$\frac{1}{g} = \int_S |\nabla_T U|^2 \, ds.$$

10-7 PHASE AND GROUP VELOCITY

When a sinusoidally time-varying electromagnetic field has phasor components whose dependence on z is of the form $e^{-j\beta z}$, we obtain real functions of the form $\cos(\omega t - \beta z)$ for the field components. It follows from the discussion given in Section 9–2 that the field wave form propagates with a phase velocity

$$u_p = \omega/\beta. \tag{10–48}$$

The significance of the phase velocity is that in a reference system moving with a velocity u_p in the direction of the positive z-axis the waveform and therefore the phase associated with the waveform remain constant.

When λ_g and λ are the wavelengths in the wave guide and in the unbounded medium, respectively, we have

$$\beta = 2\pi/\lambda_g, \qquad \omega = 2\pi u/\lambda, \tag{10–49}$$

where $u = 1/\sqrt{\mu\varepsilon}$ is the phase velocity of a plane wave in the unbounded medium. It follows from Eq. (10–49) that

$$u_p = \frac{\lambda_g}{\lambda} u = \frac{\lambda_g}{\lambda} \cdot \frac{1}{\sqrt{\mu\varepsilon}}.$$

Since $\lambda_g/\lambda \geqq 1$, we see that $u_p/u \geqq 1$. Thus the phase velocity of an electromagnetic wave in an air-filled wave guide is greater than the velocity of light in free space. However, it should be noted that the phase velocity is the velocity of propagation of the waveform and this is not, in general, equal to the velocity of energy propagation, which is called the *group velocity*. We define the group velocity u_g by the equation

$u_g \times$ (average electromagnetic energy per unit length of wave guide) $= P_A$,

where

$$P_A \triangleq \tfrac{1}{2} \operatorname{Re} \left[\int_S (\mathbf{E}_T \times \mathbf{H}_T^*) \cdot \mathbf{i}_z \, ds \right] \tag{10–50}$$

is the average rate of flow of energy in the positive z-direction (see Eq. 9–26b). We shall now determine u_g for the case of TM waves. (The case of TE waves can be discussed in a similar manner.) To obtain the desired result we must express surface integrals involving $\mathbf{E}$ and $\mathbf{H}$ in terms of surface integrals involving U only. To obtain these expressions we first note that Eq. (10–6) can be written (see Eq. 1–109) in the form

$$\nabla_T^2 U + k^2 U = 0,$$

where

$$k^2 = -\beta^2 + \omega^2 \mu\varepsilon. \tag{10–51}$$

We make use of the vector identity (see Eq. 10–43a, where $\gamma = j\beta$)

$$\nabla_T \cdot (U^* \nabla_T U) = |\nabla_T U|^2 + U^* \nabla_T^2 U = (|E_T|^2/\beta^2) - k^2 |U|^2$$

and the two-dimensional form of the divergence theorem to obtain

$$\oint_C U^* \, \nabla_T U \cdot \mathbf{n} \, ds = \int_S [(|E_T|^2/\beta^2) - k^2 |U|^2] \, ds.$$

It follows from the boundary conditions for U (see Eq. 10–7) that the left-hand integral in the above equation is zero. Thus we obtain one of the desired relations:

$$\int_S |E_T|^2 \, ds = \beta^2 k^2 \int_S |U|^2 \, ds. \tag{10–52}$$

Substituting Eq. (10–51) into Eq. (10–5) yields a second relation,

$$E_z = k^2 U e^{-j\beta z}. \tag{10–53}$$

We are now in a position to determine the peak electromagnetic energy in a unit length of the wave guide [see Eqs. 9–25b and c and note that we take $dv = (1) \, ds$]. The peak electric-field energy per unit length,

$$W_e = \frac{\varepsilon}{2} \int_S [|E_T|^2 + |E_z|^2] \, ds = \tfrac{1}{2}(\omega \varepsilon k)^2 \mu \int_S |U|^2 \, ds,$$

is evaluated with the aid of Eqs. (10–51), (10–52), and (10–53). The peak magnetic field energy per unit length,

$$W_m = \frac{\mu}{2} \int_S |H_T|^2 \, ds = \frac{\mu}{2} \left(\frac{\omega \varepsilon}{\beta}\right)^2 \beta^2 k^2 \int_S |U|^2 \, ds,$$

is evaluated with the aid of Eqs. (10–44) and (10–52). We see that $W_e = W_m$. Thus the average electromagnetic field energy per unit length is

$$\tfrac{1}{2}(W_e + W_m) = W_e = W_m.$$

The average rate of flow of energy in the positive z-direction (see Eq. 10–50) is

$$P_A = \frac{1}{2}\left(\frac{\omega \varepsilon}{\beta}\right) \int_S |E_T|^2 \, ds = \frac{1}{2}\left(\frac{\omega \varepsilon}{\beta}\right) \beta^2 k^2 \int_S |U|^2 \, ds$$

and the group velocity is

$$u_g = P_A/W_m = \beta/\omega \mu \varepsilon = u^2/u_p = (\lambda/\lambda_g)(1/\sqrt{\mu \varepsilon}). \tag{10–54}$$

We can obtain an alternative equation for u_g by differentiating Eq. (10–51) with respect to β:

$$d\omega/d\beta = \beta/u\mu \varepsilon = u_g. \tag{10–55}$$

It follows from Eq. (10–54) and $u_p \geqq u$ that $u_g \leqq u$. Thus the group velocity can never exceed the velocity of light. In the case of a plane wave in an unbounded medium or in the case of a *TEM* wave in a wave guide, the group velocity is equal to the phase velocity. This can be shown with the aid of Eq. (10–51). In the above cases we have $k = 0$; thus $\beta = \omega/u_p$, and Eq. (10–55) yields $u_g = u_p$.

10-8 ATTENUATION IN WAVE GUIDES

The walls of a wave guide have a finite conductivity σ. The resultant power loss results in an attenuation function $\alpha > 0$ for a wave propagating in the positive z-direction. For a lossy wave guide, the propagation function is therefore $\gamma = \alpha + j\beta$ and the transverse field components of an incident wave have the form

$$E_T(z) = E_T(0)e^{-(\alpha+j\beta)z}, \qquad H_T(z) = H_T(0)e^{-(\alpha+j\beta)z},$$

and the average rate of flow of energy in the positive z-direction (see Eq. 10–50) has the form $P_A(z) = P_A(0)e^{-2\alpha z}$. Given that P_D is the average power dissipated per unit length, we have $P_D = -dP_A/dz = 2\alpha P_A$. Thus

$$\alpha = \frac{P_D(z)}{2P_A(z)} = \frac{P_D(0)}{2P_A(0)}. \qquad (10\text{–}56)$$

We shall now determine a first-order approximation for α. We obtain the zero-order approximation, $\alpha = 0$, by assuming that the walls are perfect conductors so that the tangential component of $\mathbf{E}$ is zero on the walls. Using the zero-order tangential vector component $\mathbf{H}_t$ of $\mathbf{H}$ at the surface, we assume that the local electromagnetic field around a surface element of the wave-guide walls can be approximated by the electromagnetic field of a plane wave which has a magnetic field intensity of $\mathbf{H}_t$. Associated with $\mathbf{H}_t$ in the plane wave is a tangential $\mathbf{E}$ field (see Section 9–5 and Eq. 9–33) given in magnitude by $E_t = Z_c H_t$ where

$$Z_c = \sqrt{\omega\mu_c/\sigma}\; e^{j\pi/4}$$

is the transverse wave impedance and μ_c is the permeability of the conductor. The field components E_t and H_t are taken as the first-order approximation for the tangential field components at the surface of the wave guide. The average rate of flow of energy per unit length into the wave-guide walls is obtained by integrating Eq. (9–36) over a surface S formed by a unit length of the wave guide. Thus

$$P_D(0) = \frac{R_c}{2}\int_S |H_t|^2\, ds, \qquad (10\text{–}57)$$

where

$$R_c \triangleq \text{Re}\,[Z_c] = \sqrt{\omega\mu_c/2\sigma}. \qquad (10\text{–}58)$$

The attenuation computed from Eqs. (10–56) and (10–57) is reasonably accurate, provided that the field does not deviate to any great extent from the zero-order field. This is the case when the wave-guide walls are smooth, the frequency is above the cutoff frequency, and we restrict ourselves to lower-order modes. We shall now give several examples illustrating the theoretical evaluation of α.

Example 1. Let us evaluate α for the case of TE waves in a rectangular wave guide. The phasor components of the zero-order field are given by Eqs. (10–19). It follows from Eqs. (10–18) and (10–51) that

$$k_{mn} = \pi\sqrt{(m/a)^2 + (n/a)^2}. \tag{10-59}$$

The z-component of the complex Poynting vector (see Eq. 9–26a) is

$$(\mathbf{E}_T \times \mathbf{H}_T^*) \cdot \mathbf{i}_z = E_x H_y^* - E_y H_x^*.$$

Thus, substituting into Eq. (10–50), we obtain the average rate of flow of energy in the positive z-direction,

$$P_A(0) = \tfrac{1}{8}\omega\mu\beta_{mn}k_{mn}^2 ab, \qquad m \neq 0, n \neq 0. \tag{10-60}$$

We can evaluate Eq. (10–57) by using symmetry to account for all four wave-guide walls:

$$P_D(0) = \tfrac{1}{2}R_c\left\{2\int_0^b [|H_y|^2 + |H_z|^2]_{x=0}\, dy + 2\int_0^a [|H_x|^2 + |H_z|^2]_{y=0}\, dx\right\}$$

$$= \frac{k_{mn}^4 R_c}{2}\left[\left(\frac{\pi\beta_{mn}}{k_{mn}^2}\right)^2\left(\frac{m^2}{a} + \frac{n^2}{b}\right) + a + b\right].$$

Substituting the above results into Eq. (10–56) yields the attenuation function,

$$\alpha = \frac{2k_{mn}^2 R_c}{\omega\mu\beta_{mn}ab}\left[\left(\frac{\pi\beta_{mn}}{k_{mn}^2}\right)^2\left(\frac{m^2}{a} + \frac{n^2}{b}\right) + a + b\right].$$

For computational reasons it is convenient to express α in terms of the frequency f and the cutoff frequency f_c. This requires some further manipulations. We have (see Eqs. 10–18 and 10–59)

$$u\beta_{mn}/\omega = \sqrt{1 - (f_c/f)^2}, \tag{10-61a}$$

$$uk_{mn}/\omega = f_c/f. \tag{10-61b}$$

With the aid of the relations (see Eq. 10–59)

$$\left(\frac{\pi\beta_{mn}}{k_{mn}^2}\right)^2 = \left(\frac{\pi}{k_{mn}}\right)^2\left(\frac{u\beta_{mn}}{\omega}\right)^2\left(\frac{\omega}{uk_{mn}}\right)^2$$

$$= \left[\left(\frac{m}{a}\right)^2 + \left(\frac{n}{b}\right)^2\right]^{-1}\left[1 - \left(\frac{f_c}{f}\right)^2\right]\left(\frac{f}{f_c}\right)^2,$$

$$\frac{k_{mn}^2}{\omega\mu\beta_{mn}}\left(\frac{f}{f_c}\right)^2 = \frac{1}{\mu u}\left(\frac{\omega}{u\beta_{mn}}\right) = \sqrt{\frac{\varepsilon}{\mu}}\left[1 - \left(\frac{f_c}{f}\right)^2\right]^{-1/2}, \tag{10-62}$$

and by factoring out the term $a(f/f_c)^2$ we obtain

$$\alpha = \frac{2}{b}\left(\frac{R_c}{Z_w}\right)\left\{\frac{[(b/a)[(b/a)m^2 + n^2]}{(bm/a)^2 + n^2}\left[1 - \left(\frac{f_c}{f}\right)^2\right]\right.$$
$$\left. + \left(1 + \frac{b}{a}\right)\left(\frac{f_c}{f}\right)^2\right\}\frac{1}{\sqrt{1-(f_c/f)^2}}, \quad (10\text{–}63)$$

where $Z_w = \sqrt{\mu/\varepsilon}$ is the transverse-wave impedance of the infinite medium. When $n = 0$, it can be shown that

$$\alpha = \frac{2}{b}\left(\frac{R_c}{Z_w}\right)\left[\frac{1}{2} + \left(\frac{b}{a}\right)\left(\frac{f_c}{f}\right)^2\right]\frac{1}{\sqrt{1 - (f_c/f)^2}}.$$

As an application of this equation, let us compute the attenuation function for the case of a TE_{10} wave in an air-filled copper wave guide of dimensions $a = 0.9$ in. $= 2.286$ cm, $b = 0.4$ in. $= 1.016$ cm at a frequency of 10 GHz. We have $u = c = 3 \times 10^8$ m/sec, $Z_w = 120\pi$ ohms and $\sigma = 5.8 \times 10^7$ mhos/m. The cutoff frequency is $f_c = 6.56$ GHz (see the example given in Section 10–3). For copper $\mu_c \cong \mu_0$ and Eq. (10–58) yields $R_c = 2.61 \times 10^{-2}$ ohm. Thus

$$\alpha = 1.25 \times 10^{-2}\ \text{Np/m}.$$

The attenuation results in a decrease in the field intensity by a factor of e^{-1} in a distance of 80 m.

The attenuation is often expressed in decibels per 100 feet. Since 1 Np/m $= 264.54$ db/100 ft, we obtain

$$\alpha = 3.3\ \text{db/100 ft}.$$

Example 2. In this example we shall determine a formula for α in the case of TE waves in a circular wave guide. It can be shown that the phasor components of the field are given by:

$$E_r = j\frac{\omega\mu m}{r} J_m(k_{mn}r)\sin m\phi e^{-j\beta_{mn}z},$$

$$E_\phi = j\omega\mu k_{mn}J_m'(k_{mn}r)\cos m\phi e^{-j\beta_{mn}z},$$

$$E_z = 0,$$

$$H_r = -j\beta_{mn}k_{mn}J_m'(k_{mn}r)\cos m\phi e^{-j\beta_{mn}z}, \quad (10\text{–}64)$$

$$H_\phi = j\frac{\beta_{mn}m}{r} J_m(k_{mn}r)\sin m\phi e^{-j\beta_{mn}z},$$

$$H_z = k_{mn}^2 J_m(k_{mn}r)\cos m\phi e^{-j\beta_{mn}z}.$$

Here $J_m'(u)$ is the derivative of $J_m(u)$ with respect to u.

The average rate of flow of energy in the direction of the positive z-axis (see Eq. 10–50) is

$$P_A(0) = \frac{1}{2} \int_0^{2\pi} \int_0^a (E_r H_\phi^* - E_\phi H_r^*) r \, dr \, d\phi$$

$$= \frac{\omega \mu \pi \beta_{mn}}{2} \int_0^a \left\{ \left(\frac{m}{r}\right)^2 J_m^2(k_{mn}r) + [k_{mn}J_m'(k_{mn}r)]^2 \right\} r \, dr.$$

The integral is evaluated in Appendix (A–21). Thus

$$P_A(0) = \tfrac{1}{4}\omega\mu\pi\beta_{mn}a^2 k_{mn}^2 \left[1 - \left(\frac{m}{ak_{mn}}\right)^2 \right] J_m^2(k_{mn}a).$$

The average power dissipated per unit length (see Eq. 10–57) is

$$P_D(0) = \tfrac{1}{2}R_c \int_0^\pi [|H_\phi|^2 + |H_z|^2]_{r=a} \, a \, d\phi$$

$$= \frac{\pi a k_{mn}^4 R_c}{2} \left[\left(\frac{m\beta_{mn}}{ak_{mn}^2}\right)^2 + 1 \right] J_m^2(k_{mn}a).$$

Thus

$$\alpha = \frac{k_{mn}^2 R_c}{\omega\mu\beta_{mn}a} \left[\frac{1 + (m\beta_{mn}/ak_{mn}^2)^2}{1 - (m/ak_{mn})^2} \right]. \tag{10–65}$$

For computational reasons we again prefer to express α in terms of the frequency f and the cutoff frequency f_c. With the aid of Eqs. (10–51) and (10–61b), we obtain

$$1 + (m\beta_{mn}/ak_{mn}^2) = 1 - (m/ak_{mn})^2 + (mf/ak_{mn}f_c)^2.$$

Factoring out $(f/f_c)^2$ from Eq. (10–65) and using Eq. (10–62) yields

$$\alpha = \frac{1}{a}\left(\frac{R_c}{Z_w}\right)\left[\left(\frac{f_c}{f}\right)^2 + \frac{m^2}{a^2 k_{mn}^2 - m^2} \right] \frac{1}{\sqrt{1 - (f_c/f)^2}}.$$

Besides losses in the wave-guide walls, the medium within the wave guide may be lossy. If the wave-guide medium has a finite conductivity, we can introduce a complex permittivity (see Eq. 9–27b) $\varepsilon_c = \varepsilon + (\sigma/j\omega)$ into Eq. (10–21) and obtain the propagation function from the relation

$$\gamma^2 = (\alpha + j\beta)^2 = \alpha^2 - \beta^2 + j2\alpha\beta = k^2 - \omega^2\mu\varepsilon_c.$$

Thus

$$\beta^2 - \alpha^2 = (\omega/u)^2 - k^2, \qquad 2\alpha\beta = \omega\mu\sigma.$$

If σ is small, α is small, and as a first approximation we can neglect α^2. The phase function is then unchanged (see Eq. 10–61a),

$$\beta \cong (\omega/u)\sqrt{1 - (f_c/f)^2},$$

and the attenuation function for a lossy medium is

$$\alpha \cong \frac{\sigma Z_w}{2} \frac{1}{\sqrt{1 - (f_c/f)^2}}.$$

The resultant attenuation function is the sum of the attenuation function for the surface losses and the attenuation function for the lossy medium.

10–9 RESONANT CAVITIES

A volume bounded by a closed perfectly conducting surface forms a cavity in which an electromagnetic field can exist. We speak of the cavity as a *resonant cavity* and we say that the electromagnetic field exists in a *resonant mode*. For a lossless cavity of volume v bounded by a surface S, it follows from Eqs. (9–25d) and (9–25e) that $P_D = 0$ and $P_C = 0$. Since there are no mechanical sources present, $P_{mech} = 0$, and we see from Eq. (9–25a) that $W_m = W_e$. Thus the peak magnetic-field energy in the cavity is equal to the peak electric-field energy (the same applies for the average magnetic- and electric-field energies). The average electromagnetic-field energy in the cavity is

$$W_A = \tfrac{1}{2}(W_m + W_e) = W_m = W_e. \tag{10–66}$$

Let us take the surface of the cavity to coincide with coordinate surfaces determined by equating the general coordinates u_1, u_2, and u_3 to constants. We can consider that the coordinate surfaces determined by u_1 and u_2 form a wave guide which is closed by the coordinate surfaces $u_3 = c_1$ and $u_3 = c_2 > c_1$ to form a cavity. We consider that resonance results from an incident electromagnetic wave being reflected at the perfectly conducting surface $u_3 = c_2$ and combining with the reflected wave to give a standing wave. The tangential component of $\mathbf{E}$ must vanish at the conducting surfaces which form *nodes* for the electric field. The surface $u_3 = c_2$ forms such a node; further nodes occur at intervals l along the u_3-axis determined by the equation

$$l = N\lambda_g/2, \qquad N = 1, 2, \ldots,$$

where λ_g is the wavelength in the wave guide. The perfectly conducting surface $u_3 = c_1$ can be placed at these nodes without disturbing the standing wave. This results in a closed cavity and a resonant electromagnetic field. Since $\beta\lambda_g = 2\pi$, we can also write

$$\beta_N l = \pi N, \qquad N = 1, 2, \ldots \tag{10–67}$$

Here N is the number of half-periods of the field between the surfaces $u_3 = c_1$ and $u_3 = c_2$. We have introduced a subscript N on β to indicate its dependence on the mode number N.

When the walls of the cavity have a finite conductivity, energy is dissipated in the walls. When no external excitation is applied the energy content of the electromagnetic field will decay.   For a lossy cavity, let the field components have the form

$$E(t) = E(0)e^{-\alpha t}, \qquad H(t) = H(0)e^{-\alpha t}.$$

The instantaneous electromagnetic field energy will then have the form $W(t) = W(0)e^{-2\alpha t}$, and the instantaneous rate of energy dissipation is $-dW/dt = 2\alpha W$. The average rate of energy dissipation P_D is obtained by averaging the above equation over one cycle of oscillation: $P_D = 2\alpha W_A$. Thus (see Eq. 10–66)

$$\alpha = \frac{P_D}{2W_m} = \frac{P_D}{2W_e}, \tag{10–68}$$

where (see Eqs. 9–25b and 9–25c)

$$W_m = \frac{\mu}{2} \int_v |H|^2 \, dv, \qquad W_e = \frac{\varepsilon}{2} \int_v |E|^2 \, dv$$

are the peak magnetic and electric field energies in the cavity. (For computational reasons it is more convenient to use W_m in the case of TM waves and W_e in the case of TE waves.)

When the medium within the cavity is lossless, the average rate of energy dissipation is due entirely to the losses in the cavity walls. Thus P_D is given by Eq. (10–57), where S is the surface area of the cavity. Due to the losses the field components are attenuated by a factor of $e^{-2\pi\alpha/\omega} = e^{-\delta}$ in one period of oscillation. The decrement δ is defined by the equation

$$\delta \triangleq \frac{2\pi\alpha}{\omega} = \frac{\pi P_D}{\omega W_m}.$$

The quantity π/δ is known as the *unloaded Q* of the cavity, and is defined by

$$Q_u \triangleq \frac{\omega W_m}{P_D} = \frac{\omega W_e}{P_D} = \frac{\omega}{2\alpha}. \tag{10–69}$$

Since $W_D = 2\pi P_D/\omega$ is the energy dissipated during one cycle, we can also write

$$Q_u = 2\pi W_A/W_D.$$

To illustrate these concepts, we shall discuss the case of TM waves in a circular cylindrical cavity of radius a and length l. We can obtain the resonant frequencies of the cavity resonator by considering the superposition of an incident and a suitably chosen reflected wave. If, for example, the expressions for the incident wave have the factors

$$\tfrac{1}{2}e^{-j\beta_N z}, \qquad \tfrac{1}{2}j\beta_N e^{-j\beta_N z},$$

we can choose a reflected wave which has the respective factors (obtained by changing the sign of β_N)

$$\tfrac{1}{2}e^{j\beta_N z}, \qquad -\tfrac{1}{2}j\beta_N e^{j\beta_N z}.$$

The resultant field has the respective factors

$$\cos \beta_N z, \qquad \sin \beta_N z,$$

and the field is a standing wave. In the case of TM waves in a cylindrical cavity the phasor resonant field components can be obtained from Eqs. (10–22), which apply for an incident wave. Replacing β_{mn} by β_N and introducing a reflected wave as discussed above, we obtain:

$$E_r = -\beta_N k_{mn} J'_m(k_{mn}r) \cos m\phi \sin \beta_N z,$$

$$E_\phi = \frac{\beta_N m}{r} J_m(k_{mn}r) \sin m\phi \sin \beta_N z,$$

$$E_z = k_{mn}^2 J_m(k_{mn}r) \cos m\phi \cos \beta_N z,$$

$$H_r = -j\frac{\omega\varepsilon m}{r} J_m(k_{mn}r) \sin m\phi \cos \beta_N z, \qquad\qquad (10\text{–}70)$$

$$H_\phi = -j\omega\varepsilon k_{mn} J'_{mn}(k_{mn}r) \cos m\phi \cos \beta_N z,$$

$$H_z = 0.$$

The boundaries of the cavity are taken at $z = 0$ and $z = l$ and β_N is determined by Eq. (10–67). The tangential component of $\mathbf{E}$ then vanishes at the surfaces $z = 0$ and $z = l$. The resonant frequency $f_r \triangleq f_{nmN}$ is determined (see Eq. 10–21) by the equation

$$\left(\frac{\omega_r}{u}\right)^2 = \beta_N^2 + k_{mn}^2.$$

Thus

$$f_{nmN} = (u/2a)\sqrt{(k_{mn}a/\pi)^2 + (aN/l)^2}. \qquad\qquad (10\text{–}71)$$

The peak magnetic field energy in the cavity can be evaluated with the aid of Appendix (A–21):

$$W_m = \frac{\mu}{2} \int_0^l \int_0^{2\pi} \int_0^a [|H_r|^2 + |H_\phi|^2] r \, dr \, d\phi \, dz$$

$$= \frac{\mu\pi l(\omega_r\varepsilon)^2}{4} \int_0^a \left\{ \left(\frac{m}{r}\right)^2 J_m^2(k_{mn}r) + [k_{mn}J'_m(k_{mn}r)]^2 \right\} r \, dr$$

$$= \frac{\mu\pi l}{8} [\omega_r\varepsilon a k_{mn} J'_m(k_{mn}a)]^2.$$

The average rate of energy dissipation in the cavity walls is

$$P_D = \frac{R_c}{2}\left[2\int_0^{2\pi}\int_0^a [|H_r|^2 + |H_\phi|^2]_{z=0}r\, dr\, d\phi \right.$$

$$\left. + \int_0^{2\pi}\int_0^l [|H_\phi|^2 + |H_z|^2]_{r=a}a\, d\phi\, dz \right]$$

$$= \frac{\pi R_c}{2}\, [\omega_r\varepsilon k_{mn}J'_m(k_{mn}a)]^2\left(a^2 + \frac{al}{2}\right).$$

Substituting the expressions for W_m and P_D into Eq. (10–69) yields

$$Q_u = \frac{\omega_r\mu l}{4R_c}\frac{1}{1 + l/2a}, \qquad (10\text{–}72)$$

where the resonant angular frequency $\omega_r = f_{nmN}/2\pi$ can be found from Eq. (10–71).

As a numerical example let us take an air-filled cavity of radius $a = 2$ cm and of length $l = 10$ cm. The walls of the cavity are of brass with a conductivity of $\sigma = 1.45 \times 10^7$ mhos/m. To determine the resonant frequency for a TM_{011} mode in the cavity, we substitute the value $k_{01}a = 2.405$ obtained from Table 10–1 into Eq. (10–71). We find that $f_r = f_{011} = 6.47$ GHz. Since $\mu \simeq \mu_0$ for brass, Eq. (10–58) yields $R_c = 4.2 \times 10^{-2}\ \Omega$. We can then find the unloaded Q for the TM_{011} mode in the cavity from Eq. (10–72). This yields $Q_u = 8681$. Such high values of Q are characteristic of cavities, and are very difficult to obtain with lumped-parameter inductors and capacitors at lower frequencies.

A cavity can be excited by a small probe which couples to the electric field or by a small loop which couples to the magnetic field. In either case there must be an aperture in the cavity to permit excitation. The effect of the aperture is to decrease the Q of the cavity. Given that W_R is the energy radiated per cycle through the aperture, we define $Q_e \triangleq 2\pi(W_A/W_R)$ as the external Q and $Q_l \triangleq 2\pi[W_A/(W_R + W_D)]$ as the loaded Q. It follows that Q_l satisfies the equation

$$1/Q_l = (1/Q_u) + (1/Q_e).$$

To understand the distinction between Q_e, Q_l, and Q_u, let us consider the case in which a cavity is excited from a wave guide by means of a small aperture; let us suppose that we have derived a transmission-line analog for the entire system. At a fixed angular frequency ω and given that $W_m > W_e$, the voltage-current relations for the transmission line can be obtained from an equivalent circuit of the form illustrated in Fig. 10–7. The cavity is represented at a fixed frequency by a resistor R and an inductor L. The aperture coupling is represented by an ideal transformer of turns ratio n.

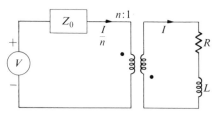

Fig. 10–7. An equivalent network for the excitation of a cavity.

Let us first discuss Q_u. The average electromagnetic field energy in the cavity is represented by the average magnetic field energy in the inductor:

$$W_A = \tfrac{1}{2}L\,|I|^2.$$

The average rate of energy dissipation in the cavity is represented by the average power dissipated in the resistor: $P_D = \tfrac{1}{2}R\,|I|^2$. Thus $Q_u = \omega L/R$. The external Q can be obtained by taking $V = 0$, assuming the existence of an energy source within the cavity which sustains the field, and determining the energy lost through the aperture. The transmission line is considered to be terminated in a matched load (its characteristic impedance being Z_0) so that the electromagnetic wave which is radiated from the aperture is not reflected back into the cavity. The rate of flow of energy out of the cavity is

$$P_R = \frac{\omega W_R}{2\pi} = \tfrac{1}{2}Z_0\,\frac{|I|^2}{n}.$$

Thus $Q_e = (\omega L/Z_0)n^2$, and the loaded Q is

$$Q_l = \frac{\omega L}{R + Z_0/n^2}.$$

10–10 FIELD PERTURBATIONS IN CAVITIES AND WAVE GUIDES

By introducing small material bodies into the electromagnetic field, one can alter the frequency of oscillation of a cavity or alter the propagation function of a wave guide. These effects can serve many useful purposes, such as the tuning of cavities and the measurement of field configurations [1, 2, 3]. We shall now derive equations for the frequency change of cavities and the change in the propagation function of wave guides produced by a small perturbation of the field. To derive the perturbation equations we consider the electromagnetic fields $\mathbf{E}_1$, $\mathbf{H}_1$ and $\mathbf{E}_2$, $\mathbf{H}_2$ of two cavities which have different material properties ($\varepsilon_1 \neq \varepsilon_2$, $\mu_1 \neq \mu_2$) but are otherwise identical. The Maxwell equations in phasor form are

$$\nabla \times \mathbf{H}_k = j\omega_k \varepsilon_k \mathbf{E}_k, \qquad \nabla \times \mathbf{E}_k = -j\omega_k \mu_k \mathbf{H}_k, \qquad k = 1, 2.$$

If we let

$$\mathbf{E} \triangleq \mathbf{E}_2 - \mathbf{E}_1, \qquad \mathbf{H} \triangleq \mathbf{H}_2 - \mathbf{H}_1, \qquad \Delta\omega \triangleq \omega_2 - \omega_1,$$

it follows that

$$\nabla \times \mathbf{E} + j\omega_1\mu_1\mathbf{H} = -j\,\Delta\omega\mu_2\mathbf{H}_2 - j\omega_1(\mu_2 - \mu_1)\mathbf{H}_2,$$

$$\nabla \times \mathbf{H} - j\omega_1\varepsilon_1\mathbf{E} = j\,\Delta\omega\varepsilon_2\mathbf{E}_2 + j\omega_1(\varepsilon_2 - \varepsilon_1)\mathbf{E}_2.$$

If we scalar-multiply the first equation by $\mathbf{H}_1^*$ and the second equation by $-\mathbf{E}_1^*$ and then add the two equations, we obtain for the left-hand side the expression

$$f \triangleq \mathbf{H}_1^* \cdot (\nabla \times \mathbf{E}) + j\omega_1\mu_1\mathbf{H} \cdot \mathbf{H}_1^* - \mathbf{E}_1^* \cdot (\nabla \times \mathbf{H}) + j\omega_1\varepsilon_1\mathbf{E} \cdot \mathbf{E}_1^*.$$

By use of the vector identities

$$\nabla \cdot (\mathbf{H}_1^* \times \mathbf{E}) = \mathbf{E} \cdot (\nabla \times \mathbf{H}_1^*) - \mathbf{H}_1^* \cdot (\nabla \times \mathbf{E})$$

$$= -j\omega_1\varepsilon_1\mathbf{E} \cdot \mathbf{E}_1^* - \mathbf{H}_1^* \cdot (\nabla \times \mathbf{E}),$$

$$\nabla \cdot (\mathbf{E}_1^* \times \mathbf{H}) = \mathbf{H} \cdot (\nabla \times \mathbf{E}_1^*) - \mathbf{E}_1^* \cdot (\nabla \times \mathbf{H})$$

$$= j\omega_1\mu_1\mathbf{H} \cdot \mathbf{H}_1^* - \mathbf{E}_1^* \cdot (\nabla \times \mathbf{H}),$$

we can express f in the following form:

$$f = -\operatorname{div}(\mathbf{H}_1^* \times \mathbf{E}) + \operatorname{div}(\mathbf{E}_1^* \times \mathbf{H}).$$

If we now integrate f over the volume of the cavity, it follows from the divergence theorem and the boundary conditions for $\mathbf{E}_1$ and $\mathbf{E}_2$ on the perfectly conducting cavity surfaces that

$$\int_v f\,dv = 0 = -j\,\Delta\omega\int_v [\mu_2\mathbf{H}_2 \cdot \mathbf{H}_1^* + \varepsilon_2\mathbf{E}_2 \cdot \mathbf{E}_1^*]\,dv$$

$$-j\omega_1\int_v [(\mu_2 - \mu_1)\mathbf{H}_2 \cdot \mathbf{H}_1^* + (\varepsilon_2 - \varepsilon_1)\mathbf{E}_2 \cdot \mathbf{E}_1^*]\,dv.$$

Thus

$$-\frac{\Delta\omega}{\omega_1} = \frac{\displaystyle\int_v [(\mu_2 - \mu_1)\mathbf{H}_2 \cdot \mathbf{H}_1^* + (\varepsilon_2 - \varepsilon_1)\mathbf{E}_2 \cdot \mathbf{E}_1^*]\,dv}{\displaystyle\int_v [\mu_2\mathbf{H}_2 \cdot \mathbf{H}_1^* + \varepsilon_2\mathbf{E}_2 \cdot \mathbf{E}_1^*]\,dv}. \tag{10–73}$$

Equation (10–73) gives the exact difference in the frequency of oscillation for the two cavities, provided that the fields are known exactly. The unperturbed field $\mathbf{E}_1$, $\mathbf{H}_1$ is usually known. If we change ε_1, μ_1 to ε_2, μ_2 within a part of the cavity volume (due to the introduction of a small material body) the field is perturbed. The perturbed field $\mathbf{E}_2$, $\mathbf{H}_2$ is not usually known and, in general, can be evaluated only approximately in terms of the unperturbed field.

If the material body which perturbs the field is lossy, the Q of the cavity will be reduced. In this case the expression on the right-hand side of Eq. (10–73) is complex and the imaginary part can be used to determine the change in Q. Let $\Delta\alpha$ be the change in the attenuation function and let $\Delta\omega_r$ be the real change in angular frequency. It follows that $\Delta\omega = \Delta\omega_r + j\,\Delta\alpha$, and since (see Eq. 10–69)

$$\Delta\alpha = \frac{\omega_1}{2}\Delta\left(\frac{1}{Q_u}\right)$$

we find that

$$\operatorname{Im}\left[\frac{\Delta\omega}{\omega_1}\right] = \Delta\left(\frac{1}{2Q_u}\right).$$

We shall now determine an expression for the change in the propagation function due to the introduction of a material body into a wave guide. We assume that the direction of propagation is the direction of the positive z-axis and that all field vectors have the form $\mathbf{F}e^{-\gamma z}$, where $\mathbf{F} = \mathbf{F}(u_1, u_2)$ and where γ is the propagation function. In order for this to be the case, the ratio of the cross-sectional dimensions of the wave guide and of the material body must be independent of z. The material body must therefore be in the form of an infinitely long slab or rod whose axis is parallel to the z-axis. Let $\mathbf{E}_1$, $\mathbf{H}_1$ be the unperturbed field. When we change ε_1, μ_1 to ε_2, μ_2 within part of the wave-guide volume in the manner discussed, we obtain a perturbed field $\mathbf{E}_2$, $\mathbf{H}_2$. Due to the manner in which the field vectors depend on z, it is convenient to introduce the transverse del operator (see Eq. 10–14). We have $\mathbf{V} = \mathbf{V}_T + \mathbf{i}_z(\partial/\partial z)$. Thus

$$\mathbf{V} \times \mathbf{F}e^{-\gamma z} = e^{-\gamma z}(\mathbf{V}_T \times \mathbf{F} - \gamma\mathbf{i}_z \times \mathbf{F}),$$

and Maxwell's equations in phasor form (note that ω is fixed by the source of excitation) are now

$$\mathbf{V}_T \times \mathbf{E}_k - \gamma_k\mathbf{i}_z \times \mathbf{E}_k = -j\omega\mu_k\mathbf{H}_k,$$

$$\mathbf{V}_T \times \mathbf{H}_k - \gamma_k\mathbf{i}_z \times \mathbf{H}_k = j\omega\varepsilon_k\mathbf{E}_k, \qquad k = 1, 2.$$

The derivation of the desired perturbation formula is based on the vector identities

$$\mathbf{V}_T \cdot (\mathbf{E}_1^* \times \mathbf{H}_2) = \mathbf{H}_2 \cdot (\mathbf{V}_T \times \mathbf{E}_1^*) - \mathbf{E}_1^* \cdot (\mathbf{V}_T \times \mathbf{H}_2)$$

$$= j\omega[\mu_1\mathbf{H}_2 \cdot \mathbf{H}_1^* - \varepsilon_2\mathbf{E}_2 \cdot \mathbf{E}_1^*] + \gamma_1^*\mathbf{H}_2 \cdot (\mathbf{i}_z \times \mathbf{E}_1^*) - \gamma_2\mathbf{E}_1^* \cdot (\mathbf{i}_z \times \mathbf{H}_2),$$

$$\mathbf{V}_T \cdot (\mathbf{E}_2 \times \mathbf{H}_1^*) = -j\omega[\mu_2\mathbf{H}_1^* \cdot \mathbf{H}_2 - \varepsilon_1\mathbf{E}_1^* \cdot \mathbf{E}_2] + \gamma_2\mathbf{H}_1^* \cdot (\mathbf{i}_z \times \mathbf{E}_2)$$

$$- \gamma_1^*\mathbf{E}_2 \cdot (\mathbf{i}_z \times \mathbf{H}_1^*).$$

We now add these two equations and integrate over the cross-sectional area S of the wave guide. Applying the two-dimensional form of the divergence theorem to the left-hand integral I and noting the boundary conditions for $\mathbf{E}_1$ and $\mathbf{E}_2$ yields $I = 0$. Thus

$$\gamma_2 + \gamma_1^* = \frac{j\omega \int_S [(\mu_2 - \mu_1)\mathbf{H}_1 \cdot \mathbf{H}_2^* + (\varepsilon_2 - \varepsilon_1)\mathbf{E}_1^* \cdot \mathbf{E}_2]\, ds}{\mathbf{i}_z \cdot \int_S [(\mathbf{E}_1^* \times \mathbf{H}_2) + (\mathbf{E}_2 \times \mathbf{H}_1^*)]\, ds}. \quad (10\text{–}74)$$

Let us look at an application of Eq. (10–73). Consider the electromagnetic field $\mathbf{E}_1$, $\mathbf{H}_1$ in an air-filled cavity and let $f_1 = \omega_1/2\pi$ be the frequency of oscillation. A small sphere of radius a, permeability $\mu_2 = \mu$, and permittivity $\varepsilon_2 = \varepsilon$ is introduced into the field. It will be shown in Section 11–11 that if $(a/\lambda) \ll 1$, where $\lambda = u/f_1$ is the wavelength in the unbounded medium, we can use quasi-static methods for the approximate evaluation of the local field around the sphere. The sphere is therefore considered to be located in a uniform quasi-static electric field $\mathbf{E}_1$ and a uniform quasi-static magnetic field $\mathbf{H}_1$. The electric and magnetic fields inside the sphere (see Eqs. 5–20 and 6–48a) are then given by

$$\mathbf{E}_2 = \frac{3}{\varepsilon_r + 2} \mathbf{E}_1, \qquad \mathbf{H}_2 = \frac{3}{\mu_r + 2} \mathbf{H}_1.$$

The integrand of the numerator integral in Eq. (10–73) is therefore constant over the volume of the sphere and zero outside the sphere. The range of integration for the denominator integral I_d in Eq. (10–73) is over the entire volume of the cavity. Since the local field around the sphere has a negligible effect on I_d, we can evaluate the integral approximately by taking $\mathbf{H}_2 \cong \mathbf{H}_1$, $\mathbf{E}_2 \cong \mathbf{E}_1$. We find that $I_d \cong 2(W_e + W_m) = 4W_A$. Thus

$$-\frac{\Delta\omega}{\omega_1} = \frac{\pi a^3}{W_A} \left[\frac{\mu_r - 1}{\mu_r + 2} \mu_0 |H_1|^2 + \frac{\varepsilon_r - 1}{\varepsilon_r + 2} \varepsilon_0 |E_1|^2 \right]. \quad (10\text{–}75)$$

We have seen that, when the sphere is a perfect conductor, we can correctly account for the local field around the sphere by taking $\varepsilon_r \to \infty$, $\mu_r \to 0$ (see Sections 5–4 and 7–7). Thus, for a perfectly conducting sphere,

$$\frac{\Delta\omega}{\omega_1} \cong \frac{\pi a^3}{2W_A} [\mu_0 |H_1|^2 - 2\varepsilon_0 |E_1|^2]. \quad (10\text{–}76)$$

10–11 THE EXCITATION OF WAVE GUIDES

Wave guides are usually used in conjunction with such devices as oscillators and antennas which involve a coupling of electromagnetic energy into or out of a wave guide. Coupling is often achieved by a small probe or loop which can efficiently excite the desired mode in the wave guide. Figure 10–8a shows how an extension of the inner conductor of a coaxial cable which is excited in a TEM mode is used to excite a TE_{10} mode in a rectangular wave guide. Figure 10–8b shows how a TE_{20} mode can be excited in a rectangular wave guide by two coaxial cables which have a 180° phase shift in their TEM fields.

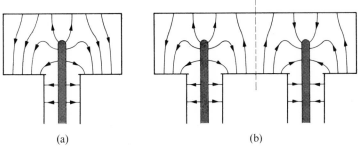

(a)　　　　　　　　　　　　(b)

Fig. 10–8. Methods for exciting TE_{10} and TE_{20} modes in a rectangular wave guide.

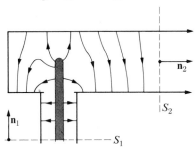

Fig. 10–9. Terminal planes for the junction of a rectangular wave guide and a coaxial cable.

Probes not only excite the desired mode but usually excite all other modes in the wave guide. If the dimensions of the wave guide are suitably chosen it is often possible to make the undesired modes evanescent. The undesired modes are then negligible at field points which are several wavelengths from the probe. Let us consider Fig. 10–9, which shows the excitation of a TE_{10} mode in a rectangular wave guide from a TEM mode in a coaxial cable. While evanescent modes exist at the junction, only a TEM mode exists in the coaxial cable at distances which are several wavelengths away from the probe. If we apply Eq. (9–25a) to the volume v bounded by the terminal planes S_1 and S_2 we have, taking $P_{\text{mech}} = 0$ and $\mathbf{n} = -\mathbf{n}_1$ over S_1,

$$P_1 = j\omega(W_m - W_e) + P_D + P_2,$$

where

$$P_1 = \tfrac{1}{2}V_1 I_1^* = \tfrac{1}{2}\int_{S_1} (\mathbf{E} \times \mathbf{H}^*) \cdot \mathbf{n}_1 \, ds$$

is the complex power supplied at terminal 1, W_m is the peak magnetic-field energy stored in v, W_e is the peak electric-field energy stored in v, P_D is the average power dissipated in v, and P_2 is the complex power available at terminal 2. At terminal 1 we can use a transmission-line analog with a phasor voltage V_1 and a phasor current I_1 and define an impedance Z_1 by the equation

$$Z_1 \triangleq \frac{2P_1}{|I_1|^2} = \frac{2[j\omega(W_m - W_e) + P_D + P_2]}{|I_1|^2}. \tag{10–77}$$

In order to obtain a matched line we require that

$$W_m - W_e + \mathrm{Im}\,[P_2] = 0 \tag{10–78}$$

and that

$$Z_0 = \frac{2\{P_D + \mathrm{Re}\,[P_2]\}}{|I_1|^2}, \tag{10–79}$$

where Z_0 is the characteristic impedance of the coaxial cable. Equation (10–78) can usually be satisfied by means of suitable tuning probes which adjust W_m and W_e. Equation (10–79) can usually be satisfied by the use of a quarter-wave matching section.

REFERENCES

1. G. L. HALL, "Measurement of resonant-cavity characteristics," *Proc. IRE* **41,** 1769–1773, December 1953
2. L. C. MAIER and J. C. SLATER, "Field-strength measurements in resonant cavities," *J. Appl. Phys.* **23,** 68–77, January 1952 ·
3. S. W. KITCHEN and A. D. SCHELBERG, "Resonant cavity field measurements." *J. Appl. Phys.* **26,** 618–621, May 1955

GENERAL REFERENCES

G. SOUTHWORTH, *Principles and Applications of Wave Guides,* New York: Van Nostrand, 1950

S. RAMO, J. R. WHINNERY and T. VAN DUZER, *Fields and Waves in Communication Electronics,* New York: John Wiley & Sons, 1965

A. F. HARVEY, *Microwave Engineering,* New York: Academic Press, 1963

R. E. COLLIN, *Foundations for Microwave Engineering,* New York: McGraw-Hill, 1966

PROBLEMS

10–1 Derive the phasor field components for *TM* waves in a rectangular wave guide. Determine the cutoff frequency and the guide wavelength at a frequency above cutoff.

10–2 Discuss the propagation of *TE, TM,* and *TEM* waves in a transmission line consisting of two parallel perfectly conducting planes a distance d apart.

10–3 Determine the cutoff frequency for the TE_{10} mode of a standard S-band air-filled wave guide of dimensions $a = 2.840$ in., $b = 1.340$ in. Evaluate the guide wavelength of a TE_{10} wave at a frequency of 3 GHz. Determine the attenuation function due to cutoff for a TE_{11} mode at a frequency of 3 GHz. What are the values for the cutoff frequency and the guide wavelength at a frequency of 3 GHz for a TE_{10} mode, given that the wave guide is filled with a dielectric of permittivity 2.6?

10–4 Determine the *TEM* field components for a biconical transmission line of half-angle ψ (Fig. 10–10). [*Hint:* Choose $u_1 = \theta$, $u_2 = \phi$, and replace z by $u_3 = r$ in Eqs. (10–4), (10–5), and (10–6).] Determine a transmission-line analog by choosing

$$I = 2\pi r \sin\theta \, H_\phi]_{\theta=\psi}$$

as the phasor current and

$$V = r \int_\psi^{\pi-\psi} E_\theta \, d\theta$$

as the phasor voltage. Show that the characteristic impedance of the transmission line is

$$Z_0 = \frac{1}{\pi} \sqrt{\frac{\mu}{\varepsilon}} \ln \cot \frac{\psi}{2}.$$

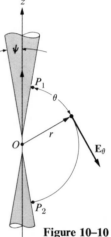

Figure 10–10

10–5 Consider the transmission-line analog for the coaxial cable discussed in Section 10–6. Prove that the phasor current defined by Eq. (10–39) and the phasor voltage defined by Eq. (10–40) satisfy the power relation (10–38), where the complex power is obtained by integrating the z-component of the complex Poynting vector over the cross-sectional area.

10–6 Prove that the phasor voltage V and the phasor current I defined by Eqs. (10–25) and (10–27), respectively, satisfy the complex power relation

$$\tfrac{1}{2}VI^* = \tfrac{1}{2}\int_S (\mathbf{E} \times \mathbf{H}) \cdot \mathbf{i}_z \, ds,$$

where S is the cross-sectional area outside the conductors. [*Hint:* Use the vector identity

$$\nabla_T \cdot (U\,\nabla_T U^*) = |\nabla_T U|^2 + U\,\nabla_T^2 U^*$$

and apply the two-dimensional form of the divergence theorem.]

10–7 A TE_{10} mode is propagating at a frequency of 3.95 GHz in an S-band air-filled wave guide of dimensions $a = 2.840$ in., $b = 1.340$ in. A safe maximum for the magnitude of the electric field intensity is considered to be 15 kV/cm. (a) Assuming that there is no reflected wave, compute the maximum power, in megawatts, which the wave guide can safely handle. [*Hint:* The phasor components given by

Eqs. (10–19) must be multiplied by a suitable factor so that the maximum magnitude of E corresponds to 15 kV/cm.] (b) Assuming that the wave guide is made of brass, which has a conductivity of $\sigma = 1.45 \times 10^7$ mhos/m, compute the attenuation function for the TE_{10} mode at a frequency of 3.95 GHz. Express α in Np/m and in db/100 ft. (c) Determine the power dissipated in a 10-m length of wave guide if the power input is 1 MW.

10–8 Derive Eqs. (10–64) for the phasor field components of a *TE* wave in a circular wave guide. Determine the cutoff frequency and the guide wavelength at a frequency above cutoff.

10–9 Consider two plane electromagnetic waves with the same plane of polarization propagating in the same direction at slightly different frequencies f and f_0. Given that $u_p = \beta_0/\omega_0$ is the phase velocity of the slower wave and that $u_m \triangleq \frac{1}{2}(\omega - \omega_0)$, show that the superposition of the two waves results in an amplitude of the form

$$\cos(\omega_0 t - \beta_0 z) + \cos(\omega t - \beta z) \cong 2\cos\omega_m(t - z/u_g)\cos\omega_0(t - z/u_p),$$

which can be interpreted as a modulation of the slower wave. Show that the modulation envelope propagates with a velocity u_g defined by the equation

$$\frac{1}{u_g} = \frac{\beta - \beta_0}{\omega - \omega_0} \cong \left[\frac{d\beta}{d\omega}\right]_{\omega=\omega_0}.$$

[Note that u_g is the group velocity as defined by Eq. (10–55).]

10–10 Prove that the attenuation function for *TEM* waves in an air-filled coaxial cable is given by

$$\alpha = \frac{R_c}{4\pi Z_0}\left(\frac{1}{a} + \frac{1}{b}\right),$$

where (see Eq. 10–42) $Z_0 = 60\ln(b/a)$ is the characteristic impedance. Here a and b are the inner and outer radii, respectively. Prove that if b is fixed, α is a minimum when $b/a = 3.6$, which gives $Z_0 = 77\ \Omega$.

10–11 For the *TEM* mode in an air-filled coaxial cable, Eq. (10–42) gives $Z_0 = 60\ln(b/a)$ and Eqs. (10–35) and (10–40) yield $V = aE\ln(b/a)$, where we can take $E = E_r(a)$ as the magnitude of the maximum electric field intensity at $z = 0$. (a) Assuming that bE is fixed, show that V is a maximum when $b/a = e$, which gives $Z_0 = 60\ \Omega$. (b) Assuming that bE is fixed, show that the power $P = \frac{1}{2}(V^2/Z_0)$ is a maximum when $b/a = 1.65$, which gives $Z_0 = 30\ \Omega$.

10–12 Prove Eq. (10–54) for the case of *TE* waves.

10–13 Determine $\mathbf{J}_s$ and σ_s for the case of *TE* waves in a rectangular wave guide. [See Eqs. (10–19) for the field components.]

10–14 Prove that the attenuation function due to wall losses for propagating *TM* waves in a circular wave guide of radius a is given by

$$\alpha = \frac{R_c}{aZ_w}\frac{1}{\sqrt{1 - (f_c/f)^2}}.$$

10–15 Determine an expression for the attenuation function due to wall losses for propagating TM waves in a rectangular wave guide. [See the answer to Problem 10–1 for the field components.]

10–16 Show that the field components for the TE_{mnN} modes of oscillation in a circular cylindrical cavity of length l and radius a are given by:

$$E_r = \frac{\omega \mu m}{r} J_m(k_{mn}r) \sin m\phi \sin \beta_N z,$$

$$E_\phi = \omega \mu k_{mn} J_m'(k_{mn}r) \cos m\phi \sin \beta_N z,$$

$$E_z = 0,$$

$$H_r = -j\beta_N k_{mn} J_m'(k_{mn}r) \cos m\phi \cos \beta_N z,$$

$$H_\phi = j \frac{\beta_N m}{r} J_m(k_{mn}r) \sin m\phi \cos \beta_N z,$$

$$H_z = -jk_{mn}^2 J_m(k_{mn}r) \cos m\phi \sin \beta_N z,$$

where $\beta_N = \pi N/l$ and where k_{mn} is determined by the boundary condition

$$J_m'(k_{mn}a) = 0.$$

Show that the frequency of oscillation is given by

$$f_{mnN} = (u/2)\sqrt{(N/l)^2 + (k_{mn}/\pi)^2},$$

where $u = 1/\sqrt{\mu\varepsilon}$ is the velocity of wave propagation in the unbounded medium.

10–17 Using the field components given in Problem 10–16, show that the average electromagnetic field energy for a TE_{mnN} mode of oscillation in a cylindrical cavity of length l and radius a is

$$W_A = \frac{\varepsilon\pi(\omega\mu)^2 l}{8}[k_{mn}^2 a^2 - m^2] \cdot J_m^2(k_{mn}a).$$

10–18 A perfectly conducting sphere of radius $b \ll a$ is introduced into an air-filled cylindrical cavity of radius a which is resonant in the TM_{1nN} mode (see Eqs. 10–70). The sphere is located on the axis at a position of maximum electric field intensity. Show that the change in frequency is determined by the equation

$$-\frac{\Delta\omega}{\omega} = \frac{2b^3}{a^2 l}\left(\frac{\beta_N}{\beta_0}\right)^2 \frac{1}{[J_1'(k_{1n}a)]^2},$$

where $\beta_0 = \omega_r/c$ and $\beta_N = \pi N/l$. Here l is the length of the cavity.

10–19 Consider a rectangular cavity of dimensions a, b, and c. Determine the resonant frequencies for the case of TM_{mnN} modes. Find an expression for the Q, given that $a = b = c = 2$ cm and that the walls are of brass with a conductivity of $\sigma = 1.45 \times 10^7$ mhos/m. Take the cavity to be air-filled.

10–20 A dielectric sphere of radius $b \ll a$ and permittivity ε is placed on the axis of a cylindrical cavity of radius a which is resonant in the TM_{01N} mode (see Eqs.

10–70). Show that the frequency change is determined by

$$-\frac{\Delta\omega}{\omega} = \frac{\varepsilon_r - 1}{\varepsilon_r + 1} \frac{\cos^2 \beta_N z}{J_1^2(k_{01}a)} \left(\frac{6v_1}{v_0}\right)\left[1 - \left(\frac{\beta_N}{\beta_0}\right)^2\right],$$

where v_1 is the volume of the sphere, v_0 is the volume of the cavity, $\beta_0 = \omega_r/c$, $\beta_N = \pi N/l$, and where k_{01} is a root of the equation $J_0(k_{01}a) = 0$.

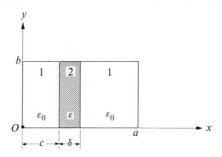

Figure 10–11

10–21 A rectangular wave guide is loaded within an infinite dielectric slab, as shown in Fig. 10–11. Determine the propagation function and the field components for a TE_{10}-type wave. [*Hint:* Choose functions V_1 and V_2 which satisfy Eq. (10–6) in the regions 1 and 2 and which satisfy the boundary conditions. One can then find the field components by applying Eqs. 10–8.]

10–22 With the aid of Eq. (10–74), solve Problem 10–21 for the case of $\delta \ll a$. [*Hint:* One can consider the field in region 2 to be uniform for a fixed z and one can find it from the boundary conditions by using the unperturbed field in region 1.]

CHAPTER 11

ANTENNAS

11-1 INTRODUCTION

In the discussion of the propagation of electromagnetic waves in Chapters 9 and 10 we considered regions of space that were source-free ($\mathbf{J} = 0$, $\rho = 0$). We derived the wave equation

$$\nabla^2 f - \frac{1}{u^2} \frac{\partial^2 f}{\partial t^2} = 0, \tag{11-1}$$

from which the components of the field vectors could be obtained. In a region of space which is source-free we can, therefore, have nonzero solutions of the wave equation. However, physical considerations require that field vectors vanish if all of space is source-free. Thus a plane electromagnetic wave can be only an approximation within a region of space to an electromagnetic wave which is produced by moving charges.

In Chapter 10 we saw that in the case of wave guides we could first obtain solutions of Maxwell's equations in the source-free region within the wave guide. By means of the boundary conditions we could then relate the vector components of the field to the sources of the field, which are the surface current density and the surface charge density (see Eqs. 10–36 and 10–37). In the case of antennas such an approach is, in general, not possible. We shall now concern ourselves with determining a direct relationship between the field vectors and the sources of the field. The physical problem is the evaluation of the electromagnetic field of an antenna. In an antenna there are charges which are constrained to move along conducting surfaces. The field associated with the moving charges is an electromagnetic field which can propagate. The application of this phenomenon to communication systems is of extreme importance. By means of an electromagnetic wave we can couple together the currents and charges in transmitting and receiving antennas over tremendous distances. Antennas have many interesting properties which are described by quantities such as input impedance, gain function, far-field components, and receiving cross section. We shall be concerned with the mathematical analysis of these quantities and with their use in the solution of antenna problems. This requires finding a particular solution for the system of equations (9–1) through (9–4) which meets the antenna boundary conditions.

11–2 VECTOR AND SCALAR
POTENTIALS OF THE ELECTROMAGNETIC FIELD

In this section we assume that all vectors and scalars are functions of position P and time t so that, for example,

$$\mathbf{J} \triangleq \mathbf{J}(P, t), \qquad \rho \triangleq \rho(P, t).$$

In antennas the current density $\mathbf{J}$ cannot be arbitrarily chosen, since it is determined by the boundary conditions at the antenna surface. However, for the moment, let us assume that $\mathbf{J}$ is a known function. The charge density ρ can be found from $\mathbf{J}$ by means of the equation of continuity. The relationship between the field vectors $\mathbf{B}$ and $\mathbf{E}$ and the sources $\mathbf{J}$ and ρ are given by Eqs. (9–1) through (9–4). To solve these equations for $\mathbf{B}$ and $\mathbf{E}$ in terms of $\mathbf{J}$ and ρ, we first note that Eq. (9–4b) is satisfied if we choose

$$\mathbf{B} = \text{curl } \mathbf{A}. \tag{11–2}$$

The vector $\mathbf{A}$ is known as the *vector potential*. The first of Maxwell's equations now takes the form

$$\text{curl } \left(\mathbf{E} + \frac{\partial \mathbf{A}}{\partial t} \right) = 0,$$

and is satisfied if we let

$$\mathbf{E} = -\frac{\partial \mathbf{A}}{\partial t} - \text{grad } U. \tag{11–3}$$

The scalar U is known as the *scalar potential*. In the case of electrostatic fields we have seen that it is possible to express $\mathbf{E}$ in the form $\mathbf{E} = -\text{grad } U$, while in the case of quasi-static fields we have seen that $\mathbf{E}$ has a vector component of the form (see Eq. 7–9) $\mathbf{E} = -\partial \mathbf{A}/\partial t$.

From Eq. (11–3) we see that in general the electric-field intensity consists of two vector components. One vector component of $\mathbf{E}$ is associated with the time-varying charge density, while a second vector component of $\mathbf{E}$ is associated with the time-varying magnetic flux density. The expressions for $\mathbf{A}$ and U given by Eqs. (3–7) and (6–5) are valid for quasi-static fields. In order to express $\mathbf{A}$ and U in terms of time-varying $\mathbf{J}$ and ρ, we must use Maxwell's equations to eliminate the field vectors $\mathbf{E}$ and $\mathbf{B}$. If we assume that μ and ε are piecewise uniform, it follows from Maxwell's second equation (9–1b) that

$$\nabla \times (\nabla \times \mathbf{A}) = \mu \mathbf{J} + \mu \varepsilon \frac{\partial \mathbf{E}}{\partial t}.$$

When we substitute Eq. (11–3) into the above equation and represent ∇ in a cartesian coordinate system, we find that

$$\nabla^2 \mathbf{A} - \mu \varepsilon \frac{\partial^2 \mathbf{A}}{\partial t^2} + \mu \mathbf{J} = \text{grad } \left(\text{div } \mathbf{A} + \mu \varepsilon \frac{\partial U}{\partial t} \right). \tag{11–4}$$

[Note that in a cartesian coordinate system $\nabla^2 \mathbf{A}$ represents the Laplacian operator operating on $\mathbf{A}$. See Section 1–22 and Eq. (1–116).]

When we substitute Eq. (11–3) into Eq. (9–4a), we obtain

$$\nabla^2 U - \mu\varepsilon \frac{\partial^2 U}{\partial t^2} + \frac{\rho}{\varepsilon} = -\frac{\partial}{\partial t}\left(\text{div } \mathbf{A} + \mu\varepsilon \frac{\partial U}{\partial t}\right). \qquad (11\text{–}5)$$

Equations (11–4) and (11–5) are a pair of coupled equations in $\mathbf{A}$ and U. We can decouple and simplify the solution of these equations if we choose $\mathbf{A}$ to be a solution of the inhomogeneous vector wave equation

$$\nabla^2 A - \mu\varepsilon \frac{\partial^2 \mathbf{A}}{\partial t^2} = -\mu\mathbf{J}, \qquad (11\text{–}6)$$

and if we choose U to be a solution of the inhomogeneous scalar wave equation

$$\nabla^2 U - \mu\varepsilon \frac{\partial^2 U}{\partial t^2} = -\frac{\rho}{\varepsilon}. \qquad (11\text{–}7)$$

We shall seek particular solutions of Eqs. (11–6) and (11–7) which satisfy the antenna boundary conditions at infinity:

$$\lim_{r \to \infty} \mathbf{A} = 0, \qquad \lim_{r \to \infty} U = 0. \qquad (11\text{–}8)$$

It then follows from Eqs. (11–4) and (11–6) that the gradient of

$$C \triangleq \text{div } \mathbf{A} + \mu\varepsilon \frac{\partial U}{\partial t} = 0 \qquad (11\text{–}9)$$

is everywhere zero, and from Eqs. (11–5) and (11–7) it follows that C must be time-invariant. Thus C is independent of P and t. The fact that $C = 0$ follows from Eqs. (11–8). Equation (11–9) is known as the *Lorentz condition*. The particular solutions $\mathbf{A}$ and U that we find must satisfy the Lorentz condition. However, we shall not concern ourselves directly with the Lorentz condition. It will subsequently be shown that the Lorentz condition is essential to account for the equation of continuity which relates $\mathbf{J}$ and ρ.

We shall first discuss a heuristic approach for finding a particular solution of Eq. (11–7). This approach is informative, since it yields the correct result and is based on simple physical considerations. For a static field Eq. (11–7) reduces to Poisson's equation $\nabla^2 U = -\rho/\varepsilon$, which has the particular solution (see Eq. 1–75)

$$U = \frac{1}{4\pi\varepsilon} \int_v \frac{\rho}{r} \, dv.$$

We can interpret the solution in the following manner. The potential at a field point P due to an element of charge $\rho \, dv$ at a distance r from the point P (Fig. 11–1) is $dU = \rho\, dv/4\pi\varepsilon r$, and the total potential at P is obtained by summing (integrating) over all elements of charge.

Suppose now that ρ is time-varying. We have seen that electromagnetic effects propagate with a finite velocity u. A time interval r/u is therefore required in order for the effect of the charge element at Q to be noticed at P. Thus the effect observed at P at an instant of time t is due to the charge element

$$\rho(Q, t - r/u)\, dv = [\rho]\, dv,$$

which was at Q at a time $t - r/u$. Here the brackets are used to denote a *retarded value*. The retarded value of any function $f = f(Q, t)$ is obtained by replacing t by $t - r/u$:

$$[f] \triangleq f(Q, t - r/u).$$

On the basis of this physical interpretation we anticipate that

$$U \triangleq U(P, t) = \frac{1}{4\pi\varepsilon} \int_v \frac{[\rho]}{r}\, dv \qquad (11\text{–}10)$$

is a solution of Eq. (11–7). Similarly, the solution of Eq. (11–6) is

$$\mathbf{A} = \frac{\mu}{4\pi} \int_v \frac{[\mathbf{J}]}{r}\, dv. \qquad (11\text{–}11)$$

Note that the solutions given by Eqs. (11–10) and (11–11) satisfy the boundary conditions at infinity (11–8).

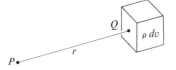

Fig. 11–1. The potential at P due to a charge element at Q.

The above derivation is heuristic. We shall now prove that the expressions found for U and $\mathbf{A}$ are solutions of Eqs. (11–7) and (11–6), respectively, and that they satisfy the Lorentz condition. The integrand of the integral in Eq. (11–10) has the form $f = g/r$, where $g \triangleq g(\tau)$, $\tau \triangleq t - r/u$, and $r^2 = x^2 + y^2 + z^2$. The Laplacian of f is

$$\nabla^2 f = g\, \nabla^2 \frac{1}{r} + 2\, \nabla g \cdot \nabla \frac{1}{r} + \frac{1}{r} \nabla^2 g.$$

The gradient of g is $\nabla g = -g'\mathbf{r}/ur$, so that

$$2\, \nabla g \cdot \nabla \frac{1}{r} = \frac{2g'}{ur^2}$$

and

$$\nabla^2 g = \frac{1}{u^2} g'' - \frac{2g'}{ur},$$

where g' is the derivative of g with respect to τ. Since $\partial^2 f / \partial t^2 = g'' / r$, we find that

$$\nabla^2 f - \frac{1}{u^2} \frac{\partial^2 f}{\partial t^2} = g \, \nabla^2 \frac{1}{r} = 0, \qquad r \neq 0, \tag{11-12}$$

and thus the function f is a solution of the homogeneous wave equation, provided that $r \neq 0$. In order to make use of the result given by Eq. (11-12), we must divide the volume v into a small spherical volume v_1 centered at the field point P and a volume $v_2 = v - v_1$. The potential U given by Eq. (11-10) is then the sum of the potential U_1 due to the elements of charge in v_1 and the potential U_2 due to the elements of charge in v_2. In the case of v_2 we have $r \neq 0$, since P is outside v_2. Thus we can differentiate under the integral sign, and by using Eq. (11-12) we obtain

$$\nabla^2 U_2 - \frac{1}{u^2} \frac{\partial^2 U_2}{\partial t^2} = \frac{1}{4\pi\varepsilon} \int_{v_2} \left(\nabla^2 f - \frac{1}{u^2} \frac{\partial^2 f}{\partial t^2} \right) dv = 0,$$

where $f \triangleq [\rho]/r$. Thus U_2 is a solution of the homogeneous wave equation. In the case of U_1 we cannot differentiate under the integral sign, since $r = 0$ when Q coincides with P. However, we can take the radius a of the spherical volume to be arbitrarily small, so that we can expand $[\rho]$ in a Taylor series in r/ut which holds uniformly throughout v_1:

$$\rho(Q, t - r/u) = \rho(Q, t) + c_1(r/ut) + c_2(r/ut)^2 + \cdots$$

Only the first term of this expansion will enter into the final expression, so that we shall not concern ourselves with the evaluation of the constants c_k. Introducing the expansion into the integral and noting that the first term

$$U_0 \triangleq U_0(P, t) = \frac{1}{4\pi\varepsilon} \int_{v_1} \frac{\rho(Q, t)}{r} dv$$

is a solution of Laplace's equation $\nabla^2 U_0 = -\rho(P, t)/\varepsilon$, we obtain

$$\nabla^2 U_1 - \frac{1}{u^2} \frac{\partial^2 U_1}{\partial t^2} = -\frac{\rho}{\varepsilon} + 0(a^2),$$

where $0(a^2)$ indicates terms the order of a^2. Combining the equations for U_1 and U_2 yields

$$\nabla^2 U - \frac{1}{u^2} \frac{\partial^2 U}{\partial t^2} = -\frac{\rho}{\varepsilon} + 0(a^2).$$

If we now let $a \to 0$, we see that U satisfies Eq. (11-7). In a similar manner we can show that Eq. (11-11) satisfies Eq. (11-6).

We must now verify that the solutions given by Eqs. (11-10) and (11-11) satisfy the Lorentz condition. To distinguish between derivatives evaluated at the field point P and the source point Q, we introduce subscripts on ∇

(see Section 1–16). We have

$$\mathbf{V}_P \cdot \mathbf{A} = \frac{\mu}{4\pi} \int_v \mathbf{V}_P \cdot \frac{[\mathbf{J}]}{r} \, dv, \tag{11–13}$$

where $r^2 = (x_P - x_Q)^2 + (y_P - y_Q)^2 + (z_P - z_Q)^2$. To carry out the proof of the Lorentz condition, we must consider the two equations

$$\mathbf{V}_P \cdot \frac{[\mathbf{J}]}{r} = \frac{1}{r} \mathbf{V}_P \cdot [\mathbf{J}] + [\mathbf{J}] \cdot \mathbf{V}_P \frac{1}{r}, \tag{11–14}$$

$$\mathbf{V}_Q \cdot \frac{[\mathbf{J}]}{r} = \frac{1}{r} \mathbf{V}_Q \cdot [\mathbf{J}] + [\mathbf{J}] \cdot \mathbf{V}_Q \frac{1}{r}, \tag{11–15}$$

where $[\mathbf{J}] \triangleq \mathbf{J}(Q, \tau)$ and where $\tau \triangleq t - r/u$. To compute the derivatives of the components of $[\mathbf{J}]$ in cartesian coordinates, we note that if $f \triangleq f(Q, \tau)$, we have

$$\frac{\partial f}{\partial x_Q} = \frac{\partial f'}{\partial x_Q} + \frac{\partial f}{\partial \tau} \frac{\partial \tau}{\partial x_Q}, \qquad \frac{\partial f}{\partial x_P} = \frac{\partial f}{\partial \tau} \frac{\partial \tau}{\partial x_P},$$

and since τ is a function of r we have $\partial \tau / \partial x_Q = -\partial \tau / \partial x_P$. Here $f' \triangleq f(Q, \tau')$ and the prime is used to indicate that τ' is to be held constant in evaluating the derivative. Expressions similar to those above hold for derivatives with respect to y_Q, y_P, z_Q, and z_P. It follows from these expressions that

$$\mathbf{V}_Q \cdot [\mathbf{J}] = [\mathbf{V}_Q \cdot \mathbf{J}] - \mathbf{V}_P \cdot [\mathbf{J}]. \tag{11–16}$$

Here we have noted that $\mathbf{V}_Q \cdot [\mathbf{J}'] = [\mathbf{V}_Q \cdot \mathbf{J}]$. The equality of this expression follows from the fact that in evaluating $\mathbf{V}_Q \cdot \mathbf{J}$, we assume that t is constant, and that after replacing t by τ we obtain $[\mathbf{V}_Q \cdot \mathbf{J}]$. With the aid of Eqs. (1–67), (11–14), (11–15), and (11–16) we can express the integrand of Eq. (11–13) in the form

$$\mathbf{V}_P \cdot \frac{[\mathbf{J}]}{r} = \frac{1}{r} [\mathbf{V}_Q \cdot \mathbf{J}] - \frac{1}{r} \mathbf{V}_Q \cdot [\mathbf{J}] - [\mathbf{J}] \cdot \mathbf{V}_Q \frac{1}{r} = \frac{1}{r} [\mathbf{V}_Q \cdot \mathbf{J}] - \mathbf{V}_Q \cdot \frac{[\mathbf{J}]}{r}.$$

$$\tag{11–17}$$

With the aid of the divergence theorem and Eq. (11–17) we obtain

$$\mathbf{V}_P \cdot \mathbf{A} + \mu\varepsilon \frac{\partial U}{\partial t} = \frac{\mu}{4\pi} \int_v \frac{1}{r} \left[\mathbf{V}_Q \cdot \mathbf{J} + \frac{\partial \rho}{\partial t} \right] dv - \frac{\mu}{4\pi} \int_S \frac{[\mathbf{J}] \cdot \mathbf{n}}{r} \, ds, \tag{11–18}$$

where S is the surface bounding the volume v. Given that $\mathbf{J}$ is a piecewise continuous function of position and that the current is restricted to flow in a finite region of space, we can choose the infinite sphere for S and the surface integral will vanish. The case of a perfectly conducting surface on which a surface current density $\mathbf{J}_s$ exists and on which $\mathbf{J}$ is infinite can be treated by taking a limit to replace $\mathbf{J}$ by $\mathbf{J}_s$. In this case $[\mathbf{J}_s] \cdot \mathbf{n} = 0$ over the surface of the conductor. We see that in either case the surface integral vanishes. The integrand of the volume integral is zero because of the equation of continuity (2-42). Since Eq. (2-42) is valid at any source point Q for all t, we may replace t by τ and obtain the retarded quantity

$$\left[\nabla_Q \cdot \mathbf{J} + \frac{\partial \rho}{\partial t} \right] = 0.$$

Thus the right-hand side of Eq. (11-18) is zero, and we see that $\mathbf{A}$ and U satisfy the Lorentz condition.

The solutions of the inhomogeneous wave equation given by Eqs. (11-10) and (11-11) are particular solutions satisfying certain boundary conditions. For the case in which μ and ε are piecewise uniform these solutions will not, in general, satisfy the boundary conditions at the interfaces of the different media. In such cases we must determine suitable solutions of the homogeneous wave equation. The situation is similar to that which was discussed in Chapter 4 in conjunction with electrostatic fields. The particular solution (4-4) cannot, in general, satisfy the boundary conditions, and suitable solutions of Laplace's equation must be found in order to satisfy these conditions.

To avoid the considerable mathematical complexity of boundary-value problems of this type, we shall restrict the discussion to antennas in free space and take $\mu = \mu_0$, $\varepsilon = \varepsilon_0$. It is fortunate that the particular solutions given by Eqs. (11-10) and (11-11) are applicable to the case of antennas in free space, a case which is of considerable practical importance. We shall also assume that $\mathbf{J}$ is a known sinusoidally time-varying function of position. For antennas composed of conducting surfaces we cannot assume a form for $\mathbf{J}$, since this form is determined by the boundary conditions at the surface. Since the solution of the boundary-value problem for $\mathbf{J}$ is mathematically involved, it will not be discussed. For our purposes it will be sufficient to choose a form for $\mathbf{J}$ which is a good approximation to the current distribution of an actual antenna. The assumed current distribution consists of current filaments in free space which are not restricted by boundary conditions. However, distributed mechanical forces must be imposed to keep the current filaments from disintegrating under the action of electromagnetic forces. We must therefore take considerable care when we evaluate the energy input to the electromagnetic field from these mechanical sources and when we attempt to relate this to the energy input to the electromagnetic field of an actual antenna driven by a transmission line.

11-3 PHASOR FORM OF VECTOR AND SCALAR POTENTIALS; THE ELECTRIC DIPOLE ANTENNA

For sinusoidally time-varying fields we use a phasor representation and express vector and scalar quantities in the exponential form

$$\mathbf{F}e^{j\omega t}, \qquad f e^{j\omega t},$$

where $\mathbf{F} \triangleq \mathbf{F}(P)$ and $f \triangleq f(P)$ are functions of the field point P. The phasor forms of Eqs. (11–2), (11–3), and (11–9) are given by

$$\mathbf{B} = \text{curl } \mathbf{A}, \tag{11-19a}$$

$$\mathbf{E} = -j\omega\mathbf{A} - \text{grad } U, \tag{11-19b}$$

$$\text{div } \mathbf{A} + j\omega\mu_0\varepsilon_0 U = 0, \tag{11-19c}$$

where we have taken $\mu = \mu_0$ and $\varepsilon = \varepsilon_0$. The phasor forms of retarded quantities are obtained by replacing t by $t - r/u$. Thus

$$[\mathbf{J}e^{j\omega t}] = \mathbf{J}e^{j\omega(t-r/u)} = \mathbf{J}e^{-j\beta r}e^{j\omega t},$$

where $\beta \triangleq \omega/u$. It follows from Eqs. (11–10) and (11–11) that the phasor scalar and vector potentials are given by

$$U = \frac{1}{4\pi\varepsilon_0} \int_v \frac{\rho e^{-j\beta r}}{r}\, dv, \tag{11-20a}$$

$$\mathbf{A} = \frac{\mu_0}{4\pi} \int_v \frac{\mathbf{J}e^{-j\beta r}}{r}\, dv. \tag{11-20b}$$

(These expressions can also be obtained by taking the Fourier transform of Eqs. 11–10 and 11–11.)

To illustrate the use of Eqs. (11–20) in determining the electromagnetic field of an antenna, let us consider the electric dipole antenna illustrated in Fig. 11–2, which consists of a thin linear current filament of length l terminated by two terminal conductors. We assume that the current, $i = I_0 \cos \omega t$, is uniform along the filament. Since the filament is considered to be infinitesimally thin, we have $\int_v \mathbf{J}\, dv = \mathbf{i}_z I_0 l$.

Equation (11–20b) yields the phasor vector potential due to the current filament: $\mathbf{A} = \mathbf{i}_z A_z$, where

$$A_z = \frac{\mu_0 I_0 l}{4\pi} \frac{e^{-j\beta r}}{r}.$$

The phasor current I_0 results in the upper terminal conductor acquiring a phasor charge, $Q = I_0/j\omega = \int_{v_c} \rho\, dv$, where v_c is the volume of the terminal conductor (note that $\rho = 0$ along the filament). Equation (11–20a) yields the phasor scalar potential due to the charged terminal conductors:

$$U = \frac{I_0}{j4\pi\varepsilon_0\omega}\left(\frac{e^{-j\beta r_1}}{r_1} - \frac{e^{-j\beta r_2}}{r_2}\right) = \frac{I_0}{j4\pi\varepsilon_0\omega} \frac{\partial}{\partial r}\left(\frac{e^{-j\beta r}}{r}\right)(-l \cos \theta)$$

$$= \frac{I_0 l \cos \theta}{j4\pi\varepsilon_0\omega}\left(\frac{1}{r^2} + \frac{j\beta}{r}\right)e^{-j\beta r}.$$

The phasor field vectors can be obtained from Eqs. (11–19). Due to symmetry the components are best determined in a spherical coordinate system. Thus $A_r = A_z \cos \theta$, $A_\theta = -A_z \sin \theta$, $A_\phi = 0$, and we obtain (see Eq. 1–106)

$$H_r = 0 = H_\theta, \qquad H_\phi = -\frac{\sin \theta}{\mu_0} \frac{\partial A_z}{\partial r} = \frac{I_0 l \sin \theta}{4\pi r}\left(j\beta + \frac{1}{r}\right)e^{-j\beta r}. \qquad (11\text{–}21)$$

For the phasor components of **E** we have

$$E_r = -j\omega A_r - \frac{\partial U}{\partial r} = \frac{I_0 l Z_0 \cos \theta}{2\pi r}\left(\frac{1}{r} + \frac{1}{j\beta r^2}\right)e^{-j\beta r}, \qquad (11\text{–}22\text{a})$$

$$E_\theta = -j\omega A_\theta - \frac{1}{r}\frac{\partial U}{\partial \theta} = \frac{I_0 l Z_0 \sin \theta}{4\pi r}\left(j\beta + \frac{1}{r} + \frac{1}{i\beta r^2}\right)e^{-j\beta r}, \qquad (11\text{–}22\text{b})$$

$$E_\phi = -j\omega A_\phi - \frac{1}{r \sin \theta}\frac{\partial U}{\partial \phi} = 0, \qquad (11\text{–}22\text{c})$$

where $Z_0 = \sqrt{\mu_0/\varepsilon_0} = 120\pi$ ohms is the intrinsic impedance of free space.

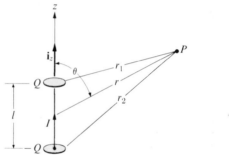

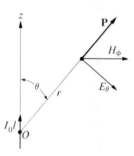

Fig. 11–2. A radiating electric dipole.   **Fig. 11–3.** The far-field components of a radiating electric dipole.

The *far-field components* are obtained by neglecting terms of higher order than $1/r$. Thus

$$H_\phi = \frac{j\beta I_0 l \sin \theta}{4\pi r} e^{-j\beta r}, \qquad (11\text{–}23\text{a})$$

$$E_\theta = \frac{j\beta I_0 l Z_0 \sin \theta}{4\pi r} e^{-j\beta r} \qquad (11\text{–}23\text{b})$$

are the far-field components for the electric dipole antenna. In the far field the vectors **E** and **H** and the radius vector **r** form a right-handed orthogonal system of vectors and the ratio E_θ/H_ϕ is equal to the intrinsic impedance of free space (Fig. 11–3). Thus we see that in the far field the vectors **E** and **H** are related to each other in the same manner as in a plane wave. The wavelength λ in the far field is determined by the condition that $e^{-j\beta r} = e^{-j\beta(r+\lambda)}$. Thus $\beta = 2\pi/\lambda$.

The complex Poynting vector **P** in the far field is real and has the direction of **r**. We have

$$P = \tfrac{1}{2} E_\theta H_\phi^* = \left[\frac{\beta I_0 l \sin \theta}{4\pi r} \right]^2 \frac{Z_0}{2}$$

and we can obtain the power radiated by integrating P over a sphere of radius r (see Eq. 9–25e):

$$P_R = \mathrm{Re} \left[\int_S \tfrac{1}{2} (\mathbf{E} \times \mathbf{H}^*) \cdot \mathbf{n}\, ds \right] = \left[\frac{\beta I_0 l}{4\pi r} \right]^2 \frac{Z_0}{2} \int_0^\pi \sin^2 \theta (2\pi r \sin \theta)(r\, d\theta).$$

$$(11–24)$$

Since $\displaystyle \int_0^\pi \sin^3 \theta\, d\theta = \tfrac{4}{3}$, we obtain

$$P_R = \frac{(\beta I_0 l)^2}{12\pi} Z_0. \qquad (11–25)$$

For both computational and physical reasons it is convenient to represent the energy radiated by an antenna in terms of the energy dissipated in a *radiation resistance R*, defined by the equation

$$P_R = \tfrac{1}{2} |I_0|^2 R. \qquad (11–26)$$

Thus the radiation resistance of the electric dipole antenna is

$$R = 80(\pi l/\lambda)^2 \text{ ohms } (\Omega). \qquad (11–27)$$

The assumed uniform current distribution is a good first approximation for physical antennas whose length l is short compared with the wavelength. Assuming that the currents are approximately the same, we can expect the same to be true for the far-field components and for the energy radiated. To illustrate the use of these equations, let us take $l = \lambda/4\pi$ and compute the peak magnitude of the current density and the electric field intensity at a distance of ten kilometers, given that the power radiated is 1 kW. Equation (11–27) yields the radiation resistance, $R = 5\,\Omega$, and Eq. (11–26) yields the peak magnitude of the current, $I_0 = 20$ A. If $\theta = \pi/2$, Eq. (11–23b) yields

$$|E_\theta| = \frac{60\pi I_0 l}{r\lambda} = 30 \text{ mV/m}.$$

The electric dipole antenna is used at low frequencies when it is necessary that the antenna length be small compared with the wavelength in order to prevent excessive antenna heights. The conductors at the ends of the current filament are essential to achieve a uniform distribution of current along the antenna axis. Without this *top loading*, the current distribution would have the form

$$i = I_0 \left(1 - \frac{2\,|z|}{l} \right) \cos \omega t, \qquad (11–28)$$

which would result in a smaller radiation resistance. This is undesirable, since for a given radiated power the current increases as R decreases and the increased current results in higher dissipative losses in a physical antenna.

It is of interest to discuss the source of energy for the electromagnetic field of the assumed current filament. In order that the current filament not disintegrate, we must have a distribution of mechanical sources which move the charges along the filament against the opposing electromagnetic forces. The complex mechanical power input due to these sources (see Eq. 9–25a) is given by

$$P_{\text{mech}} = \tfrac{1}{2} \int_{v_g} (-\mathbf{E} \cdot \mathbf{J}^*) \, dv = j\omega(W_m - W_e) + P_R. \qquad (11\text{–}29)$$

The quantity $|W_m - W_e|$ represents the peak stored electromagnetic energy in the field and P_R is the power radiated. However, a physical antenna is composed of conductors and is usually supplied with electrical energy from a transmission line, as illustrated in Fig. 11–4. If the conductors are perfect conductors, the boundary condition requires that $\mathbf{E} \cdot \mathbf{J}_s^* = 0$, so that mechanical sources are not present. The electrical energy flows from the transmission line into the field through a part S_i of the surface S. Thus

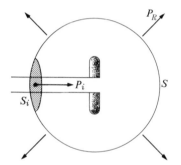

$$P_i = \tfrac{1}{2} \int_{S_i} (\mathbf{E} \times \mathbf{H}^*) \cdot (-\mathbf{n} \, ds)$$

$$= j\omega(W_m - W_e) + P_R, \qquad (11\text{–}30)$$

where

$$P_R = \tfrac{1}{2} \int_{S-S_i} (\mathbf{E} \times \mathbf{H}^*) \cdot \mathbf{n} \, ds.$$

Fig. 11–4. A dipole excited by a transmission line.

The distinction between an antenna formed by an assumed current distribution and a physical antenna should be carefully noted. By assuming a current distribution we avoid the boundary-value problem. However, we then require distributed mechanical sources to account for the complex input power to the electromagnetic field. In a physical antenna we cannot assume a current distribution; it is determined by the boundary conditions, and the complex power is supplied by a transmission line. However, if the assumed current distribution approximates the distribution obtained by solving the boundary-value problem, we can expect that the expressions for W_m, W_e, and P_R on the right-hand sides of Eqs. (11–29) and (11–30) will be approximately the same. Thus we can set

$$P_i \cong P_{\text{mech}}. \qquad (11\text{–}31)$$

From a computational point of view it is more convenient to deal with an assumed current distribution from which P_{mech} can be comparatively easily evaluated. To compute P_i from Eq. (11–30) by using the solution of the boundary-value problem is mathematically extremely complex. Thus, in nearly all cases, it is P_{mech} that we evaluate. The interesting philosophical question as to what occurs if we happen to assume the correct current distribution in computing P_{mech} will be discussed in Section 11–7.

11–4 FAR-FIELD COMPONENTS, RADIATION RESISTANCE, AND GAIN FUNCTIONS OF THIN LINEAR ANTENNAS

For a thin linear antenna we can take the z-axis as the antenna axis and let

$$\mathbf{J}\, dv = \mathbf{i}_z I\, dz, \qquad \rho\, dv = q\, dz,$$

where I is the phasor current and q the phasor linear charge density. The equation of continuity, div $\mathbf{J} + j\omega\rho = 0$, for the thin linear antenna takes the form

$$\frac{\partial I}{\partial z} + j\omega q = 0. \tag{11–32}$$

Theoretical and experimental results have shown that a sinusoidal current distribution of the form

$$I = I_0 \sin \beta \left(\frac{l}{2} - |z| \right) \tag{11–33}$$

is a good first approximation for the current distribution on a thin linear antenna of length l. The far-field components can be obtained by considering each element of current $I\, dz$ as an elementary dipole. Thus the far field (see Eqs. 11–23) is determined by

$$dE_\theta = Z_0\, dH_\phi, \qquad dH_\phi = \frac{j\beta I\, dz \sin \theta}{4\pi r'} e^{-j\beta r'},$$

where (see Fig. 11–5) $r' = r - z \cos \theta$. In the far field we have

$$\frac{1}{r'} \cong \frac{1}{r}, \qquad e^{-j\beta r'} = e^{-j\beta r}e^{j\beta z}\cos \theta,$$

and we find that

$$E_\theta = Z_0 H_\phi, \tag{11–34a}$$

$$H_\phi = \frac{j\beta I_0 l_\theta \sin \theta}{4\pi r} e^{-j\beta r}, \tag{11–34b}$$

where

$$l_\theta \triangleq \int_{-l/2}^{l/2} \frac{I}{I_0} e^{j\beta z \cos \theta}\, dz \tag{11–35}$$

is defined as the *effective antenna length*.

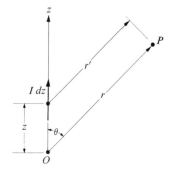

Fig. 11–5. The far field of a thin linear antenna.

The same result can be obtained from the vector and scalar potentials. In the far field we have

$$A_z = \frac{\mu_0 I_0 l_\theta}{4\pi r} e^{-j\beta r}.$$

For the phasor scalar potential we obtain, using Eq. (11–32) and integrating by parts,

$$U = \frac{e^{-j\beta r}}{4\pi\varepsilon_0 r} \int_{-l/2}^{l/2} q e^{j\beta z \cos\theta}\, dz = \frac{I_0 l_\theta \beta \cos\theta}{4\pi\omega\varepsilon_0} \frac{e^{-j\beta r}}{r}.$$

It follows from Eqs. (11–21) and (11–22b) that the far-field components are given by

$$E_\theta = -j\omega A_\theta, \qquad H_\phi = -\frac{\sin\theta}{\mu_0} \frac{\partial A_z}{\partial r}. \qquad (11\text{–}36)$$

In the far field the potentials have the same form as those derived in Section 11–3 for the electric dipole antenna. We must now, however, replace the length l by the effective length l_θ. We can see from Eqs. (11–36) that the fact that l_θ is a function of θ does not affect the result, and we again obtain Eqs. (11–23), where l must be replaced by l_θ. The integral for the effective length is readily evaluated:

$$l_\theta = \int_{-l/2}^{l/2} \sin\beta\left(\frac{l}{2} - |z|\right) e^{j\beta z \cos\theta}\, dz = 2\int_0^{l/2} \sin\beta\left(\frac{l}{2} - z\right) \cos(\beta z \cos\theta)\, dz$$

$$= \frac{2}{\beta \sin^2\theta}\left[\cos\left(\frac{\beta l}{2}\cos\theta\right) - \cos\frac{\beta l}{2}\right]. \qquad (11\text{–}37)$$

The complex Poynting vector in the far field is real, and has the radial direction:

$$P = \tfrac{1}{2} E_\theta H_\phi^* = \tfrac{1}{2} Z_0 |H_\phi|^2.$$

An antenna does not, in general, radiate equally in all directions; it has a directivity associated with its radiation. To obtain a mathematical representation for the directivity of an antenna, let us define $P(\theta, \phi)$ as the power radiated per unit solid angle in the (θ, ϕ) direction. For a thin linear antenna we have

$$P(\theta, \phi) = r^2 P = \frac{15 |I_0|^2}{\pi} \left| \frac{\cos\left[(\beta l/2)\cos\theta\right] - \cos(\beta l/2)}{\sin\theta} \right|^2,$$

which gives the power density at any point on a unit sphere which is centered at the origin.

If the antenna is isotropic, the power density is uniform over the unit sphere and is given by $P_R/4\pi$, where P_R is the average power radiated. The ratio

$$G(\theta, \phi) \triangleq \frac{P(\theta, \phi)}{P_R/4\pi} \qquad (11\text{–}38)$$

is defined as the *gain function* of the antenna. Both P_R and the radiation resistance R are determined by integrating the power density over the unit sphere:

$$P_R = \tfrac{1}{2}|I_0|^2 R = \int_0^{2\pi}\int_0^{\pi} P(\theta,\,\phi)\sin\theta\;d\theta\;d\phi.$$

Let us first determine R. Since $P(\theta,\,\phi)$ is independent of ϕ for the thin linear antenna, we find that

$$R = 60\int_0^{\pi}\left|\frac{\cos\,[(\beta l/2)\cos\theta]\,-\,\cos\,(\beta l/2)}{\sin\theta}\right|^2\sin\theta\;d\theta.$$

In order to evaluate the integral we first substitute $u = \cos\theta$, $k = \beta l/2$. Thus

$$R = 60\int_{-1}^{+1}\frac{(\cos ku - \cos k)^2}{1 - u^2}\;du = 30\int_{-1}^{+1}\frac{(\cos ku - \cos k)^2}{1 + u}\;du$$

$$+\;30\int_{-1}^{1}\frac{(\cos ku - \cos k)^2}{1 - u}\;du.$$

If we now substitute $v = k(1 + u)$ into the first integral and $v = k(1 - u)$ into the second integral, we obtain

$$R = 60\int_0^{\beta l}\frac{[\cos\,(v - k) - \cos k]^2}{v}\;dv.$$

The integral can be expressed in terms of tabulated integrals by expanding the integrand:

$$[\cos\,(v - k) - \cos k]^2 = \frac{1 + \cos 2(v - k)}{2} - 2\cos k\cos\,(v - k)$$

$$+\;\frac{1 + \cos 2k}{2} = (1 + \cos 2k)(1 - \cos v) - \frac{\cos 2k}{2}(1 - \cos 2v)$$

$$-\;\sin 2k\sin v + \frac{\sin 2k}{2}\sin v.$$

We obtain

$$R = 30[2(1 + \cos\beta l)\,\text{Cin}\,\beta l - \cos\beta l\,\text{Cin}\,2\beta l$$

$$-\;2\sin\beta l\,\text{Si}\,\beta l + \sin\beta l\,\text{Si}\,2\beta l], \quad (11\text{–}39)$$

where the following integrals are tabulated [1, 2]:

$$\text{Si}\,(u) \triangleq \int_0^u \frac{\sin x}{x}\;dx$$

$$\text{Ci}\,(u) \triangleq -\int_u^{\infty}\frac{\cos x}{x}\;dx$$

$$\text{Cin}\,(u) \triangleq \int_0^u\frac{1 - \cos x}{x}\;dx = \ln u + \gamma - \text{Ci}\,u. \quad (11\text{–}40)$$

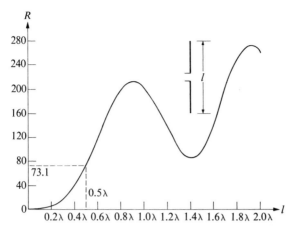

Fig. 11–6. The radiation resistance R, expressed in ohms, of a thin linear antenna.

Here $\gamma \triangleq \lim_{u \to \infty} (\text{Cin } u - \ln u) = 0.5772$.   Equation (11–39) is plotted in Fig. 11–6, where the length l is expressed in wavelengths [3].

As an example let us consider a half-wave antenna for which $l = \lambda/2$ and $\beta l = \pi$. From Eq. (11–39) and the tabulated values of Cin (u), we find that

$$R = 30 \text{ Cin } 2\pi = 73.1 \ \Omega.$$

The radiated power is $P_R = 36.5 \, |I_0|^2 \, \text{W}$ and the gain function is

$$G(\theta, \phi) = 1.64 \left| \frac{\cos \left[(\pi/2) \cos \theta \right]}{\sin \theta} \right|^2.$$

To illustrate numerical values, let us determine the peak current and the power input to the antenna if the electric field intensity is to have a maximum magnitude of 10 mV/m at a distance of 10 km.   From Eqs. (11–34) and (11–37) we obtain

$$E_\theta = j \, \frac{60 I_0 e^{-j\beta r}}{r} \, \frac{\cos \left[(\beta l/)2 \cos \theta \right] - \cos (\beta l/2)}{\sin \theta}.$$

For the half-wave antenna we have $\beta l = \pi$ and $|E_\theta|$ is a maximum when $\theta = \pi/2$. Thus

$$|I_0| = \frac{|E_\theta| \, r}{60} = 1.67 \text{ A (peak)},$$

and the power required by the antenna is

$$P_R = \tfrac{1}{2} |I_0|^2 \, R = 102 \text{ W}.$$

11–5 ANTENNA ARRAYS

In most practical applications it is desirable to have a directivity associated with the energy radiated by an antenna. A simple linear antenna has no directivity in the equatorial plane ($\theta = \pi/2$). However, by means of an antenna array and by suitable phasing between the antenna currents, a directivity in the radiation can be achieved. The component E_θ in the far field of a thin linear antenna (see Eqs. 11–34) is given by

$$E_\theta = j60I_0F_0 \frac{e^{-j\beta r}}{r} , \tag{11-41}$$

where

$$F_0 \triangleq \frac{\cos [(\beta l/2) \cos \theta] - \cos (\beta l/2)}{\sin \theta} \tag{11-42}$$

determines the relative field intensity pattern for the antenna. In order to obtain a directivity for the radiation in the equatorial plane, let us place n identical linear antennas at equal distances along the x-axis, as shown in Fig. 11–7. Let α be the phase difference between consecutive antenna currents. Thus, for the kth antenna we have $I_k = I_0e^{jk\alpha}$. The radius vector from the center of the kth antenna to a field point P in the far field is $\mathbf{r}_k = \mathbf{r} - ak\mathbf{i}_x$ and the unit normal in the (θ, ϕ) direction is

$$\mathbf{n} = \mathbf{i}_x \sin \theta \cos \phi + \mathbf{i}_y \sin \theta \sin \phi + \mathbf{i}_z \cos \theta.$$

In the far field $\mathbf{r}_k$ and $\mathbf{r}$ are parallel. Thus

$$r_k = r - ak(\mathbf{n} \cdot \mathbf{i}_x) = r - ak \sin \theta \cos \phi.$$

In the far field we use the relations

$$\frac{1}{r_k} \cong \frac{1}{r} , \qquad e^{-j\beta r_k} = e^{-j\beta r}e^{j\beta ak \sin \theta \cos \phi}$$

to obtain the resultant far-field component,

$$E_\theta = j60I_0F_0F_1 \frac{e^{-j\beta r}}{r} , \tag{11-43}$$

where

$$F_1 \triangleq \sum_{k=1}^{n} \exp [jk(\alpha + \beta a \sin \theta \cos \phi)]$$

$$= \exp\left[j\frac{n+1}{2}(\alpha + \beta a \sin \theta \cos \phi)\right] \frac{\sin (n/2)(\alpha + \beta a \sin \theta \cos \phi)}{\sin \frac{1}{2}(\alpha + \beta a \sin \theta \cos \phi)} \tag{11-44}$$

is called the *array factor*.

The average power density radiated by the array in the (θ, ϕ) direction is given by

$$P(\theta, \phi) = \frac{1}{2}\frac{|E_\theta|^2}{Z_0}r^2 = \frac{15}{\pi}|I_0F_0F_1|^2. \tag{11-45}$$

To illustrate the use of Eq. (11–45), consider the case of n half-wave antennas spaced a half-wavelength apart and with equal phasing of the currents. We have $\beta a = \pi$ and $\alpha = 0$. Thus, when we substitute these values into Eqs. (11–42) and (11–44), we obtain

$$P(\theta, \phi) = \frac{15}{\pi} |I_0|^2 \left| \frac{\cos\left[(\pi/2)\cos\theta\right]}{\sin\theta} \frac{\sin\left[(\pi n/2)\sin\theta\cos\phi\right]}{\sin\left[(\pi/2)\sin\theta\cos\phi\right]} \right|^2. \quad (11\text{–}46)$$

Figure 11–8 illustrates an equatorial plot of $P(\pi/2, \phi)$ for the case of $n = 4$. An array of this type, in which $P(\theta, \phi)$ has a maximum in a direction normal to the plane of the array, is called a *broadside array*. If $P(\theta, \phi)$ has a maximum in the plane of the array, the array is called an *end-fire array*.

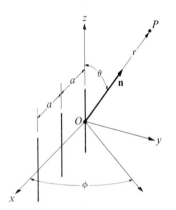
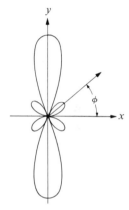

Fig. 11–7. An array of parallel linear antennas.

Fig. 11–8. The gain function of a broadside antenna.

Besides the directivity in the radiated energy, which is represented by $P(\theta, \phi)$, we are also interested in the field intensity in the far field which results from a given power input P_R. Assuming that E_1 is the value of E_θ which results when the power P_R is supplied to an isolated element of the array, we define the *gain in field intensity* by the expression

$$G_f \triangleq |E_\theta/E_1|.$$

As an example, let us determine G_f for the case of four parallel thin linear antennas which have equal input powers and equal currents. Given that R_{11} represents the radiation resistance of an isolated antenna, we have

$$|I_0| = \sqrt{\frac{2P_R}{R_{11}}} \quad \text{and} \quad |E_1| = \frac{60|F_0|}{r} \sqrt{\frac{2P_R}{R_{11}}}.$$

The four antennas in the array are considered to be excited from a common source through four transmission lines. The electromagnetic field of the transmission lines can be described in terms of phasor voltages V_k and phasor currents I_k ($k = 1, 2, 3, 4$). Since the antennas are mutually coupled through the electromagnetic field, we have a relationship of the form

$$V_k = Z_{k1}I_1 + Z_{k2}I_2 + Z_{k3}I_3 + Z_{k4}I_4, \tag{11-47}$$

where Z_{kk} is the impedance of the kth antenna and Z_{kl} ($k \neq l$) is the mutual impedance between the kth and lth antennas. These antenna impedances are measured at the input terminals to the kth antenna. When we take $I_k = I_0$ and assume that we use antenna tuning units to eliminate the reactance terms, we obtain

$$V_1 = (R_{11} + R_{12} + R_{13} + R_{14})I_0.$$

We specified that all four antennas are supplied with equal powers. Thus

$$P_R = 4(\tfrac{1}{2}V_1 I_1^*) = 2(R_{11} + R_{12} + R_{13} + R_{14})\,|I_0|^2$$

and Eq. (11-43) yields

$$|E_\theta| = \frac{60\,|I_0 F_0 F_1|}{r} = \frac{30\,|F_0 F_1|}{r}\sqrt{\frac{2P_R}{R_{11} + R_{12} + R_{13} + R_{14}}}\,.$$

The gain in field intensity is

$$G_f = \frac{|F_1|}{2}\sqrt{\frac{R_{11}}{R_{11} + R_{12} + R_{13} + R_{14}}}\,. \tag{11-48}$$

For the case of the broadside array illustrated in Fig. 11-8 we have a maximum of $F_1 = 4$ at $\phi = \pi/2$. We can compute the values of R_{kl} required in Eq. (11-48) from Eqs. (11-39) and (11-64).

11-6 SELF AND MUTUAL IMPEDANCES OF THIN LINEAR ANTENNAS; INDUCED EMF METHOD

Most transmitting antennas are excited by means of transmission lines. Suppose that P_i is the complex input power supplied to an antenna from a transmission line. We have

$$P_i = \tfrac{1}{2}Z_i\,|I_i|^2 = \tfrac{1}{2}Z_{11}\,|I_0|^2, \tag{11-49}$$

where Z_i is the *input impedance* of the antenna as seen from the transmission line terminals, $|I_i|$ is the magnitude of the peak input current, $|I_0|$ is the maximum current in the antenna, and

$$Z_{11} = R_{11} + jX_{11} \triangleq \frac{2P_i}{|I_0|^2} \tag{11-50}$$

is defined as the *self-impedance* of the antenna. It follows from Eqs. (11–26) and (11–30) that

$$X_{11} \triangleq \frac{\omega}{|I_0|^2} (W_m - W_e)$$

and that R_{11} is the radiation resistance:

$$R_{11} \triangleq \frac{2P_R}{|I_0|^2} = R. \tag{11–51}$$

If we know the current and charge distributions we can determine the field vectors from the vector and scalar potentials given by Eqs. (11–20). It is then possible to find P_R, W_m, and W_e from Eqs. (9–25b), (9–25c), and (9–25e). These quantities determine the complex power P_i from which we can find Z_{11}. However, to evaluate the volume integrals which give W_m and W_e is a formidable task even when we know the current distribution. The problem is further complicated by the fact that the current distribution is determined by the solution of a boundary-value problem. Equation (11–50) is therefore of little practical use for determining the self-impedance of an antenna. An alternative approach based on Eq. (11–31) is, however, possible. We assume a current distribution which approximates that found in real antennas. For thin linear antennas, it is known that a sinusoidal distribution is a good approximation. The assumed current distribution will not, in general, satisfy the boundary conditions. We must therefore postulate its existence in the form of current filaments in free space held together by mechanical forces. These mechanical forces also supply the complex power to the field, P_{mech}. For the thin linear antenna the computation of P_{mech} by means of Eq. (11–29) is readily carried out. The self-impedance can then be found by using Eq. (11–31):

$$Z_{11} \cong \frac{2P_{\text{mech}}}{|I_0|^2} = \int_{v_g} - \frac{\mathbf{E}}{I_0} \cdot \left(\frac{\mathbf{J}}{I_0}\right)^* dv. \tag{11–52}$$

This method for finding Z_{11} is known as the *induced emf method*, since there is a nonzero tangential component of $\mathbf{E}$ along the antenna axis. However, it is important to note that Eq. (11–52) applies only to the case of current filaments in free space which are not constrained in any manner by boundary conditions. The electromagnetic forces which act on the current filament are compensated for by distributed mechanical forces.

In order to use Eq. (11–52) to determine the self-impedance, we must evaluate the induced electric field intensity along the axis of the assumed current filament. Let us first consider the thin linear antenna illustrated in Fig. 11–9 and take the current distribution to be given by

$$I = I_0 \sin \beta u, \qquad 0 \leq u \leq l/2.$$

The linear charge density along the filament is determined by Eq. (11–32):

$$q = \frac{j\beta I_0}{\omega} \cos \beta u.$$

Noting that

$$\rho \, dv = q \, du, \qquad \mathbf{J} \, dv = \mathbf{i}_z I \, du,$$

we find from Eqs. (11–20) that the phasor vector potential, $\mathbf{A} = \mathbf{i}_z A_z$, is determined by

$$A_z = \frac{\mu_0 I_0}{4\pi} \int_0^{l/2} \frac{e^{-j\beta r}}{r} \sin \beta u \, du$$

and that the phasor scalar potential is

$$U = \frac{j I_0 \beta}{8\pi\varepsilon_0\omega} \int_0^{l/2} \left[\frac{e^{-j\beta(r-u)}}{r} + \frac{e^{-j\beta(r+u)}}{r} \right] du,$$

where $r^2 = x^2 + (z - u)^2$. The z-component of $\mathbf{E}$ is determined by the equation

$$E_z = -j\omega A_z - \frac{\partial U}{\partial z}. \qquad (11\text{–}53)$$

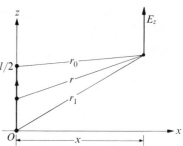

Fig. 11–9. The electric field intensity of a thin linear antenna.

The integrals for A_z and U appear formidable. However, we shall see that they need not be evaluated and that E_z can be found by a simple integration by parts. When we note that

$$\frac{\partial}{\partial z}\left(\frac{e^{-j\beta(r-u)}}{r} \right) = e^{j\beta u} \frac{\partial}{\partial z}\left(\frac{e^{-j\beta r}}{r} \right) = -e^{j\beta u} \frac{\partial}{\partial u}\left(\frac{e^{-j\beta r}}{r} \right),$$

we obtain

$$-\frac{\partial U}{\partial z} = \frac{j I_0 \beta}{8\pi\varepsilon_0\omega} \int_0^{l/2} \left[e^{j\beta u} \frac{\partial}{\partial u}\left(\frac{e^{-j\beta r}}{r} \right) + e^{-j\beta u} \frac{\partial}{\partial u}\left(\frac{e^{-j\beta r}}{r} \right) \right] du.$$

Integrating by parts and substituting

$$\beta/\varepsilon_0\omega = Z_0 = 120\pi, \qquad \beta^2/\varepsilon_0\omega = \mu_0\omega,$$

yields

$$-\frac{\partial U}{\partial z} = j30 I_0 \left(\cos \frac{\beta l}{2} \frac{e^{-j\beta r_0}}{r_0} - \frac{e^{-j\beta r_1}}{r_1} \right) + \frac{j I_0 \mu_0 \omega}{4\pi} \int_0^{l/2} \frac{e^{-j\beta r}}{r} \sin \beta u \, du.$$

The integral in the above expression is $j\omega A_z$. Thus we find from Eq. (11–53) that

$$E_z = j30 I_0 \left(\cos \frac{\beta l}{2} \frac{e^{-j\beta r_0}}{r_0} - \frac{e^{-j\beta r_1}}{r_1} \right). \qquad (11\text{–}54)$$

We shall now use Eq. (11–54) to determine the z-component of $\mathbf{E}$ for the thin linear antenna illustrated in Fig. 11–10. The current distribution is taken to be that given by Eq. (11–33). Applying Eq. (11–54) to both halves of the antenna (note that we must change the sign of both I_0 and E_z for the lower half) and adding the two results yields

$$E_z = -j30I_0 \left(\frac{e^{-j\beta r_2}}{r_2} + \frac{e^{-j\beta r_1}}{r_1} - 2 \cos \frac{\beta l}{2} \frac{e^{-j\beta r_0}}{r_0} \right). \tag{11–55}$$

Substituting $x = 0$ into Eq. (11–55) yields the tangential component of electric field intensity along the current filament. We see that $E_z \neq 0$ along the antenna. Thus the expression for E_z cannot satisfy the boundary condition $E_z = 0$ for a perfectly conducting antenna. However, for the current filament the effect of E_z is compensated for by distributed mechanical forces. The complex mechanical power input to the antenna (see Eq. 11–29) is

$$P_{\text{mech}} = \tfrac{1}{2} \int_{-l/2}^{l/2} -E_z I^* \, dz = \int_0^{l/2} - E_z I^* \, dz$$

and Eq. (11–52) yields

$$Z_{11} \cong 2 \int_0^{l/2} - \frac{E_z}{I_0} \left(\frac{I}{I_0} \right)^* dz. \tag{11–56}$$

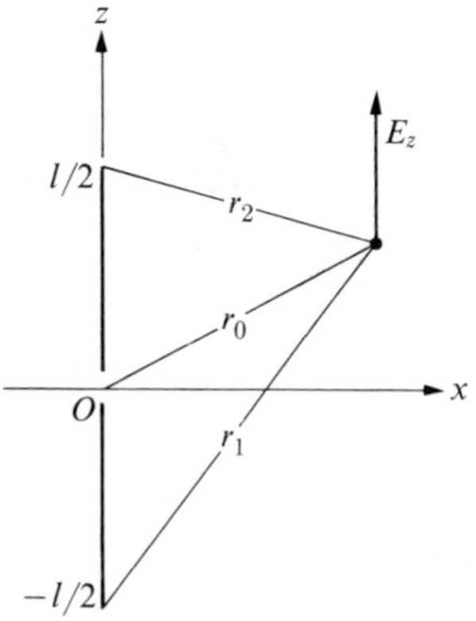

Fig. 11–10. The electric field intensity of a symmetrical thin linear antenna.

Substituting Eqs. (11–33) and (11–55) into Eq. (11–56) and evaluating the integrals yields Z_{11}. For an infinitely thin linear antenna we find that X_{11} is infinite. Thus, in order to evaluate X_{11}, we must take account of the finite radius of an antenna. However, R_{11} is finite and is given by the expression

$$R_{11} = 2\text{Re} \left[\int_0^{l/2} - \left(\frac{E_z}{I_0} \right) \left(\frac{I}{I_0} \right)^* dz \right]$$

$$= 60 \int_0^{l/2} \left(\frac{\sin \beta r_2}{r_2} + \frac{\sin \beta r_1}{r_1} - 2 \cos \frac{\beta l}{2} \frac{\sin \beta r_0}{r_0} \right) \sin \beta \left(\frac{l}{2} - z \right) dz.$$

In order to evaluate the integral we let $k \triangleq \beta l/2$ and substitute

$$u = \beta r_2 = \beta \left(\frac{l}{2} - z \right), \qquad u = \beta r_1 = \beta \left(\frac{l}{2} + z \right), \qquad u = \beta r_0 = \beta z,$$

which results in three integrals:

$$I_1 \triangleq 2 \int_0^k \frac{\sin^2 u}{u} \, du = \text{Cin } 2k,$$

$$I_2 \triangleq 2 \int_k^{2k} \frac{\sin u \sin (2k - u)}{u} \, du = \sin 2k[\text{Si } (4k) - \text{Si } (2k)]$$

$$- \cos 2k[\text{Cin } (4k) - \text{Cin } (2k)],$$

$$I_3 \triangleq -2 \cos k \int_0^k \frac{\sin u \sin (k - u)}{u} \, du$$

$$= -\sin 2k \, \text{Si } (2k) + (1 + \cos 2k) \, \text{Cin } 2k.$$

Thus $R_{11} = 30(I_1 + I_2 + I_3)$, and the resulting expression is identical to the radiation resistance R given by Eq. (11–39). This is a consequence of the fact that the current distributions are the same, so that the real powers radiated must be the same:

$$\text{Re } [P_i] = P_R = \tfrac{1}{2} |I_0|^2 R = \text{Re } [P_{\text{mech}}] = \tfrac{1}{2} |I_0|^2 R_{11}.$$

In the case of two or more antennas there is a mutual coupling through the electromagnetic field which affects the antenna impedances. A transmission-line representation for the coupling between two antennas takes the form

$$V_1 = Z_{11}I_{10} + Z_{12}I_{20}, \qquad V_2 = Z_{21}I_{10} + Z_{22}I_{20}. \tag{11–57}$$

Here we take Z_{kk} as the self-impedance and $|I_{k0}|$ as the maximum current of the kth antenna ($k = 1, 2$). It is shown in Section 11–8 that the mutual impedances Z_{12} and Z_{21} satisfy the reciprocity relation

$$Z_{12} = Z_{21}. \tag{11–58}$$

When we apply Eqs. (11–57) to two coupled antennas the question arises as to what meaning can be assigned to the phasor voltages V_1 and V_2. This question is answered by considering the complex power input to the electromagnetic field and evaluating the antenna impedances. We require that

$$P_i = \tfrac{1}{2}V_1I_{10}^* + \tfrac{1}{2}V_2I_{20}^* = \tfrac{1}{2}Z_{11} |I_{10}|^2 + \tfrac{1}{2}Z_{12}(I_{10}^*I_{20} + I_{10}I_{20}^*)$$

$$+ \tfrac{1}{2}Z_{22} |I_{20}|^2. \tag{11–59}$$

We can find the complex power input from Eq. (11–30) by determining the field vectors from the antenna currents and then evaluating W_m, W_e, and P_R (see Eqs. 9–25b and 9–25c). By comparing terms with corresponding subscripts, we can obtain formulas for Z_{11}, Z_{12}, and Z_{22}. However, the expressions obtained for the impedances are extremely difficult to evaluate. We can, however, proceed as we did in the case of a single antenna and postulate the existence of current filaments driven by mechanical forces. If the assumed current distribution approximates that of the conducting antennas, the corresponding field vectors and hence W_m, W_e, and P_R for the two fields will be approximately the same. We may then again use Eq. (11–31). Thus, if $\mathbf{E}_k$ is the electric field intensity due to $\mathbf{J}_k$ ($k = 1, 2$), we have

$$P_i \cong P_{\text{mech}} = \tfrac{1}{2}\int_{v_{g1}} (\mathbf{E}_1 + \mathbf{E}_2) \cdot (-\mathbf{J}_1^*) \, dv + \tfrac{1}{2}\int_{v_{g2}} (\mathbf{E}_1 + \mathbf{E}_2) \cdot (-\mathbf{J}_2^*) \, dv,$$

$$(11\text{–}60)$$

where the integrals are taken over the assumed current filaments. Comparing corresponding terms of Eqs. (11–59) and (11–60) yields

$$Z_{12}(I_{10}^* I_{20} + I_{10} I_{20}^*) \cong \int_{v_{g1}} -\mathbf{E}_2 \cdot \mathbf{J}_1^* \, dv + \int_{v_{g2}} -\mathbf{E}_1 \cdot \mathbf{J}_2^* \, dv. \quad (11\text{–}61)$$

It is left as an exercise to prove the reciprocity relation

$$\int_v \mathbf{E}_2 \cdot \mathbf{J}_1 \, dv = \int_v \mathbf{E}_1 \cdot \mathbf{J}_2 \, dv. \qquad (11\text{–}62)$$

Thus if we assume a real current distribution for $\mathbf{J}_1$ and $\mathbf{J}_2$ and make use of the reciprocity relation, we obtain

$$Z_{12} \cong \int_{v_{g2}} -\left(\frac{\mathbf{E}_1}{I_{10}}\right) \cdot \left(\frac{\mathbf{J}_2}{I_{20}}\right) dv.$$

$$(11\text{–}63)$$

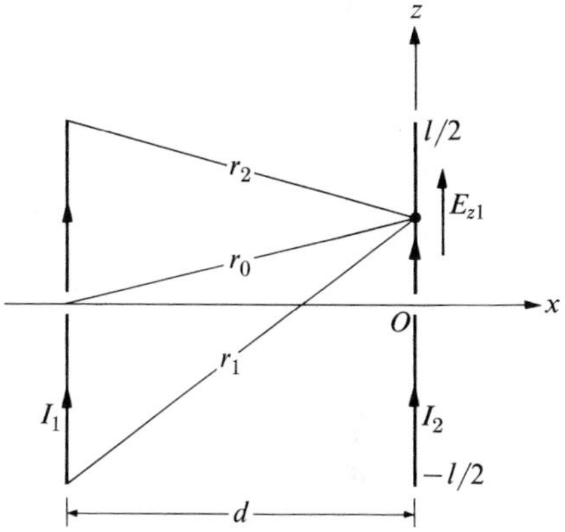

Fig. 11–11. The mutual impedance of two parallel thin linear antennas.

Let us now apply Eq. (11–63) to the case of two parallel thin linear antennas (Fig. 11–11). The current distribution in both antennas is taken to have the form given by Eq. (11–33), where we now introduce subscripts 1 and 2 which correspond to the respective antennas. Applying Eq. (11–63) to the case of a thin antenna and substituting Eqs. (11–33) and (11–55) yields

$$Z_{21} = Z_{12} = j60 \int_0^{l/2} \left(\frac{e^{-j\beta r_2}}{r_2} + \frac{e^{-j\beta r_1}}{r_1} - 2\cos\frac{\beta l}{2}\frac{e^{-j\beta r_0}}{r_0}\right) \sin \beta(l/2 - z) \, dz,$$

where $r_0^2 = d^2 + z^2$, $r_1^2 = d^2 + (l/2 + z)^2$, and $r_2^2 = d^2 + (l/2 - z)^2$. In order to evaluate the integral we express the sine functions in exponential form. The integrand will then consist of six terms which results in six separate integrals. The first integral,

$$I_1 \triangleq 30 \int_0^{l/2} \frac{e^{-j\beta(r_2+z-l/2)}}{r_2} \, dz,$$

can be evaluated by the substitution $u = \beta(r_2 + z - l/2)$, which yields $du/dz = u/r_2$. Thus

$$I_1 = 30 \int_{u_1}^{u_2} \frac{e^{-ju}}{u} \, du = 30 \, (\text{Ci } u - j \, \text{Si } u)_{u_1}^{u_2},$$

where the lower limit u_1 corresponds to $z = 0$ and the upper limit corresponds to $z = l/2$. The remaining integrals are of similar form and can be evaluated by similar substitutions. Taking the real and imaginary parts of Z_{12} yields

$$R_{12}/30 = \sin \beta l (\text{Si } x_2 - \text{Si } x_1 - 2 \, \text{Si } y_2 + 2 \, \text{Si } y_1)$$
$$- \cos \beta l (2 \, \text{Ci } y_2 + 2 \, \text{Ci } y_1 - 2 \, \text{Ci } x_0 - \text{Ci } x_2 - \text{Ci } x_1)$$
$$- 2(\text{Ci } y_2 + \text{Ci } y_1 - 2 \, \text{Ci } x_0),$$

$$X_{12}/30 = -\sin \beta l (2 \, \text{Ci } y_2 - 2 \, \text{Ci } y_1 + \text{Ci } x_1 - \text{Ci } x_2)$$
$$- \cos \beta l (\text{Si } x_2 + \text{Si } x_1 + 2 \, \text{Si } x_0 - 2 \, \text{Si } y_1 - 2 \, \text{Si } y_2)$$
$$+ 2(\text{Si } y_2 + \text{Si } y_1 - 2 \, \text{Si } x_0), \quad (11\text{–}64)$$

where

$$x_0 = \beta d,$$
$$x_1 = \beta(\sqrt{d^2 + l^2} - l), \qquad x_2 = \beta(\sqrt{d^2 + l^2} + l),$$
$$y_1 = \beta[\sqrt{d^2 + (l/2)^2} - l/2], \qquad y_2 = \beta[\sqrt{d^2 + (l/2)^2} + l/2].$$

Figure 11–12 shows a plot of R_{12} and X_{12} for parallel half-wave antennas [3].

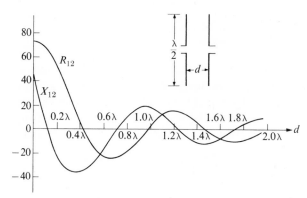

Fig. 11–12. The mutual impedance $Z_{12} = R_{12} + jX_{12}$ of parallel half-wave thin linear antennas.

11-7 THE INPUT IMPEDANCE OF CONDUCTING ANTENNAS

Most conducting antennas are driven from an open-wire or coaxial transmission line by means of a *TEM* wave. We can determine the input impedance of the antenna experimentally by measuring the standing-wave ratio and the position of the maxima and minima of the *TEM* field (see Section 9–6). From these measurements, we determine the reflection coefficient Γ and the normalized impedance ζ, where $\zeta = (1 + \Gamma)/(1 - \Gamma)$. The input impedance of the antenna is then defined by the equation

$$Z_i \triangleq \zeta Z_0, \tag{11-65}$$

where Z_0 is the characteristic impedance of the transmission line.

In order to determine Z_i analytically, we must first determine the complex power P_i supplied to the antenna. We can then define the input impedance by the equation

$$Z_i \triangleq \frac{2P_i}{|I_i|^2}, \tag{11-66}$$

and the phasor input voltage by the equation $V_i \triangleq Z_i I_i$, where I_i is the phasor input current. From the discussion given in Section 9–6, we can see that the definitions of Z_i given by Eqs. (11–65) and (11–66) are identical.

We shall discuss the case of a thin linear antenna driven by a two-wire transmission line (the same results apply in the case of a coaxial cable). Let the electric field intensities resulting from the charges and currents on the antenna and transmission line be $\mathbf{E}_a$ and $\mathbf{E}_i$, respectively, and let the surface current density on the perfectly conducting antenna surface be $\mathbf{J}_s$. The boundary condition at the antenna surface is $(\mathbf{E}_a + \mathbf{E}_i) \cdot \mathbf{J}_s = 0$. We may consider the field $\mathbf{E}_i$ of the transmission line as an impressed field which excites the antenna. The complex power input to the antenna is then

$$P_i = \tfrac{1}{2}\int_S \mathbf{E}_i \cdot \mathbf{J}_s^* \, ds = \tfrac{1}{2}\int_S -\mathbf{E}_a \cdot \mathbf{J}_s^* \, ds, \tag{11-67}$$

where S represents the antenna surface. For a fixed position at $z = a$ on the antenna (see Fig. 11–13), we have

$$\lim_{b \to 0} \mathbf{E}_i(a) = 0, \tag{11-68}$$

where $2b$ is the transmission-line spacing. We find from Eq. (11–67), as $b \to 0$ and when we take $J_s(0) \, ds = I_i \, dz$, that

$$P_i \cong \tfrac{1}{2} I_i^* \int_S E_i \, dz \cong \tfrac{1}{2} I_1^* \int_{P_1}^{P_2} E_i \, dr = \tfrac{1}{2} V_1 I_1^*.$$

To understand the evaluation of the above integral, note that due to the condition (11–68) the contribution to the value of the integral comes mainly from the region $b \leqq z \leqq a$ (we shall designate this region the transition region). For a *TEM* mode on the transmission line we have $|r^2 E_i| \leqq b^2 M$ for $r \gg b$, where M is a positive constant. Thus, as $b \to 0$, we can extend the range of integration along the antenna axis and then along a semicircle in the transverse plane. This results in a continuous path of integration from P_1 to P_2. For a *TEM* mode the value of the integral is independent of the path in the transverse plane and is equal to the scalar potential difference of the transmission line (see Eq. 10–26). When $b \to 0$ we can evaluate the electromagnetic fields of the transmission line and antenna separately and it is then possible to distinguish between the electromagnetic energy in the antenna field and the electromagnetic energy associated with the transmission line (it is otherwise not possible to define an impedance for the antenna alone). The field vectors $\mathbf{E}_a$ and $\mathbf{H}_a$ for the antenna are found from the charge and current distribution on the antenna and the quantities W_m, W_e, and P_R for the antenna can then be evaluated. However, this approach in determining P_i is not advisable, since the volume integrals are extremely difficult to evaluate. We shall therefore derive an alternative expression for P_i. The possibility of an alternative expression not involving volume integrals over an infinite space can be seen from Eqs. (5–8) and (7–24), where the static electric and magnetic field energies are expressed in terms of the sources of the field. We shall therefore investigate the relationship between P_i and the charge and current distribution on the antenna surface.

When $b \to 0$, the difference in the scalar potential of the conductors as measured at a terminal plane T (see Fig. 11–13) is determined entirely by the charges on the transmission line. This follows from the fact that the scalar potential U_a due to the charges on the antenna is a continuous function of position, so that

$$\lim_{b \to 0} [U_a(P_1) - U_a(P_2)] = 0.$$

We shall consider the limiting case as $b \to 0$, so that we have

$$V = U(P_1) - U(P_2),$$

where V is the phasor voltage for the *TEM* wave on the transmission line (see Eq. 10–26). The complex power supplied by the transmission line at the terminal plane T is

$$P = \tfrac{1}{2} V I^*,$$

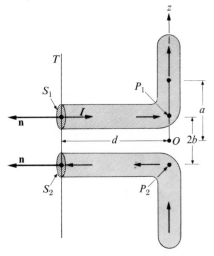

Fig. 11–13. An antenna driven by a two-wire transmission line.

and if the distance d to the antenna terminals is small we have $P_i = \tfrac{1}{2}V_iI_i^*$. Let us now consider the equation

$$\mathbf{E} \cdot \mathbf{J}^* = (-j\omega\mathbf{A} - \operatorname{grad} U) \cdot \mathbf{J}^*.$$

With the aid of the equation of continuity, we obtain

$$\nabla \cdot (U\mathbf{J}^*) = U \operatorname{div} \mathbf{J}^* + \mathbf{J}^* \cdot \operatorname{grad} U = j\omega U\rho^* + \mathbf{J}^* \cdot \operatorname{grad} U.$$

Thus

$$-\mathbf{E} \cdot \mathbf{J}^* = j\omega(\mathbf{A} \cdot \mathbf{J}^* - U\rho^*) + \operatorname{div}(U\mathbf{J}^*).$$

Integrating over the volume v bounded by the terminal plane T and the antenna and transmission line surfaces yields

$$\int_v - \mathbf{E} \cdot \mathbf{J}^* \, dv = j\omega \int_v (\mathbf{A} \cdot \mathbf{J}^* - U\rho^*) \, dv + \int_{S_1+S_2} U\mathbf{J}^* \cdot \mathbf{n} \, ds. \quad (11\text{–}69)$$

(Note that $\mathbf{J} \cdot \mathbf{n} = 0$ everywhere except over the areas S_1 and S_2 in the terminal plane.) When the radius of the transmission-line conductors is negligible we can take $U = U(P_1)$ to be constant over S_1 and take $U = U(P_2)$ to be constant over S_2. We then have

$$-V_iI_i^* = \int_{S_1+S_2} U\mathbf{J}^* \cdot \mathbf{n} \, ds,$$

and if ohmic losses are present Eq. (11–69) takes the form

$$P_i = \tfrac{1}{2}V_iI_i^* = \frac{j\omega}{2}\int_v (\mathbf{A} \cdot \mathbf{J}^* - U\rho^*) \, dv + \tfrac{1}{2}\int_v \frac{|J|^2}{\sigma} \, dv, \quad (11\text{–}70)$$

where P_i is the complex power supplied by the transmission line at the antenna terminals. In the case of perfect conductors we set †

$$\rho \, dv = \sigma_s \, ds, \qquad \mathbf{J} \, dv = \mathbf{J}_s \, ds,$$

where σ_s is the surface charge density. Equation (11–70) then takes the form (see Eq. 11–67)

$$P_i = \tfrac{1}{2}\int_S - \mathbf{E}_a \cdot \mathbf{J}_s^* \, ds = \frac{j\omega}{2}\int_S (\mathbf{A} \cdot \mathbf{J}_s^* - U\sigma_s^*) \, ds. \quad (11\text{–}71)$$

Equation (11–71) can be used to evaluate the input impedance of a perfectly conducting antenna. The boundary-value problem,

$$\mathbf{J}_s \cdot \mathbf{E}_a = 0, \qquad a \leq z \leq l/2, \quad (11\text{–}72)$$

must first be solved and the form of the current distribution determined. [Note that since the impressed field $\mathbf{E}_i$ is not initially known, we cannot determine the current distribution in the transition range $b \leq z \leq a$ and

---

† We use the subscript s to distinguish the surface charge density σ_s from the conductivity σ.

that condition (11–68) requires a to be fixed in order that Eq. (11–72) hold. After we have taken the limit as $b \to 0$ and determined the current distribution, we may then take the limit as $a \to 0$.] Only the form of the current distribution is determined by the solution of the boundary-value problem, so that we must choose an arbitrary value I_i for the input current. From a physical point of view I_i is determined by specifying the real power P_R radiated by the antenna. Once we know the current and charge distributions, we can then evaluate $\mathbf{A}$ and U on the antenna surface. We can then determine the complex input power by evaluating the right-hand integral in Eq. (11–71). It is important to note that since the range of integration for the left-hand integral in Eq. (11–67) is over the transition region where neither $\mathbf{E}_i$ or $\mathbf{J}_s$ are known, we cannot determine P_i from this equation.

In many cases it is convenient for computational reasons to assume a current distribution and consider that the complex power is supplied by distributed mechanical sources. There is then no transmission line or terminal plane and Eq. (11–69) then takes the form

$$P_{\text{mech}} = \tfrac{1}{2} \int_S - \mathbf{E} \cdot \mathbf{J}_s^* \, ds = \frac{j\omega}{2} \int_v (\mathbf{A} \cdot \mathbf{J}_s^* - U\sigma_s^*) \, ds. \quad (11\text{–}73)$$

We saw in Section 11–6 that by assuming a suitable distribution of current (usually sinusoidal) we can evaluate the left-hand integral in Eq. (11–73). If the assumed current distribution does not differ significantly from the current distribution obtained by solving the boundary-value problem, we can make use of Eq. (11–31) to obtain an approximate expression for the input impedance:

$$Z_i = R + jX \triangleq \frac{2P_i}{|I_i|^2} \simeq \frac{2P_{\text{mech}}}{|I_i|^2}.$$

At low frequencies $\mathbf{A} \cdot \mathbf{J}^*$ and $U\rho^*$ are both real; we then have (see Eqs. 5–8 and 7–24)

$$W_m = \tfrac{1}{2} \int_v \mathbf{A} \cdot \mathbf{J}^* \, dv = \tfrac{1}{2} L |I_i|^2, \quad (11\text{–}74a)$$

$$W_e = \tfrac{1}{2} \int_v U\rho^* \, dv = \frac{1}{2\omega^2 C} |I_i|^2, \quad (11\text{–}74b)$$

where W_m and W_e are the peak magnetic and electric field energies, respectively. By means of Eqs. (11–74) we can compute the inductance L and capacitance C associated with the field. Note that we have already made use of Eq. (11–71) to compute the inductance and capacitance of conductor configurations at low frequencies.

A question of philosophical interest arises as to what occurs if we should happen to assume the correct current distribution in evaluating P_{mech} from Eq. (11–73). In such a case the integrals given in Eqs. (11–71) and (11–73) are identical. The integrals on the right-hand sides of these equations are taken over a region which is outside the transition region, while the integrals on the left-hand sides are taken over the transition region. If we assume the correct current distribution, the right-hand integrals are identically equal. The left-hand integrals are equal because the effect of the distributed mechanical forces is exactly the same as the effect of the impressed field, E_i, due to the transmission line. In effect, then, if we happen to assume the correct current distribution, there is then no difference between Eqs. (11–71) and (11–73).

In this case, we must use the right-hand side of Eq. (11–71) to evaluate $P_i = P_{\text{mech}}$. The left-hand sides of Eqs. (11–71) and (11–73) cannot be used, since in the transition region the electric field intensity, in the limit as $b \to 0$, is due entirely to the transmission line. The current distribution on the transmission line can be found only after P_i is known. We see that a peculiar compromise must be made in the assumed current distribution in order that Eq. (11–31) prove useful in a simple approximate evaluation of P_i. If the assumed current distribution J_s matches the actual current distribution too closely, then the left-hand integral in Eq. (11–73) cannot be accurately evaluated, since $E \cdot J_s = 0$ over most of the antenna except in the transition region where E is not known. On the other hand, if the assumed current distribution is not a reasonable approximation to the actual current distribution, then Eq. (11–31) will no longer hold. In order for Eq. (11–31) to be applicable there must be a current distribution which is a reasonable approximation to the actual current distribution and for which the transition region has negligible effect on P_{mech}. It is a fortunate circumstance that a sinusoidal current distribution meets these conflicting requirements. We have seen that, for thin linear antennas and for a sinusoidal current distribution, we can derive analytic expressions for antenna impedances. These expressions are approximate. However, they are useful in interpreting and understanding the loading effect of mutually coupled antennas on transmission lines.

To illustrate the distinction between mechanical and electric sources of power, let us compute the complex input power for a thin lossless conducting loop at low frequencies (Fig. 11–14). For a thin loop we can set

$$J \, dv = I \, d\mathbf{r}, \qquad \rho \, dv = q \, dr$$

where I is the total current and q the linear charge density. At low frequencies, $\beta r \ll 1$, and we can set

$$\frac{e^{-j\beta r}}{r} \cong \frac{1}{r} - j\beta.$$

To avoid solving the boundary-value problem we can postulate the existence of a current filament and assume that $I = I_0$ is uniform along the filament.

Thus $q = 0$ and we have

$$\mathbf{E}_2 = -j\omega\mathbf{A}_2 = -j\frac{\omega\mu_0 I_0}{4\pi}\oint_C \frac{d\mathbf{r}_1}{r_{12}}.$$

The complex mechanical power input to the filament is

$$P_{\text{mech}} = \tfrac{1}{2}\oint_C -\mathbf{E}_2\cdot I_0^*\,d\mathbf{r}_2 = \frac{j\omega L}{2}|I_0|^2$$

where

$$L \triangleq \frac{\mu_0}{4\pi}\oint_C \oint_C \frac{d\mathbf{r}_1\cdot d\mathbf{r}_2}{r_{12}}.$$

We have thus, by this approach, obtained Neumann's formula for the inductance of a current loop.

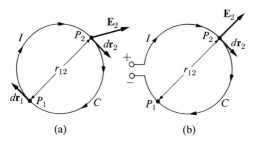

Fig. 11–14. Sources of complex power of a thin loop: (a) mechanical, (b) electrical.

In the case illustrated in Fig. 11–14b the complex input power to the perfectly conducting loop is supplied by a closely spaced transmission line. The boundary-value problem must be solved to determine the current distribution. This has the form $I = I_0(1 + \delta)$, where δ is the deviation from a uniform distribution. At low frequencies it is known that $|\delta| \ll 1$. The linear charge density q is proportional to δ, so that the product Uq^* is a quantity of higher order and can be neglected. We have, at the field point P_2,

$$\mathbf{A}_2 I_2^* \cong \frac{\mu_0 |I_0|^2}{4\pi}\oint_C \frac{1 + \delta_1 + \delta_2^*}{r_{12}}\,d\mathbf{r}_1.$$

Thus substituting into Eq. (11–71) yields

$$P_i = \frac{j\omega L}{2}|I_0|^2 + \frac{j\omega\mu_0 |I_0|^2}{4\pi}\oint_C \oint_C \frac{\delta_1 + \delta_2^*}{r_{12}}d\mathbf{r}_1\cdot d\mathbf{r}_2.$$

Since $|\delta| \ll 1$, we see that $P_{\text{mech}} \cong P_i$. It is evident that the approximate computation of L using mechanical sources is simpler.

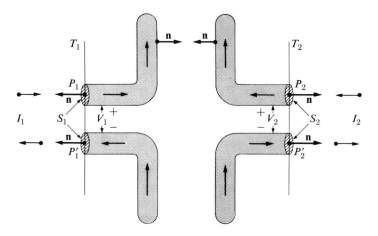

Fig. 11–15. The reciprocity relation of coupled antennas.

11-8 MUTUAL IMPEDANCE OF CONDUCTING ANTENNAS

It is possible to generalize Eq. (11–71) so that it applies to the case of coupled antennas. We shall discuss the case illustrated in Fig. 11–15, in which two conducting antennas are driven by two separate transmission lines. We take the spacing between the transmission-line conductors to be infinitesimally small so that the scalar potential difference between the conductors at the terminal planes T_1 and T_2 are due entirely to the charges on the transmission lines. We shall first prove a reciprocity theorem, from which we can derive the reciprocity relation (11–58). Let $\mathbf{A}$, U represent the potentials due to an excitation at terminal T_1 with an open circuit ($I_2 = 0$) at terminal T_2, and let $\mathbf{A}'$, U' represent the potentials due to an excitation at terminal T_2 with an open circuit ($I_1 = 0$) at terminal T_1. The proof of the reciprocity theorem is based on the vector identity

$$\mathbf{E} \cdot \mathbf{J}' - \mathbf{E}' \cdot \mathbf{J} = j\omega(\mathbf{A}' \cdot \mathbf{J} - \mathbf{A} \cdot \mathbf{J}') - \mathbf{J}' \cdot \operatorname{grad} U + \mathbf{J} \cdot \operatorname{grad} U'$$

$$= j\omega(\mathbf{A}' \cdot \mathbf{J} - \mathbf{A} \cdot \mathbf{J}') + U'\rho - U\rho') + \operatorname{div}(U'\mathbf{J} - U\mathbf{J}'),$$

where we have introduced the equation of continuity. Integrating this expression over the conductor volume v bounded by the terminal planes and the transmission line and antenna surfaces and applying the divergence theorem to the last term yields

$$\int_v (\mathbf{E} \cdot \mathbf{J}' - \mathbf{E}' \cdot \mathbf{J})\, dv = j\omega \int_v (\mathbf{A}' \cdot \mathbf{J} - \mathbf{A} \cdot \mathbf{J}' + U'\rho - U\rho')\, dv$$

$$+ \int_{S_1 + S_2} (U'\mathbf{J} - U\mathbf{J}') \cdot \mathbf{n}\, ds. \quad (11\text{–}75)$$

We note that

$$\int_v \mathbf{A}' \cdot \mathbf{J}\, dv = \int_v \left(\frac{\mu_0}{4\pi} \int_v \frac{\mathbf{J}' e^{-j\beta r}}{r}\, dv_1\right) \cdot \mathbf{J}\, dv_2$$

$$= \int_v \left(\frac{\mu_0}{4\pi} \int_v \frac{\mathbf{J} e^{-j\beta r}}{r}\, dv_2\right) \cdot \mathbf{J}'\, dv_1 = \int_v \mathbf{A} \cdot \mathbf{J}'\, dv.$$

Similarly, we find that

$$\int_v U' \rho\, dv = \int_v U \rho'\, dv.$$

Thus the first integral on the right-hand side of Eq. (11–75) vanishes.

If we apply Eq. (11–75) to the case of perfectly conducting antennas, we must replace the volume distribution of current by a surface distribution. Due to the boundary conditions, $\mathbf{E} \cdot \mathbf{J}'_s = 0$, $\mathbf{E}' \cdot \mathbf{J}_s = 0$, the integral on the left-hand side of the equation vanishes. For convenience in evaluating the remaining surface integral we still consider the current as distributed over a shell-like volume embedded in the conductor surface. Due to the open-circuit constraints we have the following conditions:

$$J'(P_1) = J'(P_1') = 0 \quad \text{on } S_1, \qquad J(P_2) = J(P_2') = 0 \quad \text{on } S_2.$$

Thus Eq. (11–75) yields

$$0 = \int_{S_1} (U'\mathbf{J}) \cdot \mathbf{n}\, ds - \int_{S_2} (U\mathbf{J}') \cdot \mathbf{n}\, ds = -V_1[I_1]_{I_2=0} + V_2[I_2]_{I_1=0}, \quad (11\text{–}76)$$

where

$$V_1 \triangleq U'(P_1) - U'(P_1'), \qquad V_2 \triangleq U(P_2) - U(P_2').$$

Equation (11–76) can be written in the form

$$\left(\frac{V_1}{I_2}\right)_{I_1=0} = \left(\frac{V_2}{I_1}\right)_{I_2=0},$$

which is known as the *reciprocity theorem*.

The voltage and current relations at the terminal planes can be represented by transmission-line equations of the form

$$V_1 = z_{11}I_1 + z_{12}I_2, \qquad V_2 = z_{21}I_1 + z_{22}I_2.$$

It follows from the reciprocity theorem that

$$z_{12} = z_{21}. \qquad (11\text{–}77)$$

Here the z_{kl} are impedances seen at the transmission-line terminals. The antenna impedances Z_{kl} given in Eq. (11–57) are defined in terms of the maximum antenna currents I_{k0} and are related to the z_{kl} by the equations $I_k z_{kl} = I_{k0} Z_{kl}$. Thus Eq. (11–58) follows immediately from Eq. (11–77).

Let us now consider the complex input power due to simultaneous excitation at both terminals. When we let $\mathbf{A} = \mathbf{A}_1$, $\mathbf{A}' = \mathbf{A}_2$, $\mathbf{J}_s = \mathbf{J}_{s1}$, and $\mathbf{J}'_s = \mathbf{J}_{s2}$, so that the resultant vector potential is $\mathbf{A}_1 + \mathbf{A}_2$ and the resultant surface current density is $\mathbf{J}_{s1} + \mathbf{J}_{s2}$, we obtain from Eq. (11–71)

$$
\begin{aligned}
\tfrac{1}{2}V_1 I_1^* + \tfrac{1}{2}V_2 I_2^* &= \tfrac{1}{2}z_{11}|I_1|^2 + \tfrac{1}{2}z_{12}(I_1^* I_2 + I_1 I_2^*) + \tfrac{1}{2}z_{22}|I_2|^2 \\
&= \frac{j\omega}{2}\int_S [(\mathbf{A}_1 + \mathbf{A}_2)\cdot(\mathbf{J}_{s1} + \mathbf{J}_{s2})^* \\
&\quad - (U_1 + U_2)(\sigma_{s1} + \sigma_{s2})^*]ds.
\end{aligned}
$$

The self-impedance at the input terminals of a single antenna has been defined in terms of Eq. (11–71). For coupled antennas the input self-impedances are

$$
z_{kk} \triangleq \frac{j\omega}{|I_k|^2}\int_S (\mathbf{A}_k \cdot \mathbf{J}_{sk}^* - U_k \sigma_{sk}^*)\, ds. \tag{11–78}
$$

It is a consequence of Eqs. (11–77) and (11–78) that the mutual impedance at the input must be taken as

$$
z_{12} \triangleq \frac{j\omega}{I_1 I_2^* + I_1^* I_2}\int_S (\mathbf{A}_1 \cdot \mathbf{J}_{s2}^* + \mathbf{A}_2 \cdot \mathbf{J}_{s1}^* - U_1 \sigma_{s2}^* - U_2 \sigma_{s1}^*)\, ds. \tag{11–79}
$$

We have seen how we can evaluate the integral in Eq. (11–78) approximately by assuming a current distribution and computing P_{mech} from Eq. (11–73). Let us now consider a similar approximation for the integral in Eq. (11–79). The transmission line is no longer present if we assume a current distribution for both antennas which are driven by mechanical forces. We can compute the complex mechanical input power required to sustain the assumed current distribution from Eq. (11–73):

$$
\begin{aligned}
\tfrac{1}{2}\int_{S_1} (-\mathbf{E}_1 - \mathbf{E}_2)\cdot\mathbf{J}_{s1}^*\, ds &+ \tfrac{1}{2}\int_{S_2} (-\mathbf{E}_1 - \mathbf{E}_2)\cdot\mathbf{J}_{s2}^*\, ds \\
&= \frac{j\omega}{2}\int_S (\mathbf{A}_1 + \mathbf{A}_2)\cdot(\mathbf{J}_{s1} + \mathbf{J}_{s2})^* - (U_1 + U_2)(\rho_{s1} + \rho_{s2})^*]\, ds.
\end{aligned}
$$

Here S_1 is the surface of antenna 1, S_2 is the surface of antenna 2 and $S = S_1 + S_2$. On comparing terms with similar subscripts in the above equation, we see that we must take

$$
\int_{S_1} (-\mathbf{E}_2 \cdot \mathbf{J}_{s1}^*)\, dv + \int_{S_2} (-\mathbf{E}_1 \cdot \mathbf{J}_{s2}^*)\, dv
$$

$$
= j\omega \int_S (\mathbf{A}_1 \cdot \mathbf{J}_{s2}^* + \mathbf{A}_2 \cdot \mathbf{J}_{s1}^* - U_1 \rho_{s2}^* - U_2 \rho_{s1}^*)\, ds. \tag{11–80}
$$

When the assumed current distribution approximates the current distribution obtained by solving the boundary-value problem, the corresponding field vectors of both fields will be approximately equal over most of space. As a consequence the integrals on the right-hand sides of Eqs. (11–79) and (11–80) will be approximately equal. Thus

$$z_{12} \cong \frac{1}{I_1 I_2^* + I_1^* I_2} \left[\int_{S_1} (-\mathbf{E}_2 \cdot \mathbf{J}_{s1}^*) \, ds + \int_{S_2} (-\mathbf{E}_1 \cdot \mathbf{J}_{s2}^*) \, ds \right]. \quad (11\text{–}81)$$

Equation (11–81) corresponds to Eq. (11–61), the difference being that z_{12} is defined in terms of the antenna input currents I_1 and I_2, while Z_{12} is defined in terms of the maximum antenna currents $|I_{10}|$ and $|I_{20}|$.

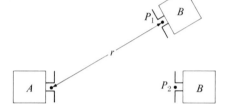

Fig. 11–16. A transmitting antenna A and a receiving antenna B.

11-9 THE RECEIVING ANTENNA

The antennas discussed in the previous sections have all been considered as transmitting. With the aid of the reciprocity relation we can obtain an important relationship between the gain function and the *receiving cross section A_r* of an antenna. The receiving cross section is defined by the equation

$$P_{\text{abs}} = P_a A_r, \quad (11\text{–}82)$$

where P_{abs} is the average power absorbed in the antenna load and where P_a is the average power per unit area of the incident electromagnetic wave at the receiving antenna (see Eq. 9–26b). It is assumed that the antenna has a matched load and that it has the proper orientation with respect to the polarization of the electromagnetic field to ensure a maximum transfer of energy to the load.

To derive the relationship between the gain function of an antenna and its receiving cross section, let us consider two antennas A and B separated a distance r (Fig. 11–16). We first consider the case of A transmitting and B receiving. Antenna B is oriented at each position to receive maximum energy. The power absorbed, $P_{\text{abs}}(P_1)$, by antenna B at a position P_1 is proportional to $G_A(P_1)$, the power per unit solid angle radiated by antenna A in the direction of B. Thus $P_{\text{abs}}(P_1) = cG_A(P_1)$, where c is a constant. If we choose a different position P_2 at the same distance r from A, we have $P_{\text{abs}}(P_2) = cG_A(P_2)$. Thus

$$\frac{P_{\text{abs}}(P_1)}{P_{\text{abs}}(P_2)} = \frac{G_A(P_1)}{G_A(P_2)}.$$

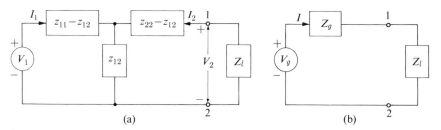

Fig. 11-17. The equivalent networks of the coupled antennas shown in Fig. 11-16.

We can express the terminal characteristics of antennas A and B, respectively, by means of transmission-line equations:

$$V_1 = z_{11}I_1 + z_{12}I_2,$$ (11-83a)

$$V_2 = z_{21}I_1 + z_{22}I_2.$$ (11-83b)

If antenna B is receiving (see Fig. 11-17), we have $V_2 = -I_2Z_l$, where Z_l is the load impedance. Substituting into Eq. (11-83b) yields

$$I_2 = -\frac{z_{21}}{z_{22} + Z_l} I_1$$

and

$$P_{\text{abs}}(P) = \text{Re}\left[\tfrac{1}{2}V_2I_2^*\right] = \frac{|I_1|^2}{2}\left|\frac{z_{21}(P)}{z_{22} + Z_l}\right|^2 \text{Re}[Z_l].$$ (11-84)

The mutual coupling between the antennas, which is represented by $z_{12} = z_{12}(P)$, depends on the position P of antenna B. Thus

$$\frac{P_{\text{abs}}(P_1)}{P_{\text{abs}}(P_2)} = \left|\frac{z_{21}(P_1)}{z_{21}(P_2)}\right|^2 = \frac{G_A(P_1)}{G_A(P_2)}.$$ (11-85)

Let us now consider a situation in which B is transmitting and A receiving. The power absorbed in the load of antenna A is $P_{\text{abs}} = P_a A_{rA}$. The receiving cross section A_{rA} depends on the position P of antenna A, while P_a is taken to be fixed. The absorbed power can be written in the form (11-84) provided that we replace z_{21} and z_{22} by z_{12} and z_{11}, respectively. Taking the ratio of the absorbed powers for two different positions P_1 and P_2 yields

$$\frac{P_{\text{abs}}(P_1)}{P_{\text{abs}}(P_2)} = \frac{A_{rA}(P_1)}{A_{rA}(P_2)} = \left|\frac{z_{12}(P_1)}{z_{12}(P_2)}\right|^2.$$ (11-86)

It follows from the reciprocity relation (11-77) that Eqs. (11-85) and (11-86) are equal. Thus we have

$$A_{rA}(P) = c_A G_A(P),$$ (11-87)

where c_A is a constant. We shall now prove that c_A is a universal constant.

For a case in which A is transmitting we can use the equivalent circuit shown in Fig. 11–17a to represent the transmission-line equations (11–83). Applying Thevenin's theorem yields the equivalent circuit shown in Fig. 11–17b, where

$$V_g \triangleq \frac{z_{12}}{z_{11}} V_1, \qquad Z_g \triangleq z_{22} - z_{12} + \frac{z_{12}(z_{11} - z_{12})}{z_{11}}.$$

In the case of antennas we usually have weak coupling, so that $Z_g \cong z_{22}$. The power absorbed in the load is a maximum when the load impedance is matched to the internal impedance of the generator. This requires that $Z_l = Z_g^*$ and the power absorbed in the case of weak coupling (see Eq. 11–84) is

$$P_{\text{abs}}(P) = \frac{1}{8} \frac{|I_1 z_{12}(P)|^2}{R_{22}}, \tag{11–88}$$

where $R_{22} \triangleq \text{Re}\,[z_{22}]$. It follows from the definition of the receiving cross section (see Eq. 11–82) and the gain function (see Eq. 11–38) that we can also write

$$P_{\text{abs}} = \frac{P_{RA}}{4\pi r^2} G_A A_{rB}, \tag{11–89}$$

where the average power radiated by A is given by

$$P_{RA} \triangleq \tfrac{1}{2} |I_1|^2 R_{11},$$

and where $R_{11} \triangleq \text{Re}\,[z_{11}]$. Substituting into Eq. (11–89) and comparing with Eq. (11–88) yields

$$G_A A_{rB} = \frac{\pi r^2 |z_{12}|^2}{R_{11} R_{22}}.$$

Similarly, if we consider B as transmitting and A as receiving, we obtain

$$G_B A_{rA} = \frac{\pi r^2 |z_{21}|^2}{R_{22} R_{11}}.$$

It follows from the above expressions and the reciprocity relation that $G_A A_{rB} = G_B A_{rA}$, where A_{rB} can be found by replacing the subscript A by the subscript B in Eq. (11–87). Substituting for A_{rB} and A_{rA}, we see that $c_A = c_B = c$. Thus c is the same for all antennas and is therefore a universal constant.

We can determine c by considering any convenient type of antenna and evaluating the gain function and the receiving cross section. Let us choose an electric dipole as a receiving antenna and evaluate the receiving cross section. The complex power absorbed from an incident plane electromagnetic wave with the electric field intensity $\mathbf{E}_i$ parallel to the dipole axis is $\tfrac{1}{2} E_i l I^*$, where l

is the length of the dipole and I is the phasor current. Thus, in the equivalent circuit for the receiving antenna shown in Fig. 11–17b, we can choose $V_g = E_i l$.

In the case of the transmitting dipole we have $V_g = 0$ in the equivalent circuit, there is no load impedance, and we consider that the complex power is supplied by distributed mechanical sources which move the charges between terminals 1 and 2. The real power supplied by the mechanical sources is radiated by the antenna. Thus we see that we must have

$$\text{Re } [Z_g] = R,$$

where R is the radiation resistance of the dipole. If the dipole is receiving we must replace the mechanical sources by suitable mechanical loads. Since we are interested only in the power relations we need not concern ourselves with the structural details of the loads, which in any case are entirely hypothetical. Maximum power is absorbed in the load when

$$\text{Re } [Z_l] = R, \qquad Z_l = Z_g^*.$$

The real power absorbed in the load is then one-half the real power absorbed by the dipole (the other half is re-radiated):

$$\tfrac{1}{4} \text{ Re } [E_i l I^*]. \tag{11–90}$$

Let us consider a unit area normal to the direction of propagation of the plane incident wave. The power per unit area in the incident wave is

$$\tfrac{1}{2} E_i H_i^* = \frac{1}{2Z_0} |E_i|^2, \tag{11–91}$$

where $Z_0 = 120\pi$ ohms is the intrinsic impedance of free space. The real power absorbed in the load is

$$\frac{A_r}{2Z_0} |E_i|^2 = \tfrac{1}{2} |I|^2 R$$

and the phasor current is determined by

$$I = \frac{E_i l}{Z_g + Z_g^*} = \frac{E_i l}{2R} .$$

Thus, substituting for R (see Eq. 11–27), we obtain the receiving cross section in the equatorial plane for the electric dipole antenna:

$$A_r = Z_0 R \left| \frac{I}{E_i} \right|^2 = \frac{3}{8\pi} \lambda^2. \tag{11–92}$$

It is left as an exercise for the reader to show that the gain function for the electric dipole antenna in the equatorial plane is $G = \tfrac{3}{2}$ (see Problem 11–10). Substituting A_r and G into Eq. (11–87) yields $c = \lambda^2/4\pi$. Thus we see that the receiving cross section of an antenna in the (θ, ϕ) direction is given by

$$A_r(\theta, \phi) = \frac{\lambda^2}{4\pi} G(\theta, \phi), \tag{11-93}$$

where $G(\theta, \phi)$ is the gain function of the antenna in the (θ, ϕ) direction.

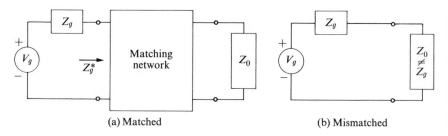

(a) Matched   (b) Mismatched

Fig. 11-18. The equivalent networks of matched and mismatched receiving antennas.

In deriving Eq. (11-93) we have assumed that the load impedance is matched to the antenna impedance. Let us now investigate the effect of a load mismatch on the receiving cross section. A transmission line of characteristic impedance $Z_0 \neq z_{22}^*$ is terminated in a matched load $(Z_l = Z_0)$ and a lossless matching network couples the transmission line to the antenna which has a source impedance $Z_g = z_{22}$ (Fig. 11-18a). This arrangement results in the maximum power transfer to the load for a given Z_0 and is the matched case for which the absorbed power is given by Eq. (11-88). In the mismatched case the matching network is not present and the power absorbed is given by Eq. (11-84), where $Z_l = Z_0$ is real. The ratio of these powers is equal to the ratio of the receiving cross sections:

$$\frac{A_{rm}}{A_r} = \frac{4R_{22}Z_0}{|z_{22} + Z_0|^2}.$$

Here A_{rm} is the receiving cross section in the case of a mismatch. The above expression is best expressed in terms of the reflection coefficient Γ, which is determined by

$$z_{22} = Z_0 \frac{1 + \Gamma}{1 - \Gamma}.$$

Thus

$$R_{22} = \tfrac{1}{2}(z_{22} + z_{22}^*) = Z_0 \frac{1 - |\Gamma|^2}{|1 - \Gamma|^2}, \qquad z_{22} + Z_0 = \frac{2Z_0}{1 - \Gamma},$$

and we obtain

$$A_{rm} = A_r(1 - |\Gamma|^2). \tag{11-94}$$

11-10 ANTENNAS USED FOR BOTH TRANSMITTING AND RECEIVING; THE SCATTERING CROSS SECTION

In radar systems a highly directional antenna is used to transmit pulses of electromagnetic energy to distant objects. The currents and charges induced in the object by the incident electromagnetic wave set up a secondary field through which some of the transmitted energy is returned to the antenna. The time interval between the transmitted and reflected pulses can be used to determine the distance of the object. In such an application the same antenna is used for transmitting and receiving. Consider an antenna A which transmits a pulse of electromagnetic energy toward an object O (Fig. 11–19). Let $\mathbf{E}_i$ represent the electric field intensity of the incident wave at O and let $\mathbf{E}_s$ represent the electric field intensity of the scattered field at A. The *scattering cross section* is defined by the equation

$$\sigma \triangleq \lim_{r \to \infty} 4\pi r^2 \left| \frac{E_s}{E_i} \right|^2, \tag{11-95}$$

where we take $\mathbf{E}_i$ and $\mathbf{E}_s$ to have the same polarization.

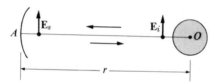

Fig. 11–19. Illustration defining the scattering cross section.

Given that P_R is the average power radiated by A during the pulse and G is the gain function of A, we have (see Eqs. 11–38 and 11–45)

$$\frac{1}{2} \frac{|E_i|^2}{Z_0} r^2 = \frac{P_R}{4\pi} G, \tag{11-96}$$

where $Z_0 = 120\pi$ ohms is the intrinsic impedance of free space. Equation (11–96) yields the magnitude of the incident electric field intensity,

$$|E_i| = \frac{1}{r} \sqrt{60 P_R G}, \tag{11-97}$$

and Eqs. (11–95) and (11–97) yield the magnitude of the reflected electric field intensity at A,

$$|E_s| = \frac{|E_i|}{r} \sqrt{\frac{\sigma}{4\pi}}. \tag{11-98}$$

The average power per unit area at A due to the scattered field is given by

$$P_a = \frac{1}{2} \frac{|E_s|^2}{Z_0}. \tag{11-99}$$

When the receiving antenna is connected to a matched load, the power absorbed from the scattered field is

$$P_r \triangleq P_a A_r, \tag{11-100}$$

which we define as the received power. Substituting Eqs. (11-95), (11-96), and (11-99) into Eq. (11-100) yields

$$\frac{P_r}{P_R} = \frac{\sigma(G\lambda)^2}{(4\pi)^3 r^4}. \tag{11-101}$$

Here we have used Eq. (11-93) to eliminate A_r. Solving Eq. (11-101) for r yeilds the *radar range equation*,

$$r = \sqrt[4]{G^2 \lambda^2 \sigma P_R / (4\pi)^3 P_r}. \tag{11-102}$$

As an example, let us take $P_R = 500 \text{ kW}$, $\lambda = 10 \text{ cm}$, $\sigma = 20 \text{ m}^2$, $r = 100 \text{ km}$, and let the antenna have a maximum gain of $G = 1000$ in the direction of the object. Using this given data we shall determine $|E_i|$, $|E_s|$, P_a, A_r, and P_r. Equation (11-97) yields the magnitude of the incident electric field intensity at O:

$$|E_i| = 1.73 \text{ V/m}.$$

The power per unit area in the incident wave at O is

$$\frac{1}{2} \frac{|E_i|^2}{Z_0} = 4 \times 10^{-3} \text{ W/m}^2.$$

The magnitude of the scattered electric field intensity at A is given by Eq. (11-98):

$$|E_s| = 2.18 \times 10^{-5} \text{ V/m}.$$

The power per unit area in the scattered wave at A is

$$P_a = \frac{1}{2} \frac{|E_s|^2}{Z_0} = 6.3 \times 10^{-13} \text{ W/m}^2.$$

The receiving cross section is

$$A_r = \frac{\lambda^2}{4\pi} G = 0.8 \text{ m}^2,$$

and the power absorbed by the antenna from the scattered wave is

$$P_r = P_a A_r = 5 \times 10^{-13} \text{ W/m}^2.$$

11-11 STATIC AND QUASI-STATIC APPROXIMATIONS

Equations (4-4) and (6-5) give the scalar and vector potentials of static time-invariant charges and currents, while Eqs. (11-20) give the phasor scalar and vector potentials for sinusoidally time-varying charges and currents.

We see that the exponential factor $e^{-j\beta r}$, which arises because of the finite velocity of propagation of electromagnetic fields, distinguishes the potentials of static fields from the potentials of sinusoidally time-varying fields. Expanding the exponential factor in a Taylor series in $j\beta r$ yields

$$e^{-j\beta r} = 1 - j\beta r - \frac{(\beta r)^2}{2} + \cdots \tag{11-103}$$

The quasi-static field is defined by the condition

$$\beta r = \omega r / c = (2\pi r / \lambda) \ll 1, \tag{11-104}$$

which holds when the frequency is sufficiently low or when the conductor dimensions are small compared with the free-space wavelength. We can then neglect all terms in the expansion, with the exception of the first, and obtain

$$U \cong \frac{1}{4\pi\varepsilon_0} \int_v \frac{\rho}{r} \, dv, \tag{11-105a}$$

$$\mathbf{A} \cong \frac{\mu_0}{4\pi} \int_v \frac{\mathbf{J}}{r} \, dv. \tag{11-105b}$$

Equations (11–105) correspond to Eqs. (4–4) and (6–5) which were used in the discussion of static and quasi-static electric and magnetic fields. The static electric and magnetic fields are determined by the conditions that ρ and $\mathbf{J}$ be constant. In the case of a quasi-static field, $\mathbf{J}$ and ρ are time-varying and are related to each other by the equation of continuity.

Let us consider the special case of a straight filament of infinite length and take the phasor current and phasor linear charge density to be given by

$$I = I_0 e^{-j\beta z}, \qquad q = q_0 e^{-j\beta z},$$

respectively, where z is the distance along the filament. Equation (11–32) yields $q/I = q_0/I_0 = \beta/\omega$. The static E-field is determined by the real vector $\mathbf{E}_0 = -\text{grad } U_0$, where

$$U_0 = \frac{q_0}{4\pi\varepsilon_0} \int_{-\infty}^{\infty} \frac{dz}{r}.$$

The quasi-static field phasors are determined by

$$\mathbf{E}' = -j\omega\mathbf{A}, \qquad \mathbf{B} = \text{curl } \mathbf{A},$$

where

$$\mathbf{A} = \mathbf{i}_z \frac{\mu_0 I_0}{4\pi} \int_{-\infty}^{\infty} \frac{dz}{r},$$

and the resultant real electric field intensity and real magnetic flux density are given by

$$\mathbf{E}_0 + \text{Re}\,[\mathbf{E}'e^{j\omega t}] \quad \text{and} \quad \text{Re}\,[\mathbf{B}e^{j\omega t}],$$

respectively.

REFERENCES

1. J. D. KRAUS, *Antennas*, New York: McGraw-Hill Book Company, 1950
2. E. JAHNKE and F. EMDE, *Tables of Functions*, New York: Dover Publications, 1945
3. P. S. CARTER, "Circuit relations in radiating systems and applications to antenna problems," *Proc. IRE* **20**, 1004–1041, June 1932

GENERAL REFERENCES

E. C. JORDON, *Electromagnetic Waves and Radiating Systems*, New York: Prentice-Hall, 1950

S. SCHELKUNOFF and H. FRIIS, *Antennas: Theory and Practice*, New York: John Wiley & Sons, 1952

PROBLEMS

11–1 Consider a circular loop antenna of radius a located in the xy-plane and centered at the origin (Fig. 11–20). Assume that the current in the loop is uniform and given by $I_0 \cos \omega t$. Determine the far-field phasors, the Poynting vector in the far field, and the radiation resistance. [*Hint:* Show that

$$r - r_1 = r_2 - r = a \cos \phi \sin \theta, \quad e^{-j\beta r_1} - e^{-j\beta r_2} = 2je^{-j\beta r} \sin (\beta a \cos \phi \sin \theta),$$

and use the fact that

$$J_1(z) = \frac{1}{\pi} \int_0^\pi \sin (z \cos \phi) \cos \phi \, d\phi,$$

where $J_1(z)$ is the Bessel function of the first kind of order one to determine the vector potential $\mathbf{A} = \mathbf{i}_\phi A_\phi$.]

11–2 Consider Problem 11–1. Given that $\beta a \ll 1$, show that the far-field components are

$$E_\phi = \frac{\mu_0 \omega \beta I_0 a^2}{4} \sin \theta \frac{e^{-j\beta r}}{r} = -Z_0 H_\theta, \qquad H_\theta = -\frac{I_0 \beta^2 a^2}{4} \sin \theta \frac{e^{-j\beta r}}{r}.$$

Prove that the radiation resistance is $R = 20\pi^2(\beta a)^4$. Note that the above components correspond to the components of an electric dipole antenna, provided that we interchange $\mathbf{E}$ and $\mathbf{H}$ (see Eqs. 11–23). A loop antenna with $\beta a \ll 1$ is known as a *magnetic dipole antenna*. Given that $\beta a = 0.1$, $I_0 = 1$ A, $\theta = \pi/2$, determine the magnitude of the electric field intensity at a distance of 1 km from the antenna. Determine P_R, the power radiated by the antenna. The loop is made of copper wire of conductivity $\sigma = 5.8 \times 10^7$ mhos/m, $a = 10$ cm, and the wire has a circular cross section of radius 0.1 cm. Determine the antenna efficiency $P_R/(P_R + P_L)$, where P_L is the power dissipated in the wire.

11–3 Two similar thin linear antennas of equal length l are parallel and spaced a distance a apart on the x-axis (Fig. 11–21). It is required that the gain function

$G(\theta, \phi)$ be zero in the direction of the negative x-axis. Determine a in terms of the free-space wavelength and determine the phase of the current in antenna 2 relative to the phase of the current in antenna 1 in order that the gain function have the required property.

11–4 Consider a thin linear antenna which is normal to a perfectly conducting plane and which is driven by a transmission line, as indicated in Fig. 11–22a. Explain how the method of images can be used to account for the boundary condition along the plane conductor. What is the input impedance of the antenna if $l = \lambda/4$? Explain how the method of images can be used to account for the boundary condition along the plane conductor if the antenna axis is parallel to the conducting plane, as shown in Fig. 11–22b. Discuss the effect of the conducting plane on the input impedance of the antenna.

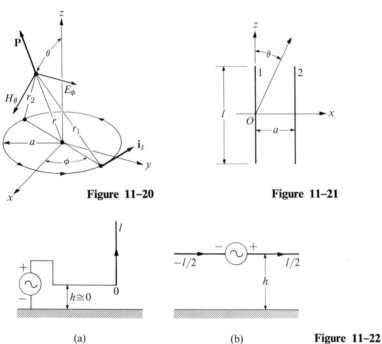

Figure 11–20   Figure 11–21

(a)   (b)   Figure 11–22

11–5 A quarter-wave antenna of the type illustrated in Fig. 11–22a is to have a maximum magnitude of electric field intensity of 1 mV/m at a distance of 1 km. Determine the power required by the antenna. What is the maximum current in the antenna?

11–6 Consider a thin linear perfectly conducting antenna of length l which is driven at the center from a transmission line (Fig. 11–10). With the aid of Eqs. (11–19) and (11–68), show that

$$\frac{d^2 A_z}{dz^2} + \beta^2 A_z = 0, \qquad a < |z| \leq l/2$$

where $\mathbf{A} = \mathbf{i}_z A_z$ is the vector potential of the antenna. Derive *Hallen's integral equation* for the current distribution:

$$C_1 \sin \beta \, |z| + C_2 \cos \beta z = \int_v \frac{J e^{-j\beta r}}{r} \, dv.$$

Here v is the volume of the antenna. The constants C_1 and C_2 are determined by the condition that $J(l/2) = J(-l/2) = 0$ and by specifying either the real power radiated by the antenna or by specifying the maximum magnitude of $\mathbf{J}$.

11-7 Two electric dipole antennas are collinear with the z-axis, are a distance a apart and have the same length l (Fig. 11–23). Given that $l \ll a$ and that I_1 and $I_2 e^{j\alpha}$ are the phasor currents in the antennas where I_1 and I_2 are real, show that the radiated power is

$$P_R = 40\pi^2 \left(\frac{l}{\lambda}\right)^2 (I_1^2 + I_2^2) + 60 I_1 I_2 \left(\frac{l}{a}\right)^2 \left(\frac{\sin \beta a}{\beta a} - \cos \beta a\right) \cos \alpha.$$

[*Hint:* In evaluating the coefficient of $I_1 I_2$ in Eq. (11–24), use the substitution $u = \cos \theta$ and integrate by parts.]

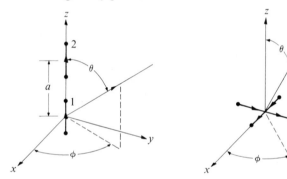

Figure 11–23   **Figure 11–24**

11-8 Figure 11–24 illustrates a turnstile type of antenna formed by two electric dipole antennas of equal length which are at right angles to each other and which have phasor currents of I and jI, respectively. Show that the far-field electric-field intensity on the z-axis is circularly polarized and determine the Poynting vector. Determine the far-field components and the Poynting vector in the xy-plane.

11-9 A plane electromagnetic wave in free space has a frequency of 1 MHz and is normally incident on a half-wave thin linear antenna. Given that the electric field intensity is parallel to the antenna axis and that it has a magnitude of 1 mV/m, determine the maximum power that can be delivered to a matched load.

11-10 Show that the gain function for an electric dipole antenna is

$$G(\theta, \phi) = \tfrac{3}{2} \sin^2 \theta.$$

11-11 Determine the gain function for the magnetic dipole antenna discussed in Problem 11-2.

11–12   Consider a long thin linear antenna which lies on the z-axis. The current distribution is a traveling wave given by

$$I(z) = I_0 e^{j(\omega t - \beta z)}.$$

Show that the phasor component E_θ in the far field is

$$E_\theta = j60I_0 \frac{e^{-j\beta r}}{r} \frac{\sin\theta}{1 - \cos\theta} \sin\left[\frac{\beta l}{2}(1 - \cos\theta)\right],$$

where l is the length of the antenna. Prove that the radiation resistance is given by

$$R = 60\left[\text{Cin}(2\beta l) - 1 + \frac{\sin 2\beta l}{2\beta l}\right].$$

11–13   Prove the reciprocity theorem for sinusoidally time-varying fields

$$\int_v \mathbf{E}_2 \cdot \mathbf{J}_1 \, dv = \int_v \mathbf{E}_1 \cdot \mathbf{J}_2 \, dv$$

where $\mathbf{E}_k$ is the phasor electric field intensity associated with the phasor current density $\mathbf{J}_k$ $(k = 1, 2)$. Is the reciprocity theorem valid if we replace $\mathbf{J}_k$ by $\mathbf{J}_k^*$?

11–14   Consider a sinusoidally time-varying plane electromagnetic wave to be incident on a dielectric sphere of permittivity ε and radius a (Fig. 11–25). Given that $\beta a \ll 1$, one can use quasi-static methods to determine the scattered field. With the aid of Eqs. (5–20) and (3–27), show that the phasor polarization current density is

$$\mathbf{J}_p = j3\frac{\varepsilon_r - 1}{\varepsilon_r + 1}\omega\varepsilon_0\mathbf{E}_i,$$

where $\mathbf{E}_i = \mathbf{i}_z E_i$ is the incident phasor electric field intensity. The polarization current can be considered to form elemental electric dipoles. Prove that the scattered electric field intensity in the far field and for $\theta = \pi/2$ is given by

$$\mathbf{E}_s = -\mathbf{i}_z j30\beta l_e I \frac{e^{-j\beta r}}{r},$$

where

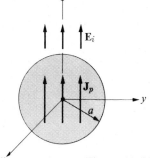

$$l_e I \triangleq \int_v \mathbf{J}_p \cdot \mathbf{i}_z \, dv = j4\pi a^3 \frac{\varepsilon_r - 1}{\varepsilon_r + 1}\omega\varepsilon_0 E_i.$$

Use these results to prove that the scattering cross section of the dielectric sphere is

$$\sigma = 4(\beta a)^4 \left|\frac{\varepsilon_r - 1}{\varepsilon_r + 1}\right|^2 \pi a^2.$$

Figure 11–25

11–15   Consider a sinusoidally time-varying plane electromagnetic wave to be incident on a perfectly conducting sphere of radius a (Fig. 11–26). If $\beta a \ll 1$, quasi-static methods can be used to determine the scattering cross section. The

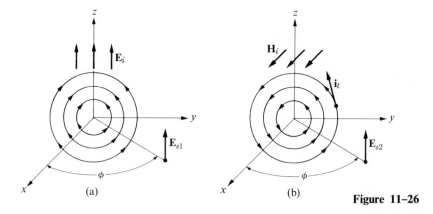

Figure 11-26

surface charge density induced on the sphere by the incident electric field intensity, $E_i = i_z E_i$ (see Example 3, Section 4–4) is given by

$$\sigma = 3\varepsilon_0 E_i \cos\theta.$$

Associated with σ is a surface current density J_s, which we can find by expressing the equation of continuity (2–42) in phasor form and substituting $D_r = D_\phi = 0$, $D_\theta = hJ_s$, and $\rho = h\sigma$, where $h \ll a$, into Eq. (1–105). Show that (see Fig. 11–24a)

$$J_s = -i_\theta j\omega\tfrac{3}{2}a\varepsilon_0 E_i \sin\theta.$$

In the far field only the z-component, $-J_s \sin\theta$, of this current density contributes to the vector potential $A = i_z A_z$. Evaluate A_z and prove that the scattered electric field intensity in the xy-plane is given by

$$E_{s1} = i_z \beta^2 a^3 E_i \frac{e^{-j\beta r}}{r}.$$

If the incident plane wave propagates in the direction of the positive y-axis so that $H_i = i_x H_i$, the time-varying magnetic flux density will cause currents to be induced in the conductor surface, as illustrated in Fig. 11–26(b). The surface current density is determined by the condition that $H = 0$ inside the sphere. It can be shown (see Problem 6–12) that

$$J_s = -i_t \frac{3H_i}{2} \sin\theta,$$

where i_t is a unit vector tangential to the sphere, directed as shown in the figure. This current distribution can be considered as a distribution of elemental current loops. Prove that the scattered electric field intensity in the xy-plane (see Problem 11–2) is given by

$$E_{s2} = -i_z \frac{\beta^2 a^3}{2} E_i \sin\phi \frac{e^{-j\beta r}}{r}.$$

The resultant scattered field in the xy-plane is $E_s = E_{s1} + E_{s2}$. Use these results to prove that the scattering cross section of the perfectly conducting sphere for $\theta = \pi/2$ is $\sigma = 4(\beta a)^4(1 - \tfrac{1}{2}\sin\phi)^2\pi a^2$.

11–16 A directive antenna with a paraboloidal reflector has an aperture area A (Fig. 11–27). Use the geometric optics approximation to justify the following estimate for the gain of the antenna in the direction of the z-axis:

$$G \cong (4\pi/\lambda^2)A.$$

Determine the gain for an aperture which has a circular cross section of radius $a = 1$ m and for a wavelength of $\lambda = 10$ cm.

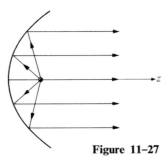

Figure 11–27

11–17 An antenna A has a gain of 1000 in the direction of a small metallic sphere of radius $a = 1$ cm which is at a distance of 1 km from A. A pulse of electromagnetic energy is transmitted by A toward the sphere. Given that $P_R = 1$ MW during the pulse and that the wavelength is 10 cm, evaluate the magnitude of the incident electric field intensity on the sphere and the magnitude of the scattered electric field intensity at A. What is the power absorbed by A in a matched load?

11–18 Determine the maximum range at which a specific target can be detected, given the following data for a radar system: $\sigma = 25$ m², $\lambda = 10$ cm, $P_R = 250$ kW, $G = 1500$, and the minimum detectable received power is $P_r = 10^{-13}$ W.

CHAPTER 12

WAVE PROPAGATION IN ANISOTROPIC MEDIA

12-1 INTRODUCTION

Up to this point we have assumed that the permittivity ε and permeability μ of material media are scalar functions of position. Material media having such properties are called isotropic; $\mathbf{D}$ and $\mathbf{E}$, $\mathbf{H}$ and $\mathbf{B}$, are then collinear at any field point P for all directions of $\mathbf{E}$ and $\mathbf{B}$. In ionized gases the interaction between a sinusoidally time-varying field and the free charges results in an effective polarization $\mathbf{P}$ which is not collinear with $\mathbf{E}$ for all directions of $\mathbf{E}$. The constitutive relation between $\mathbf{P}$ and $\mathbf{E}$ must then be described by a tensor susceptibility. In the case of plane waves this results in a number of interesting effects which we shall investigate. Similar effects are observed in magnetic media. A magnetic material of particular importance is ferrite, which consists of crystals of $MOFe_2O_3$ sintered together in a ceramic binder. Here M is a divalent metal such as iron, magnesium or nickel. The importance of the ferrites is a consequence of their high resistivity (10^6 to 10^7 Ω/cm) and the ferromagnetic resonance effects that they exhibit at very high frequencies. We shall see that the magnetization $\mathbf{M}$ resulting from a magnetic field $\mathbf{H}_i$ is not collinear with $\mathbf{H}_i$ for all directions of $\mathbf{H}_i$. The constitutive relation between $\mathbf{M}$ and $\mathbf{H}_i$ must then be described by a tensor susceptibility. This results in a number of interesting effects such as the Faraday rotation and the Cotton-Mouton effect which find application in microwave isolators and phase shifters.

12-2 EFFECTIVE TENSOR SUSCEPTIBILITY OF AN IONIZED GAS IN A UNIFORM MAGNETIC FIELD

Ionized gases in which the densities of the electrons and positive ions are approximately equal are called *plasmas*. Wave propagation in plasmas is a subject area of considerable current interest. Here we shall restrict ourselves to one aspect of it, which is of importance in communication systems and which illustrates some of the effects that may occur in plasmas. Due to radiation from the sun the upper regions of the earth's atmosphere become ionized. These regions are referred to as the *ionosphere*. The free electrons in the ionosphere are influenced by electromagnetic waves and their motion results in an effective polarization **P** which is not collinear with **E** for all directions of **E**. Consequently the effective susceptibility is a tensor quantity, and this has a considerable effect on the propagation function.

In any finite region of the ionosphere we can, as a first approximation, take the electron density N and the earth's magnetic flux density $\mathbf{B}_0$ as uniform and time-invariant. Since the positive ion is heavier than the electron, we need concern ourselves only with the equation of motion for the electron:

$$m \frac{d\mathbf{u}}{dt} = -e[\mathbf{E} + \mathbf{u} \times (\mathbf{B} + \mathbf{B}_0)]. \tag{12–1}$$

Here m is the mass of the electron and e is the magnitude of the electron charge. The field components of a plane wave in free space (see Eq. 9–12) satisfy the relation

$$E_x/B_y = \omega/\beta = c.$$

Thus $uB_y/E_x = u/c$. Since the velocity of the electrons is considerably less than the velocity of light we can, therefore, neglect the effect of **B** on the motion of the electrons. At any instant of time we consider the electromagnetic field to be uniform over the path of an electron. Thus

$$d\mathbf{u}/dt = \partial\mathbf{u}/\partial t.$$

Equation (12–1), in phasor notation, now takes the form

$$j\omega m\mathbf{u} = -e(\mathbf{E} + \mathbf{u} \times \mathbf{B}_0),$$

and if we take $\mathbf{B}_0 = \mathbf{i}_z B_0$ we obtain

$$-j \frac{\omega m}{e} u_x - B_0 u_y = E_x, \qquad B_0 u_x - j \frac{\omega m}{e} u_y = E_y, \qquad -j \frac{\omega m}{e} u_z = E_z. \tag{12–2}$$

Solving Eqs. (12–2) for u_x, u_y, and u_z and multiplying by $-N/e\varepsilon_0$ yields

$$-eNu_x/\varepsilon_0 = \frac{\omega_p^2}{\omega_0^2 - \omega^2}(j\omega E_x - \omega_0 E_y), \tag{12–3}$$

$$-eNu_y/\varepsilon_0 = \frac{\omega_p^2}{\omega_0^2 - \omega^2}(\omega_0 E_x + j\omega E_y), \qquad -eNu_z/\varepsilon_0 = -j \frac{\omega_p^2}{\omega} E_z,$$

where $\omega_0 \triangleq eB_0/m$, $\omega_p^2 \triangleq Ne^2/\varepsilon_0 m$. The frequency $f_0 = \omega_0/2\pi$ is known as the *Larmor frequency* and $f_p = \omega_p/2\pi$ is known as the *plasma frequency*. Equations (12–3) can be expressed in tensor form by taking $-eN\mathbf{u} = j\omega\varepsilon_0\boldsymbol{\chi} \cdot \mathbf{E}$, where

$$\boldsymbol{\chi} \triangleq \begin{pmatrix} \chi & -j\kappa & 0 \\ j\kappa & \chi & 0 \\ 0 & 0 & \chi_z \end{pmatrix} \tag{12–4}$$

is the *effective tensor susceptibility.* The components of χ are defined by the equations

$$\chi \triangleq \frac{\omega_p^2}{\omega_0^2 - \omega^2}, \qquad \kappa \triangleq \frac{-\omega_0\omega_p^2}{\omega(\omega_0^2 - \omega^2)}, \qquad \chi_z \triangleq -\left(\frac{\omega_p}{\omega}\right)^2. \quad (12\text{-}5)$$

The motion of the electrons results in a current density

$$\mathbf{J} = -e N \mathbf{u} = j\omega\varepsilon_0\chi \cdot \mathbf{E}, \quad (12\text{-}6)$$

and it is convenient to consider that $\mathbf{J}$ is associated with an effective polarization $\mathbf{P}$. We can define $\mathbf{P}$ by introducing $\mathbf{J}$ into the phasor form of Eq. (3–27). We may also define $\mathbf{P}$ by the equation

$$\mathbf{P} \triangleq -e N \mathbf{r}, \quad (12\text{-}7)$$

where $\mathbf{r}$ is the average vector displacement of the electrons. Expressing $\mathbf{u} = d\mathbf{r}/dt$ in phasor form, we see that Eqs. (12–6) and (12–7) yield the same result:

$$\mathbf{P} \triangleq \varepsilon_0\chi \cdot \mathbf{E}. \quad (12\text{-}8)$$

With the aid of Eq. (12–8) we can define the effective electric flux density by the equation

$$\mathbf{D} \triangleq \varepsilon_0\mathbf{E} + \mathbf{P} = \boldsymbol{\epsilon} \cdot \mathbf{E}, \quad (12\text{-}9)$$

where

$$\boldsymbol{\epsilon} \triangleq \varepsilon_0(\mathbf{e} + \chi) \quad (12\text{-}10)$$

is the *effective tensor permittivity.* Here $\mathbf{e}$ is the unit tensor (see Section 1–22). In cartesian coordinates, Eq. (12–8) takes the form

$$P_x = \varepsilon_0(\chi E_x - j\kappa E_y), \quad (12\text{-}11a)$$

$$P_y = \varepsilon_0(j\kappa E_x + \chi E_y), \quad (12\text{-}11b)$$

$$P_z = \varepsilon_0\chi_z E_z. \quad (12\text{-}11c)$$

We see from Eq. (12–8) that $\mathbf{P}$ is not, in general, collinear with $\mathbf{E}$. To investigate the possibility of a scalar susceptibility in special cases, let us consider a positively circularly polarized plane wave propagating in the positive z-direction so that $E_z = 0$. We have (see Eq. 9–70) $E_y = -jE_x$. Substituting into Eqs. (12–11), we see that $P_y = -jP_x$, $P_z = 0$, and that

$$\mathbf{P} = \varepsilon_0\chi_+\mathbf{E}, \quad (12\text{-}12)$$

where

$$\chi_+ \triangleq \chi - \kappa = \frac{\omega_p^2}{\omega(\omega_0 - \omega)} \quad (12\text{-}13)$$

For a negatively circularly polarized plane wave (see Eq. 9–69) we have $E_y = jE_x$, and we find that

$$\mathbf{P} = \varepsilon_0\chi_-\mathbf{E}, \quad (12\text{-}14)$$

where

$$\chi_- \overset{\triangle}{=} \chi + \kappa = - \frac{\omega_p^2}{\omega(\omega_0 + \omega)}. \tag{12-15}$$

Since χ_+ and χ_- are scalars, we see that $\mathbf{P}$ and $\mathbf{E}$ are collinear for circularly polarized plane waves. We can see the significance of the Larmor frequency from Eqs. (12-12) and (12-13). Given that an electron moves in a circular orbit of radius a in a right-handed sense with respect to $\mathbf{B}_0$, we can equate the centrifugal force to the Lorentz force (Fig. 12-1): $mu^2/a = eB_0u$. Substituting $u = \omega_0 a$ yields $\omega_0 = eB_0/m$. Since the electron can move in a finite orbit at the angular frequency ω_0, we can have a finite polarization with $\mathbf{E} = 0$. If one applies an $\mathbf{E}$-field which rotates in synchronism with the electron, it will cause an infinite displacement and hence an infinite polarization. Thus at the Larmor frequency we have a resonance occurring in $\mathbf{P}$ when the applied field is positively circularly polarized. However, we have neglected damping effects, such as collisions between electrons and radiation, which limit the amplitude of the electron orbits. For the negatively circularly polarized plane wave there is no resonance effect, since there is no equilibrium orbit for the electron in the absence of an impressed $\mathbf{E}$-field.

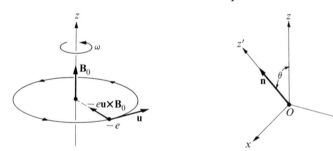

Fig. 12-1. Illustration defining the Larmor frequency.

Fig. 12-2. A plane wave propagating in an infinite anisotropic medium.

12-3 PROPAGATION OF PLANE ELECTROMAGNETIC WAVES IN A UNIFORMLY IONIZED GAS

Let us consider a sinusoidally time-varying plane electromagnetic wave that propagates in the direction of a unit vector $\mathbf{n}$ which lies in the xz-plane and which makes an angle θ with respect to the z-axis (Fig. 12-2). Let z' represent the coordinate in the $\mathbf{n}$ direction. For a plane wave,

$$\mathbf{E} = \mathbf{E}_0 e^{-\gamma z'}, \qquad \mathbf{H} = \mathbf{H}_0 e^{-\gamma z'}, \tag{12-16}$$

where γ is the propagation function and where $\mathbf{E}_0$ is normal to $\mathbf{n}$. In a cartesian (x', y', z') coordinate system, we have (see Problem 9-1)

$$\nabla \times \mathbf{E} = -\gamma \mathbf{n} \times \mathbf{E}, \tag{12-17}$$

and Maxwell's equations take the form

$$\gamma \mathbf{n} \times \mathbf{E} = j\omega\mu\mathbf{H}, \tag{12–18a}$$

$$-\gamma \mathbf{n} \times \mathbf{H} = j\omega\varepsilon_0\mathbf{E} + \mathbf{J} = j\omega\mathbf{D}. \tag{12–18b}$$

Here we have substituted Eqs. (12–6) and (12–9) into the second of Maxwell's equations. Eliminating $\mathbf{H}$ from Eqs. (12–18) yields

$$\mathbf{n} \times (\mathbf{n} \times \mathbf{E}) = \mu(\omega/\gamma)^2\mathbf{D}. \tag{12–19}$$

It follows from Eqs. (12–18) that $\mathbf{H} \cdot \mathbf{n} = 0$, $\mathbf{D} \cdot \mathbf{n} = 0$. However, since $\mathbf{D}$ and $\mathbf{E}$ do not, in general, have the same direction, we see from Eq. (12–19) that this results in a nonzero component, $\mathbf{E} \cdot \mathbf{n}$, in the direction of propagation.

Substituting Eq. (12–9) into (12–19) yields

$$(1 + a)\mathbf{E} + a\boldsymbol{\chi} \cdot \mathbf{E} - (\mathbf{n} \cdot \mathbf{E})\mathbf{n} = 0, \tag{12–20}$$

where

$$a \triangleq \mu\varepsilon_0(\omega/\gamma)^2. \tag{12–21}$$

Equations (12–20) can be reduced to a characteristic equation whose solutions determine the propagation function γ. To carry out the reduction, we note that $\boldsymbol{\chi}$ has the following properties:

$$\mathbf{i}_x \cdot \boldsymbol{\chi} = \mathbf{i}_x\chi - \mathbf{i}_y j\kappa, \qquad \mathbf{i}_y \cdot \boldsymbol{\chi} = \mathbf{i}_x j\kappa + \mathbf{i}_y\chi,$$

$$\boldsymbol{\chi} \cdot \mathbf{i}_x = \mathbf{i}_x\chi + \mathbf{i}_y j\kappa, \qquad \boldsymbol{\chi} \cdot \mathbf{i}_y = -\mathbf{i}_x j\kappa + \mathbf{i}_y\chi, \tag{12–22}$$

$$\mathbf{i}_z \cdot \boldsymbol{\chi} = \boldsymbol{\chi} \cdot \mathbf{i}_z = \mathbf{i}_z\chi_z.$$

It follows from Eqs. (12–22) that

$$\mathbf{i}_x \cdot \boldsymbol{\chi} \cdot \mathbf{E} = \chi E_x - j\kappa E_y, \qquad \mathbf{i}_y \cdot \boldsymbol{\chi} \cdot \mathbf{E} = j\kappa E_x + \chi E_y. \tag{12–23}$$

The vector $\mathbf{n}$ (see Fig. 12–2) is given by

$$\mathbf{n} = \mathbf{i}_x \sin\theta + \mathbf{i}_z \cos\theta.$$

Thus

$$\mathbf{n} \cdot \mathbf{E} = E_x \sin\theta + E_z \cos\theta. \tag{12–24}$$

When we scalar-multiply Eq. (12–20) from the left with $\mathbf{i}_x$, $\mathbf{i}_y$, and $\mathbf{i}_z$, respectively, and use Eqs. (12–23) and (21–24), we obtain

$$[1 + (1 + \chi)a - \sin^2\theta]E_x \qquad -ja\kappa E_y \qquad -\sin\theta\cos\theta \cdot E_z = 0, \tag{12–25a}$$

$$ja\kappa E_x + [1 + (1 + \chi)a]E_y + \qquad 0 \cdot E_z = 0, \tag{12–25b}$$

$$-\sin\theta\cos\theta \cdot E_x \qquad +0 \cdot E_y + [a(1 + \chi_z) + \sin^2\theta]E_z = 0. \tag{12–25c}$$

The system of equations (12–25) has a nonzero solution when the determinant vanishes; this yields the characteristic equation

$$\begin{vmatrix} 1 + (1 + \chi)a - \sin^2 \theta & -ja\kappa & -\sin \theta \cos \theta \\ ja\kappa & 1 + (1 + \chi)a & 0 \\ -\sin \theta \cos \theta & 0 & a(1 + \chi_z) + \sin^2 \theta \end{vmatrix} = 0. \quad (12\text{–}26)$$

We can solve Eq. (12–26) for a and then determine the propagation function from Eq. (12–21). There are two important cases. The first case is that of the *Faraday effect*, in which the direction of propagation is parallel to $\mathbf{B}_0$ so that $\theta = 0$. Equation (12–26) yields

$$1 + (1 + \chi)a = \pm a\kappa. \quad (12\text{–}27)$$

When we let

$$\gamma = \alpha + j\beta, \qquad u = 1/\sqrt{\mu\varepsilon_0},$$

we find two possible solutions (note Eqs. 12–13 and 12–15):

$$\gamma_+ = \alpha_+ + j\beta_+ = j\frac{\omega}{u}\sqrt{1 + \chi - \kappa} = j\frac{\omega}{u}\sqrt{1 + \chi_+}, \quad (12\text{–}28a)$$

$$\gamma_- = \alpha_- + j\beta_- = j\frac{\omega}{u}\sqrt{1 + \chi_-}. \quad (12\text{–}28b)$$

With the aid of Eqs. (12–25a) and (12–27) we obtain

$$E_x = \pm jE_y, \quad (12\text{–}29)$$

and from Eq. (12–25c) we see that $E_z = 0$. The components H_x and H_y can be determined from Eq. (12–18a) and we find that

$$\frac{H_x}{H_y} = -\frac{E_y}{E_x} = \pm j. \quad (12\text{–}30)$$

The positive and negative signs in Eqs. (12–29) and (12–30) correspond to positively and negatively circularly polarized plane waves, respectively. The propagation functions for these polarized waves are given by Eqs. (12–28). The Faraday effect is a consequence of the difference in the propagation functions.

The second case is that of the *Cotton-Mouton effect*, in which the direction of propagation is normal to $\mathbf{B}_0$ so that $\theta = \pi/2$. Equation (12–26) yields

$$[(1 + \chi_z)a + 1][1 + \chi + (1 + \chi)^2 a - a\kappa^2] = 0$$

and we find two possible solutions. These two solutions represent the propagation functions for an *ordinary wave* and for an *extraordinary wave*, respectively:

$$\gamma_1 = j\frac{\omega}{u}\sqrt{1 + \chi_z},$$ (12–31a)

$$\gamma_2 = j\frac{\omega}{u}\sqrt{\frac{(1 + \chi)^2 - \kappa^2}{1 + \chi}}.$$ (12–31b)

In the case of γ_1, where $(1 + \chi_z)a + 1 = 0$, we see from Eqs. (12–25) that $E_x = E_y = 0$ and $E_z \neq 0$, and from Eq. (12–18a) we find

$$\mathbf{H} = -\mathbf{i}_y \frac{\sqrt{1 + \chi_z}}{u\mu} E_z.$$

This is the case of a plane *TEM* wave propagating with a phase velocity

$$u/\sqrt{1 + \chi_z} = 1/\sqrt{\mu\varepsilon_0(1 + \chi_z)}.$$

For the solution γ_2 we have $(1 + \chi_z)a \neq -1$. It then follows from Eqs. (12–25) that we must have

$$E_x/E_y = j\kappa/(1 + \chi),$$ (12–32)

and $E_z = 0$. From Eq. (12–18a) we obtain

$$H_x = H_y = 0, \qquad H_z = \frac{\gamma_2}{j\omega\mu} E_y.$$

The extraordinary plane wave has a nonzero component E_x in the direction of propagation. However, it follows from Eqs. (12–9) and (12–32) that

$$D_x = \varepsilon_0 E_x + P_x = \varepsilon_0(E_x + \chi E_x - j\kappa E_y) = 0.$$

Thus both **H** and **D** are normal to the direction of propagation.

12-4 THE FARADAY ROTATION

A linearly polarized plane wave propagating in the direction of the positive z-axis can be considered to result from the superposition of two circularly polarized fields (Fig. 12–3). Thus, for the electric field intensity, we can write

$$\mathbf{E} = \mathbf{n}_+ E_0 \cos(\omega t - \beta_+ z) + \mathbf{n}_- E_0 \cos(\omega t - \beta_- z),$$

where $\mathbf{n}_+$ and $\mathbf{n}_-$ are unit vectors in the xy-plane which rotate with an angular velocity ω in a positive and negative sense, respectively. Here we take the direction of the linear polarization at $z = 0$ to be along the x-axis. In an isotropic medium $\beta_+ = \beta_-$ and the direction of polarization does not change. However, in the Faraday effect the propagation functions for the positively and negatively circularly polarized waves are different, and this results

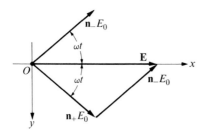

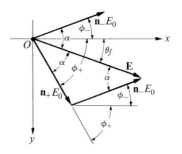

Fig. 12–3. A view in the direction of the positive z-axis of a linearly polarized electric field at $z = 0$ resolved into a positively and a negatively circularly polarized electric field.

Fig. 12–4. A view in the direction of the positive z-axis of the linearly polarized electric field at $z > 0$.

in a rotation θ_f of the direction of polarization (see Fig. 12–4). When we let

$$\phi_+ = \omega t - \beta_+ z, \qquad \phi_- = \omega t - \beta_- z,$$

we see that

$$\phi_+ + \phi_- = 2\alpha = 2(\phi_+ - \theta_f).$$

Thus

$$\theta_f = \tfrac{1}{2}(\phi_+ - \phi_-) = \frac{z}{2}(\beta_- - \beta_+). \tag{12–33}$$

Substituting Eqs. (12–28) and noting that $\alpha_+ = \alpha_- = 0$ yields the *Faraday rotation*, we have

$$\theta_f = \frac{\omega z}{2u}(\sqrt{1 + \chi_-} - \sqrt{1 + \chi_+}). \tag{12–34}$$

With the aid of Eqs. (12–13) and (12–15) we can express the Faraday rotation in the form

$$\theta_f = \frac{\omega z}{2u}\left[\sqrt{1 - \frac{\omega_p^2}{\omega(\omega + \omega_0)}} - \sqrt{1 + \frac{\omega_p^2}{\omega(\omega - \omega_0)}}\right]. \tag{12–35}$$

For the case in which $\omega > \omega_p$ and $\omega > \omega_0$, we can expand Eq. (12–35) in a Taylor series and obtain

$$\theta_f \simeq \frac{\omega_0 z}{2u}\left(\frac{\omega_p}{\omega}\right)^2. \tag{12–36}$$

Example. Let us compute the Larmor frequency, the plasma frequency, and the Faraday rotation per meter, given the following data:

$$e/m = 1.76 \times 10^{11} \text{ C/kg}, \qquad e = 1.602 \times 10^{-19} \text{ C},$$

$$B_0 = 0.5 \times 10^{-4} \text{ Wb/m}^2, \qquad N = 4 \times 10^{11} \text{ electrons/m}^3,$$

$$f = 10 \text{ MHz}.$$

We can obtain the desired frequencies by substituting the above values into the equations

$$f_0 = \frac{1}{2\pi}\frac{eB_0}{m} = 1.4 \text{ MHz}, \qquad f_p = \frac{1}{2\pi}\sqrt{\frac{e}{m}\left(\frac{Ne}{\varepsilon_0}\right)} = 5.68 \text{ MHz}.$$

Taking $\mu \cong \mu_0$, so that $u = 3 \times 10^8$ m/sec, we find, from Eq. (12–36), the Faraday rotation per meter:

$$\theta_f/z = 4.73 \times 10^{-3} \text{ rad/m} = 0.271 \text{ deg/m}.$$

12–5 GEOMETRIC OPTICS APPROXIMATION IN THE CASE OF NEGLIGIBLE MAGNETIC FIELD

The problem of wave propagation in the ionosphere is complicated by the fact that $\mathbf{B}_0$ and N are functions of position. If, as a first approximation, we neglect the effect of the earth's magnetic field, we have $\omega_0 = 0$. Thus $\chi = \chi_z$, $\kappa = 0$, and we obtain a solution which represents an ordinary plane wave (see Eq. 12–31a) with a phase velocity $u = c/\sqrt{1 + \chi_z}$. Thus we see that the ionized gas has an effective permittivity of

$$\varepsilon = \varepsilon_0(1 + \chi_z) = \varepsilon_0[1 - (\omega_p/\omega)^2], \qquad (12\text{–}37)$$

and that the index of refraction (see Section 9–9) is $n = \sqrt{1 - (\omega_p/\omega)^2}$.

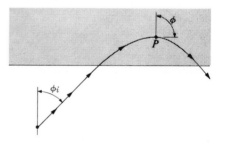

Fig. 12–5. The reflection of a plane electromagnetic wave from the ionosphere.

When we treat a plane wave in the geometric optics approximation we can apply Snell's law and obtain

$$\sin \phi_i = n \sin \phi,$$

(see Fig. 12–5). The wave is reflected back to the earth if at some field point P we have $\phi = 90°$. This requires that $\sin \phi_i = n$. In the case of vertical incidence $\phi_i = 0$, and we find the critical frequency

$$f_p = \frac{e}{2\pi}\sqrt{\frac{N}{\varepsilon_0 m}} \cong 9\sqrt{N}, \qquad (12\text{–}38)$$

above which a wave cannot propagate through the ionosphere and is totally reflected (see Problem 12–1). The above formula for f_p is useful in the experimental evaluation of N.

12-6 THE TENSOR SUSCEPTIBILITY OF A FERRITE

Let us consider an orbital electron of an atom which moves in a circular orbit of radius r with a velocity $\mathbf{u}$. The motion of the electron has a magnetic effect which is equivalent to a current loop of radius r carrying a current

$$i = -eu/2\pi r,$$

where e is the magnitude of the electron charge. The magnetic dipole moment of the orbital electron is

$$\mathbf{M} = \mathbf{n}i\pi r^2 = -\mathbf{n}\frac{eur}{2},$$

where $\mathbf{n}$ is a unit vector which is normal to the plane of the current loop and whose direction forms a right-handed system with respect to the direction of current flow in the loop (Fig. 12–6). The angular momentum of the orbital electron is

$$\mathbf{L} = \mathbf{n}\,mur = \frac{1}{\gamma}\mathbf{M},$$

where $\gamma \triangleq -e/2m$ is called the *gyromagnetic ratio*; it is the ratio of the components of the magnetic moment and the angular momentum in the $\mathbf{n}$-direction.

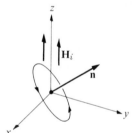

Fig. 12–6. A current loop in a magnetic field.

Magnetic effects are largely due to spinning electrons and their coupling to each other and to the crystal lattice, factors which are accounted for by the *Landé g-factor*. Thus

$$\gamma = -eg/2m.$$

For the free electron spin $g = 2$, while in materials such as ferrite g is somewhat larger. Let us consider the motion of $\mathbf{M}$ in a uniform internal magnetic field $\mathbf{H}_i$. The rate of change of angular momentum is equal to the applied torque. Thus $d\mathbf{L}/dt = \mu_0\mathbf{M} \times \mathbf{H}_i$, and we obtain

$$d\mathbf{M}/dt = \mu_0\gamma\mathbf{M} \times \mathbf{H}_i. \qquad (12\text{–}39)$$

The numerical values for a free electron are:

$$g = 2, \quad e = 1.602 \times 10^{-19}\,\text{C}, \quad m = 9.107 \times 10^{-31}\,\text{kg},$$
$$\mu_0 = 4\pi \times 10^{-7}\,\text{H/m}.$$

Since dimensional units can be determined by introducing phasor notation in Eq. 12–39, we find that

$$\mu_0\gamma = -2.21 \times 10^5 \text{ (rad/sec)(ampere-turns/m)}^{-1}.$$

When we deal with magnetic media, we usually use cgs units. Since 1 ampere-turn/m $= 4\pi \times 10^{-3}$ Oe, we have

$$\mu_0\gamma = -17.6 \times 10^6 \text{ (rad/sec)(Oe)}^{-1} = -2.8 \text{ (MHz)(Oe)}^{-1}. \quad (12\text{–}40)$$

In a ferrite the electron spins form groups which align themselves either parallel or antiparallel to the internal magnetic field $\mathbf{H}_i$. The resultant uncompensated spins are parallel and are described macroscopically by the magnetization vector $\mathbf{M}$. The ferrite is considered to be saturated when a further increase in $\mathbf{H}_i$ results in no further change in $\mathbf{M}$. Let us now superimpose an external high-frequency field $\mathbf{H}_e$ on an external dc field $\mathbf{H}_{e0}$. Due to the demagnetization effects of induced magnetic charges, the internal fields of a ferrite sample can be different. These fields are represented by $\mathbf{H}$ and $\mathbf{H}_0$, respectively (Fig. 12–7). Due to $\mathbf{H}$ there is a high-frequency torque acting on the electrons which results in a precession of $\mathbf{M}$ about $\mathbf{H}_0$. If $\mathbf{H}$ is suddenly removed, the coupling between the electron spins and the crystal lattice of the ferrite results in a damping of the precessional motion, so that $\mathbf{M}$ eventually becomes parallel to $\mathbf{H}_0$ and assumes its dc value $\mathbf{M}_0$. To account for the damping, we introduce a damping torque $\mathbf{T}_d$ on the right-hand side of Eq. (12–39). Let us assume that the damping is of such a nature that M remains constant. If $\mathbf{M} \cdot \mathbf{M} = \text{const}$, we have $\mathbf{M} \cdot (d\mathbf{M}/dt) = 0$. It follows that $\mathbf{M} \cdot \mathbf{T}_d = 0$, and we can therefore choose

$$\mathbf{T}_d = D\,\frac{\mathbf{M}}{M} \times \frac{d\mathbf{M}}{dt},$$

where D is a constant. The equation of motion is now

$$\frac{d\mathbf{M}}{dt} = \mu_0\gamma\mathbf{M} \times \mathbf{H}_i + D\gamma\,\frac{\mathbf{M}}{M} \times \frac{d\mathbf{M}}{dt}. \quad (12\text{–}41)$$

The internal magnetic field, $\mathbf{H}_i = \mathbf{i}_z H_0 + \mathbf{H}$, results in a magnetization $\mathbf{M} = \mathbf{i}_z M_0 + \mathbf{m}$. We take $|H/H_0| \ll 1$ so that $|m/M_0| \ll 1$. When we neglect terms of higher order than the first, we find from Eq. (12–41) that

$$\frac{d\mathbf{m}}{dt} = \mu_0\gamma(\mathbf{M}_0 \times \mathbf{H} + H_0\mathbf{m} \times \mathbf{i}_z) + \alpha_d\mathbf{i}_z \times \frac{d\mathbf{m}}{dt}, \quad (12\text{–}42)$$

where $\alpha_d \triangleq \gamma D$. Using phasor notation and expressing the above equation in terms of its x- and y-components yields

$$j\omega m_x = -(\omega_0 + j\omega\alpha_d)m_y + \omega_M H_y, \quad (12\text{–}43a)$$

$$j\omega m_y = (\omega_0 + j\omega\alpha_d)m_x - \omega_M H_x, \quad (12\text{–}43b)$$

where

$$\omega_0 \triangleq -\mu_0 \gamma H_0, \qquad (12\text{-}44\text{a})$$

$$\omega_M \triangleq -\mu_0 \gamma M_0. \qquad (12\text{-}44\text{b})$$

The frequency $f_0 = \omega_0/2\pi$ is known as the Larmor frequency.

In order to solve Eqs. (12–43) for **m**, we multiply Eq. (12–43a) by $-j$ and (a) add it to Eq. (12–43) and (b) subtract it from Eq. (12–43). This yields the two equations

$$m_x + jm_y = \chi_+(H_x + jH_y), \qquad (12\text{-}45\text{a})$$

$$m_x - jm_y = \chi_-(H_x - jH_y), \qquad (12\text{-}45\text{b})$$

where

$$\chi_+ \triangleq \frac{\omega_M}{\omega_0 - \omega + j\omega\alpha_d}, \qquad \chi_- \triangleq \frac{\omega_M}{\omega_0 + \omega + j\omega\alpha_d}.$$

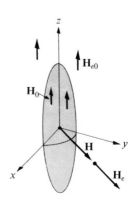

Fig. 12–7. A ferrite sample in a dc field H_{e0} superimposed on a high-frequency field **H**.

By the addition and subtraction of Eqs. (12–45) we find the components of **m**:

$$m_x = \chi H_x - j\kappa H_y, \qquad m_y = j\kappa H_x + \chi H_y, \qquad m_z = 0,$$

where

$$\chi \triangleq \tfrac{1}{2}(\chi_+ + \chi_-) = \frac{\omega_M(\omega_0 + j\omega\alpha_d)}{(\omega_0 + j\omega\alpha_d)^2 - \omega^2},$$

$$\kappa \triangleq \tfrac{1}{2}(\chi_- - \chi_+) = \frac{-\omega\omega_M}{(\omega_0 + j\omega\alpha_d)^2 - \omega^2}. \qquad (12\text{-}46)$$

The component m_z is zero, since the magnetization is saturated in the direction of the z-axis by the dc field H_0. In matrix form we have

$$\begin{pmatrix} m_x \\ m_y \\ m_z \end{pmatrix} = \begin{pmatrix} \chi & -j\kappa & 0 \\ j\kappa & \chi & 0 \\ 0 & 0 & 0 \end{pmatrix} \begin{pmatrix} H_x \\ H_y \\ H_z \end{pmatrix}. \qquad (12\text{-}47)$$

Equation (12–47) can be written in the equivalent vector form

$$\mathbf{m} = \boldsymbol{\chi} \cdot \mathbf{H}, \qquad (12\text{-}48)$$

where $\boldsymbol{\chi}$ is the *tensor susceptibility*.

The dc field required to saturate a ferrite is of the order of 100 Oe and this can result in an undesirable power dissipation in the coil supplying the magnetic field. A ferrite is therefore often used at a field strength below saturation and we then have a relation of the form

$$m_z = \chi_z H_z,$$

where χ_z approaches zero as the magnetization approaches saturation. The tensor susceptibility then has the form given by Eq. (12–4), so that

$$
\begin{pmatrix} m_x \\ m_y \\ m_z \end{pmatrix} = \begin{pmatrix} \chi & -j\kappa & 0 \\ j\kappa & \chi & 0 \\ 0 & 0 & \chi_z \end{pmatrix} \begin{pmatrix} H_x \\ H_y \\ H_z \end{pmatrix}. \tag{12–49}
$$

Equations (12–46) are no longer applicable below saturation. However, the form (12–49) remains valid provided that we introduce suitable values for χ, κ, and χ_z [1].

Due to the demagnetizing effect of induced magnetic surface charges, the field $\mathbf{H}$ inside the ferrite differs from the external field $\mathbf{H}_e$. When the dimensions of the ferrite sample are sufficiently small, we can use quasi-static methods to determine the relationship between $\mathbf{H}$ and $\mathbf{H}_e$. If $\mathbf{H}_e$ is uniform and if the sample is of uniform composition and its shape is that of an ellipsoid of revolution or of a limiting form that can be obtained from the ellipsoid, such as a cylinder or a circular disk, we can express $\mathbf{H}$ in terms of $\mathbf{H}_e$ and the demagnetization factors N_x and N_y:

$$
\mathbf{H} = \mathbf{H}_e - (\mathbf{i}_x N_x m_x + \mathbf{i}_y N_y m_y).
$$

Similarly, the relationship between $\mathbf{H}_0$ and $\mathbf{H}_{e0}$ is given by

$$
\mathbf{H}_0 = \mathbf{H}_{e0} - \mathbf{i}_z N_z M_0.
$$

The demagnetization factors satisfy the equation $N_x + N_y + N_z = 1$.

In order to determine the relationship between $\mathbf{m}$ and $\mathbf{H}_e$, we consider the equation

$$
\mathbf{m} = \boldsymbol{\chi} \cdot \mathbf{H} = \boldsymbol{\chi} \cdot [\mathbf{H}_e - (\mathbf{i}_x N_x m_x + \mathbf{i}_y N_y m_y)].
$$

We obtain the x- and y-components of the above equation by scalar multiplication by $\mathbf{i}_x$ and $\mathbf{i}_y$, respectively. Thus (see Eqs. 12–22)

$$
(1 + \chi N_x)m_x - j\kappa N_y m_y = \chi H_{xe} - j\kappa H_{ye},
$$

$$
j\kappa N_x m_x + (1 + \chi N_y)m_y = j\kappa H_{xe} + \chi H_{ye}.
$$

Solving for m_x and m_y yields

$$
m_x = \frac{\omega_M(\omega_0 + N_y \omega_M + j\omega\alpha_d)}{D} H_{xe} + j\frac{\omega\omega_M}{D} H_{ye},
$$

$$
m_y = -j\frac{\omega\omega_M}{D} H_{xe} + \frac{\omega_M(\omega_0 + N_x \omega_M + j\omega\alpha_d)}{D} H_{ye}, \tag{12–50}
$$

where

$$
\begin{aligned}
D &\triangleq [1 + \chi(N_x + N_y) + (\chi^2 - \kappa^2)N_x N_y][(\omega_0 + j\omega\alpha_d)^2 - \omega^2] \\
&= [\omega_e + (N_x - N_z)\omega_M + j\omega\alpha_d][\omega_e + (N_y - N_z)\omega_M + j\omega\alpha_d] - \omega^2,
\end{aligned}
$$

and where (see Eq. 12–44a) $\omega_e \triangleq -\mu_0 \gamma H_{e0}$. Here $H_{e0} = H_0 + N_z M_0$ is the magnitude of the externally applied dc magnetic field intensity.

Resonance occurs at angular frequencies determined by the zeros of D. Due to the assumed symmetry of the ferrite sample we have $N_x = N_y$, and if we neglect α_d the resonant frequency is determined by

$$\omega_r \triangleq \omega_e + (N_x - N_z)\omega_M = \omega_0 + N_x \omega_M. \qquad (12\text{–}51)$$

The physical significance of the resonant frequency and the Larmor frequency can be seen if we let $\mathbf{H}_e = 0$, so that only the dc field $\mathbf{H}_{e0}$ is applied. The magnetization can then precess about $\mathbf{H}_{e0}$ with an angular velocity ω_r. However, due to the damping, which has been neglected, $\mathbf{M}$ eventually becomes parallel to $\mathbf{H}_{e0}$ and assumes its dc value $\mathbf{M}_0$. If a lossless ferrite is of infinite extent so that there are no demagnetizing effects, we have $N_x = N_z = 0$ and $\omega_r = \omega_0$. Thus the magnetization $\mathbf{M}$ in an infinite lossless ferrite medium can precess at the Larmor frequency about the applied dc magnetic field $\mathbf{H}_{e0}$.

If the ferrite is lossy, a high-frequency excitation $\mathbf{H}_e$ must be applied in order for $\mathbf{M}$ to have a steady-state precession. As the frequency of excitation approaches the resonant frequency, there is a resonance absorption of energy from the field which is dissipated as heat in the ferrite.

Most of the literature on the subject of ferrites uses cgs units, in which B' gauss $= c_0(H' + 4\pi M_g')$ Oe, and in which $c_0 = 1$ gauss/Oe is a dimensional conversion factor which is often neglected, since it is of unit magnitude. We can readily accomplish the conversion between units if we note that a physical quantity F is represented as

$$F = F_1' a_1 = F_2' a_2,$$

where F_1' and F_2' are dimensionless numbers, a_1 is the fundamental unit in the first system of units and a_2 is a fundamental unit in the second system of units. If we choose $F_1' = 1$, we can then determine the numerical conversion factor F_2' between the systems of units. For example,

$$1 \text{ Oe} = \frac{10^3}{4\pi} \text{ ampere-turns/m.}$$

It is a common practice to express the numerical value of the saturation magnetization in terms of the saturation flux density B_s' gauss. Thus

$$B_s' \text{ gauss} = c_0 4\pi M_g' \text{ Oe,}$$

and the numerical value of the above equation yields $B_s' = 4\pi M_g'$. For the magnetization, when we use $F_1' = M_0'$ and $F_2' = 4\pi M_g'$, we have

$$M_0' \text{ ampere turns/m} = 4\pi M_g' \text{ Oe} = B_s' \text{ Oe} = B_s' \frac{10^3}{4\pi} \text{ ampere-turns/m.}$$

Thus

$$M_0' = B_s' \frac{10^3}{4\pi}.$$

Substituting into Eq. (12–44b) and noting Eq. (12–40), we obtain

$$f_M = \omega_M/2\pi = 2.8(\text{MHz})(\text{Oe})^{-1}B_s'(\text{Oe}) = 2.8B_s' \text{ MHz}, \quad (12\text{–}52)$$

where B_s' is the numerical value of the saturation flux density, measured in gauss. The Larmor frequency (see Eq. 12–44a) is

$$f_0 = \omega_0/2\pi = 2.8H_0' \text{ MHz}, \quad (12\text{–}53)$$

where H_0' is the numerical value of the internal dc magnetic field intensity measured in oersteds.

Example. Let us consider a ferrite sample for which the saturation flux density is B_s' gauss $= 3000$ gauss. We wish to determine the Larmor and the resonant frequency.

Substituting into Eq. (12–52) yields $f_M = 8.4$ GHz. Let the dc magnetic field strength be such that $H_0 = 1000$ Oe. The Larmor frequency is determined by Eq. (12–53): $f_0 = 2.8$ GHz. If the ferrite sample is a sphere, we have $N_x = N_y = N_z = \frac{1}{3}$, and it follows from Eq. (12–51) that the resonant frequency is $f_r = 5.6$ GHz.

Note that in the cgs system of units the numerical value of H_{e0} is given by

$$H_{e0}' = H_0' + N_z 4\pi M_0' = H_0' + \tfrac{1}{3}B_s' = 2000.$$

The external magnetic field intensity has a magnitude of 2000 Oe. We can see why cgs units are preferred when we look at the awkwardly large numerical values which are obtained when one uses mks units:

$$H_0' \text{ ampere-turns/m} = 79{,}600 \text{ ampere-turns/m},$$

$$M_0' \text{ ampere-turns/m} = B_s' \frac{10^3}{4\pi} \text{ ampere-turns/m} = 238{,}700 \text{ ampere-turns/m},$$

$$H_{e0}' \text{ ampere-turns/m} = (H_0' + N_z M_0') \text{ ampere-turns/m} = 159{,}200$$

$$\text{ampere-turns/m}.$$

12–7 THE TENSOR PERMEABILITY OF A FERRITE

The *tensor permeability* $\boldsymbol{\mu}$ is defined by the equation $\mathbf{B} = \boldsymbol{\mu} \cdot \mathbf{H}$. Thus $\boldsymbol{\mu} \triangleq \mu(\mathbf{e} + \boldsymbol{\chi})$, where $\mathbf{e}$ is the unit tensor. We shall now show that $\boldsymbol{\mu}$ can be represented by a scalar for the circularly polarized solutions of Eqs. (12–45). Equations (12–45) are satisfied if

$$H_x = jH_y, \quad m_x = jm_y.$$

The phasor magnetic field intensity in the xy-plane is then

$$\mathbf{H}_T \triangleq \mathbf{i}_x H_x - \mathbf{i}_y j H_x,$$

and if we take H_x to be real, we find that the vector

$$\text{Re } [\mathbf{H}_T e^{j\omega t}] = (\mathbf{i}_x \cos \omega t + \mathbf{i}_y \sin \omega t) H_x$$

rotates in the xy-plane in a positive sense; we speak of Re $[\mathbf{H}_T \, e^{j\omega t}]$ as a positively circularly polarized magnetic field. From Eq. (12–45a) we see that

$$\mathbf{m} = \mathbf{i}_x m_x + \mathbf{i}_y m_y = \chi_+ \mathbf{H}_T.$$

Thus, for a positively circularly polarized magnetic field, we have a permeability

$$\mu_+ \triangleq \mu_0(1 + \chi_+) = \mu_0\left(1 + \frac{\omega_M}{\omega_0 - \omega}\right). \qquad (12\text{–}54)$$

Here we have neglected α_d in the second equation (for a typical ferrite $\alpha_d \cong 0.05$). Similarly, if we take

$$H_x = -jH_y, \qquad m_x = -jm_y,$$

we obtain a solution of Eqs. (12–45) for which Re $[\mathbf{H}_T e^{j\omega t}]$ is a negatively circularly polarized magnetic field. For this case the permeability is

$$\mu_- \triangleq \mu_0(1 + \chi_-) = \mu_0\left(1 + \frac{\omega_M}{\omega_0 + \omega}\right), \qquad (12\text{–}55)$$

where we have again neglected α_d in the second equation.

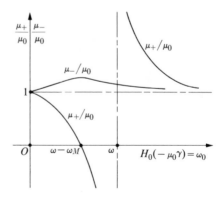

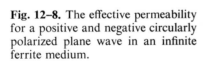

Fig. 12–8. The effective permeability for a positive and negative circularly polarized plane wave in an infinite ferrite medium.

Figure 12–8 illustrates a plot of μ_+/μ_0 and μ_-/μ_0 against the dc field H_0 for a constant value of ω. Equations (12–54) and (12–55) are still applicable below the saturation value of M_0, provided that we use the general form (12–49) of the tensor susceptibility, where the elements χ, κ, and χ_z are no longer constants but are functions of H_0 [1].

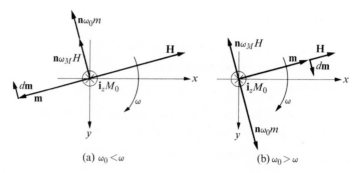

(a) $\omega_0 < \omega$ (b) $\omega_0 > \omega$

Fig. 12–9. The behavior of $\mathbf{m} = \chi_+\mathbf{H}$ as a function of ω viewed in the direction of the positive z-axis.

We can understand the behavior of μ_+ and μ_- as functions of H_0 with the aid of Eq. (12–42) and Fig. 12–9. If we neglect α_d, it follows from Eq. (12–42) that the elemental vector $d\mathbf{m}$ has the direction of the vector

$$\mu_0\gamma(\mathbf{M}_0 \times \mathbf{H} + H_0\mathbf{m} \times \mathbf{i}_z).$$

Let us consider the case in which $\mathbf{H}$ rotates with an angular velocity $\boldsymbol{\omega} = \mathbf{i}_z\omega$ in the xy-plane. Given that $\omega_0 < \omega$, where $\omega_0 \triangleq -\mu_0\gamma H_0$, $d\mathbf{m}$ has the direction of the vector

$$\mu_0\gamma H_0\mathbf{m} \times \mathbf{i}_z = \mathbf{n}\omega_0 m,$$

as shown in Fig. 12–9a; the unit vector $\mathbf{n}$ is defined by the above equation. Since $d\mathbf{m} = \mathbf{n}m\omega\, dt$ and $\mu_0\gamma\mathbf{M}_0 \times \mathbf{H} = \mathbf{n}\omega_M H$, the magnitude of Eq. (12–42) yields

$$m = \frac{\omega_M}{\omega - \omega_0}\, H.$$

Thus, noting that $\mathbf{H}$ and $\mathbf{m}$ have opposite directions,

$$\mathbf{m} = -\frac{\omega_M}{\omega - \omega_0}\, \mathbf{H} = \chi_+\mathbf{H},$$

and we see that $\chi_+ < 0$. When $\omega_0 > \omega$, the vectors $\mathbf{m}$ and $\mathbf{H}$ have the same directions, as shown in Fig. 12–9b. The magnitude of Eq. (12–42) now yields

$$m = \frac{\omega_M}{\omega_0 - \omega}\, H.$$

Thus

$$\mathbf{m} = \frac{\omega_M}{\omega_0 - \omega}\, \mathbf{H},$$

and we obtain $\chi_+ > 0$. Thus we see that the positively circularly polarized solution of Eqs. (12–45) can be represented by the vector $\mathbf{m}$ illustrated in Fig. 12–9. The vector $\mathbf{m}$ rotates with an angular velocity ω in the positive sense. The considerations for χ_- are similar. The vector **m** then rotates with an angular velocity ω in the negative sense. When $H = 0$, the vector **m** can rotate in the positive sense with an angular velocity given by the Larmor angular frequency.

When we wish to account for the effect of demagnetization due to induced magnetic surface charges, we must express Eqs. (12–50) in the form given by Eqs. (12–45). This is possible if $N_x = N_y$, and we find that

$$\chi_+ = \frac{\omega_M}{\omega_r - \omega + j\omega\alpha_d}, \qquad \chi_- = \frac{\omega_M}{\omega_r + \omega + j\omega\alpha_d},$$

where ω_r is given by Eq. (12–51). It is interesting to note that the internal field responsible for resonance is not only $H_{e0} - N_z M_0$, the internal dc field, but has a component due to magnetic surface charges induced by the high-frequency field. The effect of the latter component on the resonance frequency is accounted for by the demagnetization factors N_x and N_y.

12-8 PROPAGATION OF PLANE ELECTRO-MAGNETIC WAVES IN AN INFINITE FERRITE MEDIUM

To investigate the possibility of having a plane propagating electromagnetic wave in an infinite ferrite medium, we let **n** be a unit normal in the direction of propagation and let z' be the coordinate in the **n**-direction (see Fig. 12–2). Equations (12–16) apply in the case of a plane wave. Noting Eq. (12–17), we can write Maxwell's equations in the form

$$-\gamma \mathbf{n} \times \mathbf{E} = -j\omega \mathbf{B}, \qquad -\gamma \mathbf{n} \times \mathbf{H} = j\omega\varepsilon\mathbf{E}.$$

Thus

$$\frac{\gamma}{j\omega} \mathbf{E} \times \mathbf{n} = -\mathbf{B}, \qquad \frac{\gamma}{j\omega} \mathbf{H} \times \mathbf{n} = \varepsilon\mathbf{E}. \tag{12–56}$$

Eliminating **E** from the above equations yields

$$(\mathbf{H} \times \mathbf{n}) \times \mathbf{n} = \varepsilon(\omega/\gamma)^2 \mathbf{B}. \tag{12–57}$$

It follows from Eqs. (12–56) that $\mathbf{E} \cdot \mathbf{n} = 0$ and $\mathbf{B} \cdot \mathbf{n} = 0$. However, since **B** and **H** do not, in general, have the same direction, we see from Eq. (12–57) that we then have $\mathbf{H} \cdot \mathbf{n} \neq 0$.

Let us assume that the ferrite is saturated by an internal dc magnetic field $\mathbf{H}_0 = \mathbf{i}_z H_0$. In an infinite medium we need not consider demagnetization effects due to induced magnetic surface charges. The tensor susceptibility is then given by Eq. (12–49), and we can express Eq. (12–57) in the form

$$(1 + a)\mathbf{H} + a\boldsymbol{\chi} \cdot \mathbf{H} - (\mathbf{n} \cdot \mathbf{H})\mathbf{n} = 0, \tag{12–58}$$

where

$$a \triangleq \mu_0\varepsilon(\omega/\gamma)^2. \tag{12–59}$$

Equation (12–58) has the same form as Eq. (12–20). The characteristic equation (12–26) holds and the propagation functions are given by Eqs. (12–28) in the case of the Faraday effect ($\theta = 0$) and by Eqs. (12–31) in the case of the Cotton-Mouton effect ($\pi/2 = 0$). Here we shall discuss the case of $\theta = 0$ for a ferrite where $\alpha_d \ll 1$. The propagation functions given by Eqs. (12–28) can be written in the form

$$\gamma_+ = \alpha_+ + j\beta_+ = j\frac{\omega}{u}\sqrt{\frac{\mu_+}{\mu_0}}, \tag{12–60a}$$

$$\gamma_- = \alpha_- + j\beta_- = j\frac{\omega}{u}\sqrt{\frac{\mu_-}{\mu_0}}, \tag{12–60b}$$

where (see Eqs. 12–45)

$$\frac{\mu_+}{\mu_0} = \frac{\omega_0 - \omega + \omega_M + j\omega\alpha_d}{\omega_0 - \omega + j\omega\alpha_d},$$

$$\frac{\mu_-}{\mu_0} = \frac{\omega_0 + \omega + \omega_M + j\omega\alpha_d}{\omega_0 + \omega + j\omega\alpha_d}.$$

When $\alpha_d = 0$, μ_- is real and greater than zero. Thus $\alpha_- = 0$, and the negatively circularly polarized wave propagates without attenuation. To determine α_+, we must investigate arg $[\mu_+]$ as a function of ω_0. Given that $\alpha_d = 0$ and that $\omega - \omega_M < \omega_0 < \omega$, we see that $\mu_+ < 0$. Thus arg $[\mu_+]$ is an odd multiple of π. To determine the correct multiple of π, we let $\omega - \omega_0 = \varepsilon$, where ε is a positive arbitrarily small number, and obtain

$$\frac{\mu_+}{\mu_0} \cong -\frac{\omega_m}{\varepsilon} - \frac{j\omega\alpha_d}{\varepsilon}.$$

From this equation we see that arg $[\mu_+] \to -\pi$ as $\alpha_d \to 0$. Thus

$$\text{arg } [\mu_+] = \begin{cases} 0, & 0 < \omega_0 < \omega - \omega_M, \\ -\pi, & \omega - \omega_M < \omega_0 < \omega, \\ 0, & \omega_0 > \omega. \end{cases}$$

In the range $\omega - \omega_M < \omega_0 < \omega$, we find that

$$j\sqrt{\mu_+} = j\sqrt{|\mu_+|}\, e^{-j\pi/2} = \sqrt{|\mu_+|} > 0,$$

and as a consequence, the positively circularly polarized wave is attenuated in the direction of propagation. However, it should be noted that we are considering the case of an infinite medium. Practical considerations require that the dimensions of the medium be finite, a restriction which can result in a considerable modification of the propagation function. Thus the attenuation determined above may not be observed in a finite medium.

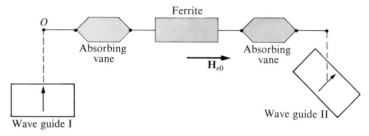

Fig. 12–10. A microwave isolator utilizing the Faraday rotation in a ferrite.

12–9 THE FARADAY ROTATION IN A FERRITE MEDIUM

The Faraday rotation in an anisotropic medium is given by Eq. (12–34). If we neglect α_d we can substitute Eqs. (12–54) and (12–55) and obtain the Faraday rotation in an infinite ferrite medium:

$$\theta_f = \frac{\omega_z}{2u}\left[\sqrt{1 + \frac{\omega_M}{\omega_0 + \omega}} - \sqrt{1 + \frac{\omega_M}{\omega_0 - \omega}}\right]. \qquad (12\text{--}61)$$

Example. In the case of weak fields and low saturation magnetization, we have $\omega_0 \ll \omega$ and $\omega_M \ll \omega$. Thus we can expand Eq. (12–61) in a Taylor series in ω^{-1} to obtain the Faraday rotation per unit length,

$$\theta_f/z \simeq \tfrac{1}{2}\omega_M\sqrt{\mu_0\varepsilon}.$$

Given that the ferrite parameters are B_s' gauss $= 3000$ gauss and $\varepsilon = 10\varepsilon_0$, we have (see Eq. 12–52)

$$f_M = \omega_M/2\pi = 8.4 \text{ GHz}$$

and the Faraday rotation per unit length is

$$\theta_f/z = 2.79 \text{ rad/cm} = 160 \text{ deg/cm}.$$

Figure 12–10 illustrates the application of the Faraday effect in an isolator which allows energy to flow in one direction only. In the isolator there are absorbing vanes which are normal to the incident and transmitted electric field intensities of TE_{10} waves in two rectangular wave guides. A linearly polarized TE_{10} wave in a rectangular wave guide is converted at the origin O into a TE_{11} wave of a circular wave guide by means of a gradual transition. The absorbing vane has a negligible effect on this field. The linearly polarized wave can be resolved into positively and negatively circularly polarized waves and the Faraday effect results in a rotation θ_f of the E-field. At the output, the circularly polarized waves can be combined into a linearly polarized wave. For the isolator, $\theta_f = 45°$, and the electric field intensity at the output is parallel to the electric field intensity of a TE_{10} wave in wave guide II, whose xy-axes are at an angle of $45°$ with respect to the xy-axes of wave guide I. A gradual transition is used at the output to convert the TE_{11} wave of the circular wave guide into a TE_{10} wave of the rectangular wave guide. There is thus negligible attenuation for energy flow from wave guide I to wave guide II.

Let us now consider the backward flow of energy. The Faraday effect is nonreciprocal, so that if there is a reflected TE_{10} wave in wave guide II it will be rotated in the same direction as before and the reflected electric field intensity in wave guide I will then be parallel to the absorbing vane. This results in an evanescent wave in wave guide I and the vane attenuates the field enough so that there is negligible energy reflected back into wave guide II.

12-10 FERRITE IN CAVITIES

When a ferrite sample is placed in a resonant cavity, the resonant frequency changes. This can serve the useful purpose of tuning the cavity by means of an externally applied dc magnetic field. Furthermore, we can determine the susceptibility parameters experimentally by locating the sample in regions in which the E-field is zero and in which the H-field is linearly or circularly polarized. We can obtain the equation giving the change in resonant frequency caused by a ferrite sample from Eq. (10–73) by replacing $\mu_2 H_2$ by B_2. Thus

$$-\frac{\Delta\omega}{\omega_1} = \frac{\int_v [(\mathbf{B}_2 \cdot \mathbf{H}_1^* - \mu_1 \mathbf{H}_2 \cdot \mathbf{H}_1^*) + (\varepsilon_2 - \varepsilon_1)\mathbf{E}_2 \cdot \mathbf{E}_1^*]\, dv}{\int_v [\mathbf{B}_2 \cdot \mathbf{H}_1^* + \varepsilon_2 \mathbf{E}_2 \cdot \mathbf{E}_1^*]\, dv}. \qquad (12\text{-}62)$$

To illustrate the application of Eq. (12–62), let us consider the case of a thin ferrite rod placed on the axis of a circular cylindrical cavity of length l and radius a which is resonant in the TM_{110} circularly polarized mode. This mode is obtained by choosing

$$U = J_1(k_{11}r)e^{-j\phi},$$

where $J_1(k_{11}a) = 0$. The phasor field components are then given by Eqs. (10–4) and (10–5), where we take $u_1 = r$, $u_2 = \phi$, $h_1 = 1$, and $h_2 = r$. The nonzero field components for the unperturbed cavity are

$$E_{z1} = k_{11}^2 J_1(k_{11}r)e^{-j\phi},$$

$$H_{r1} = \frac{\omega\varepsilon_0}{r} J_1(k_{11}r)e^{-j\phi}, \qquad (12\text{-}63)$$

$$H_{\phi 1} = -j\omega\varepsilon_0 k_{11} J_1'(k_{11}r)e^{-j\phi}.$$

Let the applied dc magnetic field $\mathbf{H}_{e0} = \mathbf{i}_z H_{e0}$ saturate the ferrite. Suppose that the ferrite sample is a circular cylinder whose dimensions are small compared with a and l; we can use quasi-static methods to determine the perturbed field within the ferrite rod. Let us place the rod axis on the z-axis where $E_{z1} = 0$. In order to determine the local field about the z-axis, we make use of the expansions

$$J_1(u) = \frac{u}{2} + \cdots, \qquad J_1'(u) = \tfrac{1}{2} + \cdots \qquad (12\text{–}64)$$

We shall see that $\mathbf{B}_2$ and $\mathbf{H}_2$ are uniform throughout the rod, so that Eq. (12–62) takes the form

$$-\frac{\Delta\omega}{\omega} \cong \frac{I_H v_f}{4W_m}, \qquad (12\text{–}65)$$

where

$$I_H \triangleq \mathbf{B}_2 \cdot \mathbf{H}_1^* - \mu_0 \mathbf{H}_2 \cdot \mathbf{H}_1^*, \qquad (12\text{–}66)$$

and where v_f if the volume of the ferrite rod. In Eq. (12–62) we approximated the denominator term by taking $\mathbf{B}_2 \cong \mathbf{B}_1$ and $\mathbf{E}_2 \cong \mathbf{E}_1$, which holds over most of the volume, and we have made use of the equality (see Eq. 10–66)

$$W_m = \frac{\mu_0}{2} \int_v |H_1|^2 \, dv = \frac{\varepsilon_0}{2} \int_v |E_1|^2 \, dv. \qquad (12\text{–}67)$$

We can evaluate Eq. (12–67) with the aid of Appendix A–21:

$$W_m = \pi\mu_0 l(\omega\varepsilon_0)^2 \int_0^a \left\{ \frac{J_1^2(k_{11}r)}{r^2} + [k_{11}J_1'(k_{11}r)]^2 \right\} r \, dr$$

$$= \frac{\pi\mu_0 l}{2} [\omega\varepsilon_0 k_{11} a J_1'(k_{11}a)]^2. \qquad (12\text{–}68)$$

We can find the unperturbed field in the neighborhood of the axis with the aid of Eqs. (12–63) and (12–64). This yields

$$H_{x1} = H_{r1} \cos\phi - H_{\phi 1} \sin\phi = H,$$

where $H \triangleq \omega\varepsilon_0 k_{11}/2$. Similarly,

$$H_{y1} = H_{r1} \sin\phi + H_{\phi 1} \cos\phi = -jH.$$

Hence

$$\mathbf{H}_1 = H(\mathbf{i}_x - j\mathbf{i}_y),$$

and we see that the unperturbed field is a positively circularly polarized magnetic field. To determine the perturbed field $\mathbf{H}_2$ inside the ferrite, we make use of the result given in Problem 6–23, which applies to the case of a ferrite cylinder placed in a uniform magnetic field $\mathbf{H}_e = \mathbf{i}_x H$. We must now extend this result to account for the effect of the magnetic field $\mathbf{H}_e = \mathbf{i}_y(-jH)$, which we can do by replacing H_x, H_y, and H by H_y, $-H_x$, and $-jH$, respectively. The resultant field is determined by superposition:

$$H_{x2} = 2\frac{1 + \mu_r}{(1 + \mu_r)^2 - \kappa^2} H + \frac{j2\kappa}{(1 + \mu_r)^2 - \kappa^2}(-jH) = \frac{2H}{1 + \mu_r - \kappa},$$

$$H_{y2} = \frac{-j2\kappa}{(1 + \mu_r)^2 - \kappa^2} H + 2\frac{1 + \mu_r}{(1 + \mu_r)^2 - \kappa^2}(-jH) = \frac{-j2H}{1 + \mu_r - \kappa},$$

where $\mu_r \triangleq 1 + \chi$. Substituting $\mathbf{B}_2 = \mu_0(\mathbf{e} + \boldsymbol{\chi}) \cdot \mathbf{H}_2$ into Eq. (12–66) and using the tensor form of $\boldsymbol{\chi}$ given by Eq. (12–47) yields

$$I_H = \mu_0(\chi H_{x2} - j\kappa H_{y2})H_{x1}^* + \mu_0(j\kappa H_{x2} + \chi H_{y2})H_{y1}^* = \frac{4\mu_0(\chi - \kappa)}{1 + \mu_r - \kappa}|H|^2.$$

Using the value $u_{11} = 3.832$ given in Table 10–1, Section 10–4, we obtain

$$-\frac{\Delta\omega}{\omega_1} = 3.1\frac{\mu_r - \kappa - 1}{\mu_r - \kappa + 1}\frac{v_f}{v_c}, \tag{12–69}$$

where v_c is the volume of the cavity. By reversing the polarity of the externally applied dc magnetic field, we can change the sense of the circularly polarized field inside the cavity and the resulting change in frequency is found from Eq. (12–69) by replacing κ by $-\kappa$. We can obtain $\mu_r \pm \kappa$ from Eq. (12–69) by measuring the frequency changes and we can then determine μ_r and κ.

REFERENCE

R. F. Soohoo, "Ferrite microwave phase shifters," *IRE Convention Record* **4**, Part 5, 84–98, 1956

GENERAL REFERENCES

R. F. Soohoo, *Theory and Application of Ferrites*, Englewood Cliffs, N.J., Prentice-Hall, 1960

K. J. Button and B. Lax, *Microwave Ferrites and Ferrimagnetics*, New York: McGraw-Hill, 1962

PROBLEMS

12–1 A semi-infinite plasma has a uniform electron density of $N = 10^{17}$ electrons/m^3. A sinusoidally time-varying plane electromagnetic wave is normally incident on plasma region 2 (Fig. 12–11). If region 1 is a free-space region, determine the reflection and transmission coefficients. Determine the cutoff frequency f_c at which there is no propagated wave in region 2. Discuss the E and H fields at this frequency. What is the penetration depth at a frequency of $f = 2$ GHz?

12–2   Determine the numerical values of the susceptibility parameters χ, κ, and χ_z at a frequency of $f = 5$ MHz, given that $N = 10^{12}$ electrons/m^3 and $B_0 = 0.5 \times 10^{-4}$ Wb/m^2.

12–3   Consider a region of the earth's ionosphere in which $\mathbf{B}_0 = \mathbf{i}_z B_0$ is uniform and in which $B_0 = 0.5 \times 10^{-4}$ Wb/m^2. Assume that the plasma frequency is $f_p = 5$ MHz and that the frequency of a plane wave is $f = 10$ MHz. Evaluate the phase velocities for the case of $\theta = 0$ and the case of $\theta = 90°$ (see Fig. 12–2). Determine the electron density N for this value of f_p and determine the Faraday rotation per unit length for a linearly polarized plane wave propagating in the $\mathbf{i}_z$ direction.

12–4   A uniform ferrite in the shape of a sphere is saturated by an external magnetic dc field $\mathbf{H}_{e0} = \mathbf{i}_z H_{e0}$ and a high-frequency external magnetic field $\mathbf{H}_e = \mathbf{i}_x H_e \cos \omega t$ is applied (see Fig. 12–7). Resolve $\mathbf{H}_e$ into a positive and a negative rotating component in the xy-plane and prove that

$$\mathbf{m} = \frac{\omega_M H_e}{2} \left(\frac{\mathbf{n}_+}{\omega_r - \omega} + \frac{\mathbf{n}_-}{\omega_r + \omega} \right)$$

(see Fig. 12–3 for the definition of $\mathbf{n}_+$ and $\mathbf{n}_-$). Discuss the motion of the resultant magnetization $\mathbf{M} = \mathbf{M}_0 + \mathbf{m}$ for a case in which the frequency of excitation is near the resonance frequency. Can you explain the increase in the amount of energy absorbed by the ferrite as the excitation frequency approaches the resonance frequency?

12–5   Consider Fig. 12–7. The ferrite sample has a saturation flux density of $B_s = 2500$ gauss and is saturated by an external field of $H_{e0} = 1500$ Oe. Determine the dc field H_0 inside the ferrite and the values of f_M, f_0, and f_r for the following cases. [For the definition of f_M, f_0, and f_r see Eqs. (12–51), (12–52) and (12–53).] (a) The ferrite medium is of infinite extent. (b) The ferrite medium has the shape of a sphere. (c) The ferrite medium has the shape of a circular cylinder whose axis coincides with the z-axis.

12–6   Consider Fig. 12–7 and the data given in Problem 12–5. A high-frequency external magnetic field $\mathbf{H}_e = \mathbf{i}_x H_e \cos 2\pi f t$ is superimposed on the dc field $\mathbf{H}_{e0}$. It is often convenient to express the magnetization in terms of $\mathbf{H}_e$ by means of a susceptibility tensor χ_e, so that $\mathbf{m} = \chi_e \cdot \mathbf{H}_e$. Given that $f = 2$ GHz, evaluate the scalar components χ_e, κ_e of χ_e for the cases (a), (b), and (c) of Problem 12–5.

12–7   A plane electromagnetic wave is normally incident on a semi-infinite ferrite medium magnetized to saturation in the direction of propagation (Fig. 12–12).

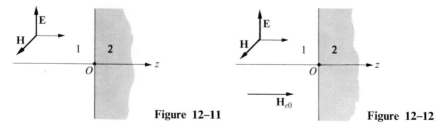

Figure 12–11   Figure 12–12

Determine the field components in regions 1 and 2 for cases in which (a) the wave is positively circularly polarized, (b) the wave is negatively circularly polarized.

12-8 A very thin straight circular rod is placed on the axis of a circular cylindrical cavity of length l and radius a which is resonant in the linearly polarized TM_{110} mode see Eqs. 10–70). Show that Eq. (12–62) now takes the form

$$- \frac{\Delta\omega}{\omega_1} = 3.1 \frac{\mu_r^2 - 1 - \kappa^2}{(1 + \mu_r)^2 - \kappa^2} \frac{v_f}{v_c}.$$

12-9 A small ferrite sphere of radius b is placed on the axis of a circular cylindrical cavity of length l and radius a. The cavity axis is taken as the z-axis and the ferrite is saturated by a dc field $\mathbf{H}_{e0} = \mathbf{i}_z H_{e0}$. Consider a mode of oscillation in the empty cavity for which the field has zero electric field intensity at a point P on the axis and for which the magnetic field intensity at P is circularly polarized in a plane transverse to the z-axis, so that it has the form

$$\mathbf{H}_{T1} = \frac{H_1}{\sqrt{2}} (\mathbf{i}_x \pm j\mathbf{i}_y).$$

Use Eq. (6–71) to show that the perturbed field inside the sphere is

$$\mathbf{H}_{T2} = \frac{3\mathbf{H}_{T1}}{\mu_r + 2 \pm \kappa}.$$

Show that (see Eq. 12–66)

$$I_H = 3\mu_0 \frac{\mu_r - 1 \pm \kappa}{\mu_r + 2 \pm \kappa} |H_1|^2 \quad \text{and that} \quad \frac{\Delta\omega}{\omega_1} = - k \frac{\mu_r - 1 \pm \kappa}{\mu_r + 2 \pm \kappa}$$

where

$$k \triangleq \mu_0 \pi b^3 \frac{|H_1|^2}{W_m},$$

and where W_m is the peak magnetic energy stored in the cavity.

12-10 A circularly polarized TE_{11N} mode of oscillation in a circular cylindrical cavity of length l and radius a has field components given by:

$$E_r = - \frac{\omega\mu_0}{r} J_1(k_{11}r)e^{-j\phi} \sin \beta_N z, \qquad H_r = k_{11}\beta_N J_1'(k_{11}r)e^{-j\phi} \cos \beta_N z,$$

$$E_\phi = j\omega\mu_0 k_{11} J_1'(k_{11}r)e^{-j\phi} \sin \beta_N z, \qquad H_\phi = -j\frac{\beta_N}{r} J_1(k_{11}r)e^{-j\phi} \cos \beta_N z,$$

$$E_z = 0, \qquad H_z = k_{11}^2 J_1(k_{11}r)e^{-j\phi} \sin \beta_N z.$$

(We can show this by choosing $V = J_1(k_{11}r)e^{-j\phi} \sin \beta_N z$, expressing $\sin \beta_N z$ in exponential form, and applying Eqs. 10–8.) Here k_{11} is defined by the equation $J_1'(k_{11}a) = 0$ and the resonant frequency f_r is determined by Eq. (10–71). Show that the peak electric (or magnetic) field energy in the cavity is

$$W_e = \frac{\pi\epsilon_0(\omega_r\mu_0)^2 l}{4} (k_{11}^2 a^2 - 1)J_1^2(k_{11}a),$$

and use this result to determine the factor k defined in Problem 12–9.

CHAPTER 13

INTERACTION OF CHARGED PARTICLES WITH ELECTROMAGNETIC FIELDS

13-1 INTRODUCTION

Many important devices depend for their operation on the interaction of moving charges with electromagnetic fields. Cathode-ray tubes, electron microscopes, mass spectrographs, traveling-wave tubes, backward-wave oscillators, magnetrons, and klystrons are examples of such devices. We shall discuss two methods for analyzing the motion of charged particles in an electromagnetic field. The *ballistic method* considers the motion of a single charged particle in an electromagnetic field and the assumption is made that the particle does not appreciably affect the field. The *field method* accounts for the interaction between the charges and the field. Both the ballistic method and the field method are useful in the analysis of the above-mentioned devices.

13-2 MOTION OF CHARGED PARTICLES IN STATIC ELECTRIC FIELDS

The equation of motion for a charged particle of mass m and charge Q moving in an electromagnetic field is given by

$$m \frac{d\mathbf{u}}{dt} = Q(\mathbf{E} + \mathbf{u} \times \mathbf{B}).$$ (13-1)

If we scalar-multiply Eq. (13-1) by the velocity $\mathbf{u}$ and note that $\mathbf{u} \cdot (\mathbf{u} \times \mathbf{B}) = 0$, we obtain

$$m\mathbf{u} \cdot \frac{d\mathbf{u}}{dt} = \frac{m}{2} \frac{d}{dt}(u^2) = Q\mathbf{E} \cdot \mathbf{u} = Q\mathbf{E} \cdot \frac{d\mathbf{r}}{dt},$$ (13-2)

where $\mathbf{r}$ is the radius vector from the origin O to the charged particle. Equation (13-2) expresses the rate of change of kinetic energy of the particle in terms of the power supplied by the field. It is interesting to note that because of the vanishing of the scalar triple product, $\mathbf{B}$ does not occur in Eq. (13-2). The magnetic flux density does not affect the kinetic energy of a charged particle. It can, however, alter the direction of motion of the particle.

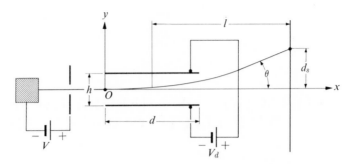

Fig. 13–1. Deflection of an electron beam in a cathode-ray tube.

In the case of an electrostatic field the electric field intensity can be expressed as the negative gradient of a scalar potential U: $\mathbf{E} = -\text{grad } U$. Since

$$\frac{dU}{dt} = \text{grad } U \cdot \frac{d\mathbf{r}}{dt} = -\mathbf{E} \cdot \frac{d\mathbf{r}}{dt},$$

we can integrate Eq. (13–2) and obtain

$$\frac{m}{2}(u_2^2 - u_1^2) = -Q(U_2 - U_1) = -QV, \qquad (13\text{–}3)$$

where V is the potential difference between positions 1 and 2 in the field. The kinetic energy acquired by an electron in moving through a potential difference of one volt is referred to as the *electron volt* (eV). The numerical value of the electron volt is obtained by substituting

$$u_1 = 0, \qquad V = 1, \qquad -Q = e = 1.6 \times 10^{-19}$$

into Eq. (13–3), which yields

$$1 \text{ eV} = \frac{m}{2} u^2 = 1.6 \times 10^{-19} \text{ joule (J)}.$$

We shall now discuss several applications of Eqs. (13–1) and (13–3) for the case of electrostatic fields in which $\mathbf{B} = 0$. Let us first consider the deflection of an electron beam by the deflection plates of a cathode-ray tube (Fig. 13–1). The electrons are emitted by a cathode, focused into a narrow beam, and then accelerated through a potential difference V. The electron beam enters the region between the deflecting plates with a velocity given by

$$u = \sqrt{2 \text{ eV}/m}. \qquad (13\text{–}4)$$

Let $E_y = -E$ be the y-component of the electric field intensity between the deflection plates and let us consider E to be uniform. An electron is deflected by the electric field and emerges into the field-free region at an angle θ with respect to the x-axis and strikes the screen at a distance d_s from the axis. We have

$$\tan \theta = \frac{u_y}{u_x} = \frac{d_s}{l},$$

where u_x and u_y are the x- and y-components of the velocity of the electron in the field-free region after the electron passes through the deflection region. Given that t is the time it takes for the electron to pass through the deflection region of width d, we have $d = ut$ and the y-component of Eq. (13–1) can be integrated to give

$$u_y = \frac{eEt}{m} = \frac{eEd}{mu}. \tag{13–5}$$

In the deflection region the source V_d of the field $\mathbf{E}$ does work on the electron, increasing its kinetic energy. However, after the electron leaves the deflection region it is slowed down by the force of attraction between the deflection plates and its charge. In the field-free region its speed is again u. We can see this from the fact that there is no resultant transfer of charge through the source V_d and therefore there is no resultant work done on the electron. Thus

$$u_x = \sqrt{u^2 - u_y^2}.$$

For the case of small deflections we have $u_x \simeq u$ and we find from Eqs. (13–4) and (13–5) that

$$\tan \theta = \frac{eEd}{mu^2} = \frac{Ed}{2V}. \tag{13–6}$$

An important performance measure for the cathode-ray tube is the *deflection sensitivity*, which is defined by the equation

$$d_s/V_d = ld/2Vh,$$

where $V_d = Eh$ is the potential difference applied to the deflection plates.

To illustrate a further case of a simple ballistic motion of a charged particle in an electrostatic field, let us now consider the motion of an electron in the radial field E_r of a uniformly charged infinitely long straight transmission line (Fig. 13–2). The radial force on the electron has two components: one is due to the electric field and the other to centrifugal force. Thus, using cylindrical coordinates (see Eqs. 1–122), we have

$$m\frac{d^2r}{dt^2} = mr\left(\frac{d\phi}{dt}\right)^2 - eE_r. \tag{13–7}$$

Since the torque on the electron is zero, the angular momentum is constant:

$$mr^2\frac{d\phi}{dt} = mr_0u_1. \tag{13–8}$$

Here u_1 is the tangential component of the velocity at a radial distance r_0. It is known that, for a uniformly charged infinitely long straight transmission line, E_r behaves as $1/r$. Let us write E_r in the form

$$E_r = mu_0^2/er,$$

and let u_0 be defined by this equation. Equation (13–7) now has the form

$$\frac{d^2r}{dt^2} = \frac{r_0^2 u_1^2}{r^3} - \frac{u_0^2}{r}. \tag{13–9}$$

A simple solution of Eq. (13–9) occurs for the case of $u_1 = u_0$ and $r = r_0$, where the electron moves in a circular orbit of radius r_0 with a speed u_0.

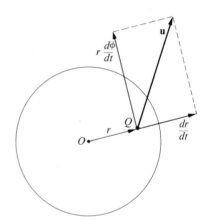

Fig. 13–2. The motion of a charge in the field of a uniformly charged infinitely long straight transmission line.

In order to determine the trajectory in the form $r = r(\phi)$, we use Eq. (13–8) and obtain

$$\frac{dr}{dt} = \frac{dr}{d\phi}\frac{d\phi}{dt} = \frac{r_0 u_1}{r^2}\frac{dr}{d\phi}, \qquad \frac{d^2r}{dt^2} = \left(\frac{r_0 u_1}{r}\right)^2 \frac{d}{d\phi}\left(\frac{1}{r^2}\frac{dr}{d\phi}\right).$$

Substituting into Eq. (13–9) yields the differential equation for electron trajectories:

$$\frac{d}{d\phi}\left(\frac{1}{r^2}\frac{dr}{d\phi}\right) = \frac{1}{r}\left[1 - \left(\frac{u_0 r}{u_1 r_0}\right)^2\right]. \tag{13–10}$$

As an example of the application of Eq. (13–10), let us discuss the radial-field focusing of the velocity spectrograph illustrated in Fig. 13–3. Electrons enter the radial electric field at point O. Let u_1 and $r_0\dot{\delta}_1$ represent the tangential and radial components of the velocity at O. Electrons with the same value of u_1 will be focused at a point P_1 on a plane located at an angle α, as shown in the figure. Electrons entering with a tangential velocity u_0 and zero radial velocity will travel along a circular arc of radius r_0 and strike the plane at P_0. Let

$$u_1 \overset{\triangle}{=} u_0(1 + \varepsilon), \qquad r \overset{\triangle}{=} r_0(1 + \delta),$$

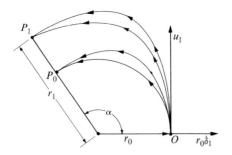

Fig. 13–3. A velocity spectrograph.   **Fig. 13–4.** An ideal planar diode.

where we take $|\varepsilon| \ll 1$ and $|\delta| \ll 1$. Substituting into Eq. (13–10) and neglecting higher-order powers of ε and δ yields

$$\frac{d^2\delta}{d\phi^2} + 2\delta = 2\varepsilon. \qquad (13–11)$$

The solution of Eq. (13–11) which satisfies the specified initial conditions at $\phi = 0$ is

$$\delta = \frac{\dot{\delta}_1}{\sqrt{2}} \sin \sqrt{2}\phi + \varepsilon(1 - \cos \sqrt{2}\phi). \qquad (13–12)$$

When $\phi = \alpha = \pi/\sqrt{2}$, we obtain from Eq. (13–12) the focusing relation

$$\frac{r_1 - r_0}{r_0} = 2\frac{u_1 - u_0}{u_0}.$$

Since this relation is independent of $\dot{\delta}_1$, it shows that the desired focusing action is realized; that is, electrons with the same u_1 but different $\dot{\delta}_1$ will all focus at the same point P_1.

The previous discussions have illustrated the ballistic method, in which the electromagnetic field is assumed to be unaffected by the moving charge. Let us now discuss the field method, as it is applied in the analysis of an ideal planar diode (Fig. 13–4). A cathode, which is taken to be at zero potential, emits electrons. The electrons are attracted to the anode, which is at a potential V. The charge density ρ between the plates is related to the potential U through Poisson's equation,

$$\frac{d^2U}{dx^2} = -\frac{\rho}{\varepsilon_0}. \qquad (13–13)$$

The electron velocity u (see Eq. 13–3) is given by

$$\tfrac{1}{2}mu^2 = eU \qquad (13–14)$$

and the current density in the direction of the positive x-axis is

$$J = -\rho u. \tag{13-15}$$

Substituting Eqs. (13-14) and (13-15) into Eq. (13-13) yields

$$\frac{d^2 U}{dx^2} = \frac{J}{\varepsilon_0 u} = \frac{J}{\varepsilon_0} \sqrt{\frac{m}{2eU}}.$$

Multiplying this equation by $2(dU/dx)$ and integrating yields

$$\left(\frac{dU}{dx}\right)^2 = \frac{4J}{\varepsilon_0} \sqrt{\frac{mU}{2e}}, \tag{13-16}$$

where we have taken $dU/dx = 0$ for $x = 0$. This is the space-charge-limited case, in which an unlimited supply of electrons is available from the cathode. So long as the component of electric field intensity $E_x(0)$ normal to the cathode surface is greater than zero, electrons will be emitted at an increasing rate. Equilibrium is established when the space charge reduces $E_x(0)$ to zero. Taking the square root of Eq. (13-16), separating the variables, and integrating from $x = 0$ to $x = d$ yields the *Langmuir-Child* equation,

$$J = \frac{4\varepsilon_0}{9d^2} \sqrt{\frac{2e}{m}} V^{3/2}. \tag{13-17}$$

13-3 MOTION OF CHARGED PARTICLES IN STATIC MAGNETIC FIELDS

In the case of a charged particle moving with a velocity $\mathbf{u} = \mathbf{i}u$ which is normal to a uniform magnetic field $\mathbf{B}$, the equation of motion can be written in the form (see Eq. 1-120)

$$m\left(\mathbf{i}\frac{du}{dt} + \mathbf{n}\frac{u^2}{R}\right) = nQuB,$$

where $\mathbf{n}$ is a unit vector in the direction of $\mathbf{u} \times \mathbf{B}$ and where R is the radius of curvature. The two orthogonal vector components of the above equation yield

$$m(du/dt) = 0, \tag{13-18}$$

$$m(u^2/R) = QuB. \tag{13-19}$$

The solution of Eq. (13-18) which satisfies the condition (13-19) is $u =$ const. Thus the magnetic field does not change the speed of the particle. Equation (13-19) yields

$$R = mu/QB. \tag{13-20}$$

Thus the particle moves on a circular orbit of radius R.

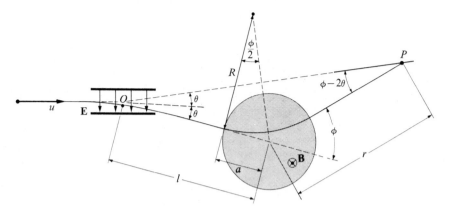

Fig. 13-5. Aston's mass spectrograph.

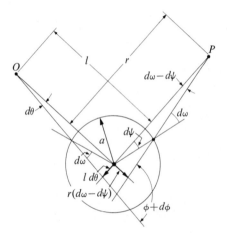

Fig. 13-6. Evaluation of the focusing condition.

Let us consider the application of Eqs. (13-6) and (13-20) to the focusing problem of a mass spectrograph of Aston's type (Fig. 13-5). A charged particle of mass m, charge Q, and speed u enters a uniform electric field **E** and is deflected through an angle θ. The particle then enters a uniform magnetic field **B** and is deflected through an angle ϕ, after which it strikes a photographic plate at P. It is convenient in the analysis of the focusing problem to consider that the particles originate at the point O. Let $d\theta$ be the angular spread of the particles leaving point O. We then have an angular spread $d\phi$ of the particles leaving the magnetic field. From Fig. 13-6 we obtain the relations

$$l \, d\theta = a \, d\omega = r(d\omega - d\psi), \qquad d\phi = d\theta + d\omega - d\psi.$$

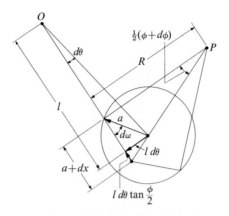

Fig. 13–7. Evaluation of the derivative.

Thus

$$r = \frac{l}{(d\phi/d\theta) - 1}.$$

The angle ϕ is a function of u and θ. Thus

$$\frac{d\phi}{d\theta} = \frac{\partial \phi}{\partial u}\frac{du}{d\theta} + \frac{\partial \phi}{\partial \theta}. \qquad (13\text{–}21)$$

In order to evaluate Eq. (13–21), we first differentiate Eq. (13–6) with respect to θ:

$$\frac{du}{d\theta} = -\frac{u}{\sin 2\theta}. \qquad (13\text{–}22)$$

With the aid of Fig. 13–5 and Eq. (13–20), we obtain

$$\tan\frac{\phi}{2} = \frac{a}{R} = \frac{aQB}{mu}. \qquad (13\text{–}23)$$

Differentiating Eq. (13–23) with respect to ϕ for a constant value of θ yields

$$\partial\phi/\partial\mu = -\sin\phi/u. \qquad (13\text{–}24)$$

In order to determine the derivative $\partial\phi/\partial\theta$, we consider Fig. 13–7. Since u is now constant, R is constant. We then have the relations

$$a + dx = a\cos d\omega + (l\,d\theta)\tan\frac{\phi}{2}, \qquad \tan\tfrac{1}{2}(\phi + d\phi) = \frac{a + dx}{R},$$

from which we obtain

$$\frac{\partial\phi}{\partial\theta} = \frac{\partial\phi}{\partial x}\frac{dx}{d\theta} = \frac{l}{a}(1 - \cos\phi). \qquad (13\text{–}25)$$

Substituting Eqs. (13–22), (13–24), and (13–25) into Eq. (13–21) yields the focusing relation,

$$r = \frac{l \sin 2\theta}{\sin \phi - \sin 2\theta + (l/a)(1 - \cos \phi) \sin 2\theta}. \qquad (13\text{–}26)$$

When θ and ϕ are both small, we find from Eq. (13–26) that $r(\phi - 2\theta) = 2l\theta$. The focusing point P then lies on a straight line through O, located as shown in Fig. 13–5.

13-4 MOTION OF CHARGED PARTICLES IN STATIC ELECTROMAGNETIC FIELDS

Figure 13–8 illustrates the motion of a charged particle in a planar magnetron where the electric field intensity **E** lies in the plane of motion and where **B** is normal to **E**. Both **E** and **B** are taken to be uniform and time-invariant. The equation of motion, given by Eq. (13–1), has a particular solution $\mathbf{u} = \mathbf{i}_x u_0$, where

$$E = u_0 B, \qquad (13\text{–}27)$$

and the particle moves parallel to the x-axis with a speed u_0. In this case the force on the particle due to the electric field is compensated by the force due to the magnetic field, and the resultant force is zero.

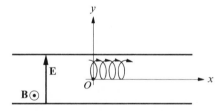

Fig. 13–8. A planar magnetron.

It is informative to consider the motion of the particle as viewed from a coordinate system which moves with a velocity $\mathbf{u}_0$ in the direction of the positive x-axis. Let

$$\mathbf{u} = \mathbf{i}_x u_0 + \mathbf{u}'.$$

With the aid of Eq. (13–27) we can obtain the equation of motion in the moving coordinate system:

$$m \frac{d\mathbf{u}'}{dt} = Q\mathbf{u}' \times \mathbf{B}. \qquad (13\text{–}28)$$

Here quantities observed in the moving coordinate system are represented by primed symbols. Equation (13–28) represents the motion of a charged particle in a uniform magnetic field. We have seen that the particle then moves with a uniform speed u' along a circle of radius R (see Eq. 13–20). The angular velocity of this motion is given by

$$\omega = \frac{u'}{R} = \frac{QB}{m},$$

and the coordinates of the moving particle in the xy-coordinate system are

$$x = u_0 t + R \cos \frac{QBt}{m},$$

$$y = R \sin \frac{QBt}{m}.$$

(13–29)

The trajectory of the particle is a *trochoid*, which is the locus of the terminus of a radial arm of length R attached to a circle of unit radius rolling on the line $y = -R$.

It is of interest to consider the solution (13–29) from a different point of view. The electric field intensity $\mathbf{E}'$ and the magnetic flux density $\mathbf{B}'$ in the moving system can be expressed in terms of $\mathbf{E}$ and $\mathbf{B}$ (see Eq. 2–59):

$$E' = E - u_0 B = 0,$$

$$B' = B.$$

We observe only a magnetic field in the moving system; the particle in this system must, therefore, have a circular trajectory.

Figure 13–9 illustrates a cylindrical magnetron in which a uniform axial magnetic flux density $\mathbf{B} = \mathbf{i}_z B$ is applied. A radial component of electric field intensity $\mathbf{E}_r$ results from a potential difference V between the cathode and anode. The angular momentum of an electron with respect to the z-axis is $mr^2(d\phi/dt)$, and the z-component of the torque acting on the electron is $Ber(dr/dt)$. Equating the rate of change of angular momentum to the torque yields the equation of motion,

$$\frac{d}{dt}\left(r^2 \frac{d\phi}{dt}\right) = \frac{Ber}{m}\frac{dr}{dt},$$

which can be integrated to

$$mr^2 \frac{d\phi}{dt} = \frac{Be}{2}(r^2 - a^2). \qquad (13\text{–}30)$$

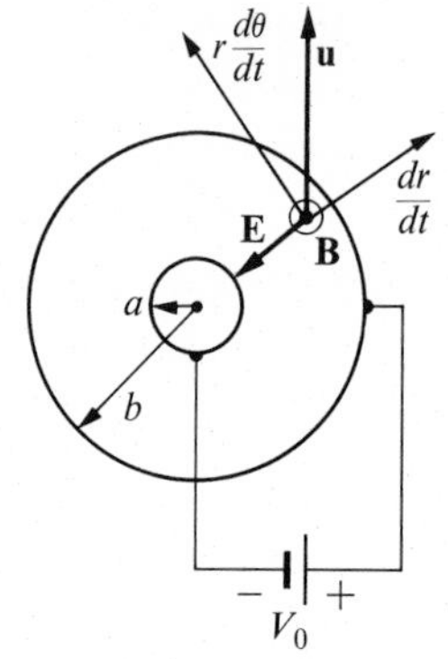

Fig. 13–9. A cylindrical magnetron.

Here we have taken the angular velocity to be zero at the cathode surface. (The electrons are assumed to be emitted normal to the cathode surface.) Taking the cathode surface to be at zero potential, we find that the energy equation (13–3) yields

$$u^2 = \left(\frac{dr}{dt}\right)^2 + \left(r\frac{d\phi}{dt}\right)^2 = \frac{2eU}{m}. \tag{13–31}$$

where U is the potential at a distance r from the cathode. We can use Eqs. (13–30) and (13–31) to obtain the cutoff condition for the magnetron. This is the minimum value of B for which no current flows from the cathode to the anode. At the maximum radius of the electron trajectory we have $dr/dt = 0$. For the cutoff condition the maximum radius is the anode radius b, since no electron is to be intercepted by the anode. Thus from Eqs. (13–30) and (13–31) we obtain the cutoff condition

$$B = \frac{6.74 \times 10^{-6}}{b[1 - (a/b)^2]}\sqrt{V}.$$

13-5 THE FOCUSING OF LONG STRAIGHT ELECTRON BEAMS

The operation of many electron devices depends on a straight beam of electrons. Due to the forces of repulsion between the electrons it is necessary to apply external focusing fields in order to keep the beam in the desired form. In the case of long straight electron beams we shall use cylindrical coordinates and assume that all quantities are functions of r and z only.

Let us first discuss the case of *Brillouin focusing* [1]. A cathode emits electrons which are electrostatically focused into a circular cylindrical beam of radius a in a region in which $B_z = 0$. The electrons then enter a region in which $B_z = B_0$. In the case of Brillouin focusing, the forces of repulsion between the electrons as well as the centrifugal forces are compensated for by the forces due to the magnetic field. The electron beam, therefore, retains its cylindrical form. We shall show that an axial element of the electron beam can be considered as a solid rotating body moving in the axial direction with a constant velocity.

In cylindrical coordinates we can write Eq. (13–1) (see Eqs. 1–122) in the form

$$\frac{d^2r}{dt^2} - r\left(\frac{d\phi}{dt}\right)^2 = -\frac{e}{m}\left(E_r + B_z r\frac{d\phi}{dt}\right), \tag{13–32a}$$

$$\frac{1}{r}\frac{d}{dt}\left(r^2\frac{d\phi}{dt}\right) = -\frac{e}{m}\left(-B_z\frac{dr}{dt} + B_r\frac{dz}{dt}\right), \tag{13–32b}$$

$$\frac{d^2z}{dt^2} = -\frac{e}{m}\left(E_z - B_r r\frac{d\phi}{dt}\right). \tag{13–32c}$$

The condition div $\mathbf{B} = 0$ requires that

$$\frac{\partial}{\partial r}(rB_r) + r\frac{\partial B_z}{\partial z} = 0, \tag{13-33}$$

where we have taken $B_\phi = 0$. When B_z is chosen to be independent of r, it follows from Eq. (13-33) that

$$B_r = -\frac{r}{2}\frac{\partial B_z}{\partial z}. \tag{13-34}$$

We see, therefore, that there is associated with a sudden change in B_z in the axial direction a large value of the radial field component B_r. This radial field can be used to impart an angular velocity to the electron beam.

Let us now investigate this angular velocity. For a field point P moving with the electron we have

$$\frac{dB_z}{dt} = \frac{\partial B_z}{\partial t}\frac{dz}{dt} = -\frac{2}{r}B_r\frac{dz}{dt}.$$

With the aid of the above equation, we can integrate Eq. (13-32b):

$$r^2\frac{d\phi}{dt} = \frac{e}{m}\int_0^t \left(B_z r\frac{dr}{dt} + \frac{r^2}{2}\frac{dB_z}{dt}\right) dt = \omega_0 r^2 - \omega_c r_c^2, \tag{13-35}$$

where

$$\omega_0 \triangleq \frac{eB_0}{2m} \tag{13-36}$$

is the Larmor frequency, $\omega_c \triangleq (eB_c/2m)$, and where B_c is the axial component of the magnetic flux density at the cathode surface. Substituting Eq. (13-35) into Eq. (13-32a) yields

$$\frac{d^2r}{dt^2} = -\frac{e}{m}E_r + r\left[\omega_c^2\left(\frac{r_c}{r}\right)^4 - \omega_0^2\right]. \tag{13-37}$$

We shall subsequently prove that an axial element of the electron beam can be considered as a rigid body rotating with an angular velocity $\boldsymbol{\omega}_0 = \mathbf{i}_z\omega_0$ and moving with a velocity $\mathbf{u}_0 = \mathbf{i}_z u_0$ (Fig. 13-10). The charge density in the beam is therefore constant. Suppose that I_0 is the beam current in the direction of the positive z-axis. We have

$$I_0 = -\rho\pi a^2 u_0.$$

Applying Gauss' law to a circular cylinder of radius $r < a$ and of unit length yields

$$2\pi r\varepsilon_0 E_r = \pi r^2\rho = -\left(\frac{r}{a}\right)^2\frac{I_0}{u_0}. \tag{13-38}$$

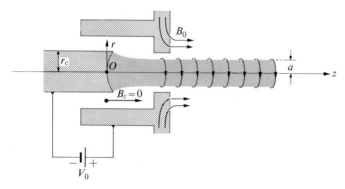

Fig. 13–10. Brillouin focusing of an electron beam.

Substituting Eq. (13–38) into Eq. (13–37) yields

$$\frac{d^2r}{dt^2} = \left[\frac{eI_0}{2\pi\varepsilon_0 mu_0 a^2} + \omega_c^2 \left(\frac{r_c}{r}\right)^4 - \omega_0^2 \right] r. \qquad (13\text{–}39)$$

In the case of Brillouin focusing we have $B_c = 0$. Thus $\omega_c = 0$ and we see that $d^2r/dt^2 = 0$, provided that the right-hand side of Eq. (13–39) vanishes. This gives the condition for Brillouin focusing,

$$I_0 = 2\pi\varepsilon_0 u_0 a^2 \omega_0^2 \frac{m}{e}. \qquad (13\text{–}40)$$

In the case of Brillouin focusing we have $r = $ const, $d\phi/dt = $ const, and we shall now prove that $dz/dt = u_0 = $ const. Substituting $u_1 = 0$, $U_1 = 0$, $U_2 = U$ into the energy relation (13–3) and noting that the velocity has two orthogonal components of magnitude u_0 and $r\omega_0$ yields

$$u_0^2 + (r\omega_0)^2 = 2eU/m. \qquad (13\text{–}41)$$

We can obtain the potential U by substituting Eq. (13–38) into $E_r = -\partial U/\partial r$ and integrating with respect to r. With the aid of Eq. (13–38) we obtain

$$U = V_0 - \frac{m}{2e} \omega_0^2 (a^2 - r^2),$$

where V_0 is the externally applied potential difference between the cathode and the surface of the beam. Substituting the above expression for U into Eq. (13–41) yields

$$u_0 = \sqrt{(2e/m)V_0 - a^2\omega_0^2} = \sqrt{(2e/m)U(0)}.$$

Thus we see that u_0 is constant throughout the beam and that the velocity u_0 is that obtained by an electron starting from rest at the cathode surface and moving through a potential difference of $U(0)$. It should be noted that this potential difference is equal to the potential of the z-axis and is different from the applied potential difference V_0. Eliminating u_0 from Eq. (13–40) yields

$$I_0 = 2\pi\varepsilon_0 a^2\omega_0^2\frac{m}{e}\sqrt{\frac{2eV_0}{m} - a^2\omega_0^2}. \tag{13-42}$$

The direction of the axial magnetic field determines the direction of rotation of the beam. The direction of rotation can be reversed without affecting the focusing action. We can, therefore, obtain Brillouin focusing by periodically reversing the direction of the magnetic field along the z-axis. A periodic field of this type can be set up if one employs a large number of small magnets, a procedure which is often more advantageous than employing a single large magnet [2].

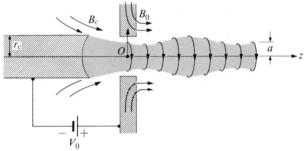

Fig. 13–11. Confined focusing of an electron beam.

Instead of attempting to achieve a perfect circular cylindrical beam we could choose the case of confined focusing, in which the transverse motion is restricted to an acceptable amount (Fig. 13–11). The magnetic field in the cathode region ($z < 0$) is adjusted so that the electron trajectories near the cathode surface coincide with the magnetic stream lines. The electrons in the beam are set in rotation near the origin $z = 0$. Let

$$r = a(1 + \delta)$$

describe the radial coordinate of the beam surface and let $|\delta| \ll 1$. In order to determine E_r at the beam surface we consider the charge per unit length q along the beam, which can be defined by the equation $I_0 = -qu_0$. Gauss' law applied to a unit length of the beam yields

$$2\pi r\varepsilon_0 E_r = q = -I_0/u_0.$$

We can obtain the equation for the radial motion at the beam surface by substituting the value of E_r given by the above equation into Eq. (13–37). If we then expand Eq. (13–37) in a Taylor series in δ and neglect higher-order terms, we obtain the two equations

$$\frac{eI_0}{2\pi\varepsilon_0 a u_0 m} + a\left[\omega_c^2\left(\frac{r_c}{a}\right)^4 - \omega_0^2\right] = 0, \qquad (13\text{–}43a)$$

$$\frac{d^2\delta}{dt^2} = -\left[\frac{eI_0}{2\pi\varepsilon_0 a^2 u_0 m} + 3\omega_c^2\left(\frac{r_c}{a}\right)^4 + \omega_0^2\right]\delta = -2\omega_0^2\left[1 + \left(\frac{\omega_c}{\omega_0}\right)^2\left(\frac{r_c}{a}\right)^4\right]\delta$$

$$= -k^2\omega_0^2\,\delta. \qquad (13\text{–}43b)$$

We can solve Eq. (13–43a) for the equilibrium radius a; this equation for a has been used to obtain Eq. (13–43b). Suppose that we set $z = u_0 t$ and that we assume that the initial conditions at $z = 0$ are $\delta = 0$ and $d\delta/dz = \tan\alpha$. We find from Eq. (13–43b) that the deflection from the equilibrium radius is given by

$$\delta = \frac{u_0\tan\alpha}{k\omega_0}\sin\left(\frac{k\omega_0 z}{u_0}\right).$$

13-6 SPACE-CHARGE WAVES

In a linear beam of electrons moving in an electromagnetic field the interaction between the electrons and the field can result in a periodic bunching and debunching of the electrons. The electron bunches give rise to space-charge waves which propagate along the beam. The electron trajectories in a beam are, in general, extremely complicated. We therefore make suitable assumptions which greatly simplify the analysis. The results obtained with these assumptions are useful in predicting the behavior of electron devices.

We consider that there is a positive ion charge density ρ_0 which compensates for the steady-state electron charge density $-\rho_0$. The resultant steady-state charge density is zero. In the steady state we need not, therefore, consider the forces of repulsion between the electrons, since these are compensated for by attractive forces due to the positive ions. We also consider that an infinitely strong axial magnetic field is applied, so that there is no transverse motion of the electrons. The electrons are emitted by a cathode and are accelerated to an axial velocity u_0 by a potential difference V (see Fig. 13–12). The electrons then enter a space-charge region ($z > 0$). Because of their much larger mass, the positive ions are considered to be immobile under the action of time-varying fields. Let E_z represent the axial component of the electric field intensity of a sinusoidally time-varying electromagnetic field. The E-field will modulate both the charge density ρ and the velocity $\mathbf{u}$:

$$\mathbf{u} = \mathbf{u}_0 + \mathbf{u}_1, \qquad \rho = -\rho_0 + \rho_1.$$

(The subscript 1 is used to indicate the time-varying components.) We assume that the modulation is small so that $|u_1/u_0| \ll 1$, $|\rho_1/\rho_0| \ll 1$. The

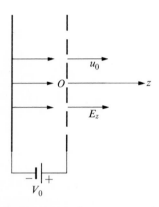

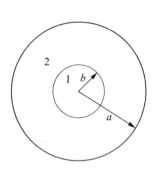

Fig. 13–12. Space-charge waves in a linear electron flow.

Fig. 13–13. A cylindrical beam of electrons which is coaxial with a circular wave guide.

current density is $\mathbf{J} = \rho\mathbf{u} = \mathbf{J}_0 + \mathbf{J}_1$. When we neglect higher-order terms, the time-varying current density is

$$\mathbf{J}_1 = -\rho_0\mathbf{u}_1 + \rho_1\mathbf{u}_0 \qquad (13\text{--}44)$$

and the equation of continuity yields

$$\partial J_1/\partial z = -\partial\rho_1/\partial t. \qquad (13\text{--}45)$$

In the case of sinusoidally time-varying fields, we introduce phasor notation and consider all quantities to vary as $e^{j\omega t}e^{-\gamma z}$. For example, we set

$$u_1(z, t) = u_1 e^{j\omega t}e^{-\gamma z}, \qquad (13\text{--}46)$$

where $u_1 \triangleq u_1(z)$. Expressing Eqs. (13–44) and (13–45) in phasor form yields

$$J_1 = \frac{j\omega\rho_0}{u_0\gamma - j\omega} \cdot u_1. \qquad (13\text{--}47)$$

The equation of motion for an electron is

$$-\frac{e}{m}E_z = \frac{du}{dt} = \frac{\partial u_1}{\partial t} + u_0\frac{\partial u_1}{\partial z}.$$

Using the phasor representation given by Eq. (13–46) yields

$$u_1 = \frac{e/m}{\gamma u_0 - j\omega}E_z. \qquad (13\text{--}48)$$

Combining Eqs. (13–47) and (13–48), we obtain the result

$$J_1 = -j\omega\varepsilon_0\left(\frac{\omega_p}{\omega + j\gamma u_0}\right)^2 E_z, \qquad (13\text{--}49)$$

where
$$\omega_p^2 \triangleq \frac{e\rho_0}{m\varepsilon_0}. \tag{13-50}$$

The quantity $f_p = \omega_p/2\pi$ is known as the *electron plasma frequency*.

The interaction of the current with the electromagnetic field can be determined with the aid of Eq. (10–6) by introducing cylindrical coordinates. If we let

$$k_0^2 = -(\gamma^2 + \omega^2 \mu_0 \varepsilon_0), \tag{13-51}$$

it follows from Eqs. (10–5) that

$$E_z = -k_0^2 U, \tag{13-52}$$

where U satisfies the equation

$$\frac{1}{r}\frac{d}{dr}\left(r\frac{dU}{dr}\right) - k_0^2 U = -\frac{J_1}{j\omega\varepsilon_0}.$$

With the aid of Eqs. (13–52) and (13–49), we find that

$$\frac{1}{r}\frac{d}{dr}\left(r\frac{dU}{dr}\right) + k^2 U = 0, \tag{13-53}$$

where

$$k^2 \triangleq k_0^2 \left[\left(\frac{\omega_p}{\omega + j\gamma u_0}\right)^2 - 1\right]. \tag{13-54}$$

A problem of practical interest which has an analytic solution is to determine the space charge waves in a circular cylindrical beam of radius b which is coaxial with a circular cylindrical wave guide of radius a (Fig. 13–13). In the beam region, $0 \leqq r \leqq b$, the function U must satisfy Eq. (13–53). In the charge-free region we have $\omega_p = 0$, $k^2 = -k_0^2$. Thus

$$\frac{1}{r}\frac{d}{dr}\left(r\frac{dU}{dr}\right) - k_0^2 U = 0, \qquad b \leqq r \leqq a. \tag{13-55}$$

A solution of Eq. (13–53) which is finite at the origin is the Bessel function J_0 of the first kind of order zero. The general solution of Eq. (13–55) is a linear combination of the modified Bessel functions I_0 and K_0 (see Appendix A–27). Thus

$$U = \begin{cases} C_1 J_0(kr), & 0 \leqq r \leqq b, \\ C_2 I_0(k_0 r) + C_3 K_0(k_0 r), & b \leqq r \leqq a. \end{cases}$$

To establish the existence of space-charge waves we must determine constants C_1, C_2, C_3, and k so that the boundary conditions are satisfied. The boundary condition $E_z]_{r=a} = 0$ is satisfied (see Eq. 13–52) if

$$C_2 I_0(k_0 a) + C_3 K_0(k_0 a) = 0. \tag{13-56}$$

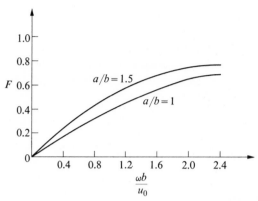

Fig. 13–14. The space-charge reduction factor for a cylindrical electron beam which is coaxial with a circular wave guide.

The boundary condition at $r = b$ requires that $E_{z1} = E_{z2}$ and $E_{r1} = E_{r2}$. If we note that

$$E_r = -\gamma \frac{\partial U}{\partial r} e^{-\gamma z}$$

(see Eqs. 10–5), we obtain

$$C_1 J_0(kb) = C_2 I_0(k_0 b) + C_3 K_0(k_0 b),$$

$$C_1 k J_1(kb) = -C_2 k_0 I_1(k_0 b) + C_3 k_0 K_1(k_0 b), \tag{13–57}$$

where we have made use of Eqs. (A–17), (A–29), and (A–30). Taking the ratio of Eqs. (13–57) and eliminating C_3/C_2 with the aid of Eq. (13–56) yields the characteristic equation

$$-\frac{kb J_1(kb)}{k_0 b J_0(kb)} = \frac{I_1(k_0 b) K_0(k_0 a) + I_0(k_0 a) K_1(k_0 b)}{I_0(k_0 b) K_0(k_0 a) - I_0(k_0 a) K_0(k_0 b)}.$$

This equation can be solved numerically for k in terms of a, b, and k_0. There are, in general, an infinite number of solutions resulting in an infinite number of space-charge waves. However, we usually assume that only the lowest order (dominant) mode is excited. Figure 13–14 illustrates the numerical values for the dominant mode [3]. Reference 3 also gives the solutions for numerous other geometries.

Once we know k, we can determine the propagation function from Eq. (13–54). Let us use Eq. (13–54) to define a *space-charge reduction factor F* so that

$$k^2 = k_0^2 \left(\frac{1}{F^2} - 1 \right).$$

It follows that

$$\pm F \triangleq \frac{\omega + j\gamma u_0}{\omega_p},$$

and we obtain the propagation function

$$\gamma = j\beta = j\,\frac{\omega \pm F\omega_p}{u_0}.$$

We therefore have two possible dominant-mode space-charge waves which have phase velocities

$$\frac{\omega}{\beta} = \frac{u_0}{1 \pm F\omega_p/\omega}.$$

With respect to the steady-state beam velocity u_0, we see that there is a fast and a slow space-charge wave. The rate of flow of energy is determined by the group velocity

$$u_g = \frac{d\omega}{d\beta} = u_0,$$

which is equal to the steady-state beam velocity for both waves.

Example. Let us determine the wavelengths for the dominant-mode space charge waves, given that

$$b = 0.3 \text{ cm}, \qquad I_0 = 50 \text{ mA}, \qquad a = 0.45 \text{ cm},$$

$$V_0 = 1000 \text{ volts}, \qquad f = 1 \text{ GHz}.$$

The wavelength can be determined from the equation

$$\lambda = \frac{u_0}{f}\,\frac{1}{1 \pm F\omega_p/\omega}.$$

The steady-state beam velocity is

$$u_0 = \sqrt{2eV_0/m} = 1.88 \times 10^7 \text{ m/sec}.$$

To determine the electron plasma frequency we substitute $\rho_0 = J_0/u_0$ into Eq. (13–50) which yields

$$\omega_p^2 = \frac{e}{m\varepsilon_0}\,\frac{J_0}{u_0}$$

The magnitude of the current density is

$$J_0 = I_0/\pi b^2 = 1.77 \times 10^3 \text{ A/m}^2$$

and the electron plasma frequency is

$$f_p = \omega_p/2\pi = 0.218 \text{ GHz}.$$

To determine F we note that

$$\omega b/u_0 = 1, \qquad a/b = 1.5,$$

and obtain $F = 0.5$ from Fig. 13–14. All numerical data for determining the wavelengths are now available. We find that

$$\lambda_1 = 1.7 \text{ cm}, \qquad \lambda_2 = 2.1 \text{ cm}.$$

It is interesting to note that the free-space wavelength of a plane electromagnetic wave at a frequency of 1 GHz is 30 cm.

13–7 THE TRAVELING-WAVE TUBE

Figure 13–15 illustrates a traveling-wave tube which operates in the following manner. Electrons emitted by a cathode are focused into a beam, and a focusing coil or magnet is used to restrict the transverse motion of the electrons (confined flow) so that the form of the beam remains essentially a circular cylinder. An electromagnetic wave is coupled into the tube helix from a wave guide and propagates along the helix with a phase velocity approximately equal to the steady-state beam velocity. The electromagnetic wave absorbs energy from the beam and is amplified. At the output, the amplified wave is coupled into a wave guide.

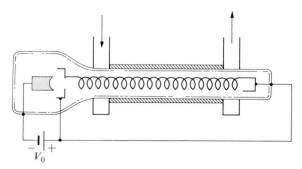

Fig. 13–15. A traveling-wave tube.

The theory of the traveling-wave tube can be treated from a field or a ballistic point of view [4]. We shall first discuss Pierce's ballistic theory. Equations (13–47) and (13–48) can be applied to the case of a cylindrical beam of radius a and remain unchanged. The axial phasor electric field intensity now consists of two components:

$$E_z = E_h + E_s.$$

Here E_h is the axial phasor field due to the helix and E_s is the axial phasor field due to the space-charge effects of the electron beam. An approximation to E_s can be obtained by considering the charge distribution to be independent of x and y so that the field E_s is one-dimensional. We can then use either Poisson's equation or Gauss' law to find E_s:

$$\partial E_s / \partial z = -\gamma E_s = \rho_1 / \varepsilon_0.$$

We can eliminate ρ_1 from the above equation by using the phasor form of the equation of continuity (13–45):

$$E_s = -\frac{1}{j\omega\varepsilon_0}J_1. \tag{13–58}$$

Equations (13–48) and (13–58) yield

$$u_1(j\omega - \gamma u_0) = -\frac{e}{m}\left(E_h - \frac{1}{j\omega\varepsilon_0}J_1\right). \tag{13–59}$$

Eliminating u_1 from Eqs. (13–47) and (13–59) yields

$$(j\beta_e - \gamma)^2 + \left(\frac{\omega\rho}{u_0}\right)^2 = j\frac{e}{m}\frac{\omega\rho_0}{u_0^2}\frac{E_h}{J_1} = j\frac{\beta_e I_0 E_h}{2V_0 I}, \tag{13–60}$$

where we have made use of the energy relation $u_0^2 = 2(e/m)V_0$ and where we have set

$$\beta_e \triangleq \omega/u_0, \qquad I_0 \triangleq \pi a^2\rho_0 u_0, \qquad I \triangleq \pi a^2 J_1.$$

Equation (13–60) is known as the *electronic equation*. To determine a characteristic equation for γ, we must now derive a second relation for E_h/I which is known as the *circuit equation*. Let γ_0 represent the propagation function for the fundamental mode of the unperturbed helix, that is, where no electron beam is present. The electron beam will perturb this mode, changing the propagation function to γ. In order to determine the circuit equation, we must represent the fundamental mode of propagation along the helix by a transmission-line analog. We let $V = V_+ e^{-\gamma z} + V_- e^{\gamma z}$ represent the potential difference for the transmission-line analog of the perturbed mode and let V be defined by the equation

$$E_h = -dV/dz,$$

where E_h is the axial component of the electric field intensity due to the helix. The transmission-line current is defined by the equation

$$I = \frac{1}{Z_c}(V_+ e^{-\gamma z} - V_- e^{\gamma z}) = -\frac{1}{\gamma Z_c}\frac{dV}{dz} = \frac{E_h}{\gamma Z_c}, \tag{13–61}$$

where Z_c is the characteristic impedance of the transmission line. Given that P is the rate at which energy is transported by the wave, we have

$$P = \tfrac{1}{2}Z_c|I|^2 = \frac{1}{2Z_c}\left|\frac{E_h}{\gamma}\right|^2.$$

The above equation can be used to define Z_c:

$$Z_c \triangleq \frac{1}{2P}\left|\frac{E_h}{\gamma}\right|^2. \tag{13–62}$$

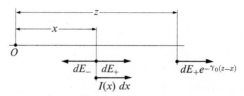

Fig. 13–16. The generation of elemental waves due to an element of beam current.

Let us now consider an element of beam current $I(x) \, dx$ (Fig. 13–16). Due to the coupling with the helix, two waves are generated on the helix by the element of beam current. One wave travels to the right and the other travels to the left of the position x. These waves are considered to be on the unperturbed helix and thus have a propagation function γ_0. Due to symmetry, the complex power supplied to both waves is identical. The power relationship is

$$-\tfrac{1}{2}I^* (x) \, dx \, dE_h = 2\tfrac{1}{2}Z_c \, |dI_+|^2, \tag{13–63}$$

where $dE_h = dE_+ + dE_- = 2 \, dE_+$ is the axial electric field intensity due to both waves. It follows from Eq. (13–61) that $dI_+ = dE_+/\gamma Z_c$ and Eq. (13–63) yields

$$dE_+ = -Z_c \, |\gamma|^2 \, I(x) \, dx. \tag{13–64}$$

With the aid of Eq. (13–64) we can now determine the resultant axial field $E_h(z)$ by the superposition of elemental unperturbed waves:

$$E_h(z) = E_0 e^{-\gamma_0 z} + \int_0^z dE_+ e^{-\gamma_0(z-x)} + \int_z^l dE_- e^{\gamma_0(z-x)}. \tag{13–65}$$

The first term in Eq. (13–65) represents an initial incident wave on the helix moving to the right. The first integral results from the superposition at z of all waves generated in the interval from zero to z which move to the right. The second integral results from the superposition of all waves generated in the interval from z to l which move to the left (the quantity l is the effective length of the helix). Since $dE_+ = dE_- = dE_h/2$, we obtain with the aid of Eq. (13–64) the equation

$$E_h(z) = E_0 e^{-\gamma_0 z} - Z_c \, |\gamma|^2 e^{-\gamma_0 z} \int_0^z e^{\gamma_0 x} I(x) \, dx - Z_c \, |\gamma|^2 e^{\gamma_0 z} \int_z^l e^{-\gamma_0 x} I(x) \, dx,$$

which can be differentiated to yield

$$\frac{d^2 E_h(z)}{dz^2} - \gamma_0^2 E_h(z) = 2Z_c \gamma_0 \, |\gamma|^2 I.$$

Substituting $E_h(z) = E_h e^{-\gamma z}$ yields the circuit equation

$$\frac{E_h}{I} = \frac{2Z_c \gamma_0 \, |\gamma|^2}{\gamma^2 - \gamma_0^2}. \tag{13–66}$$

Combining Eqs. (13–60) and (13–66) yields the characteristic equation

$$\frac{(\gamma^2 - \gamma_0^2)[(j\beta_e - \gamma)^2 + (\omega_p/u_0)^2]}{j\beta_e\,|\gamma|^2\gamma_0} = \frac{I_0Z_c}{V_0} = 2C^3. \tag{13–67}$$

The solutions of Eq. (13–67) yield the perturbed propagation function γ.

We shall now discuss the approximate solution of Eq. (13–67) for the case of negligible ω_p/ω_0 and of weak coupling so that $C \ll 1$. In order that the electromagnetic wave interact with the electron beam, the phase velocity of the unperturbed wave on the helix must be approximately equal to the steady-state beam velocity. We therefore set

$$\gamma_0 = j\beta_e, \qquad \gamma = j\beta_e(1 + \delta), \tag{13–68}$$

where $|\delta| \ll 1$. We have

$$(\gamma_0^2 - \gamma^2) = (\gamma_0 - \gamma)(\gamma_0 + \gamma) \simeq 2\beta_e^2\,\delta, \qquad \gamma^2 \simeq -\beta_e^2.$$

Substituting into Eq. (13–67) yields $\delta^3 = -C^3$. The solution of this cubic equation yields three roots, and thus there are three propagation functions which represent incident waves:

$$\gamma_1 \simeq j\beta_e(1 + C/2) - \frac{\beta_e C}{2}\sqrt{3},$$

$$\gamma_2 \simeq j\beta_e(1 + C/2) + \frac{\beta_e C}{2}\sqrt{3}, \tag{13–69}$$

$$\gamma_3 \simeq j\beta_e(1 - C).$$

Equation (13–67) is a quartic equation in γ. The fourth root γ_4 represents a reflected wave and it can be shown that

$$\gamma_4 \simeq -j\beta_e(1 - C^3/4).$$

When the helix is suitably designed and terminated, only incident waves are generated. The wave with the propagation function γ_1 has a phase velocity slightly slower than the steady-state beam velocity. Since the real part of γ_1 is negative, there is an exponential increase in amplitude of this wave as it moves to the right.

The relative amplitudes of the incident waves depends on the boundary conditions at the input. Let E_i represent the axial component of the electric field intensity due to the input wave. Both the velocity and the current density modulation are zero at the input. Thus $u_1 = 0$, $J_1 = 0$, and (see Eq. 13–58) $E_s = 0$. It follows that $E_z = E_i$ and

$$u_1 = u_{11} + u_{12} + u_{13} = 0, \tag{13–70a}$$

$$J_1 = J_{11} + J_{12} + J_{13} = 0, \tag{13–70b}$$

$$E_z = E_{z1} + E_{z2} + E_{z3} = E_i. \tag{13–70c}$$

The subscripts 1, 2, and 3 correspond to the waves with propagation functions γ_1, γ_2, and γ_3, respectively. From Eq. (13–48) we obtain

$$u_{1k} = \frac{-(e/m)}{u_0(j\beta_e - \gamma_k)} E_{zk}, \qquad k = 1, 2, 3.$$

Substituting the above equation into Eq. (13–70a) and using $\gamma_k = j\beta_e(1 + \delta_k)$ yields

$$\frac{E_{z1}}{\delta_1} + \frac{E_{z2}}{\delta_2} + \frac{E_{z3}}{\delta_3} = 0. \tag{13–71}$$

From Eq. (13–49) we obtain

$$J_{1k} = \frac{j\omega\varepsilon_0}{u_0^2}\left(\frac{\omega_p}{\gamma_k - j\beta_e}\right)^2 E_{zk}, \qquad k = 1, 2, 3.$$

Substituting the above equation into Eq. (13–70b) yields

$$\frac{E_{z1}}{\delta_1^2} + \frac{E_{z2}}{\delta_2^2} + \frac{E_{z3}}{\delta_3^2} = 0. \tag{13–72}$$

Equations (13–70c), (13–71), and (13–72) form a system of linear equations and can be solved by Cramer's rule. The determinant of the system of equations is

$$\Delta = \begin{vmatrix} 1 & 1 & 1 \\ 1/\delta_1 & 1/\delta_2 & 1/\delta_3 \\ 1/\delta_1^2 & 1/\delta_2^2 & 1/\delta_3^2 \end{vmatrix}.$$

This is a determinant of Vandermonde's type; we can evaluate it by subtracting the first column from the remaining columns. We obtain

$$\Delta = \left(\frac{1}{\delta_1} - \frac{1}{\delta_2}\right)\left(\frac{1}{\delta_2} - \frac{1}{\delta_3}\right)\left(\frac{1}{\delta_3} - \frac{1}{\delta_1}\right),$$

$$E_{z1} = \frac{E_i}{[1 - (\delta_2/\delta_1)][1 - (\delta_3/\delta_1)]} = \frac{E_i}{3},$$

$$E_{z2} = E_{z3} = E_i/3.$$

To determine the amplification of the traveling-wave tube, we must now relate E_z to the helix field E_h. The field E_h can be expressed in the form

$$E_h = E_{h1}e^{-\gamma_1 z} + E_{h2}e^{-\gamma_2 z} + E_{h3}e^{-\gamma_3 z}.$$

We can determine the ratio E_{hk}/E_{zk} from Eq. (13–49) by eliminating J_1 with the aid of Eq. (13–58) and substituting $\gamma = \gamma_k$:

$$E_{hk}/E_{zk} = 1 - \left(\frac{\omega_p}{\omega\,\delta_k}\right)^2. \tag{13–73}$$

Since we have taken $(\omega_p/\omega) \ll 1$, we obtain $E_{hk} \cong E_i/3$.

At $z = l$ the amplified helix wave has an amplitude given by

$$E_0 \simeq \tfrac{1}{3}E_i \exp \left(\frac{\beta_e Cl}{2}\sqrt{3}\right)$$

and the power gain in decibels is

$$G = 20 \log_{10} |E_0/E_i| = 7.5CL - 9.54, \qquad (13\text{–}74)$$

where $L \triangleq \omega l/u_0 = \beta_e l$.

13-8 THE FIELD THEORY OF THE TRAVELING-WAVE TUBE

In the analysis of the traveling-wave tube given in this section, we shall assume that the beam radius is equal to the radius a of the helix. This results in a substantial simplification of the mathematics without any significant loss in the physical information obtainable from the mathematical results. The boundary conditions can only be satisfied by a combination of TE and TM waves. For the TM wave we let U_1 be the solution of Eq. (13–53) for the beam region 1, $0 \leqq r \leqq a$, and let U_2 be the solution of Eq. (13–55) for region 2 where $r \geqq a$. For typical traveling-wave tube parameters, k is nearly real. Thus the appropriate solutions are

$$U_1 = C_1 J_0(kr), \qquad 0 \leqq r \leqq a, \qquad U_2 = C_2 K_0(k_0 r), \qquad r \geqq a.$$
$$(13\text{–}75)$$

For the modified Bessel functions (see Appendix A–30) we have the asymptotic relations

$$I_0(r) \sim \sqrt{1/2\pi r}\, e^r, \qquad I_0/I_1 \simeq 1,$$
$$(13\text{–}76)$$
$$K_0(r) \sim \sqrt{\pi/2r}\, e^{-r}, \qquad K_0/K_1 \simeq 1.$$

Thus we see that $U_2 \to 0$ as $r \to \infty$, which we take as the boundary condition for U_2. The components of the TM field can be obtained from Eqs. (10–4) and (10–5), where $u_1 = r$, $u_2 = \phi$, $h_1 = 1$, and $h_2 = r$. The nonzero field components are:

$$
\left.
\begin{aligned}
E_{r1} &= \gamma C_1 k J_1(kr)e^{-\gamma z} \\
E_{z1} &= -k_0^2 C_1 J_0(kr)e^{-\gamma z} \\
H_{\phi 1} &= j\omega\varepsilon_0 C_1 k J_1(kr)e^{-\gamma z}
\end{aligned}
\right\}, \qquad 0 \leqq r \leqq a,
$$

$$(13\text{–}77)$$

$$
\left.
\begin{aligned}
E_{r2} &= \gamma C_2 k_0 K_1(k_0 r)e^{-\gamma z} \\
E_{z2} &= -k_0^2 C_2 K_0(k_0 r)e^{-\gamma z} \\
H_{\phi 2} &= j\omega\varepsilon_0 C_2 k_0 K_1(k_0 r)e^{-\gamma z}
\end{aligned}
\right\}, \qquad a \leqq r.
$$

The TM field is associated with the beam and helix currents. However, TM field components alone will not satisfy the boundary conditions. To meet these conditions requires an additional TE field which is associated with the helix current only. For the *TE* field we therefore set

$$H_{zk} = -k_0^2 V_k e^{-\gamma z}, \qquad k = 1, 2,$$

and we choose V_k to be the appropriate solution of Eq. (13–55). Thus

$$V_1 = C_3 I_0(k_0 r), \qquad 0 \leqq r \leqq a, \qquad V_2 = C_4 K_0(k_0 r), \qquad a \leqq r.$$

We can now obtain the nonzero field components from Eqs. (10–8):

$$
\left.
\begin{aligned}
H_{r1} &= -\gamma C_3 k_0 I_1(k_0 r) e^{-\gamma z} \\
H_{z1} &= -k_0^2 C_3 I_0(k_0 r) e^{-\gamma z} \\
E_{\phi 1} &= j\omega\mu_0 C_3 k_0 I_1(k_0 r) e^{-\gamma z}
\end{aligned}
\right\}, \qquad 0 \leqq r \leqq a,
$$

$$
\left.
\begin{aligned}
H_{r2} &= \gamma C_4 k_0 K_1(k_0 r) e^{-\gamma z} \\
H_{z2} &= -k_0^2 C_4 K_0(k_0 r) e^{-\gamma z} \\
E_{\phi 2} &= -j\omega\mu_0 C_4 k_0 K_1(k_0 r) e^{-\gamma z}
\end{aligned}
\right\}, \qquad a \leqq r.
$$

(13–78)

The resultant field is taken to be

$$\mathbf{E} = \mathbf{E}(TE) + \mathbf{E}(TM), \qquad \mathbf{H} = \mathbf{H}(TE) + \mathbf{H}(TM). \qquad (13\text{–}79)$$

We must now determine values of the constants C_1, C_2, C_3, C_4, and k so that the boundary conditions are satisfied. The boundary conditions for a conducting helix are extremely complicated. We shall therefore discuss a simplified model of the helix which results in simpler boundary conditions. The helix is represented by a sheath model in which a current sheet is constrained to flow on a circular cylindrical surface at an angle $(\pi/2) - \psi$ with respect to the z-axis. We take the component of the electric field intensity in the direction of the current flow to be zero. This choice approximates the boundary condition on a perfectly conducting flat helix. Thus (see Fig. 13–17)

$$E_{\phi k}/E_{zk} = -\tan \psi, \qquad k = 1, 2. \qquad (13\text{–}80)$$

The component of the electric field intensity tangential to the current sheet and normal to the direction of the current flow must be continuous. Thus

$$E_{z1} \cos \psi - E_{\phi 1} \sin \psi = E_{z2} \cos \psi - E_{\phi 2} \sin \psi.$$

(13–81)

From Eqs. (13–80) and (13–81) we obtain

$$E_{z1} = E_{z2}, \qquad E_{\phi 1} = E_{\phi 2}. \qquad (13\text{–}82)$$

Substituting Eqs. (13–77) and (13–78) into the conditions (13–82) yields

$$C_1/C_2 = K_0(k_0 a)/J_0(ka), \qquad (13\text{–}83)$$

$$C_3/C_4 = -K_1(k_0 a)/I_1(k_0 a), \qquad (13\text{–}84)$$

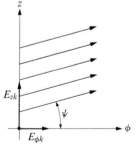

Fig. 13–17. Sheath model for a helix.

and the condition (13–80) yields

$$\frac{C_3}{C_1} = \frac{k_0}{j\omega\mu_0} \frac{J_0(ka)}{I_1(k_0a)} \tan \psi. \tag{13-85}$$

The component of $\mathbf{H}$ which is tangential to the current sheet and parallel to the direction of current flow must be continuous. Thus

$$H_{\phi 1} + H_{z1} \tan \psi = H_{\phi 2} + H_{z2} \tan \psi,$$

$$j\omega\varepsilon_0 k J_1(ka) - k_0^2 \frac{C_3}{C_1} I_0(k_0a) \tan \psi = j\omega\varepsilon_0 k_0 \frac{C_2}{C_1} K_1(k_0a) - k_0^2 \frac{C_4}{C_1} K_0(k_0a) \tan \psi.$$

With the aid of Eqs. (13–83), (13–84), and (13–85) we obtain the characteristic equation

$$k \frac{J_1(ka)}{J_0(ka)} = k_0 \frac{K_1(k_0a)}{K_0(k_0a)} - k_0 \left(\frac{ck_0 \tan \psi}{\omega}\right)^2 \left(\frac{K_0(k_0a)}{K_1(k_0a)} + \frac{I_0(k_0a)}{I_1(k_0a)}\right). \tag{13-86}$$

We can solve Eq. (13–86) numerically for k and we can then find the propagation function from Eq. (13–54). Let us first discuss the unperturbed propagation function for the fundamental mode of the helix. Since the electron beam is absent, we have $\omega_p = 0$ (see Eq. 13–54) and

$$k = jk_0, \qquad k \frac{J_1(jk_0a)}{J_0(jk_0a)} = -k_0 \frac{I_1(k_0a)}{I_0(k_0a)}.$$

For the fundamental mode of the helix we anticipate a wave moving slowly with respect to the velocity of light. Thus we set $\gamma = j\omega/u_p$, where $u_p \ll c$. We then have

$$k_0^2 = \left(\frac{\omega}{u_p}\right)^2 \left[1 - \left(\frac{u_p}{c}\right)^2\right] \simeq \left(\frac{\omega}{u_p}\right)^2 \qquad \text{and} \qquad k_0a \simeq \frac{a\omega}{u_p} = 2\pi \left(\frac{a}{\lambda}\right)\left(\frac{c}{u_p}\right) \gg 1$$

(see Eq. 13–51). The latter inequality is valid provided that a is of the same order of magnitude as the free-space wavelength λ. Using the asymptotic relations given by Eqs. (13–76), we see that Eq. (13–86) takes the form

$$-1 = 1 - 2\left(\frac{ck_0 \tan \psi}{\omega}\right)^2,$$

which yields

$$\gamma = j \frac{\omega}{c \sin \psi}$$

(again see Eq. 13–51). The phase velocity of the wave is $u_p = c \sin \psi$, and can be interpreted as the axial phase velocity of a wave propagating along the helical conductor with a phase velocity c.

Let us now return to Eq. (13–86) and consider the case in which an electron beam is present. Beck [5] has pointed out that k is nearly real for typical traveling-wave tube parameters. The equation can then be solved only by numerical methods. However, in the case of a very weak beam current, we can use the previous approximations and obtain a simple and useful result. For a very weak beam current, k is nearly purely imaginary. Thus we set $k = jf$ and obtain

$$jf\frac{J_1(jfa)}{J_0(jfa)} = -f\frac{I_1(fa)}{I_0(fa)} = -f,$$

where we have again used the asymptotic relations for the Bessel functions. If the unperturbed phase velocity is approximately equal to the steady-state beam velocity, we can expect a strong interaction between the electron beam and the wave on the helix:

$$u_0 = c \sin \psi \cong c \tan \psi.$$

Since the wave is a slow wave (see Eq. 13–51), we have

$$k_0^2 \cong -\gamma^2.$$

Substituting the above results into Eq. (13–86) gives

$$-\frac{f}{k_0} = 1 + 2\left(\frac{\gamma u_0}{\omega}\right)^2.$$

Squaring the above equation and taking into account Eq. (13–54) yields

$$1 - \left[\frac{\omega_p}{u_0(\beta_e + j\gamma)}\right]^2 = \left[1 + 2\left(\frac{\gamma}{\beta_e}\right)^2\right]^2. \tag{13–87}$$

Equation (13–87) determines the propagation function γ. By introducing a parameter δ defined by the equation

$$\gamma = j\beta_e(1 + \delta)$$

and taking $|\delta| \ll 1$ so that only the linear term in δ need be retained on the right-hand side of Eq. (13–87), we obtain the equation $\delta^3 = -C^3$, where

$$C \triangleq \frac{1}{2}\left(\frac{\omega_p}{\omega}\right)^{2/3}.$$

A discussion of the above equation was given in Section 13–7. We see that field theory can be used to determine an analytical expression for the parameter C.

13-9 THE BACKWARD-WAVE OSCILLATOR

There is an infinite number of possible modes of propagation for a helix. In a traveling-wave tube the *forward-wave modes*, in which the phase velocity has same direction as the energy flow, are excited. Figure 13–18(a) shows a transmission-line analog for forward-wave modes.

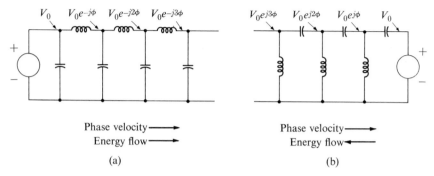

Fig. 13–18. Transmission line analogs for (a) a forward-wave structure, (b) a backward-wave structure.

However, it is also possible to have *backward-wave modes*, in which the phase velocity and the energy flow have opposite directions. Figure 13–18(b) illustrates a transmission-line analog for a backward-wave mode. The backward-wave mode of a helix is utilized in the backward-wave oscillator, which is similar in appearance to the traveling-wave tube (Fig. 13–15). However, the input-output terminals are interchanged. In the backward-wave oscillator there is an interaction between the electron beam and the backward wave. The backward wave increases in amplitude toward the left, since this is the direction of energy flow on the helix. However, the phase velocity is to the right and consequently the field configuration travels nearly in synchronism with the electron beam and can interact with it, causing a modulation. The modulated electron beam in moving to the right gives up energy to the backward wave. Since the energy flow on the helix is to the left we have, therefore, a feedback loop.

Let us consider the feedback loop illustrated in Fig. 13–19. For the coupling, we assume that the rate of change of the response v_0 is proportional to the excitation v_i. In phasor form we have $V_0 = cV_i/j\omega$, where c is a real constant, so that there is a phase lag of $\pi/2$ introduced into the feedback loop by the coupling. One of the conditions for oscillation for the positive feedback loop shown is that the phase shift around the loop must be an even multiple of π. Thus, since we have a phase advance of βl for the backward-wave

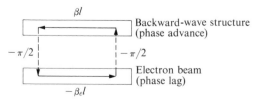

Fig. 13–19. Phase relations for a backward-wave oscillator.

structure, a phase lag of $\beta_e l$ for the electron beam, and a phase lag of $2(\pi/2)$ due to the coupling, we obtain the following condition for oscillation:

$$(\beta - \beta_e)l = (2n + 1)\pi. \tag{13–88}$$

The above expression is approximate, since the interaction between the electron beam and the backward wave cannot be accurately described by a simple feedback loop. However, a more accurate analysis by ballistic theory will show that Eq. (13–88) is a useful first approximation.

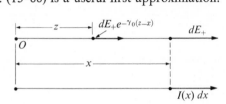

Fig. 13–20. The generation of elemental backward waves due to an element of beam current.

We shall now discuss the ballistic theory of the backward-wave oscillator. Equation (13–60) remains unchanged. However, the circuit equation differs from that of the traveling-wave tube. Let us consider a fixed position z and a position $x > z$ on the transmission-line analog. The current element $I(x)\,dx$ at x induces waves of amplitude dE_+ and dE_- at x (Fig. 13–20). Since the energy flow is to the left, we must consider the amplitude

$$dE_+ e^{-\gamma_0(z-x)}$$

which is observed at z and is associated with the amplitude dE_+ induced by the current element at x. A similar consideration for $x < z$ and the superposition of all elemental waves yields the resultant helix field observed at z:

$$E_h(z) = E_0 e^{-\gamma_0 z} + \int_0^z dE_- e^{\gamma_0(z-x)} + \int_z^l dE_+ e^{-\gamma_0(z-x)}. \tag{13–89}$$

Comparing Eq. (13–89) with Eq. (13–65), we see that the sign of γ_0 is changed for the generated waves in the backward-wave mode. Thus Eq. (13–66) now has the form

$$\frac{E_h}{I} = -\frac{2Z_c\gamma_0\,|\gamma|^2}{\gamma^2 - \gamma_0^2} \tag{13–90}$$

Combining Eq. (13–60) with Eq. (13–90) yields

$$\frac{(\gamma^2 - \gamma_0^2)[(j\beta_e - \gamma)^2 + (\omega_p/u_0)^2]}{j\beta_e\,|\gamma|^2\,\gamma_0} = -2C^3, \tag{13–91}$$

where C is defined by Eq. (13–67). If we let

$$\gamma_0 = j\beta_e(1 + Cb), \qquad \gamma = j\beta_e(1 + C\,\delta), \qquad C \ll 1,$$

and if we neglect ω_p/u_0, we obtain

$$\delta^2(\delta - b) = 1. \tag{13-92}$$

The three roots δ_1, δ_2, and δ_3 of Eq. (13-92) result in three incident waves with propagation functions γ_1, γ_2, and γ_3, respectively.

To determine the axial component of the helix field we note that Eqs. (13-70c), (13-71), and (13-73) remain valid. Thus

$$E_h(z) = E_1 e^{-\gamma_1 z} + E_2 e^{-\gamma_2 z} + E_3 e^{-\gamma_3 z} = E_i e^{-j\beta_e z}\left[\frac{\delta_1^2}{(\delta_1 - \delta_2)(\delta_1 - \delta_3)} e^{-j\delta_1\beta_e Cz}\right.$$

$$\left. + \frac{\delta_2^2}{(\delta_2 - \delta_3)(\delta_2 - \delta_1)} e^{-j\delta_2\beta_e Cz} + \frac{\delta_3^2}{(\delta_3 - \delta_1)(\delta_3 - \delta_2)} e^{-j\delta_3\beta_e Cz}\right].$$

The condition for oscillation is that for zero input, $E_h(l) = 0$, we have a nonzero response, $E_i \neq 0$. Thus we must have

$$\frac{\delta_1^2}{\delta_1 - \delta_2)(\delta_1 - \delta_3)} e^{-j\delta_1\beta_e Cl} + \frac{\delta_2^2}{(\delta_2 - \delta_3)(\delta_2 - \delta_1)} e^{-j\delta_2\beta_e Cl}$$

$$+ \frac{\delta_3^2}{(\delta_3 - \delta_1)(\delta_3 - \delta_2)} e^{-j\delta_3\beta_e Cl} = 0.$$

Equating the real and imaginary parts of this equation to zero yields two equations [6] which can be solved simultaneously with Eq. (13-92) to obtain δ_1, δ_2, δ_3, b, and Cl/β_e. For the lowest-order mode we obtain

$$\delta_1 = -0.150 + j0.725, \qquad b = 1.522,$$

$$\delta_2 = -0.150 - j0.725, \qquad C\frac{\beta_e l}{2\pi} = 0.3141,$$

$$\delta_3 = 1.823, \qquad (\beta - \beta_e)l = 3.003.$$

Table 13-1 shows the value of $(\beta - \beta_e)l$ compared with the value given by Eq. (13-88). We can see that $(2n + 1)\pi$ gives a reasonable estimate for the value of $(\beta - \beta_e)l$.

The backward-wave oscillator can be tuned over a wide frequency range by simply varying the accelerator voltage, so that the beam velocity u_0 remains approximately equal to the phase velocity of the backward wave.

Table 13-1

n	$(\beta - \beta_e)l$	$(2n + 1)\pi$
0	3.003	3.1416
1	9.860	9.4248
2	16.388	15.708
3	21.403	21.991

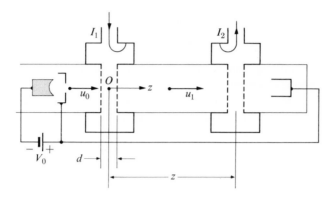

Fig. 13–21. A klystron amplifier.

13–10 THE KLYSTRON

The klystron tube can function as an amplifier or oscillator at very high frequencies. In a klystron an electron beam is accelerated to a velocity u_0. The accelerated beam is then velocity-modulated by the electric field between the grids of an input cavity (Fig. 13–21). The velocity-modulated electrons enter a drift space in which the velocity distribution results in the formation of electron bunches. Several cavities may be used to enhance the bunching effect and to obtain a suitable power gain over a specified bandwidth. The electron bunches can give up energy to the output cavity, provided that the electric field intensity has the proper phase relationship with respect to the electron bunches. We can obtain a simple first approximation to the performance characteristics of a klystron by using the ballistic method. Let the axial component of the electric field intensity in the input cavity be given by

$$E_1 = \frac{V_1}{d} \sin \omega t$$

and let us consider the motion of a particular electron which is at the center ($x = 0$) of the input cavity at a time of departure $t = t_1$. If the change in velocity through the gap is small, we can set

$$t \cong t_1 + x/u_0$$

for the instant of time at which the electron is at a position x. The change in energy of the electron in traversing the input cavity is given by the work done by the field:

$$\tfrac{1}{2}m(u_1^2 - u_0^2) \cong \frac{eV_1}{d} \int_{-d/2}^{d/2} \sin \omega(t_1 + x/u_0)\, dx = eV_1 M \sin \omega t_1. \quad (13\text{–}93)$$

Here we define

$$M \triangleq \frac{\sin(\omega d/2u_0)}{\omega d/2u_0}$$

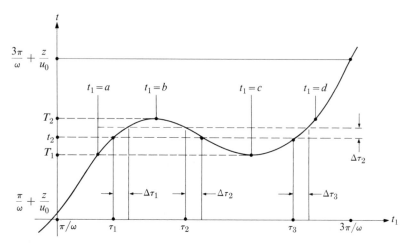

Fig. 13–22. The time of arrival t as a function of departure time t_1 for $MX = 2$.

as the *modulation coefficient*. Since $\frac{1}{2}mu_0^2 = eV_0$, where V_0 is the accelerating voltage, we can express Eq. (13–93) in the form

$$\frac{u_0}{u_1} = \left(1 + M\frac{V_1}{V_0}\sin \omega t_1\right)^{-1/2} = 1 - \frac{1}{2}M\frac{V_1}{V_0}\sin \omega t_1 + \cdots, \quad (13–94)$$

where the Taylor expansion (13–94) is valid if $|V_1/V_0| \ll 1$.

Let us now say that t represents the time of arrival of the electron at the output cavity. We consider that the electron travels in the drift space at the constant velocity u_1. Thus, given that z is the distance between the centers of the input and output cavities, we have

$$t = t_1 + z/u_1 = t_1 + z/u_0 - \frac{MX}{\omega}\sin \omega t_1 + \cdots \quad (13–95)$$

where

$$X \triangleq \frac{1}{2}\frac{\omega z}{u_0}\frac{V_1}{V_0} \quad (13–96)$$

is called the *bunching parameter*. Figure 13–22 is a plot of Eq. (13–95). Note that when $MX > 1$, there can be more than one departure time for a given time of arrival. As shown in the figure, electrons that depart at times τ_1, τ_2, and τ_3 all arrive at the time t_2. Let I_0 represent the input current and i the output current. The conservation of charge requires that at $t = t_2$ we must have

$$i\,|\Delta t_2| = I_0(\,|\Delta \tau_1| + |\Delta \tau_2| + |\Delta \tau_3|\,).$$

Noting that Δt_2 and $\Delta \tau_2$ have opposite signs, we can write

$$i\,\Delta t_2 = I_0(\Delta \tau_1 - \Delta \tau_2 + \Delta \tau_3). \quad (13–97)$$

Differentiating Eq. (13–95) with respect to t yields

$$\frac{dt_1}{dt} = \frac{1}{1 - MX \cos \omega t_1}.$$

Thus, when we let $\Delta t_2 \to 0$, we obtain the current

$$i(t, z) = I_0 \sum_{k=1}^{3} \frac{1}{|1 - MX \cos \omega \tau_k|},$$

where the τ_k are the one or more departure times which correspond to an arrival time t. Note that the sum reduces to one term if t_1 is uniquely determined by t; such is the case when $MX < 1$. Figure 13–23 illustrates the current waveform i which, for a fixed z, is a periodic function of time. The current waveform can be resolved into harmonics and we are usually interested only in the amplitude of the fundamental. The Fourier series representation has the form

$$i = \sum_{k=-\infty}^{+\infty} c_k e^{jk\omega t} \tag{13–98}$$

and the fundamental component c_1 is given by the Fourier coefficient formula,

$$c_1 = \frac{1}{2\pi} \int_{-\pi}^{\pi} i e^{-j\omega t} \, d(\omega t). \tag{13–99}$$

In order to evaluate c_1 we introduce t_1 as the integration variable. In the case of $MX > 1$, careful consideration must be given to the interval $T_1 \leqq$

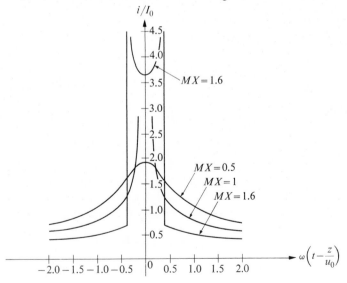

Fig. 13–23. The current waveform in the drift space of a klystron.

$t \leqq T_2$, where t_1 is a multivalued function of t (see Fig. 13–22). Thus, using Eq. (13–97), we have

$$\frac{\omega I_0}{2\pi} \int_{t=T_1}^{t=T_2} e^{-j\omega t}(d\tau_1 - d\tau_2 + d\tau_3)$$

$$= \frac{\omega I_0}{2\pi}\left(\int_a^b e^{-j\omega t}\, dt_1 + \int_b^c e^{-j\omega t}\, dt_1 + \int_c^d e^{-j\omega t}\, dt_1 \right) = \frac{\omega I_0}{2\pi} \int_a^d e^{-j\omega t}\, dt_1.$$

Using the above result and noting that an interval of length $2\pi/\omega$ on the t-axis corresponds to the same interval on the t_1-axis, we can transform Eq. (13–99) into the form,

$$c_1 = \frac{I_0}{2\pi} \int_{-\pi}^{\pi} e^{-j\omega t}\, d(\omega t_1).$$

In order to express t in terms of t_1 we substitute $\phi \triangleq \omega t_1$ into Eq. (13–95) and obtain

$$\omega t = \phi + \omega z/u_0 - MX \sin \phi.$$

Thus, using the integral representation for the Bessel function J_1, we find that

$$c_1 = \frac{I_0 e^{-j\omega z/u_0}}{2\pi} \int_{-\pi}^{\pi} e^{-j(\phi - MX \sin \phi)}\, d\phi = I_0 \exp\left(-\frac{j\omega z}{u_0} \right) J_1(MX),$$

and in a similar manner we find that

$$c_{-1} = I_0 e^{j\omega z/u_0} J_1(MX).$$

Equation (13–98) takes the form

$$i = I_0 + 2I_0 J_1(MX) \cos \omega(t - z/u_0) + \cdots , \qquad (13\text{–}100)$$

which gives the current as a function of the position z and the time of arrival t. It should be noted that the amplitude of the fundamental is a function of the bunching parameter X which is linearly dependent on z (see Eq. 13–96). From Eq. (13–100) we obtain the fundamental current i_f at the center of the output cavity at a time t_2:

$$i_f \triangleq 2I_0 J_1(MX) \cos \omega(t_2 - z/u_0).$$

We assume i_f to be uniform over the small cavity-gap width d. We assume further that the output cavity is tuned to the fundamental frequency and that the axial component of the electric field intensity in the output cavity is given by

$$E_2 = \frac{V_2}{d} \cos (\omega t + \theta - \omega z/u_0), \qquad (13\text{–}101)$$

where θ is a phase angle. During the transit time of an electron through the output gap, the field E_2 will change. To account for this change, we note that

$$t \cong t_2 + x/u_0,$$

where we take t_2 as the instant of time at which a particular electron is at the center ($x = 0$) of the output cavity, so that t is the instant of time when the electron is at a position x. Substituting the above relation into Eq. (13–101), we find the instantaneous power supplied by the beam to the output cavity to be given by

$$P = \int_{-d/2}^{d/2} i_f E_2 \, dx = 2I_0 M V_2 J_1(MX) \cos \omega(t_2 - z/u_0) \cos [\omega(t_2 - z/u_0) + \theta],$$

where M is the modulation coefficient (see Eq. 13–93). The average power is

$$P_a = \tfrac{1}{2} I_2 V_2 \cos \theta,$$

where

$$I_2 \triangleq 2I_0 M J_1(MX). \tag{13–102}$$

We see that the average power is a function of the bunching parameter X. The power is a maximum when $\theta = 0$ and when I_2 is a maximum. This occurs when

$$\frac{dJ_1(MX)}{dX} = 0,$$

which yields

$$MX = 1.84, \qquad J_1(MX) = 0.582. \tag{13–103}$$

Since $M \cong 1$, we see that $|V_1/V_0|$ must not be excessively small for optimum power output. We therefore refer to this case as one of high-level modulation. When $|V_1/V_0|$ is small compared with unity, we have $J_1(MX) \cong MX/2$, and from Eq. (13–102) we obtain the magnitude of the *transadmittance*,*

$$G_T = \frac{I_2}{V_1} = M^2 \frac{\omega z}{2u_0} \frac{I_0}{V_0}. \tag{13–104}$$

Let us now consider the equivalent circuit for the output cavity illustrated in Fig. 13–24. We assume that the cavity is tuned so that the admittances are real and can be represented by conductances:

$$G_C = \text{cavity conductance},$$

$$G_B = \text{equivalent shunt conductance to account}$$
$$\text{for beam loading of cavity},$$

$$G_L = \text{load conductance}.$$

---

* *Transadmittance* is defined as the ratio of the phasor output current and the phasor input voltage.

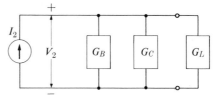

The average power supplied to the load is

$$P_L = \tfrac{1}{2} I_2 V_2 \frac{G_L}{G_L + G_B + G_C}.$$

If there is no restriction on P_L, we obtain the maximum P_L when $G_L = G_B + G_C$. Thus under this condition

$$P_L = \tfrac{1}{4} I_2 V_2. \qquad (13\text{--}105)$$

In the output cavity there is an upper limit on the possible output power. This results from the fact that some electrons may be stopped in the cavity and returned. The slowest electrons have passed through a potential difference of $V_0 - V_1$ in the input cavity gap. So that these will not be brought to rest in the output cavity gap and returned, we must have

$$V_2 \leqq V_0 - V_1. \qquad (13\text{--}106)$$

The maximum average power P_M that can be supplied to the output cavity under the condition (13–106) occurs when we take the equality sign. Thus

$$P_M = \tfrac{1}{2} I_2 V_0 (1 - V_1/V_0). \qquad (13\text{--}107)$$

Example. Let us take the simple ballistic theory that we have developed and apply it to a klystron having the following specifications:

$V_0 = 2200$ volts, $f = 3$ GHz,

$I_0 = 80$ mA,   Output cavity $G_2 = G_B + G_C = 2.5 \times 10^{-5}$ mhos,

$d = 0.25$ cm,   Input cavity $G_1 = G_B + G_C = 2.7 \times 10^{-5}$ mhos,

$z = 3$ cm.

We have

$$u_0 = \sqrt{2eV_0/m} = 2.78 \times 10^7 \text{ m/sec}, \qquad \omega d/2u_0 = 0.846,$$

and the modulation coefficient is

$$M = \frac{\sin (0.846)}{0.846} = 0.88.$$

Let us first consider the case of optimum high-level operation. From the value of MX for optimum operation (see Eq. 13–103) we can determine the bunching parameter, $X = 1.84/M = 2.08$, and from Eq. (13–96) we obtain $V_1/V_0 = 0.205$. The peak value of the voltage at the input gap is $V_1 = 451$ volts. Equation (13–102) yields the peak value of the fundamental output current, $I_2 = 82$ mA and we find that the peak value of the voltage at the output gap is

$$V_2 = I_2/2G_2 = 1.64 \times 10^3 \text{ volts.}$$

The average power supplied to the output cavity is twice the value given by Eq. (13–105): $2P_L = 67.2$ W, and the maximum power that can be supplied is given by Eq. (13–107): $P_M = 71.7$ W. The efficiency is defined as the ratio of load power and beam power, expressed as a percentage: $100P_L/I_0V_0 = 19\%$. The ratio of P_L and the power input, $P_1 = \frac{1}{2}V_1^2G_1 = 2.75$ W, gives the power gain, $G = P_L/P_1 = 12.2$.

In the case of low-level operation we use Eq. (13–104) to obtain $G_T = 2.86 \times 10^{-4}$ mhos. The input power is given by $P_1 = \frac{1}{2}V_1^2G_1$, and the power gain is

$$G = \frac{P_L}{P_1} = \frac{1}{2}\frac{G_T^2}{G_1G_2} = 61.$$

It would appear from Eq. (13–104) that when the drift length is increased the transadmittance and therefore the power gain can be increased. This results from the fact that at low power levels the bunching appears to increase with increasing drift length. However, we have neglected space-charge effects, which tend to counteract the bunching as the drift length is increased. Thus G_T does not increase indefinitely with z and there is an optimum drift length at low power levels (see Problem 13–9).

13–11 INTERACTION OF ELECTROMAGNETIC WAVES WITH ATOMS; QUANTUM ELECTRONICS

In the preceding sections as well as in Chapter 12 we have discussed various aspects of the interaction of electromagnetic waves with free charges and with anisotropic media. So far in our discussion, simple macroscopic models and classical laws have sufficed. However, there are numerous important phenomena which cannot be described by classical laws. This is the case when electromagnetic waves are absorbed and emitted by atoms. We know from quantum mechanics that an orbital electron of an atom can exist only in discrete energy levels E_n ($n = 0, 1, 2, \ldots$). The atom can absorb (or emit) pulses of electromagnetic energy (photons) in discrete amounts given by the difference in energy of the energy levels. The relationship between the frequency f_{nm} of the electromagnetic wave and the change in energy of the atom is given by *Planck's law*,

$$hf_{nm} = |E_n - E_m|, \tag{13–108}$$

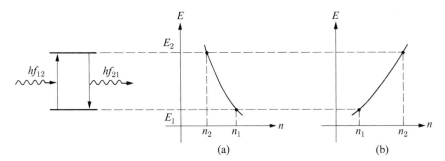

Fig. 13–25. Energy-level diagram and population distribution for (a) the normal case, (b) the inverted case.

where $h = 6.547 \times 10^{-34}$ J/sec is Planck's constant. In general, the absorption and emission of photons by atoms is of a random incoherent nature. An atom in an energy level $E_2 > E_1$ can emit a photon of energy hf_{21} and make a transition to the energy level E_1 (Fig. 13–25). For an isolated atom such a transition is known as *spontaneous emission* and is governed by the laws of probability. However, in the presence of an electromagnetic wave of frequency f_{21} the atom can be stimulated to make the transition $E_2 \rightarrow E_1$ and the emitted wave has the same field distribution and frequency as the stimulating radiation. The emission of numerous atoms can therefore be made coherent under the stimulation of an electromagnetic wave. This phenomenon occurs in the maser (Microwave Amplification by Stimulated Emission of Radiation) and the laser (Light Amplification by Stimulated Emission of Radiation). To understand the conditions for maser operation, let us compute the power absorbed P_{abs} from an incident electromagnetic wave, given that there are n_1 atoms in state E_1 and n_2 atoms in state E_2. Given that W_{12} is the *stimulated transition probability*, the number of atoms per second making the transition $E_1 \rightarrow E_2$ is $W_{12}n_1$. Similarly, the number of atoms per second making the transition $E_2 \rightarrow E_1$ is $W_{21}n_2$. Making use of the fact that $W_{12} = W_{21}$, we obtain

$$P_{abs} = hf_{12}W_{12}(n_1 - n_2). \tag{13–109}$$

From Eq. (13–109) we see that the population difference $n_1 - n_2$ determines the absorbed power. If a large number of atoms is in thermal equilibrium the ratio of the populations of two energy levels is given by the *Boltzmann equation*,

$$n_2/n_1 = e^{-(E_2-E_1)/kT}, \tag{13–110}$$

where $k = 1.38 \times 10^{-23}$ J/°K is the Boltzmann constant (see Fig. 13–25a). The thermal equilibrium population difference $n_1 - n_2$ is always positive, and according to Eq. (13–109) always results in power being absorbed. However, if a mechanism can be found which can invert the population

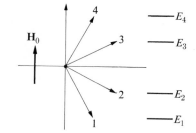

Fig. 13–26. Quantized orientation of a magnetic dipole in a magnetic field and associated energy levels.

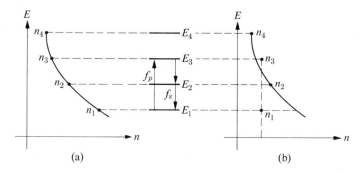

Fig. 13–27. Population distribution for (a) the normal case, (b) the inverted case.

distribution given by Eq. (13–110), as shown in Fig. 13–25b, then power can be supplied to the signal and amplification results. Population inversion is a necessary condition for maser operation.

To understand how population inversion can be accomplished, let us discuss the case of a ruby maser. Ruby is a crystal of Al_2O_3 with a small amount of Cr_2O_3 as an impurity. It is the energy levels of the Cr^{3+} ions which are used to achieve maser operation. The uncompensated spins of the orbital electrons of the chromium ion result in a permanent magnetic dipole moment. Such an atom is called *paramagnetic.* According to the laws of quantum mechanics the magnetic dipole moment can have only discrete orientations in an applied magnetic field (Fig. 13–26). Associated with each orientation is an energy level. In the case of the ruby maser, applied fields of several kilogauss result in transition frequencies between these levels in the gigahertz range. The splitting of energy levels in this manner by a magnetic field is known as the *Zeeman effect*; the energy levels which result are known as *Zeeman levels.*

Figure 13–27(a) illustrates the population distribution among the four energy levels in the case of thermal equilibrium. Now consider Fig. 13–27(b). A pump consisting of an externally applied electromagnetic wave of frequency f_{13} can be used to achieve a population inversion of level 2 with respect to level 1. Initially, since $n_1 > n_3$, there are more atoms at level 1 that will

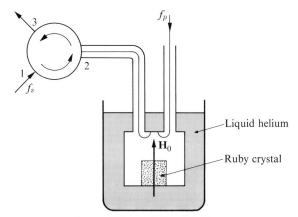

Fig. 13–28. A maser amplifier.

absorb photons than there are atoms at level 3 that will emit photons. If the pump is sufficiently strong, equilibrium is reached when $n_1 \simeq n_3$, as shown in the figure. In this case the transition $E_1 \to E_3$ is said to be saturated. Due to the pump, an inversion of level 2 with respect to level 1 has been accomplished. When a second electromagnetic wave of frequency f_{21} is allowed to interact with the crystal, the stimulated transition $E_2 \to E_1$ will result in amplification of the wave. The frequencies $f_p = f_{13}$ and $f_s = f_{21}$ are referred to as the pump and signal frequencies, respectively. The ruby maser is known as a 3-level maser, since transitions occur among three of the Zeeman energy levels. One can see from Fig. 13–27 that n_2 remains approximately at its thermal equilibrium value. A necessary condition for effective maser operation is that n_2 should be as large as possible with respect to n_1. One can see from Eq. (13–110) that this condition requires that the temperature T be as small as possible. Thus most maser amplifiers operate at low temperatures; for example, a liquid helium bath of $T = 4.2°$K is often used.

Figure 13–28 illustrates the principle of a maser amplifier. A ruby crystal is situated in a low-temperature bath in an applied magnetic field $\mathbf{H}_0$. The pump power at a frequency f_p induces the population inversion. A signal at a frequency f_s is amplified by stimulating the transition $E_2 \to E_1$. To keep the input signal and the amplified output signal separated in order to prevent amplifier instability, a circulator can be used. The circulator allows energy to flow from port 1 to port 2 only and from port 2 to port 3 only.

13–12 LASERS

By a suitable choice of materials and energy levels one can obtain highly intense sources of coherent light by laser action. The laser is the equivalent, at optical frequencies, of the maser which operates at microwave frequencies.

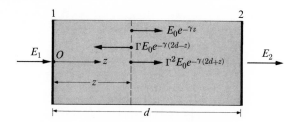

Fig. 13–29. A simple model of a laser amplifier.

Let us first consider a simplified model of a laser amplifier. At optical frequencies *Fabry-Perot resonators* are usually used. These consist of two adjacent reflecting surfaces. The medium between the reflecting surfaces is the active medium in which laser action occurs.

Now consider Fig. 13–29. For simplicity we assume that the electromagnetic waves can be described by plane waves and we take $\gamma = \alpha + j\beta$ as the propagation function in the active medium. An incident wave E_1 passes through the plate, is amplified by the active laser medium, and exits as the amplified wave E_2. To understand the action of the Fabry-Perot resonator, we consider that the field in the active region arises out of an infinite sequence of incident and reflected waves. Thus an incident wave $E_0 e^{-\gamma z}$ strikes plate 2 and gives rise to a reflected wave $\Gamma E_0 e^{-\gamma(2d-z)}$, where Γ is the reflection coefficient and $2d - z$ is the distance traveled by the wave from the origin O. This reflected wave moves to the left, and when it strikes plate 1 it gives rise to another reflected wave, $\Gamma^2 E_0 e^{-\gamma(2d+z)}$, which moves to the right. Continuing in this manner, we see that the resultant field is

$$E = E_0 e^{-\gamma z} + \Gamma E_0 e^{-\gamma(2d-z)} + \Gamma^2 E_0 e^{-\gamma(2d+z)} + \cdots$$

$$= \frac{e^{-\gamma z} + \Gamma e^{-\gamma(2d-z)}}{1 - \Gamma^2 e^{-\gamma 2d}} \cdot E_0. \quad (13\text{--}111)$$

(The infinite series can be summed by noting that it consists of two infinite

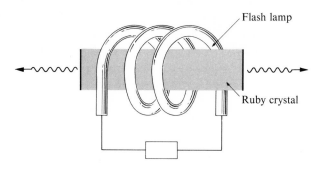

Fig. 13–30. A pulsed ruby laser.

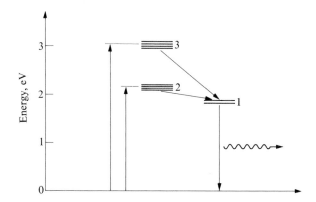

Fig. 13–31. Energy-level diagram for chromium atoms in ruby.

geometric series.) The gain in field intensity due to amplification is defined by the equation

$$G \triangleq \frac{E(d)}{E(0)} = e^{-\gamma d},$$

and we see that $|G| > 1$ if $\alpha < 0$. This is the case for a laser medium. The medium will oscillate if the denominator of Eq. (13–111) is zero. If we let $\Gamma = |\Gamma| e^{j\theta}$, we obtain the following conditions for oscillation:

$$\alpha = \frac{1}{d} \ln |\Gamma|, \qquad \beta d = \theta - \pi n. \qquad (13\text{–}112)$$

Figure 13–30 illustrates these principles as they are applied to a pulsed ruby laser and Fig. 13–31 illustrates a simplified energy-level diagram for chromium atoms. The light of a pulsed flash lamp is concentrated on the ruby and supplies the pump power required to raise the electrons of the chromium atoms to the energy levels at 2 or 3. The transition to the levels at 2 requires a green light and the transition to the levels at 3 requires a blue light. The excited atoms give up some energy to the crystal lattice and relax to the metastable levels at 1. A few atoms dropping from the levels at 1 to the ground state start the oscillation. The silvered ends of the ruby rod act as a Fabry-Perot resonator and a regenerative process rapidly triggers all atoms into making a downward transition. A high-energy pulse of coherent red light is then radiated from the partially transparent ends.

Figure 13–32 illustrates the same principles, except that here the active medium is a mixture of neon and helium gases contained in a discharge tube. The electrical discharge is maintained by an oscillator which sets up a radio-frequency field across electrodes placed around the tube, as shown. A Fabry-Perot resonator is used and the discharge tube is sealed by glass windows placed at the Brewster angle to prevent reflections.

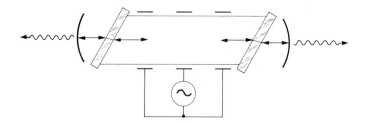

Fig. 13–32. The neon-helium gas laser.

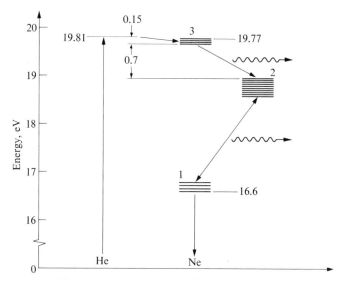

Fig. 13–33. Energy-level diagram for neon and helium.

Figure 13–33 illustrates a simplified energy-level diagram for neon and helium atoms [7]. The electrons in the discharge, because of collisions, excite the helium atoms to an energy level of 19.81 eV. This level is a metastable state in which the transition probability for an isolated atom is negligible. Consequently many atoms accumulate at this level. The excited He atoms collide with unexcited Ne atoms and exchange energies. Due to the small difference in the energy levels, a small part of the energy is taken up by the kinetic energy of the colliding atoms. The helium therefore converts the broad distribution of energy of the discharge electrons into a discrete distribution of energy in the quantum states at 3. The excited neon atoms decay by stimulated emission $(3 \rightarrow 2)$ and by incoherent photon emission $(2 \rightarrow 1)$ to the energy levels at 1, which are metastable. Neon atoms in the energy states at 1 are returned to the ground state as a result of collision with the walls of the discharge tube.

13–13   SEMICONDUCTOR LASERS

Thus far we have considered materials whose energy levels are associated with localized atoms, in which case the condition for amplification is that there be a population inversion between two energy levels. In semiconductors, the electronic states are defined over the entire crystal and the condition for stimulated emission takes a different form. In an n-type semiconductor, donor impurities donate electrons to the conduction band. The energy levels in the conduction band are not discrete, so that it is not strictly correct to speak of a population inversion between energy levels. Similarly, in a p-type semiconductor, acceptor impurities bind valence electrons, leaving a deficiency of electrons in the valence band. We can account for the deficiency of electrons by introducing the concept of holes. The energy levels for holes in the valence band are also not discrete. To satisfy the condition for laser operation in semiconductors, a highly doped (degenerate) junction diode is used at low temperatures.

To understand the reason for this choice and to derive the condition for laser operation, we must investigate the distribution of quantum states at the diode junction. For an n-type semiconductor which is not in thermal equilibrium, the probability of occupation of any state E_c in the conduction band is given by the *Fermi-Dirac distribution function*,

$$f_c = \frac{1}{1 + \exp\left[(E_c - F_c)/kT\right]}, \tag{13–113}$$

where F_c is the *quasi-Fermi level*. When we replace the subscript c by the subscript v we obtain a similar expression which applies for the valence band. In thermal equilibrium, when no external voltage is applied to the diode, we have $F_c = F_v = F_0$. Here F_0 represents the energy at which the probability of occupation is $\frac{1}{2}$.

Figure 13–34 illustrates the energy-band structure in a gallium arsenide (GaAs) injection laser. The shaded area indicates states filled with electrons. Because of degeneracy, the electron levels just below the forbidden gap on the p-side are empty, while those just above the gap on the n-side are full. Furthermore, at low temperatures very few of the states above the Fermi level contain holes and electrons. Consequently no photons with energies $hf \cong E_g$ can be absorbed by transitions within these levels. To achieve laser operation it is essential to prevent those transitions which result in undesirable absorption. This is essentially the reason for choosing a degenerate semiconductor and a low temperature. As the forward diode current is increased, a threshold current is reached at which laser operation occurs. In the depletion region at the junction, an effective population inversion exists in the sense that electrons in the conduction band, by a downward transition, can combine with holes and emit photons. The

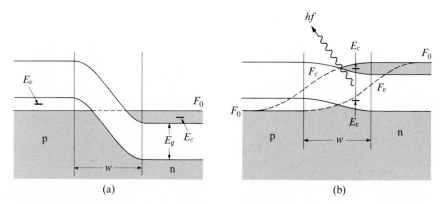

Fig. 13–34. The energy bands at low temperature in a degenerate pn-junction diode with (a) zero forward current, (b) nonzero forward current.

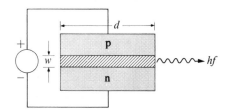

Fig. 13–35. A diode injection laser.

forward-biased diode is not in thermal equilibrium; the distribution function is given by Eq. (13–113).

To determine the threshold condition we proceed as follows. In order for a photon to be absorbed there must be an electron in the valence band that can absorb the photon and an empty state in the conduction band to which the electron can jump. The probability of an electron being in a valence-band state is f_v; the probability of an empty state in the conduction band is $1 - f_c$. Thus the number of photons absorbed per second is

$$n_a = cW_{vc}f_v(1 - f_c),$$

where c is a constant that depends on the density of photons of energy hf and the density of states and where W_{vc} is the probability for the transition $E_v \rightarrow E_c = E_v + hf$. Similarly, the number of photons emitted per second is

$$n_e = cW_{cv}f_c(1 - f_v).$$

The condition for laser operation is that $n_e > n_a$. Since $W_{vc} = W_{cv}$, it follows from Eq. (13–113) that

$$F_c - F_v > hf = E_c - E_v. \tag{13–114}$$

When Eq. (13–114) is satisfied the depletion layer at the junction is an active laser region. The depletion layer is bounded by the p- and n-regions and acts as a dielectric loaded cavity.

When the faces of the diode are polished, a Fabry-Perot resonator is formed, as shown in Fig. 13–35. When the forward current equals the threshold current, the condition (13–114) is satisfied, and electrons in the conduction band in the depletion region are stimulated to emit photons and combine with holes in the valence band. The depletion layer, acting as a dielectric loaded cavity, resonates in one or more modes, and electromagnetic energy is radiated through the partially reflecting faces of the diode.

13–14 THE GUNN EFFECT

The dynamical effects on free charges due to a bulk negative resistance which can exist in certain types of semiconductors give rise to what is known as the *Gunn effect* [8]. The mechanism of the Gunn effect is very different from the maser mechanism. We can describe the motion of free charges in a semiconductor by an equation of the type given by Eq. (13–1). However, we must take considerable care when we define an *effective mass* to be used in this equation. The internal field in a crystal usually differs considerably from the externally applied field. Furthermore, the motion of an electron consists of a sequence of transitions between available quantum states. As a consequence of the laws of quantum mechanics which govern these transitions, the effective mass of a free electron in a semiconductor differs from the mass of an electron in free space. The effective mass is usually a tensor quantity, since the internal field and the available quantum states are different for different directions of motion.

In heavily doped GaAs semiconductors the available quantum states give rise to two classes of electrons, which have different effective masses m_1 and m_2. The mobilities μ_1 and μ_2 of these two classes will therefore be different. If $m_2 > m_1$, we have

$$a \triangleq \mu_2/\mu_1 < 1. \tag{13–115}$$

The electrons of class 2 have much less mobility than the electrons of class 1. For GaAs, $a \cong 0.02$ and $\mu_1 \cong 5000$ (cm²/V)/sec. Let n_1 and n_2 be the respective densities of the two classes. Normally most of the electrons are of class 1. When an electric field E is applied to the semiconductor, the electrons of class 1 acquire energy and can make transitions to class 2. A relation of the form

$$n_2/n_1 = b^k \tag{13–116}$$

holds approximately, where $b \triangleq E/E_0$ and where E_0 is a reference field. The individual electron densities are given by

$$n_1 = \frac{n}{1 + b^k}, \qquad n_2 = \frac{nb^k}{1 + b^k},$$

where $n = n_1 + n_2$ and the average drift velocity is

$$v = \frac{\mu_1 E n_1 + \mu_2 E n_2}{n} = v_0 \frac{b + ab^{k+1}}{1 + b^k}, \qquad (13\text{–}117)$$

where $v_0 \triangleq \mu_1 E_0$.

To investigate the possibility of a negative resistance effect we must determine whether there is a negative slope in the graph of v as a function of b. The slope is the differential mobility given by

$$\mu \triangleq \frac{dv}{dE} = \frac{1}{E_0}\frac{dv}{db} = \frac{\mu_1}{(1 + b^k)^2}\{1 - [(k - 1) - a(k + 1)]b^k + ab^{2k}\}.$$

$$(13\text{–}118)$$

From Eq. (13–118) we see that $\mu = 0$ when

$$b^k = \frac{1}{2a}\{[(k - 1) - a(k + 1)] \pm \sqrt{[(k - 1) - a(k + 1)]^2 - 4a}\}.$$

$$(13\text{–}119)$$

The condition for a negative resistance region is that $\mu < 0$ over a region which is bounded by the two values given by Eq. (13–119). This requires that the square root in Eq. (13–119) be real and greater than zero. A graph of v as a function of E is shown in Fig. 13–36.

The Gunn effect is a consequence of the electrical instability which arises in the semiconductor when a certain threshold voltage across the semi-conductor is reached. To understand this instability, consider Fig. 13–36 and Fig. 13–37. The threshold is exceeded when the applied voltage results in an electric field intensity such as E_0, which corresponds to a point zero on the negative-resistance portion of the curve (Fig. 13–36). This state is unstable and leads to a breakup into domains of lower and higher fields, corresponding to points 1 and 2. This breakup is illustrated in Fig. 13–37, where the dashed line indicates the uniform initial state and the solid straight lines indicate the final state. The formation of the high-field domain 2 is associated with a decrease in the field intensity outside this domain to a value below threshold, thereby inhibiting the formation of further domains. In the final state the potential distribution adjusts itself as shown in Fig. 13–37, and, as a consequence of the continuity of current, the drift velocities are equal, as shown in Fig. 13–36.

A charge density is associated with the rapid change in electric field intensity in the region of the domain walls. The two domain walls appear, therefore, to be like a dipole layer. Since the free charges in an n-type semiconductor are electrons, the charge distribution and hence the domain walls drift toward the anode at a velocity equal to the drift velocity $v = v_1 = v_2$ of the electrons. (Note that the positive charge distribution is caused by a deficiency of electrons. Actually the domain dynamics are quite complicated

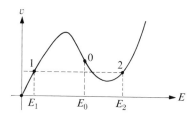

Fig. 13–36. Drift velocity as a function of the applied field.

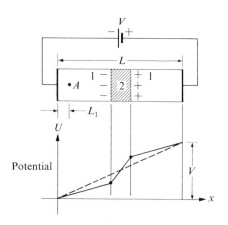

Fig. 13–37. Domain formation due to the Gunn effect.

and involve drift, diffusion, and transitions between high- and low-mobility quantum states.) Each domain is nucleated at a point such as A, which is usually close to the cathode, and grows to an equilibrium form, which it maintains as it drifts to the anode. The domain vanishes when it reaches the anode and a new domain is then nucleated at A. The process repeats cyclically with a period $T = (L - L_1)/v$, where L is the length of the semiconductor and L_1 is the distance of the nucleating center from the cathode end of the semiconductor. The current, which rises momentarily during the extinction and nucleating process, consists of a series of pulses with a period T. These current pulses can be used as an excitation source for microwave cavities.

To understand the nucleating process at A, let us take a closer look at the instability associated with the negative-resistance region. For the one-dimensional model illustrated in Fig. 13–37, Eqs. (2–47b) and (2–42) take the form

$$\text{div } \mathbf{E} = \frac{\partial E_x}{\partial x} = \frac{\rho}{\varepsilon}, \qquad \text{div } \mathbf{J} = \frac{\partial J_x}{\partial x} = -\frac{\partial \rho}{\partial t}.$$

Hence

$$\frac{\partial}{\partial x}\left(\frac{\partial E_x}{\partial t}\right) = -\frac{1}{\varepsilon}\frac{\partial J_x}{\partial x}. \tag{13–120}$$

When we integrate Eq. (13–120) over a small interval from x to $x + \Delta x$ at the domain boundary, we obtain

$$\frac{dF}{dt} = -\frac{1}{\varepsilon}[J_x(x + \Delta x) - J_x(x)] \cong -\frac{1}{\varepsilon}\frac{dJ_x}{dE_x}F, \tag{13–121}$$

where

$$F \triangleq E_x(x + \Delta x) - E_x(x).$$

Now we have taken the E-field and the positive current density to have the direction of the negative x-axis. Hence $E_x = -E$ and $J_x = -J$, where $J = env$. It follows that

$$\frac{dJ_x}{dE_x} = \frac{dJ}{dE} = en\frac{dv}{dE},$$

and Eq. (13–121) yields

$$\frac{dF}{dt} \cong -\frac{1}{\tau}F, \tag{13–122}$$

where $1/\tau \triangleq (en/\varepsilon)(dv/dE)$. The solution of Eq. (13–122) is

$$F(t) = F(0)e^{-t/\tau}. \tag{13–123}$$

In a negative resistance region $\tau < 0$. It follows from Eq. (13–123) that if $F(0) > 0$ in a negative-resistance region, F and consequently the field grow exponentially. The initial field E_0 then grows to an equilibrium value E_2 (see Fig. 13–36). Similarly, when $F(0) < 0$ in a negative-resistance region, the initial field E_0 decreases to an equilibrium value E_1. The nucleation center A is caused by a nonuniformity in doping and by field variations due to the proximity of the cathode.

REFERENCES

1. L. BRILLOUIN, "A theorem of Larmor and its importance for electrons in magnetic focusing," *Phys. Rev.* **67**, 260–266, April 1945
2. J. E. STERRETT and H. HEFFNER, "The design of periodic magnetic focusing structures," *Trans. IRE*, PGED-5, 35–42, January 1958
3. G. M. BRANCH and T. G. MIHRAN, "Plasma frequency reduction factors in electron beams," *Trans. IRE*, PGED-2, 3–11, April 1955
4. J. R. PIERCE, *Traveling-Wave Tubes*, New York: Van Nostrand, 1950
5. A. H. W. BECK, *Space-Charge Waves*, New York: Pergamon Press, 1958
6. H. R. JOHNSON, "Backward-wave oscillators," *Proc. IRE* **42**, 684–697, June 1955
7. A. JAVAN, W. R. BENNETT and O. R. HERRIOTT, "Population inversion and continuous optical maser oscillation in a gas discharge containing a He-Ne mixture," *Phys. Rev. Letters* **6**, 3, 106–110, February 1, 1961
8. *IEEE Trans. on Elec. Devices*, ED-13, No. 1, January 1966

GENERAL REFERENCES

J. SLATER, *Microwave Electronics*, New York: Van Nostrand 1950
H. REICH, P. ORDUNG, H. KRAUS, and J. SKALNIK, *Microwave Theory and Techniques*, New York: Van Nostrand, 1953
G. SIMS and I. STEPHENSON, *Microwave Tubes and Semiconductor Devices*, New York: Interscience, 1963

R. G. E. HUTTER, *Beam and Wave Electronics in Microwave Tubes*, New York: Van Nostrand, 1960

R. E. COLLIN, *Foundations for Microwave Engineering*, New York: McGraw-Hill, 1966

A. E. SIEGMAN, *Microwave Solid-State Masers*, New York: McGraw-Hill 1964

G. BIRNBAUM, "Optical Masers." *Advances in Electronics and Electron Physics*, Supplement 2, New York: Academic Press, 1964

Proc. IEEE, Special Issue on Quantum Electronics, January 1963

G. BURNS and M. I. NATHAN, "P-N junction lasers," *Proc. IEEE* **52**, 7, 770–791, July 1964

PROBLEMS

13-1 (a) Consider the ballistic motion of an electron in an xy-plane under the influence of an electric field with components E_x and E_y. Show that the trajectory of the electron can be expressed in the differential equation form

$$2U\frac{d^2y}{dx^2} = \left(E_x\frac{dy}{dx} - E_y\right)\left[1 + \left(\frac{dy}{dx}\right)^2\right].$$

(b) Given that the electric field is symmetric about the x-axis and that the deviation y of the electron from the axis is small, use the result of Problem 4–10 and part (a) above to derive the so-called *paraxial ray equation*,

$$\frac{d^2y}{dx^2} + \frac{f^{(1)}}{2f}\frac{dy}{dx} + \frac{f^{(2)}}{2f}y = 0.$$

13-2 An electron starts at rest at a position of zero potential in an electrostatic field. It is accelerated by an electric field and moves with a velocity $\mathbf{u}_1$ from a region of potential U_1 into a region of potential U_2 where its velocity is $\mathbf{u}_2$ (see Fig. 13–38). Prove Snell's law,

$$\frac{\sin\theta_1}{\sin\theta_2} = \frac{u_2}{u_1} = \sqrt{\frac{U_2}{U_1}}.$$

13-3 An electron is emitted from the axis of a long straight coil with a velocity $\mathbf{u}$ at an angle α with respect to the x-axis (Fig. 13–39). The magnetic flux density $\mathbf{B}$ is directed along the x-axis and is uniform throughout the coil. Show that the electron crosses the x-axis again when $x = 2\pi mu \cos\alpha/eB$. Describe the motion of the electron.

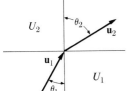

Figure 13-38

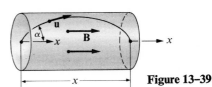

Figure 13-39

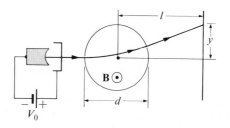

Figure 13–40

13–4 An electron beam is deflected by means of magnetic deflection coils onto a screen (Fig. 13–40). Show that the magnetic deflection sensitivity is given by

$$y/B = l\,d\sqrt{e/2mV_0},$$

where the quantities are defined by the figure. Given that $V_0 \gg 1$, and that a large deflection is desired, would you choose magnetic or electrostatic deflection? Explain.

13–5 (a) Show that Eq. (13–42) can be written in the form

$$I_0 = 0.066\,V_0^{3/2} X \sqrt{1 - X}\ \text{mA},$$

where

$$X \triangleq \frac{1}{8V_0}\left(\frac{e}{m}\right)(aB_0)^2.$$

(b) Given that $I_0 = 50$ mA, $V_0 = 1000$ volts, and $a = 0.3$ cm, determine the magnetic flux density B_0 required for Brillouin focusing. Evaluate the Larmor frequency. (c) Show that I_0 has a maximum for $X = \frac{2}{3}$ and that

$$I_{0\,\text{max}} = 0.0254\,V_0^{3/2}\ \text{mA}.$$

13–6 Express Eq. (10–6) in cartesian coordinates, eliminate $J = J_1$ by means of Eq. (13–49), and discuss the case of plane space-charge waves propagating in the positive z-direction. Show that

$$\beta_{1,2} = \frac{\omega \pm \omega_p}{u_0}.$$

Given that $V_0 = 1000$, $f = 1$ GHz, $J_0 = 1.77 \times 10^3$ A/m², determine the wavelengths of the space-charge waves.

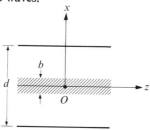

Figure 13–41

13–7 A beam of electrons in the form of an infinite sheet of thickness b is symmetrically spaced with respect to parallel conducting walls which are a distance d apart (Fig. 13–41). The beam moves with an average velocity $\mathbf{u}_0 = \mathbf{i}_z u_0$. Consider that the assumptions made in Section 13–6 are applicable and show that the characteristic equation for space-charge waves in the beam is

$$k_0 \coth \frac{k_0}{2} (d - b) = k \tan \frac{kb}{2}.$$

[*Hint:* Express Eq. 10–6 in cartesian coordinates and show that

$$\frac{\partial^2 U_1}{\partial x^2} + \frac{\partial^2 U_1}{\partial y^2} + k^2 U_1 = 0, \quad 0 \leqq x \leqq b/2,$$

$$\frac{\partial^2 U_2}{\partial x^2} + \frac{\partial^2 U_2}{\partial y^2} - k_0^2 U_2 = 0, \quad b/2 \leqq x \leqq d/2,$$

where k and k_0 are defined by Eqs. (13–51) and (13–54). The field components can be obtained from Eqs. (10–4) and (10–5). Note that due to symmetry we have $E_x = 0$ on the z-axis.]

13–8 The incremental electron velocity and incremental current density for the incident fundamental space-charge waves in a circular cylindrical beam are determined by the phasors,

$$u_1 = u_{11}e^{-\gamma_1 z} + u_{12}e^{-\gamma_2 z}, \quad J_1 = J_{11}e^{-\gamma_1 z} + J_{12}e^{-\gamma_2 z},$$

where the coefficients can be found from the boundary conditions. Consider the case of the velocity modulation of an electron beam at the input of a klystron in which we have $J_1 = 0$ at $z = 0$. Assume that the velocity modulation has a maximum value of $u_1(0)$ at $z = 0$ and at a time $t = \pi/2\omega$ and that it is zero at $z = 0$ when $t = 0$. Show that the incremental velocity in the drift space $z > 0$ is given by

$$u_1(z, t) = u_1(0) \cos Z \sin \omega(t - z/u_0),$$

where

$$Z \triangleq \frac{z\omega_p F}{u_0}.$$

13–9 The ballistic theory of the klystron given in Section 13–10 can be improved on by accounting for the space-charge waves on the electron beam. The electron velocity in the drift space then has the form

$$v = u_0 + u_1(z, t),$$

where u_0 is the steady-state beam velocity and $u_1(z, t)$ is the velocity modulation given in Problem 13–8. (a) Replace u_1 in Eq. (13–94) by v and show that

$$u_1(z, t) = \frac{u_0}{2} \frac{V_1}{V_0} M \cos Z \sin \omega t_1, \quad t - t_1 = \int_0^z \frac{dz}{v} \cong \frac{z}{u_0} - \frac{MX \sin Z}{\omega} \frac{\sin Z}{Z} \sin \omega t_1.$$

(b) Show that Eq. (13–102) now takes the form

$$I_2 = 2I_0 M J_1 \left(MX \frac{\sin Z}{Z} \right)$$

and that the low-level power gain is a maximum for $z = \pi u_0/2F\omega_p$. (c) Find the value of z and the value for the maximum low-level power gain G for the klystron discussed in Example 1, Section 13–10, given the further data that the beam radius is $a = 0.3$ cm and that $F = 0.8$.

13–10   Given that the transition frequency between two energy levels in $f = 10$ GHz, what is the ratio n_1/n_2 in the case of thermal equilibrium at (a) $T = 290°K$, (b) $T = 4.2°K$?

13–11   The four Zeeman levels of a ruby crystal have a spacing of approximately 4.08×10^{-5} eV for a field of 3 kG with respect to a particular crystal axis. Using the three-level scheme illustrated in Fig. 13–27, determine the pump and signal frequencies.

13–12   Compute the frequencies for the transitions $3 \rightarrow 2$, $2 \rightarrow 1$ in the He-Ne laser using the data given in Fig. 13–33. Given that $N = 10^{15}$ atoms/sec make these transitions, compute the power radiated at these frequencies and compute the power dissipated in wall losses.

13–13   Compute the frequency of oscillation of a Gunn-effect oscillator, given that $L = 100 \, \mu$, $L_1 \cong 0$, $v = 5 \times 10^6$ cm/sec.

LEGENDRE AND BESSEL FUNCTIONS

A–1 LEGENDRE FUNCTIONS

We have seen that $1/r$ is a solution of Laplace's equation and that further solutions can be obtained by successive differentiations with respect to z (see Section 4–3). Thus

$$\frac{\partial}{\partial z}\frac{1}{r} = -\frac{z}{r^3} = -\frac{u}{r^2} = -\frac{P_1(u)}{r^2}, \qquad (A-1)$$

where we have substituted $z = ru$ and $u \triangleq \cos\theta$, is a solution of Laplace's equation. A second differentiation yields

$$\frac{\partial^2}{\partial z^2}\frac{1}{r} = \frac{3u^2 - 1}{r^2} = \frac{2P_2(u)}{r^3}. \qquad (A-2)$$

The functions $P_n(u)$ obtained in this manner are defined as the *Legendre polynomials:* $P_1(u) = u$, $P_2(u) = \frac{1}{2}(3u^2 - 1)$, $P_3(u) = \frac{1}{2}(5u^3 - 3u)$, ... The Legendre polynomials are normalized so that $P_n(1) = 1$.

Let us consider the function

$$\frac{1}{r_1} = \frac{1}{\sqrt{r^2 + a^2 - 2ar\cos\theta}}, \qquad (A-3)$$

which is a solution of Laplace's equation, and represent it by means of Legendre polynomials. Expanding in a Taylor series in a yields

$$\frac{1}{r_1} = \frac{1}{r} + \left(\frac{\partial}{\partial a}\frac{1}{r_1}\right)_{a=0} a + \left(\frac{\partial^2}{\partial a^2}\frac{1}{r_1}\right)_{a=0}\frac{a^2}{2} + \cdots$$

In cartesian coordinates we have $r_1^2 = x^2 + y^2 + (z - a)^2$ and if $f = f(r_1)$ is a function of r_1 we note that $\partial f/\partial a = -\partial f/\partial z$. Thus

$$\frac{1}{r_1} = \frac{1}{r} - \frac{\partial}{\partial z}\left(\frac{1}{r}\right)a + \frac{\partial^2}{\partial z^2}\left(\frac{1}{r}\right)\frac{a^2}{2} + \cdots$$

$$= \frac{1}{r}\left[P_0(u) + \frac{a}{r}P_1(u) + \frac{a^2}{r^2}P_2(u) + \cdots\right], \qquad (A-4)$$

where we have made use of the relations given by Eqs. (A–1) and (A–2).

When we substitute $\theta = 0$ and $\theta = \pi$ into Eq. (A–4), we find that $P_n(1) = 1$ and that $P_n(-1) = (-1)^n$.

To determine the differential equation satisfied by $P_n(u)$ we substitute $U = r^{-n-1}P_n(\cos \theta)$ into the Laplacian given by Eq. (1–107), which we then equate to zero. This yields

$$\frac{d}{du}\left[(1 - u^2)\frac{dP_n}{du}\right] + n(n + 1)P_n = 0, \qquad (A-5)$$

where we have introduced the substitution $u \triangleq \cos \theta$. Note that if we replace $n + 1$ by $-m$ in the exponent of r, then $n(n + 1) = (m + 1)m$. Thus $U = r^n P_n(\cos \theta)$ is also a solution of Laplace's equation and a general solution is given by

$$U = \sum_{n=0}^{\infty}(A_n r^n + B_n r^{-n-1})P_n(\cos \theta). \qquad (A-6)$$

To determine a solution of Eq. (A–5), let us consider the equation

$$(1 - u^2)\frac{d^2f}{du^2} + 2(n - 1)u\frac{df}{du} + 2nf = 0. \qquad (A-7)$$

Differentiating Eq. (A–7) $n - 1$ times with respect to u, we find that

$$(1 - u^2)\frac{d^{n+1}f}{du^{n+1}} + n(n + 1)\frac{d^{n-1}f}{du^{n-1}} = 0. \qquad (A-8)$$

If we substitute $P_n = d^n f/du^n$ and then differentiate Eq. (A–8) with respect to u we obtain Eq. (A–5). A solution of Eq. (A–7) is $f = c_n(u^2 - 1)^n$. Since $P_n(1) = 1$ we must choose $c_n = 1/2^n!$. Thus we obtain *Rodrigues' formula*

$$P_n(u) = \frac{1}{2^n n!} \cdot \frac{d^n}{du^n}(u^2 - 1)^n. \qquad (A-9)$$

With the aid of Eq. (A–9) we obtain the formula

$$\frac{dP_{n+1}}{du} - \frac{dP_{n-1}}{du} = (2n + 1)P_n. \qquad (A-10)$$

To discuss the orthogonality of the Legendre polynomials, let us consider P_n and P_m, where $n \neq m$. Multiplying Eq. (A–5) by P_m, interchanging n and m, and then subtracting the two equations yields

$$\frac{d}{du}\left[(1 - u^2)\left(P_m\frac{dP_n}{du} - P_n\frac{dP_m}{du}\right)\right] + [n(n + 1) - m(m + 1)]P_nP_m = 0. \qquad (A-11)$$

Integrating Eq. (A–11) between the limits $u = -1$ and $u = 1$ yields the orthogonality relation for the Legendre polynomials:

$$\int_{-1}^{1} P_n P_m \, du = 0, \qquad n \neq m. \tag{A–12}$$

To evaluate the integral in the case of $n = m$, we first consider successive applications of Eq. (A–10): $dP_{n+1}/du = (2n + 1)P_n + (2n - 3)P_{n-2} + \cdots$ Multiplying the above equation by P_n, using Eq. (A–12), and integrating by parts yields

$$\int_{-1}^{1} P_n \frac{dP_{n+1}}{du} \, du = (2n + 1) \int_{-1}^{1} P_n^2 \, du = P_n P_{n+1}]_{-1}^{1} - \int_{-1}^{1} \frac{dP_n}{du} P_{n+1} \, du = 2.$$

In the final step we have made use of the fact that $P_n(1) = 1$, $P_n(-1) = (-1)^n$. By substituting

$$\frac{dP_n}{du} = (2n - 1)P_{n-1} + (2n - 5)P_{n-3} + \cdots$$

into the integrand, we see that the final integral vanishes. Thus

$$\int_{-1}^{1} P_n^2 \, du = \frac{2}{2n + 1}. \tag{A–13}$$

With the aid of Eqs. (A–12) and (A–13), we can determine the constant c_n in an expansion of the form $f(u) = \sum_{n=0}^{\infty} c_n P_n(u)$. We find that

$$c_n = \frac{2n + 1}{2} \int_{-1}^{1} f(u) P_n(u) \, du. \tag{A–14}$$

A–2 BESSEL FUNCTIONS

Solutions of the equation

$$\frac{d^2 y}{dr^2} + \frac{1}{r} \frac{dy}{dr} + \left(k^2 - \frac{n^2}{r^2} \right) y = 0 \tag{A–15}$$

are called *Bessel functions*. If we let $u = kr$, we can show by direct substitution that

$$J_n(u) = \frac{u^n}{2^n n!} \left[1 - \frac{u^2}{2^2(n + 1)} + \frac{u^4}{2^4 2! \, (n + 1)(n + 2)} + \cdots \right] \tag{A–16}$$

is a solution of Eq. (A–16). The function J_n is called the *Bessel function of the first kind of order n*. We find from Eq. (A–16) that

$$J_1 = -dJ_0/du. \tag{A–17}$$

When we evaluated the magnetic and electric field energy in wave guides and cavities, we made use of various integral formulas involving Bessel functions. To derive these formulas, let us consider the identity

$$-(k^2r^2 - n^2)J_n\frac{dJ_n}{dr} = k^2rJ_n^2 - \frac{1}{2}\frac{d}{dr}[(k^2r^2 - n^2)J_n^2]$$

$$= \left(r^2\frac{d^2J_n}{dr^2} + r\frac{dJ_n}{dr}\right)\frac{dJ_n}{dr} = \frac{k^2}{2}\frac{d}{dr}(rJ_n')^2, \quad (A–18)$$

where

$$J_n' \triangleq \frac{dJ_n}{du} = \frac{1}{k}\frac{dJ_n}{dr}$$

and where we have made use of Eq. (A–15) to transform the left-hand side of Eq. (A–18). Integration of Eq. (A–18) yields *Lommel's integral*,

$$2k^2\int_0^a rJ_n^2\,dr = [(k^2r^2 - n^2)J_n^2 + (krJ_n')^2]_0^a. \quad (A–19)$$

Let us now consider the identity

$$\frac{d}{dr}\left(rJ_n\frac{dJ_n}{dr}\right) = r\left(\frac{dJ_n}{dr}\right)^2 + J_n\frac{dJ_n}{dr} + rJ_n\frac{d^2J_n}{dr^2}$$

$$= r\left[(kJ_n')^2 + \left(\frac{n^2}{r^2} - k^2\right)J_n^2\right]. \quad (A–20)$$

Here we have again made use of Eq. (A–15). Integration of Eq. (A–20) yields

$$[krJ_nJ_n']_0^a = \int_0^a r\left[(kJ_n')^2 + \left(\frac{nJ_n}{r}\right)^2\right]dr - k^2\int_0^a rJ_n^2\,dr.$$

If the boundary conditions require that $J_n = 0$ or $J_n' = 0$, we can use Lommel's integral (A–19) in the above expression to obtain

$$\int_0^a r\left[(kJ_n')^2 + \left(\frac{nJ_n}{r}\right)^2\right]dr = \begin{cases} \frac{1}{2}(k^2a^2 - n^2)J_n^2(ka), & J_n'(ka) = 0, \\ \frac{1}{2}[kaJ_n'(ka)]^2, & J_n(ka) = 0. \end{cases} \quad (A–21)$$

To investigate the orthogonality of the Bessel functions, we substitute $y = (1/\sqrt{kr})f$ into Eq. (A–15) and obtain

$$\frac{d^2f}{dr^2} + \left(k^2 - \frac{n^2 - \frac{1}{4}}{r^2}\right)f = 0. \quad (A–22)$$

Let us consider two solutions of Eq. (A–22)

$$f = J_n(\alpha r)\sqrt{\alpha r}, \qquad g = J_n(\beta r)\sqrt{\beta r}, \quad (A–23)$$

where α and β are two different values of k_{mn} which are determined by boundary conditions of the type

$$J_n(k_{mn}a) = 0 \qquad \text{or} \qquad J_n'(k_{mn}a) = 0. \quad (A–24)$$

We now multiply Eq. (A–22) by g, interchange f and g, and then subtract the two equations. Integrating the result yields

$$\left[g\frac{df}{dr} - f\frac{dg}{dr}\right]_0^a = (\beta^2 - \alpha^2)\int_0^a gf\,dr.$$

With the aid of the boundary conditions for the upper limit and Eqs. (A–16) and (A–23) for the lower limit, we can show that the left-hand side is zero. Thus

$$\int_0^a rJ_n(\alpha r)J_n(\beta r)\,dr = 0, \qquad \alpha \neq \beta, \tag{A–25}$$

and we see that the functions $J_n(k_{mn}r)\sqrt{k_{mn}r}$, $(m = 0, 1, 2 \ldots)$ are orthogonal functions.

The asymptotic behavior of the Bessel functions for large values of the argument is often required in the discussion of electromagnetic fields. If $r/n \gg 1$, it follows from Eq. (A–22) that

$$J_n \cong \frac{1}{\sqrt{kr}}(c_{n1}e^{jkr} + c_{n2}e^{-jkr}).$$

We can determine the constants c_{n1} and c_{n2} from the behavior of the solution for small r. In the case of J_n we have the asymptotic formula

$$J_n(u) \sim \sqrt{\frac{2}{\pi u}}\cos\left(u - \frac{\pi}{4} - \frac{\pi n}{2}\right). \tag{A–26}$$

The modified Bessel function of the first kind, I_n, is convenient to use when $k < 0$ in Eq. (A–15). We then have

$$\frac{d^2I_n}{du^2} + \frac{1}{u}\frac{dI_n}{du} - \left(1 + \frac{n^2}{u^2}\right)I_n = 0, \tag{A–27}$$

where

$$I_n = \frac{u^n}{2^n n!}\left[1 + \frac{u^2}{2^2(n+1)} + \frac{u^4}{2^4 2!\,(n+1)(n+2)} + \cdots\right]. \tag{A–28}$$

From Eq. (A–28) we obtain the formula

$$dI_0/du = I_1. \tag{A–29}$$

A second linearly independent solution of Eq. (A–27) is K_n, the modified Bessel function of the second kind. We can obtain the form of the asymptotic behavior for I_n and K_n in the same manner as was done for J_n. It can be shown that we have the following relations:

$$I_n \sim \frac{e^u}{\sqrt{2\pi u}}, \qquad K_n \sim \sqrt{\frac{\pi}{2u}}e^{-u}, \qquad \frac{dK_0}{du} = -K_1. \tag{A–30}$$

THE ELECTROMAGNETIC FIELD
AND RELATIVITY THEORY

B-1 CLASSICAL TRANSFORMATION EQUATIONS

In this section we shall derive the classical transformation equations for the vector components of an electromagnetic field. We shall then, in a subsequent section, compare these equations with the exact relativistic transformations. Let $\mathscr{F}'(x', y', z')$ represent a coordinate system which moves with a velocity $\mathbf{u}$ relative to a coordinate system $\mathscr{F}(x, y, z)$ and let $\mathbf{E}'$, $\mathbf{B}'$ and $\mathbf{E}$, $\mathbf{B}$ represent the electric field intensity and magnetic flux density in $\mathscr{F}'$ and $\mathscr{F}$, respectively.

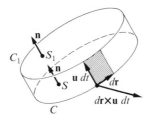

Figure B-1

In order to determine the transformation relating the vector components of the electromagnetic field in $\mathscr{F}'$ and $\mathscr{F}$, we consider Maxwell's first equation (2-54a) in $\mathscr{F}'$,

$$-\oint_C \mathbf{E}' \cdot d\mathbf{r} = \frac{d\phi_m}{dt},\qquad\qquad\text{(B-1)}$$

and we compute the rate of change of magnetic flux in terms of the vector $\mathbf{B}$ in the system $\mathscr{F}$. During a time interval dt the contour C, as seen in $\mathscr{F}$, is translated into a contour C_1 (see Fig. B-1). We have

$$\frac{d\phi_m}{dt} = \frac{\displaystyle\int_{S_1} \mathbf{B}(t + dt) \cdot \mathbf{n}\, ds - \int_S \mathbf{B}(t) \cdot \mathbf{n}\, ds}{dt}.\qquad\qquad\text{(B-2)}$$

To evaluate the integrals in Eq. (B-2) we apply the divergence theorem to the volume swept out by C during the time dt. This yields (note that the normal to the surface S is inwardly directed)

$$\int_{S_1} \mathbf{B}(t + dt) \cdot \mathbf{n} \, ds - \int_{S} \mathbf{B}(t + dt) \cdot \mathbf{n} \, ds$$

$$+ \oint_{C} \mathbf{B}(t + dt) \cdot (d\mathbf{r} \times \mathbf{u} \, dt) = \oint_{v} \operatorname{div} \mathbf{B} \, dv. \quad \text{(B-3)}$$

On the surface S we have

$$\mathbf{B}(t + dt) = \mathbf{B}(t) + (\partial \mathbf{B}/\partial t),$$

and Stokes' theorem yields

$$\oint_{C} \mathbf{B} \cdot (d\mathbf{r} \times \mathbf{u}) = \oint_{C} (\mathbf{u} \times \mathbf{B}) \cdot d\mathbf{r} = \int_{S} \mathbf{n} \cdot \operatorname{curl}(\mathbf{u} \times \mathbf{B}) \, ds.$$

Thus Eq. (B–3) can be expressed in the form

$$\int_{S_1} \mathbf{B}(t + dt) \cdot \mathbf{n} \, ds - \int_{S} \mathbf{B}(t) \cdot \mathbf{n} \, ds - \int_{S} \frac{\partial \mathbf{B}}{\partial t} \cdot \mathbf{n} \, ds$$

$$+ \int_{S} \mathbf{n} \cdot \operatorname{curl}(\mathbf{u} \times \mathbf{B}) \, ds = \int_{S} (\operatorname{div} \mathbf{B})(\mathbf{u} \cdot \mathbf{n} \, dt \, ds). \quad \text{(B-4)}$$

Substituting Eq. (B–4) into Eq. (B–2) yields

$$\frac{d\phi_m}{dt} = \int_{S} \left(\frac{\partial \mathbf{B}}{\partial t} - \operatorname{curl}(\mathbf{u} \times \mathbf{B}) + \mathbf{u} \operatorname{div} \mathbf{B} \right) \cdot \mathbf{n} \, ds. \quad \text{(B-5)}$$

By applying Stokes' theorem to Eq. (B–1) and using Eq. (B–5), we can obtain a relation between the vector components in $\mathscr{F}'$ and $\mathscr{F}$:

$$\operatorname{curl} \mathbf{E}' = -\frac{\partial \mathbf{B}}{\partial t} + \operatorname{curl}(\mathbf{u} \times \mathbf{B}) - \mathbf{u} \operatorname{div} \mathbf{B}. \quad \text{(B-6)}$$

Since Maxwell's equations are valid in both $\mathscr{F}'$ and $\mathscr{F}$, we have

$$\operatorname{curl} \mathbf{E} = -\partial \mathbf{B}/\partial t.$$

Furthermore, since $\operatorname{div} \mathbf{B} = 0$, we see that Eq. (B–6) is satisfied if

$$\mathbf{E}' = \mathbf{E} + \mathbf{u} \times \mathbf{B}. \quad \text{(B-7)}$$

Equation (B–7) is one of the transformation equations relating the vector components of the electromagnetic field in $\mathscr{F}'$ and $\mathscr{F}$.

We shall now derive a second transformation equation by considering Maxwell's second equation (2–54b):

$$\oint_{C} \mathbf{H}' \cdot d\mathbf{r} = \frac{d\phi_e}{dt} + \int_{S} \mathbf{J}' \cdot \mathbf{n} \, ds. \quad \text{(B-8)}$$

When we apply Eq. (B–5) to ϕ_e we obtain

$$\frac{d\phi_e}{dt} = \int_S \left(\frac{\partial \mathbf{D}}{\partial t} - \text{curl} \, (\mathbf{u} \times \mathbf{D}) + \mathbf{u} \, \text{div} \, \mathbf{D} \right) \cdot \mathbf{n} \, ds.$$

With the aid of Stokes' theorem we can write Eq. (B–8) in the differential form

$$\text{curl} \, \mathbf{H}' = \frac{\partial \mathbf{D}}{\partial t} - \text{curl} \, (\mathbf{u} \times \mathbf{D}) + \mathbf{u} \, \text{div} \, \mathbf{D} + \mathbf{J}'.$$

This equation is satisfied by the relation

$$\mathbf{H}' = \mathbf{H} - \mathbf{u} \times \mathbf{D}, \tag{B–9}$$

which can be seen from the fact that it then reduces to Maxwell's second equation in $\mathcal{F}$:

$$\text{curl} \, \mathbf{H} = (\partial \mathbf{D}/\partial t) + \mathbf{J}.$$

Here $\mathbf{J} = \mathbf{J}' + \mathbf{u}\rho'$ is the current density observed in $\mathcal{F}$. This current density consists of the superposition of $\mathbf{J}'$, the current density observed in $\mathcal{F}'$, and the additional current density observed in $\mathcal{F}$ due to the translation of the charge density ρ' with a velocity $\mathbf{u}$. It should be noted that we have taken $\rho \simeq \rho'$, which follows from the invariance of electric charge and the fact that classical theory assumes that corresponding volume elements in $\mathcal{F}'$ and $\mathcal{F}$ are equal. For free space we can write Eqs. (B–7) and (B–9) in the forms

$$\mathbf{D}' = \mathbf{D} + \frac{\mathbf{u}}{c^2} \times \mathbf{H}, \tag{B–10a}$$

$$\mathbf{B}' = \mathbf{B} - \frac{\mathbf{u}}{c^2} \times \mathbf{E}. \tag{B–10b}$$

Our study of the transformation properties of the vector components of the electromagnetic field has resulted in the following equations

$$\mathbf{E}' = \mathbf{E} + \mathbf{u} \times \mathbf{B}, \qquad \mathbf{B}' = \mathbf{B} - \frac{\mathbf{u}}{c^2} \times \mathbf{E}, \qquad \mathbf{D}' = \mathbf{D} + \frac{\mathbf{u}}{c^2} \times \mathbf{H},$$

$$\mathbf{H}' = \mathbf{H} - \mathbf{u} \times \mathbf{D}, \qquad \mathbf{J}' + \mathbf{u}\rho' = \mathbf{J}. \tag{B–11}$$

An exact relativistic investigation of the transformation equations shows that the above equations are accurate to within terms the order of $(u/c)^2$ and that the equations can also be applied to moving media.

B–2 RELATIVITY THEORY

We shall not need any detailed account of the relativity theory. For our purposes it is sufficient to postulate that the quadratic form

$$x^2 + y^2 + z^2 - c^2t^2 = x'^2 + y'^2 + z'^2 - c^2t'^2 \tag{B–12}$$

should remain invariant. Here x', y', and z' are the coordinates of a reference system $\mathscr{F}'$ which moves with a velocity $\mathbf{u} = \mathbf{i}_z u$ relative to a reference system $\mathscr{F}(x, y, z)$. Since there is no motion along the x- and y-axes, we can assume that $x = x'$ and $y = y'$. If u is small we expect a transformation of the type

$$z' = k(z - ut),$$

where $k \simeq 1$. If we consider z and jct as the coordinates of a two-dimensional coordinate system, it follows from Eq. (B–12) that the transformation from $\mathscr{F}$ to $\mathscr{F}'$ is a rotation. Thus we must have

$$\begin{pmatrix} z' \\ jct' \end{pmatrix} = \begin{pmatrix} k & j\beta k \\ -j\beta k & k \end{pmatrix} \begin{pmatrix} z \\ jct \end{pmatrix}, \tag{B–13}$$

where $\beta \triangleq u/c$ and where k is a constant. The condition imposed by Eq. (B–12) requires that $k^2 + (jk\beta)^2 = 1$. Thus $k = 1/\sqrt{1 - \beta^2}$, and we obtain the *Lorentz transformation*

$$z' = \frac{1}{\sqrt{1 - \beta^2}} (z - ut), \qquad t' = \frac{1}{\sqrt{1 - \beta^2}} \left(t - \frac{uz}{c^2} \right). \tag{B–14}$$

The inverse transformation corresponding to (B–14) is obtained by interchanging the primed and unprimed coordinates and changing the sign of u.

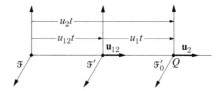

Fig. B–2. Motion of coordinate systems $\mathscr{F}_0'$ and $\mathscr{F}'$ relative to $\mathscr{F}$.

For the discussion in the next section we require equations relating three coordinate systems in relative motion. Let $\mathscr{F}_0'$, $\mathscr{F}'$, and $\mathscr{F}$ represent three coordinate systems and let $\mathscr{F}_0'$ move with a velocity $\mathbf{u}_2 = \mathbf{i}_z u_2$ relative to $\mathscr{F}$ and with a velocity $\mathbf{u}_1 = \mathbf{i}_z u_1$ relative to $\mathscr{F}'$ (see Fig. B–2). To determine the transformation between $\mathscr{F}$ and $\mathscr{F}'$, we use the inverse transformation

$$\begin{pmatrix} z' \\ jct' \end{pmatrix} = \begin{pmatrix} \gamma_1 & -j\beta_1\gamma_1 \\ j\beta_1\gamma_1 & \gamma_1 \end{pmatrix} \begin{pmatrix} z_0 \\ jct_0 \end{pmatrix},$$

where $\gamma_1 \triangleq 1/\sqrt{1 - \beta_1^2}$ and $\beta_1 \triangleq u_1/c$, and the transformation

$$\begin{pmatrix} z_0 \\ jct_0 \end{pmatrix} = \begin{pmatrix} \gamma_2 & j\beta_2\gamma_2 \\ -j\beta_2\gamma_2 & \gamma_2 \end{pmatrix} \begin{pmatrix} z \\ jct \end{pmatrix},$$

where $\gamma_2 \triangleq 1/\sqrt{1 - \beta_2^2}$ and $\beta_2 \triangleq u_2/c$. Combining the transformations and letting $\mathbf{u}_{12} = \mathbf{i}_z u_{12}$ be the relative velocity of $\mathscr{F}'$ with respect to $\mathscr{F}$, we find that

$$\begin{pmatrix} z' \\ jct' \end{pmatrix} = \begin{pmatrix} \gamma_{12} & j\beta_{12}\gamma_{12} \\ -j\beta_{12}\gamma_{12} & \gamma_{12} \end{pmatrix} \begin{pmatrix} z \\ jct \end{pmatrix},$$

where

$$\gamma_{12} = \gamma_1\gamma_2(1 - \beta_1\beta_2), \qquad \beta_{12}\gamma_{12} = \gamma_1\gamma_2(-\beta_1 + \beta_2).$$

Thus

$$\beta_{12} = \frac{-\beta_1 + \beta_2}{1 - \beta_1\beta_2}. \tag{B-15}$$

Equation (B-15) can be written in the following forms

$$\sqrt{\frac{1 - \beta_2^2}{1 - \beta_1^2}} = \frac{1 - \beta_{12}\beta_2}{\sqrt{1 - \beta_{12}^2}}, \tag{B-16a}$$

$$\beta_1(1 - \beta_{12}\beta_2) = \beta_2 - \beta_{12}. \tag{B-16b}$$

B-3 TRANSFORMATION OF THE ELECTRIC FIELD OF A POINT CHARGE

We shall now discuss a method for formulating the laws of electrodynamics, a method based on the relativistic transformation of the electric flux density of a point electric charge. Let us first consider a point charge at rest in a system $\mathscr{F}'$. The field is an electric field given by

$$\mathbf{E}' = \frac{Q}{4\pi\varepsilon_0 r'^2} \mathbf{i}_r,$$

where $\mathbf{i}_r$ is a unit radial vector. Now let $\mathscr{F}'$ move with a velocity $\mathbf{u} = \mathbf{i}_z u$ relative to a coordinate system $\mathscr{F}$ and let us compute the field in $\mathscr{F}$ at a time $t = 0$. It follows from Eq. (B-14) that

$$z = z'\sqrt{1 = \beta^2}, \qquad x = x', \qquad y = y'. \tag{B-17}$$

If we introduce polar coordinates $x = \rho \cos \phi$ and $y = \rho \sin \phi$, we see from the above equations that $\rho = \rho'$ and $\phi = \phi'$.

The electric field intensity in $\mathscr{F}$ can be determined by postulating that the elemental electric flux $d\phi_e$ of the charge is an invariant (Fig. B-3). Thus

$$d\phi_e \triangleq \varepsilon_0 E'(2\pi\rho' r'\, d\theta') = \varepsilon_0 E(2\pi\rho r\, d\theta)$$

and we obtain

$$r'E'\, d\theta' = rE\, d\theta. \tag{B-18}$$

We must now determine several relations between the angles and distances in $\mathscr{F}'$ and $\mathscr{F}$. We have

$$\rho' = r'\sin\theta' = \rho = r\sin\theta \tag{B-19}$$

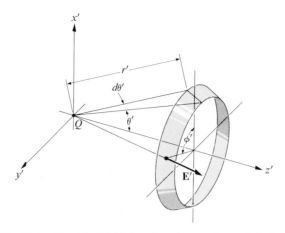

Fig. B–3. Electric field intensity of a moving point charge.

and (see Eq. B–17)

$$r' \cos \theta' = z' = \frac{z}{\sqrt{1 - \beta^2}} = \frac{r \cos \theta}{\sqrt{1 - \beta^2}}. \qquad (B\text{–}20)$$

Equations (B–19) and (B–20) yield the relations

$$r'^2 = \frac{r^2}{1 - \beta^2}(1 - \beta^2 \sin^2 \theta), \qquad (B\text{–}21)$$

$$\tan \theta' = \sqrt{1 - \beta^2} \tan \theta. \qquad (B\text{–}22)$$

Differentiating Eq. (B–22) yields

$$\frac{1}{\cos^2 \theta'}\frac{d\theta'}{d\theta} = \frac{\sqrt{1 - \beta^2}}{\cos^2 \theta}. \qquad (B\text{–}23)$$

With the aid of Eqs. (B–20) and (B–22), we can express Eq. (B–18) in the form

$$E = E' \frac{r'}{r}\frac{d\theta'}{d\theta} = E' \frac{\cos \theta'}{\cos \theta}. \qquad (B\text{–}24)$$

We can now use Eq. (B–24) to determine the components of **E**. We find that

$$E_z = E \cos \theta = E' \cos \theta' = E_z',$$

$$E_x = E \sin \theta \cos \phi = E' \sin \theta' \frac{\tan \theta}{\tan \theta'} \cos \phi' = \frac{1}{\sqrt{1 - \beta^2}} E_x',$$

where we have made use of Eq. (B–22). A similar equation can be obtained for the component E_y. The transformation equations for the components of

E are therefore

$$E_x = \frac{E_x'}{\sqrt{1 - \beta^2}}, \qquad E_y = \frac{E_y'}{\sqrt{1 - \beta^2}}, \qquad E_z = E_z'. \qquad (B\text{-}25)$$

From Eqs. (B–24) and (B–22), we obtain

$$E = \frac{E'}{\sqrt{1 - \beta^2 \sin^2 \theta}} = \frac{Q}{4\pi\varepsilon_0 r'^2} \frac{1}{\sqrt{1 - \beta^2 \sin^2 \theta}} = \frac{Q}{4\pi\varepsilon_0 r^2} \frac{1 - \beta^2}{(1 - \beta^2 \sin^2 \theta)^{3/2}},$$

$$(B\text{-}26)$$

where we have used Eq. (B–21). Equation (B–26) gives the magnitude of the force on a unit test charge at rest in $\mathscr{F}$ due to a point charge Q which moves with a velocity $\mathbf{u} = \mathbf{i}_z u$ relative to $\mathscr{F}$. Note that the motion of the charge Q results in a considerable modification of Coulomb's law for charges at rest.

B-4 THE TRANSFORMATION FOR THE E AND H FIELDS

In the present formulation of the field equations of electrodynamics, we shall see that the magnetic field is a result of the manner in which the force on a moving charge transforms between coordinate systems in relative motion. Let a point charge Q be at rest in a reference system $\mathscr{F}_0'$ and let $\mathscr{F}_0'$ move with a velocity $\mathbf{u}_2 = \mathbf{i}_z u_2$ relative to a system $\mathscr{F}$ and with a velocity $\mathbf{u}_1 = \mathbf{i}_z u_1$ relative to a system $\mathscr{F}'$. Let $\mathbf{u}_{12} = \mathbf{u}$ be the velocity of $\mathscr{F}'$ relative to $\mathscr{F}$ (see Fig. B–2). If E_{x0} is the x-component of the electric field intensity in $\mathscr{F}_0'$, we can apply Eqs. (B–25) to determine the corresponding components in $\mathscr{F}$ and $\mathscr{F}'$:

$$E_x = \frac{E_{x0}}{\sqrt{1 - \beta_2^2}}, \qquad E_x' = \frac{E_{x0}}{\sqrt{1 - \beta_1^2}}. \qquad (B\text{-}27)$$

Equations (B–27) can be used to determine the x-components of the forces on unit test charges Q_1 and Q_1' at rest in $\mathscr{F}$ and $\mathscr{F}'$, respectively. However, an observer in $\mathscr{F}$ sees the test charge Q_1' moving with a velocity $\mathbf{u}$. Experimentally we know that there is a magnetic field in $\mathscr{F}$ which is associated with the moving charge Q and which can be detected by the moving test charge Q_1'. Thus, when we express E_x' in terms of E_x, we expect to be able to identify one of the terms as representing the effect of the magnetic field associated with Q. Eliminating E_{x0} from Eqs. (B–27) and using Eq. (B–16a) (note that we let $\beta_{12} = \beta \triangleq u/c$) yields

$$E_x' = \sqrt{\frac{1 - \beta_2^2}{1 - \beta_1^2}} E_x = \frac{1}{\sqrt{1 - \beta^2}} (1 - \beta\beta_2)E_x, \qquad (B\text{-}28)$$

$$E_x' = \frac{1}{\sqrt{1 - \beta^2}} (E_x - uB_y), \qquad (B\text{-}29)$$

where we have set

$$B_y \triangleq \frac{u_2}{c^2} E_x. \tag{B-30}$$

Similarly, we obtain

$$E_y' = \frac{1}{\sqrt{1 - \beta^2}} (E_y + uB_x). \tag{B-31}$$

where

$$B_x \triangleq -\frac{u_2}{c^2} E_y. \tag{B-32}$$

Since $E_z = E_z'$, we can take $B_z = B_z' = 0$, and Eqs. (B–30) and (B–32) can be combined into the vector equation

$$\mathbf{B} \triangleq \frac{\mathbf{u_2}}{c^2} \times \mathbf{E}, \tag{B-33}$$

which defines the magnetic flux density in $\mathscr{F}$ due to Q.

Let us now determine the transformation equations for the **B** field. If we apply Eq. (B–30) to the **B**′ field in $\mathscr{F}'$ and use Eqs. (B–28) and (B–16b), where we take $\beta_{12} = \beta$, we obtain

$$B_y' = \frac{\beta_1}{c} E_x' = \frac{\beta_2 - \beta}{c\sqrt{1 - \beta^2}} E_x = \frac{1}{\sqrt{1 - \beta^2}} \left(B_y - \frac{u}{c^2} E_x \right). \tag{B-34}$$

In the final step of the above derivation we have used Eq. (B–30). Similarly we can show that

$$B_x' = \frac{1}{\sqrt{1 - \beta^2}} \left(B_x + \frac{u}{c^2} E_y \right). \tag{B-35}$$

The transformations given by Eqs. (B–29), (B–31), (B–34), and (B–35) are identical to the transformations given by Eqs. (B–11) if we take $\mathbf{u} = \mathbf{i}_z u$ and $\beta = 0$.

B–5 DERIVATION OF THE MAXWELL EQUATIONS

We are now in a position to prove that the **E** and **B** vectors are related to each other through the Maxwell equations. Equation (B–26) gives the electric field intensity of a charge Q which moves with a velocity $\mathbf{u} = \mathbf{i}_z u$ relative to a reference system $\mathscr{F}$. The field has symmetry about the z-axis (see Fig. B–3) and we can therefore set

$$x^2 + y^2 = r^2 \sin^2 \theta.$$

Thus, using Eq. (B–26), we obtain

$$E_z = E \cos \theta = Kz, \tag{B-36}$$

where

$$K \triangleq \frac{Q(1 - \beta^2)}{4\pi\varepsilon_0 S^3}, \qquad S \triangleq r\sqrt{1 - \beta^2 \sin^2 \theta} = \sqrt{z^2 + (1 - \beta^2)(x^2 + y^2)}.$$

Similarly, we find that

$$E_x = Kx, \qquad E_y = Ky. \tag{B-37}$$

Equation (B–33) yields

$$B_z = 0, \qquad B_x = -\frac{u}{c^2} E_y, \qquad B_y = \frac{u}{c^2} E_x. \tag{B-38}$$

We can now compute curl **E** in cartesian coordinates, using the components given by Eqs. (B–36) and (B–37). We find that

$$\text{curl } \mathbf{E} = \frac{3\beta^2 Kz}{S^2} (\mathbf{i}_x y - \mathbf{i}_y x). \tag{B-39}$$

To compute the time derivative of **B**, we first note that due to the uniform velocity of the charge we have

$$\mathbf{B}(z, t + \Delta t) = \mathbf{B}(z - \Delta t/u, t).$$

This relation allows us to take $\partial/\partial t = -u(\partial/\partial z)$, so that with the aid of Eqs. (B–38) we obtain

$$-\frac{\partial \mathbf{B}}{\partial t} = \frac{3\beta^2 Kz}{S^2} (\mathbf{i}_x y - \mathbf{i}_y x). \tag{B-40}$$

Comparing Eqs. (B–39) and (B–40), we see that we have derived Maxwell's first equation: curl $\mathbf{E} = -\partial \mathbf{B}/\partial t$.

Similarly, we can divide Eqs. (B–38) by μ_0 and compute

$$\text{curl } \mathbf{H} = \frac{\varepsilon_0 u K}{S^2} [\mathbf{i}_z(3z^2 - S^2) + \mathbf{i}_x 3xz + \mathbf{i}_y 3yz]. \tag{B-41}$$

With the aid of Eqs. (B–36) and (B–37), we obtain

$$\frac{\partial \mathbf{E}}{\partial t} = -\mathbf{i}_z u K + \mathbf{r}\frac{3uKz}{S^2}, \tag{B-42}$$

where $\mathbf{r} \triangleq \mathbf{i}_x x + \mathbf{i}_y y + \mathbf{i}_z z$. Comparing Eqs. (B–41) and (B–42), we see that we have derived Maxwell's second equation

$$\text{curl } \mathbf{H} = \varepsilon_0 \frac{\partial \mathbf{E}}{\partial t}.$$

The laws of electrodynamics can be based on the electric field of a point charge at rest and the Lorentz transformation of the field with respect to moving coordinate systems. The magnetic field intensity and the Maxwell equations express various aspects of the properties of the field transformation.

THE MKS SYSTEM OF UNITS

The international system of electric units was originally defined in terms of quantities which could be conveniently measured in the laboratory:

1. The ohm is the resistance offered to an unvarying electrical current by a column of mercury at the temperature of melting ice. This column of mercury has a constant cross-sectional area, a mass of 14.4521 g, and a length of 106.300 cm.

2. The ampere is the unvarying electric current which, when passed through a specified solution of silver nitrate in water, deposits silver at the rate of 0.00111800 g/sec.

3. The volt is defined in terms of the ohm and the ampere. The standard used is a Weston normal cell containing a saturated solution of cadmium sulfate which has a voltage of 1.0183 V at 20°C.

Electrical units can be defined in terms of absolute measurements, which are now sufficiently accurate to serve as primary standards. From an experimental standpoint it is convenient to take

$$\mu_0 \triangleq 4\pi \times 10^{-7} \text{ H/m}$$

as an absolute quantity. The absolute ampere can then be defined by the force between two circular coils. A so-called Rayleigh balance is used to measure the force F_x between two current-carrying coils. We see from Eq. (7–46) that we can express the current $i = i_1 = i_2$ in terms of F_x, the dimensions of the coil, and μ_0.

The absolute ohm can be defined in terms of a standard inductance or mutual inductance. We see from Eq. (7–16) that we can express the mutual inductance of two coils in terms of the dimensions of the coils and μ_0. A resistor can be compared with a standard inductor with the aid of a precision bridge. The quantities measured are the dimensions of the coil and the frequency of oscillation.

One can determine the permittivity of free space, ε_0, by using a precision bridge and comparing a standard resistor with a capacitor of known dimensions. However, it is also possible to determine ε_0 from the equation

$$\varepsilon_0 = 1/\mu_0 c^2$$

by means of a precision measurement of the velocity of light, $c = 2.998 \times 10^8$ m/sec. (In the text we have used the approximate value of 3×10^8 m/sec.)

The absolute volt is defined in terms of the absolute current and the absolute ohm. The relationship between the international units and the absolute units vary, since they depend on statistical fluctuations. The following figures indicate the order of the accuracy:

1 mean international ohm = 1.00049 absolute ohm,

1 mean international volt = 1.00034 absolute volt.

REFERENCES

F. B. SILSBEE, *Establishment and maintenance of the electrical units*, National Bureau of Standards Circular 475, Washington, D.C., June 1949

H. L. CURTIS, *Electrical Measurements*, New York: McGraw-Hill, 1937

MISCELLANEOUS CONSTANTS
AND CONVERSION FACTORS

The following is a table of conversion factors for converting the numerical value of often-used magnetic quantities in mks units to the numerical value of these quantities in cgs units. The conversion factor for converting the numerical value of a force in newtons to its numerical value in pounds is also given.

Multiply the numerical value of	by	to obtain the numerical value of
ϕ_m webers	10^8	ϕ_m maxwells
B webers/meter^2	10^4	B gauss
H ampere-turns/meter	$4\pi/10^3$	H oersteds
F newtons	0.2248	F pounds of force

Physical constants

Magnitude of electron charge $= e = 1.602 \times 10^{-19}$ coulomb
Rest mass of the electron $= m = 9.107 \times 10^{-31}$ kilogram
$e/m = 1.76 \times 10^{11}$ coulomb/kilogram
Permeability of free space $= \mu_0 = 4\pi \times 10^{-7}$ henry/meter
Permittivity of free space $= \varepsilon_0 = (1/36\pi)10^{-9}$ farad/meter
(The above value is based on the choice of $c = 3 \times 10^8$ meters/second for the velocity of light.)
Velocity of light $= c = 2.998 \times 10^8$ meters/second
Boltzmann's constant $= k = 1.38 \times 10^{-23}$ joule/°K
Planck's constant $= h = 6.547 \times 10^{-34}$ joule-sec.

ANSWERS TO ODD-NUMBERED PROBLEMS

Chapter 1

1-5 $\nabla \times (\mathbf{A} \times \mathbf{B}) = \mathbf{A}(\nabla \cdot \mathbf{B}) - \mathbf{B}(\nabla \cdot \mathbf{A}) + \mathbf{B} \cdot (\nabla \mathbf{A}) - \mathbf{A} \cdot (\nabla \mathbf{B})$

where $\mathbf{B} \cdot (\nabla \mathbf{A}) = (\mathbf{B} \cdot \nabla)\mathbf{A} = B_x \dfrac{\partial \mathbf{A}}{\partial x} + B_y \dfrac{\partial \mathbf{A}}{\partial y} + B_z \dfrac{\partial \mathbf{A}}{\partial z}$.

(For the definition of $\nabla \mathbf{A}$ in general coordinates see Eq. 1–117.)

1-7 $\phi = \theta = 45°$

1-17   Rectangular coordinates where $h_1 = h_2 = 1$, $u_1 = x$, $u_2 = y$

1-19 $\Omega = (amg/I\omega)$, where g is the acceleration due to gravity

Chapter 2

2-1   The resistance of the ring is $R = 3.45 \times 10^{-3}$ ohm and $i = 36.4$ mA.

2-3 $T = \varepsilon_0/\sigma = 1.52 \times 10^{-19}$ sec

2-5 $E_\phi = -\tfrac{1}{2}\omega B_0 r[1 - \tfrac{1}{2}(r/a)^2] \cos \omega t, \qquad 0 \leqq r \leqq a$

2-7   (a) $\phi_e = \dfrac{3\pi\varepsilon_r}{\varepsilon_r + 2} \varepsilon_0 E_0 r^2 \sin^2 \theta, \qquad r < a,$

      $\phi_e = \pi\varepsilon_0 E_0 \left[1 + 2\left(\dfrac{a}{r}\right)^3 \dfrac{\varepsilon_r - 1}{\varepsilon_r + 1} \right] r^2 \sin^2 \theta, \qquad r > a;$

      (b) $H_\phi = \dfrac{3}{2} \dfrac{\varepsilon_r}{\varepsilon_r + 2} \varepsilon_0 \dfrac{dE_0}{dt} r \sin \theta, \qquad r < a,$

      $H_\phi = \tfrac{1}{2}\varepsilon_0 \dfrac{dE_0}{dt} \left[1 + \left(\dfrac{a}{r}\right)^3 \dfrac{\varepsilon_r - 1}{\varepsilon_r + 2} \right] r \sin \theta, \qquad r > a.$

2-9 $R = 1.08 \times 10^{-3}$ ohm, $v_{e\,\text{max}} = 1.97 \times 10^{-2}$ V, $i_{\text{max}} = 18.2$ A

2-11 $V = aB\omega$

2-13 $V = uBh - E_y'h$, where $E_y' = i/b\sigma_b$ is the y-component of $\mathbf{E}'$ as seen by an observer inside the moving conductor; $i = uBh/(R_a + R_b)$, where $R_a = (h + 2x)/a\sigma_a$ and $R_b = h/b\sigma_b$.

Chapter 3

3–1 $\cos \theta_2 - 4 \cos \theta_1 = 3$, $\cos \alpha = -\frac{3}{4}$, $d = a$

3–3 $dr/E_r = r\, d\phi/E_\phi = dz/E_z$

3–5 $E_1 = Q/4\pi\varepsilon r^2$, $a \leqq r < b$,
$E_2 = Q/4\pi\varepsilon_0 r^2$, $b < r \leqq c$,

$$C = \frac{4\pi\varepsilon_0}{(1/b) - (1/c) + (1/\varepsilon_r)[(1/a) - (1/b)]}.$$

3–9 $C = 6.75\ \mu\mu\text{f}$, $V = 99.5\ \text{kV}$

3–11 $V = \dfrac{q}{2\pi}\left(\dfrac{1}{\varepsilon_1}\ln\dfrac{b}{a} + \dfrac{1}{\varepsilon_2}\ln\dfrac{c}{b}\right)$, where $q/2\pi$ is equal to the smaller of the two quantities $\varepsilon_1 a E_{c1}$ and $\varepsilon_2 b E_{c2}$. Simultaneous breakdown occurs if $\varepsilon_1 a E_{c1} = \varepsilon_2 b E_{c2}$.

3–13 $Z_0 = \dfrac{120}{1+k}\left(\ln\dfrac{d}{b} + k\ln\dfrac{d+h}{h}\right)$ where $k = \dfrac{\ln\,(d/b)[h/(d+h)]}{\ln\,[(d+2h)/b][h/(d+h)]}$
(a) $h = 1.38$ in. $k = 0.91$;   (b) $V = 140$ kV

Chapter 4

4–1 $\sigma = \dfrac{kQ}{4\pi a^3}\left[1 - k(1 - k^2)\left(\dfrac{a}{r_1}\right)^3\right]$ where $k = a/d$

4–3 $\sigma = 2\varepsilon_0 E_0 \cos\theta$

4–5 $F_x = -\dfrac{1}{\pi\varepsilon_1}\dfrac{\varepsilon_2 - \varepsilon_1}{\varepsilon_2 + \varepsilon_1}\left(\dfrac{Q}{2d}\right)^2$

4–9 $U = \dfrac{Q}{4\pi\varepsilon_0}\left(\dfrac{1}{r_2} - \dfrac{k}{r_1} + \dfrac{k}{r_1'} - \dfrac{1}{r_2'}\right)$

where $r_2^2 = (x - d)^2 + y^2 + z^2$, $(r')^2 = (x + d)^2 + y^2 + z^2$,
$r_1^2 = (x - b)^2 + y^2 + z^2$, $(r_1')^2 = (x + b)^2 + y^2 + z^2$,

and where $k = a/d$ and $b = a^2/d$. On the plane conductor ($x = 0$, $y^2 + z^2 > a^2$), the surface charge density is

$$\sigma = -\frac{Qd}{2\pi r^3}\left[1 - \left(\frac{a}{d}\right)^3\right],$$

where $r^2 = d^2 + y^2 + z^2$. On the hemisphere the surface charge density is

$$\sigma = -\frac{Qak(1 - k^2)}{4\pi}\left(\frac{1}{r_1^3} - \frac{1}{r_1'^3}\right),$$

where $r_1^2 = a^2 + b^2 - 2ab\cos\theta$, $r_1'^2 = a^2 + b^2 + 2ab\cos\theta$.

4–17 $C = 4\varepsilon K'/K$, where $k = 1/\cosh\,(\pi a/2b)$, $k' = \sqrt{1 - k^2}$

Chapter 5

5-3 $k = 2.46 \times 10^{-8}$ N-m/deg

5-5 $\dfrac{\Delta C}{C} = \left(\dfrac{c}{r}\right)^2 \dfrac{1}{\ln (b/a)}$, where $C = \dfrac{2\pi\varepsilon}{\ln (b/a)}$ is the unperturbed capacitance per unit length.

5-7 $W = \dfrac{Q^2}{2} \dfrac{d \ln (\varepsilon_1/\varepsilon_2)}{A(\varepsilon_1 - \varepsilon_2)}$, $C = \dfrac{A(\varepsilon_1 - \varepsilon_2)}{d \ln (\varepsilon_1/\varepsilon_2)}$, $F_x = -\dfrac{V^2 C}{2x}$

Chapter 6

6-5   (a) $H_x = \dfrac{in}{2} (\cos \theta_1 - \cos \theta_2)$, where $\cos \theta_1 = \dfrac{l + x}{\sqrt{b^2 + (l + x)^2}}$,

$\cos \theta_2 = \dfrac{x}{\sqrt{b^2 + x^2}}$;

(b) $H_x = \dfrac{in}{2} (\cos \theta_1 + \cos \theta_2)$, where $\cos \theta_1 = \dfrac{(l/2) + x}{\sqrt{b^2 + [(l/2) + x]^2}}$,

$\cos \theta_2 = \dfrac{(l/2) - x}{\sqrt{b^2 + [(l/2) - x]^2}}$

and where $x = 0$ corresponds to the center of the coil.

6-7 $\Omega = 2\theta$; $\mathbf{A} = \mathbf{i}_z A_z$ where $A_z = \dfrac{\mu_0 i}{2\pi} \ln \dfrac{r_1}{r_2}$;

$\mathbf{B} = -\mathbf{i}_z \times \operatorname{grad} A_z = \dfrac{\mu_0 i}{4\pi} \operatorname{grad} \Omega$

6-9 $a = 2d$

6-11 $in(\theta) = (3H_i/2) \sin \theta$

6-13 $\mathbf{J}_m = 0$, $\mathbf{J}_{sm} = \mathbf{i}_\phi \dfrac{\mu_r - 1}{\mu_r + 2} \cdot 3H_0 \sin \theta$

6-15 $H_i/4H_0 = \dfrac{\mu_r}{(\mu_r + 1)^2 - (\mu_r - 1)^2(b/a)^2}$

6-17 $H_1/H_2 = 1 + \tfrac{2}{9} \mu_r(\mu_r - 1)^2 \left[1 - \left(\dfrac{a}{b}\right)^3\right]$,

where H_1 and H_2 are the magnitudes of the magnetic field intensities at an exterior point for the case in which there is no shell and the case in which there is a shell, respectively.

6-21   See Example 1, Section 7-4.

Chapter 7

7-1   (a) $L \cong L_0 \triangleq \mu_0 \dfrac{\pi a^2 N^2}{l}$,   (b) $L \cong L_0 \dfrac{\sqrt{l^2 + a^2} - a}{l}$;

here $N = nl$ is the total number of turns.

7-3 $M = \mu_0 d(1 - \cos \alpha)$, $F = \mu_0 i_1 i_2\left(1 - \dfrac{1}{\cos \alpha}\right)$, where $\dfrac{1}{\cos \alpha} = \dfrac{d}{\sqrt{d^2 - a^2}}$

7-5 $F_z = -\dfrac{1}{2}\dfrac{\mu_r - 1}{\mu_r + 2}\left(\dfrac{a^3 b^2}{d^5}\right)\mu_0 \pi b^2 (iN)^2$

7-7 $\delta\sigma = 3/\omega\mu_0 a$

7-9 $P_D = v_e^2/R$, $T = v_e^2/\omega_1 R$, where $v_e = -\pi a^2 B_0 \dfrac{d}{dt}(\sin \omega_2 t \sin \omega_1 t)$

7-11 $L = \frac{2}{9}\mu_0 \pi a N^2$

7-13 $\Delta L = \dfrac{\mu_0(\mu_r - 1)(\mu_r + 2)}{3\mu_r + (\mu_r - 1)^2 \dfrac{2\delta}{b}}\left(\dfrac{\delta}{b}\right)\dfrac{\pi c^4 N^2}{2b^3}$

Chapter 8

8-1   (a) $L_1 = 10$ H, $L_2 = 0.1$ H, $i_1 = 27$ mA   (b) $V_m = 108$ V, $i_1 = 0.027 \cos \omega t + 1.08 \sin \omega t$, $i_2 = 10.8 \sin \omega t$. (Note that $i_1 N_1 - i_2 N_2 = \phi R_m$, where R_m is the reluctance of the magnetic circuit.)

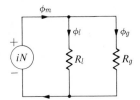

8-3   See the figure above for the equivalent circuit. The reluctances are:

$$R_l = \dfrac{1}{\mu_0 \pi l}\ln\dfrac{b}{a}, \qquad R_g = \dfrac{1}{8\mu_0 a}\left(1 + \dfrac{2b + c}{a}\right)\left[1 + \dfrac{a^2}{c^2 + 2c(a + b)}\right].$$

8-7 $B_p = 1.1$ kG, $-H_p = 540$ Oe, $M = J_{sm} = 129{,}000$ ampere-turns/m

Chapter 9

9-3 $\varepsilon_{r1} = \sqrt{\varepsilon_{r2}/\mu_{r2}}$, $a = \dfrac{\pi}{2\omega\sqrt{\mu_0 \varepsilon_1}}$

9-5 $\sigma = 1/120\pi b$

9-7 $R_c = 1.07 \times 10^{-2}$ ohm (see Eq. 9-34); $|J_s| = |H_t| = \sqrt{2/R_c} = 13.7$ A/m (see Eq. 9-36); $|E|_{min} = |E_t| = |Z_c H_t| = 0.207$ V/m; $|\Gamma_l| \cong 1 - (2R_c/Z_0)$ (see Eq. 9-25b), $r \cong Z_0/R_c = 3.52 \times 10^4$ (see Eq. 9-46), $|E|_{max} = r|E|_{min} = 7.28 \times 10^3$ V/m.

9-9 $\Gamma = \dfrac{n_1 \cos \theta_i - n_2 \cos \theta_t}{n_1 \cos \theta_i + n_2 \cos \theta_t}, \qquad T = \dfrac{2n_1 \cos \theta_i}{n_1 \cos \theta_i + n_2 \cos \theta_t}$

9-11   The frequencies of oscillation are $f = nc/2d$ ($n = 1, 2, \ldots$). (c) $n = 800$, $f = 3000$ GHz, $R_c = 0.439$ ohm, $J_s = 0.265$ A/m, $P_D = 0.031$ W. (d) $Q = 540{,}000$.

Chapter 10

10–1 $E_x = -j \dfrac{\beta_{mn}\pi m}{a} \cos \dfrac{\pi m x}{a} \sin \dfrac{\pi n y}{b} e^{-j\beta_{mn}z}$,

$E_y = -j \dfrac{\beta_{mn}\pi n}{b} \sin \dfrac{\pi m x}{a} \cos \dfrac{\pi n y}{b} e^{-j\beta_{mn}z}$,

$E_z = \left[\left(\dfrac{\pi m}{a} \right)^2 + \left(\dfrac{\pi n}{b} \right)^2 \right] \sin \dfrac{\pi m x}{a} \sin \dfrac{\pi n y}{b} e^{-j\beta_{mn}z}$,

$H_x = j \dfrac{\omega \varepsilon \pi n}{b} \sin \dfrac{\pi m x}{a} \cos \dfrac{\pi n y}{b} e^{-j\beta_{mn}z}$,

$H_y = -j \dfrac{\omega \varepsilon \pi m}{a} \cos \dfrac{\pi m x}{a} \sin \dfrac{\pi n y}{b} e^{-j\beta_{mn}z}$,

$H_z = 0$;

$f_c = u \sqrt{\left(\dfrac{m}{2a} \right)^2 + \left(\dfrac{n}{2b} \right)^2}$, $\dfrac{\lambda}{\lambda_g} = \sqrt{1 - \left(\dfrac{\lambda m}{2a} \right)^2 - \left(\dfrac{\lambda n}{2b} \right)^2}$,

where $u = 1/\sqrt{\mu\varepsilon}$, $\lambda = u/f$, $\beta_{mn} \triangleq \sqrt{(\omega/u)^2 - (\pi m/a)^2 - (\pi n/b)^2}$.

10–3   For the air-filled wave guide, $f_c = 2.08$ GHz, $\lambda_g = 43.9$ cm, $\alpha = 80.5$ Np/m. For the dielectric-filled wave guide, $f_c = 1.29$ GHz, $\lambda_g = 6.86$ cm.

10–7   (a) 3.1 MW, (b) $\alpha = 0.38 \times 10^{-2}$ Np/m = 1 db/100 ft, (c) 38 kW

10–13 The phasor surface charge density and components of the phasor current density on the surface at $x = 0$ are

$$\sigma_s = j\omega\mu\varepsilon \dfrac{\pi n}{b} \sin \dfrac{\pi n y}{b} e^{-j\beta_{mn}z},$$

$$J_{sz} = j\beta_{mn} \dfrac{\pi n}{b} \sin \dfrac{\pi n y}{b} e^{-j\beta_{mn}z},$$

$$J_{sy} = -\left[\left(\dfrac{\pi m}{a} \right)^2 + \left(\dfrac{\pi n}{b} \right)^2 \right] \cos \dfrac{\pi m y}{b} e^{-j\beta_{mn}z}.$$

10–15 $\alpha = \dfrac{2R_c}{aZ_w} \dfrac{m^2 + n^2(a/b)^3}{m^2 + (an/b)^2} \dfrac{1}{\sqrt{1 - (f_c/f)^2}}$, $m \neq 0, n \neq 0$

10–19 $Q = \dfrac{\mu\omega_r l}{4R_c} \dfrac{an^2/b + bm^2/a}{n^2(a/b)(1 + l/b) + m^2(b/a)(1 + l/a)}$,

If $a = b = l$, then $Q = \dfrac{a}{4} \sqrt{\pi\sigma\mu f_{mnN}} \times 10^9 = 3.26(m^2 + n^2 + N^2)^{1/4} \times 10^3$.

The resonant frequency is $f_{nmN} = 7.5\sqrt{m^2 + n^2 + N^2}$ GHz.

10–21 $E_x = E_z = 0$, $E_y = ju\mu \dfrac{\partial V}{\partial x} e^{-\gamma z}$,

$H_x = -\gamma \dfrac{\partial V}{\partial x} e^{-\gamma z}$, $H_y = -\gamma \dfrac{\partial V}{\partial y} e^{-\gamma z}$, $H_z = (-\gamma^2 + \omega^2\mu\varepsilon)V e^{-\gamma z}$,

where

$$V = \begin{cases} C_1 \cos k_1 x, & 0 \leq x < c, \\ C_2 \cos k_2 x + C_3 \sin k_2 x, & c < x < c + \delta, \\ C_4 \cos k_1(a - x), & c + \delta < x \leq a, \end{cases}$$

and where $k_1^2 \triangleq \gamma^2 + \omega^2 \mu_0 \varepsilon_0$, $k_2^2 \triangleq \gamma^2 + \omega^2 \mu \varepsilon$. The boundary conditions yield the following equation for γ in terms of k_1 and k_2:

$$k_1 k_2 \cos k_2 \delta \sin k_1(a - \delta) + \tfrac{1}{2} \sin k_2 \delta[(k_1^2 + k_2^2) \cos k_1(a - \delta)$$
$$+ (k_1^2 - k_2^2) \cos k_1(a - 2c - \delta)] = 0.$$

If $\delta/a \ll 1$, this equation yields

$$\beta_2 \cong \beta_1 + \frac{\delta}{a\beta_1} \beta_0^2 (\varepsilon_r - 1) \sin^2 \frac{\pi c}{a},$$

where $\beta_0 = \omega/c$.

Chapter 11

11-1 The phasor components are

$$A_\phi = j\mu_0 I_0 a J_1(\beta a \sin \theta) \frac{e^{-j\beta r}}{2r}, \qquad E_\phi = \mu_0 \omega I_0 a J_1(\beta a \sin \theta) \frac{e^{-j\beta r}}{2r},$$

$$H_\theta = -I_0 \beta a J_1(\beta a \sin \theta) \frac{e^{-j\beta r}}{2r},$$

the Poynting vector is

$$\mathbf{P} = i_r 15\pi \left[\frac{\beta a I_0}{r} J_1(\beta a \sin \theta) \right]^2$$

and the radiation resistance in the case of $\beta a \ll 1$ is $R \cong 20\pi^2(\beta a)^4$. These results are found by use of the relations

$$J_0(z) = \frac{1}{2\pi} \int_{-\pi}^{\pi} \cos (z \sin \phi) \, d\phi, \qquad J_1(z) = -\frac{dJ_0(z)}{dz},$$

$$J_1(\beta a \sin \theta) \cong \frac{\beta a}{2} \sin \theta.$$

11-3 The required pattern is obtained by choosing α and a so that $\beta a - \alpha = \pi N$, where N is a nonzero odd integer. Possible solutions are $N = 1$, $\alpha = 0$, $a = \lambda/2$, and $N = 1$, $\alpha = -\pi/2$, $a = \lambda/4$.

11-5 $P_R = 5.07$ mW, $I_0 = 16.7$ mA

11-9 $P_r = 1.56 \times 10^{-5}$ W

11-11 $G(\theta, \phi) = \tfrac{3}{2} \sin^2 \theta$

11-17 $E_i = 245$ V/m, $E_s = 1.45 \times 10^{-3}$ V/m, $P_r = 2.2 \times 10^{-9}$ W

Chapter 12

12-1 $\Gamma = \dfrac{1 - Z_0/Z_1}{1 + Z_0/Z_1}$, $T = \dfrac{2}{1 + Z_0/Z_1}$,

where $Z_1 = \sqrt{\mu_0/\varepsilon}$, $\varepsilon = \varepsilon_0[1 - (f_p/f)^2]$ and $f_p = 2.84$ GHz. The cutoff frequency is $f_c = f_p$. When $f = f_c$, then $Z_1 = \infty$, $\Gamma = 1$, and $T = 2$. The magnetic field intensity in the plasma is then zero, and, since $\gamma = 0$, the electric field intensity is uniform. At $f = 2$ GHz, the field intensities vary as $e^{-\alpha z}$ with respect to z, where $\alpha = 42.3$ Np/m. The penetration depth is 2.36 cm.

12–3 $N = 3.09 \times 10^{11}$ electrons/m³, $\theta = 0.21z$ deg/m.

12–5 For all three cases $f_M = 7$ GHz, $f_0 = 4.2$ GHz, (a) $f_r = 4.2$ GHz, $H_0 = 1500$ Oe, (b) $f_r = 6.53$ GHz, $H_0 = 667$ Oe, (c) $f_r = 7.7$ GHz, $H_0 = 1500$ Oe.

12–7 The incident field at $z = 0$ is given by $\mathbf{E}_i = E_0(\mathbf{i}_x \mp j\mathbf{i}_y)$ and $\mathbf{H}_i = (1/Z_0)\mathbf{i}_z \times \mathbf{E}_i$, where the negative and positive signs correspond to positively and negatively circularly polarized waves, respectively, and where $Z_0 = 120\pi$ ohms. The reflected wave at $z = 0$ is given by $\mathbf{E}_r = \Gamma\mathbf{E}_i$ and $\mathbf{H}_r = -\Gamma\mathbf{H}_i$, and the transmitted wave by $\mathbf{E}_T = (1 + \Gamma)\mathbf{E}_i$ and $\mathbf{H}_T = (1 - \Gamma)\mathbf{H}_i$, where

$$\Gamma = \frac{\gamma - j\omega\varepsilon Z_0}{\gamma + j\omega\varepsilon Z_0}$$

and where $\gamma = \gamma_+$ or $\gamma = \gamma_-$, depending on the sense of polarization of the incident wave. (For γ_+ and γ_-, see Eqs. 12–60.)

Chapter 13

13–5 (b) $B_0 = 110$ G, $f_0 = 154$ MHz

13–9 (c) $z = 3.84$ cm, $G = 41$

13–11 $f_p = 20$ GHz, $f_s = 10$ GHz

13–13 $f = 0.5$ GHz

INDEX